FORMULAS FROM GEOMETRY

Triangle

$h = a \sin \theta$

Area $= \dfrac{1}{2}bh$

(Law of Cosines)
$c^2 = a^2 + b^2 - 2ab \cos \theta$

Right Triangle

(Pythagorean Theorem)
$c^2 = a^2 + b^2$

Equilateral Triangle

$h = \dfrac{\sqrt{3}s}{2}$

Area $= \dfrac{\sqrt{3}s^2}{4}$

Parallelogram

Area $= bh$

Trapezoid

Area $= \dfrac{h}{2}(a + b)$

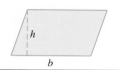

Circle

Area $= \pi r^2$
Circumference $= 2\pi r$

Sector of Circle

(θ in radians)

Area $= \dfrac{\theta r^2}{2}$

$s = r\theta$

Circular Ring

(p = average radius,
w = width of ring)

Area $= \pi(R^2 - r^2)$

$\quad = 2\pi pw$

Sector of Circular Ring

(p = average radius,
w = width of ring,
θ in radians)
Area $= \theta pw$

Ellipse

Area $= \pi ab$

Circumference $\approx 2\pi\sqrt{\dfrac{a^2 + b^2}{2}}$

Cone

(A = area of base)

Volume $= \dfrac{Ah}{3}$

Right Circular Cone

Volume $= \dfrac{\pi r^2 h}{3}$

Lateral Surface Area $= \pi r\sqrt{r^2 + h^2}$

Frustum of Right Circular Cone

Volume $= \dfrac{\pi(r^2 + rR + R^2)h}{3}$

Lateral Surface Area $= \pi s(R + r)$

Right Circular Cylinder

Volume $= \pi r^2 h$
Lateral Surface Area $= 2\pi rh$

Sphere

Volume $= \dfrac{4}{3}\pi r^3$

Surface Area $= 4\pi r^2$

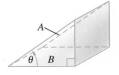

Wedge

(A = area of upper face,
B = area of base)

$A = B \sec \theta$

MULTIVARIABLE CALCULUS

MULTIVARIABLE CALCULUS

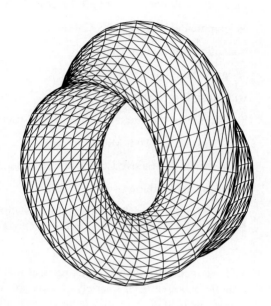

FIFTH EDITION

ROLAND E. LARSON

ROBERT P. HOSTETLER
The Pennsylvania State University
The Behrend College

BRUCE H. EDWARDS
University of Florida

with the assistance of DAVID E. HEYD
The Pennsylvania State University
The Behrend College

D. C. Heath and Company
Lexington, Massachusetts Toronto

Address editorial correspondence to:
D. C. Heath and Company
125 Spring Street
Lexington, MA 02173

Acquisitions Editors: Ann Marie Jones and Charles Hartford

Developmental Editor: Cathy Cantin

Production Editor: Ron Hampton

Designer: Sally Steele

Art Editor: Elinor Stapleton

Production Coordinators: Lisa Merrill and Richard Tonachel

Photo Researcher: Toni Michaels

Composition: Interactive Composition Corporation

Technical Art: Folium

Cover: "Umbilic Torus NC" by Sculptor/Mathematician Helaman Ferguson
(Bronze 27" x 27" x 9"). Photo by Terry Clough.

We have included examples and exercises that use real-life data as well as
technology output from a variety of software. This would not have been possible
without the help of many people and organizations. Our wholehearted thanks goes to
all for their time and effort.

Preface

Multivariable Calculus, Fifth Edition, is designed for use in a course for students in engineering, mathematics, the physical and life sciences, and economics.

Calculus Reform

During the past several years, much has been written about the need for reform in mathematics education. Most suggestions for reform have fallen into four categories: (1) problem solving, (2) technology, (3) communicating mathematics, and (4) real-life applications. *Multivariable Calculus*, Fifth Edition, embodies each of these features in the spirit of reform.

PROBLEM SOLVING Helping students learn to be efficient and creative problem solvers is the primary goal of any mathematics course. The nearly 3,000 exercises in this text cover a broad range of problem types. While the text contains an abundance of exercises that are designed to develop skills, it now has many other types of exercises as well: some have several parts that lead students through an exploration of a concept or application (Exercises 37 and 38 in Section 11.4), some ask for interpretations (Exercises 25 and 26, Section 13.1), some have many correct answers (Exercises 31–34, Section 12.1), and there are *many* other new types. Often, students are asked to consider solving a problem *numerically*, *graphically*, and *analytically* (Exercise 51, Section 13.7).

TECHNOLOGY Much of calculus reform has centered around the appropriate integration of technology in calculus instruction. Because graphing utilities and symbolic algebra systems are readily available, we have incorporated their use throughout the prose and exercises of *Multivariable Calculus*, Fifth Edition. Sometimes technology is used as a means of discovery (Exercise 19, Section 15.5), sometimes technology is used to reinforce concepts (Exercises 5 and 6, Section 15.4), and sometimes it is used as an efficient problem-solving tool (Exercise 33, Section 13.5).

Multivariable Calculus, Fifth Edition, is also available in an interactive edition. This complete learning package for calculus is a multimedia resource containing the entire fifth edition and much more—preprogrammed and editable explorations, animated art, historical notes, and real-life connections. It is also capable of interfacing with Derive, Maple, MathCad, and Mathematica.

COMMUNICATING MATHEMATICS   The third important aspect of calculus reform is a renewed emphasis on development of communication skills. To address this, we have included many exercises that ask for interpretations, descriptions, discussions, justifications, and conjectures. For instance, look at Exercises 19 and 20 in Section 15.5 and Exercise 50 in Section 12.5.

REAL-LIFE APPLICATIONS   The fourth important aspect of calculus reform is a renewed dedication to the applied nature of calculus. Almost all of the early development of calculus was written in the context of real-life problem solving. In writing this text, we included many interesting real-life applications. For instance, see Example 7 in Section 16.2, Exercise 38 in Section 14.5, and Exercise 72 in Section 13.1.

Features

Multivariable Calculus, Fifth Edition, has many design features that enhance the relevance of the text and make it an effective teaching tool. These are shown on the following pages.

Chapter Openers
Each chapter opens with a photograph of a mathematical application that is keyed to an exercise in the chapter.

Section Topics
Each section begins with a list of sub-section topics. This outline will help instructors with class planning and students with studying and synthesizing the material in the section.

Examples
The text contains over 250 examples, each titled for easy reference, which increase the usefulness of the text as a study tool. Many of the examples include side comments that clarify the steps of the solution.

Definitions and Theorems
All definitions and theorems are shown in color for emphasis and easy reference.

---

816   Chapter 12 / Vector-Valued Functions

SECTION 12.5   Arc Length and Curvature

Arc Length • Arc Length Parameter • Curvature • Applications

Arc Length

In Section 10.2, you saw that the arc length of a smooth *plane* curve C given by the parametric equations $x = x(t)$ and $y = y(t)$, $a \le t \le b$, is

$$s = \int_a^b \sqrt{[x'(t)]^2 + [y'(t)]^2}\, dt.$$

In vector form, where C is given by $\mathbf{r}(t) = x(t)\mathbf{i} + y(t)\mathbf{j}$, you can rewrite this equation for arc length as

$$s = \int_a^b \|\mathbf{r}'(t)\|\, dt.$$

EXAMPLE 1   Finding the Arc Length of a Plane Curve

Find the arc length of the curve given by $\mathbf{r}(t) = \cos t\,\mathbf{i} + \sin t\,\mathbf{j}$ from $t = 0$ to $t = 2\pi$.

Solution   Using $x(t) = \cos t$ and $y(t) = \sin t$, you obtain $x'(t) = -\sin t$ and $y'(t) = \cos t$. Thus, the arc length from $t = 0$ to $t = 2\pi$ is

$$\begin{aligned}
s &= \int_0^{2\pi} \sqrt{[x'(t)]^2 + [y'(t)]^2}\, dt = \int_0^{2\pi} \sqrt{\sin^2 t + \cos^2 t}\, dt \\
&= \int_0^{2\pi} dt \\
&= t\Big]_0^{2\pi} = 2\pi.
\end{aligned}$$

In Figure 12.26, notice that the curve is a circle of radius 1. Thus, the arc length formula confirms that the circumference of the circle is 2π.

$\mathbf{r}(t) = \cos t\,\mathbf{i} + \sin t\,\mathbf{j}$

FIGURE 12.26
The arc length of the circle is 2π.

The formula for the arc length of a plane curve has a natural extension to a smooth curve in *space*, as stated in the following theorem.

THEOREM 12.6   Arc Length of Space Curve

If C is a smooth curve given by $\mathbf{r}(t) = x(t)\mathbf{i} + y(t)\mathbf{j} + z(t)\mathbf{k}$, on an interval $[a, b]$, then the arc length of C on the interval is

$$s = \int_a^b \sqrt{[x'(t)]^2 + [y'(t)]^2 + [z'(t)]^2}\, dt = \int_a^b \|\mathbf{r}'(t)\|\, dt.$$

EXAMPLE 2   Finding an Equation of a Tangent Plane

Find an equation of the tangent plane to the hyperboloid given by

$$z^2 - 2x^2 - 2y^2 = 12$$

at the point $(1, -1, 4)$.

Solution   Begin by writing the equation of the surface as

$$z^2 - 2x^2 - 2y^2 - 12 = 0.$$

Then, considering

$$F(x, y, z) = z^2 - 2x^2 - 2y^2 - 12$$

you have

$$F_x(x, y, z) = -4x, \qquad F_y(x, y, z) = -4y, \qquad F_z(x, y, z) = 2z.$$

At the point $(1, -1, 4)$, the partial derivatives are

$$F_x(1, -1, 4) = -4, \qquad F_y(1, -1, 4) = 4, \qquad F_z(1, -1, 4) = 8.$$

Therefore, an equation of the tangent plane at $(1, -1, 4)$ is

$$
\begin{aligned}
-4(x - 1) + 4(y + 1) + 8(z - 4) &= 0 \\
-4x + 4 + 4y + 4 + 8z - 32 &= 0 \\
-4x + 4y + 8z - 24 &= 0 \\
x - y - 2z + 6 &= 0.
\end{aligned}
$$

Figure 13.57 shows a portion of the hyperboloid and tangent plane.

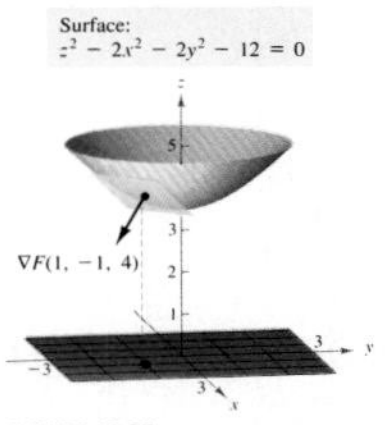

FIGURE 13.57
Tangent plane to surface.

Surface:
$z^2 - 2x^2 - 2y^2 - 12 = 0$
$\nabla F(1, -1, 4)$

TECHNOLOGY   Some three-dimensional graphing utilities are capable of sketching tangent planes to surfaces. Two examples are shown in Figure 13.58. The first of these computer drawings depicts a tangent plane to the sphere $x^2 + y^2 + z^2 = 1$, and the second depicts a tangent plane to the paraboloid $z = 2 - x^2 - y^2$.

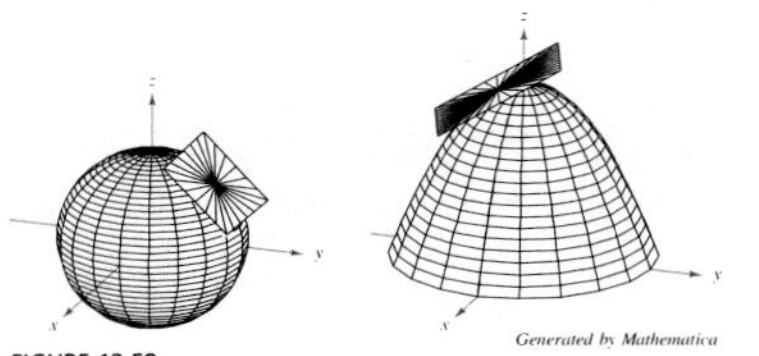

FIGURE 13.58

Generated by Mathematica

Graphics

The Fifth Edition has over 800 figures. Of these, over 350 are in the examples and exposition, over 250 are in the exercise sets, and over 200 are in the answers to odd-numbered exercises. Computer-generated for accuracy and designed with full color, this art program will help students better visualize mathematical concepts. This is particularly true in the presentation of complex, three-dimensional material, for which the art was drawn in true perspective. Many figures were created using Derive, Mathematica, Maple, and Axiom graphing utilities.

In Example 1, you could have projected the surface S onto any one of the three coordinate planes. In the next example, the surface is a portion of a cylinder centered about the z-axis, and you have the option of projecting S onto either the xz-plane or the xy-plane.

EXAMPLE 2   Evaluating a Surface Integral

Evaluate the surface integral

$$\iint_S (x + z)\, dS$$

where S is the first-octant portion of the cylinder $y^2 + z^2 = 9$ between $x = 0$ and $x = 4$, as shown in Figure 15.47.

Solution   Begin by projecting onto the xy-plane, so that $z = g(x, y) = \sqrt{9 - y^2}$, and obtain

$$
\sqrt{1 + [g_x(x, y)]^2 + [g_y(x, y)]^2} = \sqrt{1 + \left(\frac{-y}{\sqrt{9 - y^2}}\right)^2}
$$

$$
= \frac{3}{\sqrt{9 - y^2}}.
$$

Theorem 15.10 does not apply directly, because g_y is not continuous when $y = 3$. However, you can apply the theorem for $0 \le b < 3$ and then take the limit as b approaches 3, as follows.

$$
\begin{aligned}
\iint_S (x + z)\, dS &= \lim_{b \to 3} \int_0^b \int_0^4 \left(x + \sqrt{9 - y^2}\right) \frac{3}{\sqrt{9 - y^2}}\, dx\, dy \\
&= \lim_{b \to 3} 3 \int_0^b \int_0^4 \left(\frac{x}{\sqrt{9 - y^2}} + 1\right) dx\, dy \\
&= \lim_{b \to 3} 3 \int_0^b \left[\frac{x^2}{2\sqrt{9 - y^2}} + x\right]_0^4 dy \\
&= \lim_{b \to 3} 3 \int_0^b \left(\frac{8}{\sqrt{9 - y^2}} + 4\right) dy \\
&= \lim_{b \to 3} 3 \left[4y + 8 \arcsin \frac{y}{3}\right]_0^b \\
&= \lim_{b \to 3} 3 \left(4b + 8 \arcsin \frac{b}{3}\right) \\
&= 36 + 24\left(\frac{\pi}{2}\right) \\
&= 36 + 12\pi
\end{aligned}
$$

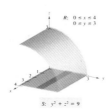

$R: \ 0 \le x \le 4$
$\quad\ 0 \le y \le 3$

$S: \ y^2 + z^2 = 9$

FIGURE 15.47

TECHNOLOGY   Some symbolic integration utilities are capable of evaluating improper integrals. If you have access to such computer software, try using it to evaluate the improper integral

$$\int_0^3 \int_0^4 \left(x + \sqrt{9 - y^2}\right) \frac{3}{\sqrt{9 - y^2}}\, dx\, dy.$$

Do you obtain the same result that was obtained in Example 2?

Technology

Students are encouraged to use a graphing utility or symbolic algebra system as a tool for exploration and discovery as well as a problem-solving tool to execute complicated computations, to visualize theoretical concepts, to offer alternative approaches, and to verify the results of other solution methods.

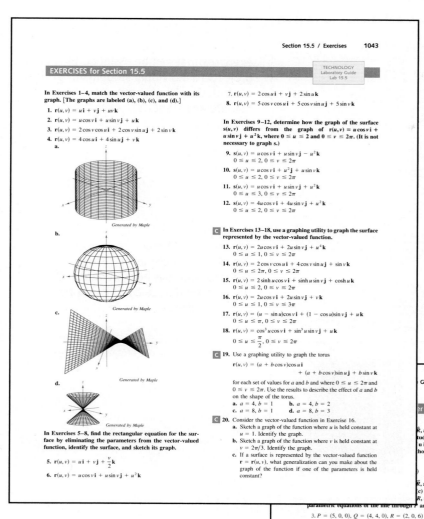

Section 15.5 / Exercises 1043

EXERCISES for Section 15.5

TECHNOLOGY
Laboratory Guide
Lab 15.5

In Exercises 1–4, match the vector-valued function with its graph. [The graphs are labeled (a), (b), (c), and (d).]

1. $\mathbf{r}(u, v) = u\mathbf{i} + v\mathbf{j} + uv\mathbf{k}$

2. $\mathbf{r}(u, v) = u\cos v\,\mathbf{i} + u\sin v\,\mathbf{j} + u\mathbf{k}$

3. $\mathbf{r}(u, v) = 2\cos v\cos u\,\mathbf{i} + 2\cos v\sin u\,\mathbf{j} + 2\sin v\,\mathbf{k}$

4. $\mathbf{r}(u, v) = 4\cos u\,\mathbf{i} + 4\sin u\,\mathbf{j} + v\mathbf{k}$

a.

Generated by Maple

b.

Generated by Maple

c.

Generated by Maple

d.

Generated by Maple

In Exercises 5–8, find the rectangular equation for the surface by eliminating the parameters from the vector-valued function, identify the surface, and sketch its graph.

5. $\mathbf{r}(u, v) = u\mathbf{i} + v\mathbf{j} + \dfrac{v}{2}\mathbf{k}$

6. $\mathbf{r}(u, v) = u\cos v\,\mathbf{i} + u\sin v\,\mathbf{j} + u^2\mathbf{k}$

7. $\mathbf{r}(u, v) = 2\cos u\,\mathbf{i} + v\mathbf{j} + 2\sin u\,\mathbf{k}$

8. $\mathbf{r}(u, v) = 5\cos v\cos u\,\mathbf{i} + 5\cos v\sin u\,\mathbf{j} + 5\sin v\,\mathbf{k}$

In Exercises 9–12, determine how the graph of the surface $s(u, v)$ differs from the graph of $\mathbf{r}(u, v) = u\cos v\,\mathbf{i} + u\sin v\,\mathbf{j} + u^2\mathbf{k}$, where $0 \le u \le 2$ and $0 \le v \le 2\pi$. (It is not necessary to graph s.)

9. $s(u, v) = u\cos v\,\mathbf{i} + u\sin v\,\mathbf{j} - u^2\mathbf{k}$
   $0 \le u \le 2,\ 0 \le v \le 2\pi$

10. $s(u, v) = u\cos v\,\mathbf{i} + u^2\mathbf{j} + u\sin v\,\mathbf{k}$
    $0 \le u \le 2,\ 0 \le v \le 2\pi$

11. $s(u, v) = u\cos v\,\mathbf{i} + u\sin v\,\mathbf{j} + u^2\mathbf{k}$
    $0 \le u \le 3,\ 0 \le v \le 2\pi$

12. $s(u, v) = 4u\cos v\,\mathbf{i} + 4u\sin v\,\mathbf{j} + u^2\mathbf{k}$
    $0 \le u \le 2,\ 0 \le v \le 2\pi$

C In Exercises 13–18, use a graphing utility to graph the surface represented by the vector-valued function.

13. $\mathbf{r}(u, v) = 2u\cos v\,\mathbf{i} + 2u\sin v\,\mathbf{j} + u^4\mathbf{k}$
    $0 \le u \le 1,\ 0 \le v \le 2\pi$

14. $\mathbf{r}(u, v) = 2\cos v\cos u\,\mathbf{i} + 4\cos v\sin u\,\mathbf{j} + \sin v\,\mathbf{k}$
    $0 \le u \le 2\pi,\ 0 \le v \le 2\pi$

15. $\mathbf{r}(u, v) = 2\sinh u\cos v\,\mathbf{i} + \sinh u\sin v\,\mathbf{j} + \cosh u\,\mathbf{k}$
    $0 \le u \le 2,\ 0 \le v \le 2\pi$

16. $\mathbf{r}(u, v) = 2u\cos v\,\mathbf{i} + 2u\sin v\,\mathbf{j} + v\mathbf{k}$
    $0 \le u \le 1,\ 0 \le v \le 3\pi$

17. $\mathbf{r}(u, v) = (u - \sin u)\cos v\,\mathbf{i} + (1 - \cos u)\sin v\,\mathbf{j} + u\mathbf{k}$
    $0 \le u \le \pi,\ 0 \le v \le 2\pi$

18. $\mathbf{r}(u, v) = \cos^3 u\cos v\,\mathbf{i} + \sin^3 u\sin v\,\mathbf{j} + u\mathbf{k}$
    $0 \le u \le \dfrac{\pi}{2},\ 0 \le v \le 2\pi$

C 19. Use a graphing utility to graph the torus
   $\mathbf{r}(u, v) = (a + b\cos v)\cos u\,\mathbf{i}$
   $\qquad\qquad + (a + b\cos v)\sin u\,\mathbf{j} + b\sin v\,\mathbf{k}$

   for each set of values for a and b and where $0 \le u \le 2\pi$ and $0 \le v \le 2\pi$. Use the results to describe the effect of a and b on the shape of the torus.
   a. $a = 4, b = 1$ b. $a = 4, b = 2$
   c. $a = 8, b = 1$ d. $a = 8, b = 3$

C 20. Consider the vector-valued function in Exercise 16.
   a. Sketch a graph of the function where u is held constant at $u = 1$. Identify the graph.
   b. Sketch a graph of the function where v is held constant at $v = 2\pi/3$. Identify the graph.
   c. If a surface is represented by the vector-valued function $\mathbf{r} = \mathbf{r}(u, v)$, what generalization can you make about the graph of the function if one of the parameters is held constant?

Exercises

The text contains nearly 2800 exercises. The exercises are graded, progressing from skill-development problems to more challenging problems involving applications and proofs. Many exercise sets begin with a group of exercises that provide the graphs of functions involved. Review exercises are included at the end of each chapter. Answers to all odd-numbered exercises are included in the back of the text.

Graphing Utilities

Many exercises in the text can be solved using technology; however, the symbol **C** identifies all exercises in which students are specifically instructed to use a graphing utility or a symbolic algebra system.

Geometry of Space

r 11

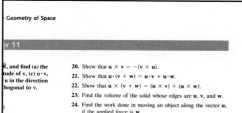

$\tilde{R}$, and find (a) the ...tude of v, (c) u·v, ...u in the direction ...gonal to v.

$\tilde{R}$, and find (a the ...c) u × v, (d) an $\tilde{R}$, and (e) a set of parametric equations of the line through P and Q.

3. $P = (5, 0, 0),\ Q = (4, 4, 0),\ R = (2, 0, 6)$

4. $P = (2, -1, 3),\ Q = (0, 5, 1),\ R = (5, 5, 0)$

In Exercises 5 and 6, determine if the vectors are orthogonal or parallel, or neither.

5. $\langle -4, 3, -6 \rangle$ 6. $\langle 7, -2, 3 \rangle$
   $\langle 16, -12, 24 \rangle$ $\langle -1, 4, 5 \rangle$

In Exercises 7–10, find the angle θ between the vectors u and v.

7. $\mathbf{u} = 5\left[\cos\left(\dfrac{3\pi}{4}\right)\mathbf{i} + \sin\left(\dfrac{3\pi}{4}\right)\mathbf{j}\right]$
   $\mathbf{v} = 2\left[\cos\left(\dfrac{2\pi}{3}\right)\mathbf{i} + \sin\left(\dfrac{2\pi}{3}\right)\mathbf{j}\right]$

8. $\mathbf{u} = \langle 4, -1, 5 \rangle$
   $\mathbf{v} = \langle 3, 2, -2 \rangle$

9. $\mathbf{u} = \langle 10, -5, 15 \rangle$ 10. $\mathbf{u} = \langle 1, 0, -3 \rangle$
   $\mathbf{v} = \langle -2, 1, -3 \rangle$ $\mathbf{v} = \langle 2, -2, 1 \rangle$

In Exercises 11–14, find the component form of u.

11. The angle, measured counterclockwise, from the positive x-axis to u is 135°, and $\|\mathbf{u}\| = 4$.

12. The angle between u and the positive x-axis is 180°, and $\|\mathbf{u}\| = 8$.

13. u is perpendicular to the plane $x - 3y + 4z = 0$, and $\|\mathbf{u}\| = 3$.

14. u is a unit vector perpendicular to the lines
    $x = 4 - t$ $x = -3 + 7s$
    $y = 3 + 2t$ $y = -2 + s$
    $z = 1 + 5t$ $z = 1 + 2s$.

In Exercises 15–24, let $\mathbf{u} = \langle 3, -2, 1 \rangle$, $\mathbf{v} = \langle 2, -4, -3 \rangle$, and $\mathbf{w} = \langle -1, 2, 2 \rangle$.

15. Find $\|\mathbf{u}\|$.

16. Find the angle between u and v.

17. Show that $\mathbf{u} \cdot \mathbf{u} = \|\mathbf{u}\|^2$.

18. Determine a unit vector perpendicular to the plane containing v and w.

19. Determine the projection of w onto u.

20. Show that $\mathbf{u} \times \mathbf{v} = -(\mathbf{v} \times \mathbf{u})$.

21. Show that $\mathbf{u} \cdot (\mathbf{v} + \mathbf{w}) = \mathbf{u} \cdot \mathbf{v} + \mathbf{u} \cdot \mathbf{w}$.

22. Show that $\mathbf{u} \times (\mathbf{v} + \mathbf{w}) = (\mathbf{u} \times \mathbf{v}) + (\mathbf{u} \times \mathbf{w})$.

23. Find the volume of the solid whose edges are u, v, and w.

24. Find the work done in moving an object along the vector u, if the applied force is w.

25. *Load Supports* Find the tension in each of the supporting cables shown in the figure.

26. *Equilibrium* A 100-pound collar slides on a frictionless vertical rod (see figure). Find the distance y for which the system is in equilibrium if the counterweight weighs 120 pounds.

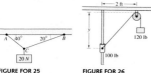

FIGURE FOR 25   FIGURE FOR 26

27. *Minimum Length* In a manufacturing process, an electric hoist lifts 500-pound ingots (see figure). Find the shortest cable connecting points P, O, and Q that can be used if the tension in the cable cannot exceed 750 pounds. (Assume that O is at the midpoint of the cable.)

28. *Torque* The specifications for a tractor state that the torque on a bolt with head size $\frac{7}{8}$ inch cannot exceed 200 foot-pounds. Determine the maximum force $\|\mathbf{F}\|$ that can be applied to the wrench in the figure.

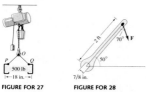

FIGURE FOR 27   FIGURE FOR 28

In Exercises 29–32, find (a) a set of parametric equations for the given line, and (b) a set of symmetric equations for the given line.

29. The line passes through $(1, 2, 3)$ and is perpendicular to the xz-coordinate plane.

30. The line passes through $(1, 2, 3)$ and is parallel to the line given by $x = y = z$.

Technology Labs

A *Technology Laboratory Guide*, referenced at the beginning of most exercise sets, offers additional technology assignments, explorations, and projects. Appropriate for any graphing technology, each lab opens with a list of the graphing capabilities required.

Computer Graphics

The usefulness of technology in representing graphs in two and three dimensions is illustrated by a variety of computer-generated graphs. Some are graphing calculator screens, and some were generated from commercial software such as Derive, Maple, Mathematica, and Axiom.

[C] 51. *Approximation* Consider the following approximations centered at $(0, 0)$ for a function $f(x, y)$.

Linear Approximation

$$P_1(x, y) \approx f(0, 0) + f_x(0, 0)x + f_y(0, 0)y$$

Quadratic Approximation

$$P_2(x, y) \approx f(0, 0) + f_x(0, 0)x + f_y(0, 0)y$$
$$+ \frac{1}{2}f_{xx}(0, 0)x^2 + f_{xy}(0, 0)xy + \frac{1}{2}f_{yy}(0, 0)y^2$$

[Note that the linear approximation is the tangent plane to the surface at $(0, 0, f(0, 0))$.]

a. Find the linear approximation of $f(x, y) = e^{(x-y)}$ centered at $(0, 0)$.

b. Find the quadratic approximation of $f(x, y) = e^{(x-y)}$ centered at $(0, 0)$.

c. If $x = 0$ in the quadratic approximation, then you obtain the second-degree Taylor polynomial for what function? Answer the same question for $y = 0$.

d. Complete the table.

x	y	f(x,y)	$P_1(x,y)$	$P_2(x,y)$
0	0			
0	0.1			
0.2	0.1			
0.2	0.5			
1	0.5			

e. Use a graphing utility to graph the surfaces given by $z = f(x, y)$, $z = P_1(x, y)$, and $z = P_2(x, y)$.

52. *Approximation* Repeat Exercise 51 for the function $f(x, y) = \cos(x + y)$.

53. Let f be a differentiable function, and consider the surface $z = xf(y/x)$. Show that the tangent plane at any point $P = (x_0, y_0, z_0)$ on the surface passes through the origin.

FOR FURTHER INFORMATION Biologists use the concept of diversity to measure the proportions of different types of organisms within an environment. For more information on this, see the article "Information Theory and Biological Diversity" by Steven Kolmes and Kevin Mitchell in the 1990 *UMAP Modules*.

54. *Wildflower Diversity* The diversity of wildflowers in a meadow can be measured by counting the number of daisies, buttercups, shooting stars, and so on. If there are n types of wildflowers, each with a proportion of p_i of the total population, then it follows that $p_1 + p_2 + \cdots + p_n = 1$. The measure of diversity of the population is defined as

$$H = -\sum_{i=1}^{n} p_i \log_2 p_i.$$

In this definition, it is understood that $p_i \log_2 p_i = 0$ when $p_i = 0$. The tables show the proportions of wildflowers in a meadow in May, June, August, and September.

a. Determine the wildflower diversity for each month. How would you interpret September's diversity? Which month had the greatest diversity?

b. If the meadow contains 10 types of wildflowers in roughly equal proportions, is the diversity of the population greater or less than the diversity of a similar distribution of four types of wildflowers? What type of distribution (of 10 types of wildflowers) would produce a maximum diversity?

c. Let H_n represent the maximum diversity of n types of wildflowers. Does H_n approach a limit as n approaches infinity?

May

Flower type	1	2	3	4
Proportion	$\frac{5}{16}$	$\frac{5}{16}$	$\frac{5}{16}$	$\frac{1}{16}$

June

Flower type	1	2	3	4
Proportion	$\frac{1}{4}$	$\frac{1}{4}$	$\frac{1}{4}$	$\frac{1}{4}$

August

Flower type	1	2	3	4
Proportion	$\frac{1}{4}$	0	$\frac{1}{4}$	$\frac{1}{2}$

September

Flower type	1	2	3	4
Proportion	0	0	0	1

Challenging Problems

New to the Fifth Edition are several exercises that can be assigned as special projects to individual students or groups of students. All of these exercises are real-life applications.

Journal References

References to articles in readily available journals help students understand that calculus is a current, dynamic field.

In Exercises 47–50, find an equation of the tangent plane and equations for the normal line to the given surface at the specified point.

Surface	Point
47. $f(x, y) = x^2 y$	$(2, 1, 4)$
48. $f(x, y) = \sqrt{25 - y^2}$	$(2, 3, 4)$
49. $z = -9 + 4x - 6y - x^2 - y^2$	$(2, -3, 4)$
50. $z = \sqrt{9 - x^2 - y^2}$	$(1, 2, 2)$

In Exercises 51 and 52, find symmetric equations of the tangent line to the curve of intersection of the given surfaces at the indicated point.

Surfaces	Point
51. $z = x^2 - y^2, z = 3$	$(2, 1, 3)$
52. $z = 25 - y^2, y = x$	$(4, 4, 9)$

In Exercises 53–56, locate and classify any extrema of the function.

53. $f(x, y) = x^3 - 3xy + y^2$

54. $f(x, y) = 2x^2 + 6xy + 9y^2 + 8x + 14$

55. $f(x, y) = xy + \dfrac{1}{x} + \dfrac{1}{y}$

56. $z = 50(x + y) - (0.1x^3 + 20x + 150)$
$\qquad - (0.05y^3 + 20.6y + 125)$

Essay In Exercises 57 and 58, write a short paragraph about the surface whose level curves are given. Comment on possible extrema, saddle points, the magnitude of the gradient, etc.

57.   **58.**

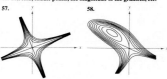

In Exercises 59 and 60, locate and classify any extrema of the function by using Lagrange multipliers.

59. $z = x^2 y$
Constraint: $x + 2y = 2$

60. $w = xy + yz + xz$
Constraint: $x + y + z = 1$

61. *Profit* A corporation manufactures a product at two locations. The cost functions for producing x_1 units at location 1 and x_2 units at location 2 are given by

$C_1 = 0.05x_1^2 + 15x_1 + 5400$

$C_2 = 0.03x_2^2 + 15x_2 + 6100$

and the total revenue function is

$R = [225 - 0.4(x_1 + x_2)](x_1 + x_2)$.

Find the production levels at the two locations that will maximize the profit $P(x_1, x_2) = R - C_1 - C_2$.

Chapter 13 Review Exercises

62. *Cost* A manufacturer has an order for 1000 units tha[t are] produced at two locations. Let x_1 and x_2 be the num[ber of] units produced at the two locations. Find the num[ber that] should be produced at each location to meet the or[der and] minimize cost, if the cost function is

$C = 0.25x_1^2 + 10x_1 + 0.15x_2^2 + 12x_2$.

63. *Production Level* The production function for a [manufac-]turer is

$f(x, y) = 4x + xy + 2y$.

Assume that the total amount available for labor an[d capital] is \$2000, and that units of labor and capital cost \$2[0 and \$4,] respectively. Find the maximum production level [for this] manufacturer.

64. *Motor Vehicle Sales* The following table gives pass[enger car] retail sales (y in millions) and truck and bus retail sa[les (x in] millions) in the United States for selected years. (Sou[rce: U.S.] Department of Commerce)

Year	1975	1980	1983	198[5]
Trucks/Buses (x)	2.4	2.2	2.7	3.[ ]
Cars (y)	8.6	9.0	9.2	10.[ ]

Year	1985	1986	1987	198[ ]
Trucks/Buses (x)	4.0	4.0	4.2	4.[ ]
Cars (y)	11.0	11.5	10.3	10.[ ]

a. Find the least squares regression line for these d[ata.]
b. What information does the slope of the regression line give about the relationship between the sales of passenger cars and trucks?

65. *Aerodynamics* The following table gives the drag force y in kilograms for a certain motor vehicle at specified speeds x in kilometers per hour.

Speed (x)	25	50	75	100	125
Drag (y)	28	38	54	75	102

a. Find the least squares regression quadratic for these data.
b. Use the quadratic to estimate the total drag when the vehicle is moving at 80 kilometers per hour.

True or False In Exercises 66–68, determine whether the statement is true or false. If it is false, explain why or give an example that shows it is false.

66. Of all parallelepipeds having a fixed surface area, the cube has the largest volume.

67. The gradient $\nabla f(x_0, y_0)$ is normal to [the surface] $z = f(x, y)$ at the point (x_0, y_0, z_0).

68. The plane $x_0 x + y_0 y + z_0 z = c^2$ is [tangent to] $x^2 + y^2 + z^2 = c^2$ at the point $(x_0, y_0[, z_0])$.

71. *Cornu Spiral* The cornu spiral is given by

$x = \displaystyle\int_0^s \cos\frac{\pi u^2}{2}\, du, \qquad y = \int_0^s \sin\frac{\pi u^2}{2}\, du.$

The spiral shown in the figure was plotted over the interval $-\pi \le x \le \pi$.

a. Find the arc length of this curve from $s = 0$ to $s = a$.
b. Find the curvature of the graph when $s = a$.
c. The cornu spiral was discovered by James Bernoulli. He found that the spiral has an amazing relationship between curvature and arc length. What is this relationship?

FIGURE FOR 71

Variety of Problems
Many new types of problems have been added to the exercise sets, offering opportunities for writing, for individual and group projects, for solving multi-part applications, for working quantitative as well as qualitative problems, and for working with real data. To help instructors make homework assignments, many of the exercises in the text are labeled to indicate the area of application (as in *Cornu Spiral*) or the type of exercise (as in *Essay*).

True or False Questions
To help students understand the logical structure of calculus, a set of true or false questions are included toward the end of most exercise sets. These questions help students focus on concepts, common errors, and the correct statements of definitions and theorems.

Career Interviews
Career interviews with engineers, scientists, mathematicians, and other professionals who use calculus in their jobs encourage students to understand that calculus is a modern, problem-solving language.

806   Chapter 12 / Vector-Valued Functions

45. *Throwing a Shot-Put* The path of a shot-put thrown at an angle θ is given by

$\mathbf{r}(t) = (v_0 \cos\theta)t\,\mathbf{i} + [h + (v_0 \sin\theta)t - \frac{1}{2}gt^2]\mathbf{j}$

where v_0 is the initial speed, h is the initial height, t is time in seconds, and g is the acceleration due to gravity. Verify that the shot-put will remain in the air for a total of

$t = \dfrac{v_0 \sin\theta + \sqrt{v_0^2 \sin^2\theta + 2gh}}{g}$ sec

and will travel a horizontal distance of

$\dfrac{v_0^2 \cos\theta}{g}\left(\sin\theta + \sqrt{\sin^2\theta + \dfrac{2gh}{v_0^2}}\right)$ ft.

46. *Throwing a Shot-Put* A shot-up is thrown from a height of $h = 6$ feet with an initial speed of $v_0 = 45$ feet per second. Find the total time of travel and the total horizontal distance traveled if the shot-put was thrown at an angle of $\theta = 42.5°$ with the horizontal.

47. Prove that if an object is traveling at a constant speed, its velocity and acceleration vectors are orthogonal.

48. Prove that an object moving in a straight line at a constant speed has an acceleration of 0.

49. *Essay* Consider a particle moving on the path $\mathbf{r}_1(t) = x(t)\mathbf{i} + y(t)\mathbf{j} + z(t)\mathbf{k}$. Discuss any changes in the position, velocity, or acceleration of the particle if its position is given by the vector-valued function $\mathbf{r}_2(t) = \mathbf{r}_1(2t)$. Generalize the results for the position function $\mathbf{r}_3(t) = \mathbf{r}_1(\omega t)$.

Supplements

Multivariable Calculus, Fifth Edition, by Larson, Hostetler, and Edwards is accompanied by a comprehensive supplements package with ancillaries for students, for instructors, and for classroom resources. Most items are keyed directly to the book.

PRINTED RESOURCES

For the instructor

Instructor's Guide by Ann R. Kraus, Pennsylvania State University, The Behrend College
- Notes to the new teacher
- Chapter summaries
- Ready-made chapter tests
- Teaching strategies

Complete Solutions Guide, Volume III, by Dianna L. Zook, Indiana University—Purdue University at Fort Wayne
- Detailed solutions to all text exercises

Test Item File by Ann R. Kraus, Pennsylvania State University, The Behrend College
- Printed test bank
- Multiple-choice and open-ended questions coded by level of difficulty
- Technology required to solve some test questions
- Also available as test-generating software

Graphing Calculator Demonstration Problems by August J. Zarcone and Russell Lundstrom, College of DuPage
- Classroom demonstration problems using TI-81 and TI-82 graphing calculators

Transparency package
- Color transparencies of figures from the text

For the student

Study and Solutions Guide by David E. Heyd, The Pennsylvania State University, The Behrend College
- Detailed solutions to selected odd-numbered text exercises
- Algebra review
- Study strategies

Technology Laboratory Guide by David E. Heyd, The Pennsylvania State University, The Behrend College
- Supplementary exercises using graphics calculators and/or a computer algebra system
- Worksheet format

Graphing Technology Guide: Calculus by Benjamin N. Levy
- Keystroke-level commands and instructions
- Step-by-step examples with numerous screen displays
- Technology tips

Computer Projects in Calculus by Bruce H. Edwards, University of Florida
- Guided exploration labs
- Brief introductions to Mathematica, Maple, and Derive

Calculus Applications in Engineering and Science by Stuart Goldenberg and Harvey Greenwald, California Polytechnic State University—San Luis Obispo
- Extended applications

Technology Resources

Computerized Testing
- Test-generating software
- Also available as a printed test bank

Derive
- Symbolic mathematics package
- Available to adopters at a discount

PC-81 Emulation Software
Simulates the functions of the TI-81 graphics calculator

Graphing Calculator Instructional Videotape by Dana Mosely

Acknowledgments

We would like to thank the many people who have helped us at various stages of this project during the past seventeen years. Their encouragement, criticisms, and suggestions have been invaluable to us.

FIFTH EDITION REVIEWERS   James Angelos, Central Michigan University; Norman Biernes, University of Regina; Brian Blank, Washington University; Jack Ceder, University of California—Santa Barbara; Kathy Davis, University of Texas; Russell Euler, Northwest Missouri State University; Michael Frantz, University of La Verne; Elgin Johnston, Iowa State University; Toni Kasper, Borough of Manhattan Community College; Ronnie Khuri, University of Florida; Murray Lieb, New Jersey Institute of Technology; Mauricio Marroquin, Los Angeles Valley College; Robert McMaster, John Abbott College; Philip Montgomery, University of Kansas; Charlotte Newsom, Tidewater Community College; Luis Ortiz-Franco, Chapman University; Donald Poulson, Mesa Community College; Enid Steinbart, University of New Orleans; Marjorie Valentine, North Side ISD; Carroll G. Wells, Western Kentucky University; Paul D. Zahn, Borough of Manhattan Community College

FOURTH EDITION FOCUS GROUP   Homer F. Bechtell, University of New Hampshire; K. Elayn Gay, University of New Orleans; Hideaki Kaneko, Old Dominion University; Judith A. Palagallo, University of Akron; John Tweed, Old Dominion University

FOURTH EDITION REVIEWERS   Keith Bergeron, United States Air Force Academy; Jorge Cossio, Miami-Dade Community College; Rosario Diprizio, Oakton Community College; Ali Hajjafar, University of Akron; Ransom Van B. Lynch, Phillips Exeter Academy; Bennet Manvel, Colorado State University; Duff A. Muir, United States Air Force Academy; Charlotte J. Newsom, Tidewater Community College; Terry J. Newton, United States Air Force Academy; Wayne J. Peeples, University of Texas; Jorge A. Perez, LaGuardia Community College; Barry J. Sarnacki, United States Air Force Academy; George W. Schultz, St. Petersburg Junior College; Frank Soler, De Anza College; Michael Steuer, Nassau Community College; John Tweed, Old Dominion University; Jay Wiestling, Palomar College; August J. Zarcone, College of DuPage; Li Fong, Johnson County Community College

THIRD EDITION REVIEWERS   Dennis Albér, Palm Beach Junior College; Garret J. Etgen, University of Houston; William R. Fuller, Purdue University; Timothy J. Kearns, Boston College; Norbert Lerner, State University of New York at Cortland; Robert L. Maynard, Tidewater Community College; Barbara L. Osofsky, Rutgers University; Jean E. Rubin, Purdue University; Lawrence A. Trivieri, Mohawk Valley Community College; J. Philip Smith, Southern Connecticut State University

SECOND EDITION REVIEWERS   Harry L. Baldwin, Jr., San Diego City College; Phillip A. Ferguson, Fresno City College; Thomas M. Green, Contra Costa College; Arnold J. Insel, Illinois State University; William J. Keane, Boston College; David C. Lantz, Colgate University; Richard E. Shermoen, Washburn University; Thomas W. Shilgalis, Illinois State University; Florence A. Warfel, University of Pittsburgh

FIRST EDITION REVIEWERS   Paul W. Davis, Worcester Polytechnic Institute; Eric R. Immel, Georgia Institute of Technology; Frank T. Kocher, Jr., Pennsylvania State University; Joseph F. Krebs, Boston College; Maurice L. Monahan, South Dakota State University; Robert A. Nowlan, Southern Connecticut State University; N. James Schoonmaker, University of Vermont; Bert K. Waits, Ohio State University

We would also like to thank users of the Third Edition who answered a questionnaire concerning changes they wanted in the new edition. They are George Anderson, Rhode Island College; Frank P. Battles, Massachusetts Maritime Academy; Derek I. Bloomfield, Orange County Community College; Karen J. Edwards, Paul Smith's College; Theodore Hanley, State University of New York at Utica/Rome; Peter Herron, Suffolk County Community College; Ann M. Joyce, Chestnut Hill College; Arthur Kaufman, College of Staten Island; Alan Levine, Franklin and Marshall College; James Magliano, Union County College; Frank Morgan, Castleton State College; Raymond Pluta, Castleton State College; M. Susan Richman, Pennsylvania State University; Carmen Vlad, Pace University; Christopher White, Castleton State College.

A special thanks to all the people at D. C. Heath and Company who worked with us in the development of the Fifth Edition, especially Ann Marie Jones, Mathematics Acquisitions Editor; Cathy Cantin, Developmental Editor; Ron Hampton, Production Editor; Sally Steele, Designer; Elinor Stapleton, Art Editor; Wing-Harn Chen, Developmental Assistant; Carolyn Johnson, Editorial Associate; Mike O'Dea, Production Manager; and Toni Michaels, Photo Researcher.

We would also like to thank the staff at Larson Texts, Inc. who assisted with proofreading the manuscript; preparing and proofreading the art package; and checking and typesetting the supplements.

A special note of thanks goes to the over 1,000,000 students who have used earlier editions of the text.

On a personal level, we are grateful to our wives, Deanna Gilbert Larson, Eloise Hostetler, and Consuelo Edwards, for their love, patience, and support. Also, a special thanks goes to R. Scott O'Neil.

If you have suggestions for improving this text, please feel free to write to us. Over the past two decades we have received many useful comments from both instructors and students, and we value these very much.

Roland E. Larson, Robert P. Hostetler, Bruce H. Edwards

Calculus

To accommodate the different methods of teaching calculus, D. C. Heath offers the programs listed below.

Calculus with Analytic Geometry, Fifth Edition
Larson/Hostetler/Edwards

Calculus with Analytic Geometry, Alternate Fifth Edition with Late Trigonometry
Larson/Hostetler/Edwards

Calculus of a Single Variable, Fifth Edition
Larson/Hostetler/Edwards

Multivariable Calculus, Fifth Edition
Larson/Hostetler/Edwards

Calculus: Early Transcendental Functions
Larson/Hostetler/Edwards

Calculus of a Single Variable: Early Transcendental Functions
Larson/Hostetler/Edwards

Interactive Calculus
Larson/Hostetler/Edwards

Contents

Chapter 11   Vectors and the Geometry of Space   714

Chapter 12   Vector-Valued Functions   782

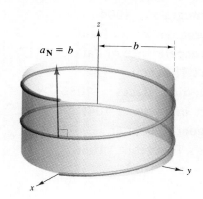

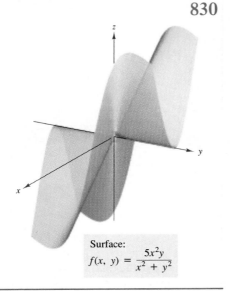

Surface:
$$f(x, y) = \frac{5x^2y}{x^2 + y^2}$$

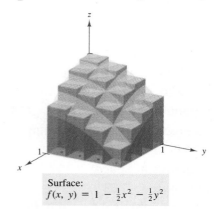

Surface:
$$f(x, y) = 1 - \tfrac{1}{2}x^2 - \tfrac{1}{2}y^2$$

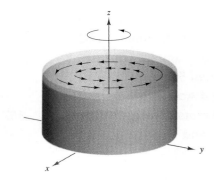

Chapter 16   Differential Equations

ABOUT THE COVER

The "Umbilic Torus NC" is a sculptural expression of timeless mathematical theorems in new silicon bronze created by Helaman Ferguson in 1987–88. Ferguson thought about the binary quadratic forms $ax^2 + bxy + cy^2$ where $b^2 - 4ac$ tells when the coefficients (a, b, c) represent the quadratic part of conic sections for hyperbolas ($b^2 - 4ac > 0$), ellipses ($b^2 - 4ac < 0$), or parabolas ($b^2 - 4ac = 0$). Then he thought about the binary cubic forms $ax^3 + bx^2y + cxy^2 + dy^3$ where the discriminant $\Delta = b^2c^2 - 4ac^3 - 4b^3d + 18abcd - 27a^2d^2$ tells when the coefficients (a, b, c, d) represent hyperbolic umbilics ($\Delta < 0$), elliptic umbilics ($\Delta > 0$), and parabolic umbilics ($\Delta = 0$). He saw an umbilic torus here by looking at the real cubic form with four real coefficients a, b, c, d as an equivalent complex cubic form with two complex coefficients u, v. He substituted z by $e^{i\theta}z$ and changed (u, v) into $(uc^{3i\theta}, vc^{i\theta})$, so u rotates thrice while v rotates once. He set $u = 1$, differentiated, and solved for the torus cross-section curve $v = 2e^{i\varnothing} - e^{-2i\varnothing}$, a hypocycloid with three cusps. From this he got the umbilic torus in two complex dimensions as ($e^{3i\theta}$, $2e^{i(\theta+\varnothing)} - e^{i(\theta-2\varnothing)}$). He felt how the space curve of cusps of this hypocycloid wound the umbilic torus three times the long way and once the short way. He developed three real dimensional equations to get the umbilic torus in a sculpture-like space, computed normal vectors, tool offset vectors, and an NC (numerically controlled) tool path. For surface texture he chose the computer-driven cutting ball end mill tool path to be a stage of the surface filling Hilbert curve or 2-adic space filling Peano curve. This positive form so carved, he put through the traditional lost-wax bronze casting process: a negative silicone rubber mold, positive wax image, negative ceramic flask, and positive silicon bronze which was chased and corroded to give a permanent antique green finish. For more about this sculpture read "Two Theorems, Two Sculptures, Two Posters" appearing in the *American Mathematical Monthly*, Volume 97, Number 7, August–September 1990, pp. 589–610. For more about the sculptor's work, read the full-color book *Helaman Ferguson: Mathematics in Stone and Bronze* by Claire Ferguson, published by Meridian Creative Group, 1994.

Applications

BUSINESS AND ECONOMICS

THE SOCIAL AND BEHAVIORAL SCIENCES

What Is Calculus?

We begin to answer this question by saying that calculus is the reformulation of elementary mathematics through the use of a limit process. From an elementary point of view, we may think of calculus as a "limit machine" that generates new formulas from old. By now you should be familiar with the limit process and may have already noticed that the study of calculus involves three distinct stages of mathematics: precalculus mathematics (the length of a line segment, the area of a rectangle, and so forth), the limit process, and new calculus formulations (derivatives, integrals, and so forth).

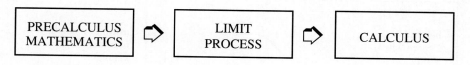

Some students try to learn calculus as if it were simply a collection of new formulas. This is unfortunate. When students reduce calculus to the memorization of differentiation and integration formulas, they miss a great deal of understanding, self-confidence, and satisfaction.

On the following two pages we have listed some familiar precalculus concepts coupled with their more powerful calculus versions. Precalculus formulas and techniques are used as building blocks to produce the more general calculus formulas and techniques.

As you proceed through this text, we suggest that you come back to this discussion repeatedly. Try to keep track of where you are relative to the three stages involved in the study of calculus. We wish you well in your venture into calculus.

WITHOUT CALCULUS	WITH DIFFERENTIAL CALCULUS
value of $f(x)$ when $x = c$	limit of $f(x)$ as x approaches c
slope of a line	slope of a curve
secant line to a curve	tangent line to a curve
average rate of change between $t = a$ and $t = b$	instantaneous rate of change at $t = c$
curvature of a circle	curvature of a curve
height of a curve when $x = c$	maximum height of a curve on an interval
tangent plane to a sphere	tangent plane to a surface
direction of motion along a straight line	direction of motion along a curved line

WITHOUT CALCULUS	WITH INTEGRAL CALCULUS
area of a rectangle	area under a curve
work done by a constant force	work done by a variable force
center of a rectangle	centroid of a region
length of a line segment	length of an arc
surface area of a cylinder	surface area of a solid of revolution
mass of a solid of constant density	mass of a solid of variable density
volume of a rectangular solid	volume of a region under a surface
sum of a finite number of terms $\qquad a_1 + a_2 + \cdots + a_n = S$	sum of an infinite number of terms $\qquad a_1 + a_2 + a_3 \cdots = S$

Chapter 11

Vectors and the Geometry of Space

Vectors in the Plane

11.1 Component Form of a Vector • Vector Operations • Standard Unit Vectors • Applications of Vectors

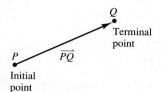

FIGURE 11.1
A directed line segment.

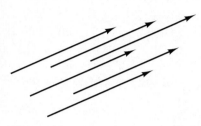

FIGURE 11.2
Equivalent directed line segments.

Component Form of a Vector

Many quantities in geometry and physics, such as area, volume, temperature, mass, and time, can be characterized by single real numbers scaled to appropriate units of measure. We call these **scalar quantities,** and the real number associated with each is called a **scalar.**

Other quantities, such as force and velocity, involve both magnitude and direction and cannot be characterized completely by single real numbers. A **directed line segment** is used to represent such a quantity, as shown in Figure 11.1. The directed line segment $\overrightarrow{PQ}$ has **initial point** P and **terminal point** Q, and its **length** is denoted by $\|\overrightarrow{PQ}\|$. Directed line segments that have the same length and direction are **equivalent,** as shown in Figure 11.2. The set of all directed line segments that are equivalent to a given directed line segment $\overrightarrow{PQ}$ is a **vector in the plane** and is denoted by $\mathbf{v} = \overrightarrow{PQ}$. In typesetting, vectors are usually denoted by lowercase, boldface letters such as $\mathbf{u}$, $\mathbf{v}$, and $\mathbf{w}$. When written by hand, however, vectors are often denoted by letters with arrows above them, such as $\vec{u}$, $\vec{v}$, and $\vec{w}$.

Be sure you see that a vector in the plane can be represented by many different directed line segments—all pointing in the same direction and all of the same length.

EXAMPLE 1   Vector Representation by Directed Line Segments

Let $\mathbf{v}$ be represented by the directed line segment from $(0, 0)$ to $(3, 2)$, and let $\mathbf{u}$ be represented by the directed line segment from $(1, 2)$ to $(4, 4)$. Show that $\mathbf{v} = \mathbf{u}$.

Solution   Let $P = (0, 0)$, $Q = (3, 2)$, $R = (1, 2)$, and $S = (4, 4)$, as shown in Figure 11.3. You can use the Distance Formula to show that $\overrightarrow{PQ}$ and $\overrightarrow{RS}$ have the *same length.*

$$\|\overrightarrow{PQ}\| = \sqrt{(3 - 0)^2 + (2 - 0)^2} = \sqrt{13}$$
$$\|\overrightarrow{RS}\| = \sqrt{(4 - 1)^2 + (4 - 2)^2} = \sqrt{13}$$

Both line segments have the *same direction,* because they both are directed toward the upper right on lines having the same slope.

$$\text{Slope of } \overrightarrow{PQ} = \frac{2 - 0}{3 - 0} = \frac{2}{3} \quad \text{and} \quad \text{Slope of } \overrightarrow{RS} = \frac{4 - 2}{4 - 1} = \frac{2}{3}$$

Because $\overrightarrow{PQ}$ and $\overrightarrow{RS}$ have the same length and direction, you can conclude that $\mathbf{v} = \mathbf{u}$.

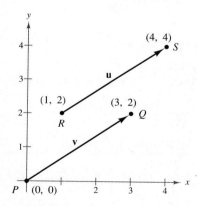

FIGURE 11.3
The vectors $\mathbf{u}$ and $\mathbf{v}$ are equal.

◀ *This photo of a crane shows many intersecting lines. In Section 11.5, Exercises 15–18, you are asked to find the points of intersection of lines in space.*

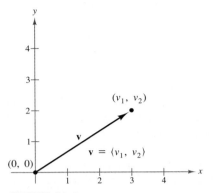

FIGURE 11.4
The standard position of a vector.

The directed line segment whose initial point is the origin is often the most convenient representative of a set of equivalent directed line segments such as those shown in Figure 11.3. This representation of **v** is said to be in **standard position.** A directed line segment whose initial point is at the origin can be uniquely represented by the coordinates of its terminal point $Q = (v_1, v_2)$, as shown in Figure 11.4.

Definition of Component Form of a Vector in the Plane

If **v** is a vector in the plane whose initial point is the origin and whose terminal point is (v_1, v_2), then the **component form of v** is given by

$$\mathbf{v} = \langle v_1, v_2 \rangle.$$

The coordinates v_1 and v_2 are called the **components of v.** If both the initial point and the terminal point lie at the origin, then **v** is called the **zero vector** and is denoted by $\mathbf{0} = \langle 0, 0 \rangle$.

This definition implies that two vectors $\mathbf{u} = \langle u_1, u_2 \rangle$ and $\mathbf{v} = \langle v_1, v_2 \rangle$ are **equal** if and only if $u_1 = v_1$ and $u_2 = v_2$.

The following procedures can be used to convert directed line segments to component form or vice versa.

REMARK It is important to understand that a vector represents a *set* of directed line segments (each having the same length and direction). In practice, however, it is common not to distinguish between a vector and one of its representatives.

1. If $P = (p_1, p_2)$ and $Q = (q_1, q_2)$, then the component form of the vector **v** represented by $\vec{PQ}$ is $\langle v_1, v_2 \rangle = \langle q_1 - p_1, q_2 - p_2 \rangle$. Moreover, the **length of v** is

$$\|\mathbf{v}\| = \sqrt{(q_1 - p_1)^2 + (q_2 - p_2)^2}$$
$$= \sqrt{v_1{}^2 + v_2{}^2}.$$

Length of a vector

2. If $\mathbf{v} = \langle v_1, v_2 \rangle$, then **v** can be represented by the directed line segment, in standard position, from $P = (0, 0)$ to $Q = (v_1, v_2)$.

The length of **v** is also called the **norm of v.** If $\|\mathbf{v}\| = 1$, then **v** is a **unit vector.** Moreover, $\|\mathbf{v}\| = 0$ if and only if **v** is the zero vector **0.**

EXAMPLE 2   Finding the Component Form and Length of a Vector

Find the component form and length of the vector **v** that has initial point $(3, -7)$ and terminal point $(-2, 5)$.

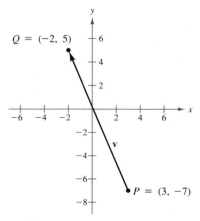

FIGURE 11.5
Component form of **v**: $\mathbf{v} = \langle -5, 12 \rangle$.

Solution   Let $P = (3, -7) = (p_1, p_2)$ and $Q = (-2, 5) = (q_1, q_2)$. Then the components of $\mathbf{v} = \langle v_1, v_2 \rangle$ are

$$v_1 = q_1 - p_1 = -2 - 3 = -5$$
$$v_2 = q_2 - p_2 = 5 - (-7) = 12.$$

Thus, as shown in Figure 11.5, $\mathbf{v} = \langle -5, 12 \rangle$, and the length of **v** is

$$\|\mathbf{v}\| = \sqrt{(-5)^2 + 12^2}$$
$$= \sqrt{169}$$
$$= 13.$$

Vector Operations

The two basic vector operations are **scalar multiplication** and **vector addition.**

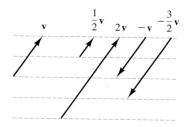

FIGURE 11.6
The scalar multiplication of **v**.

Definitions of Vector Addition and Scalar Multiplication

Let $\mathbf{u} = \langle u_1, u_2 \rangle$ and $\mathbf{v} = \langle v_1, v_2 \rangle$ be vectors and let k be a scalar.

1. The **vector sum** of **u** and **v** is the vector $\mathbf{u} + \mathbf{v} = \langle u_1 + v_1, u_2 + v_2 \rangle$.
2. The **scalar multiple** of k and **u** is the vector $k\,\mathbf{u} = \langle ku_1, ku_2 \rangle$.
3. The **negative** of **v** is the vector $-\mathbf{v} = (-1)\mathbf{v} = \langle -v_1, -v_2 \rangle$.
4. The **difference** of **u** and **v** is $\mathbf{u} - \mathbf{v} = \mathbf{u} + (-\mathbf{v}) = \langle u_1 - v_1, u_2 - v_2 \rangle$.

Geometrically, the product of a vector **v** and a scalar k is the vector that is k times as long as **v**, as shown in Figure 11.6. If k is positive, then $k\,\mathbf{v}$ has the same direction as **v**. If k is negative, then $k\,\mathbf{v}$ has the opposite direction.

To add two vectors geometrically, position them (without changing their magnitudes or directions) so that the initial point of one coincides with the terminal point of the other, as shown in Figure 11.7. The vector $\mathbf{u} + \mathbf{v}$ (called the **resultant vector**) is the diagonal of a parallelogram having **u** and **v** as its adjacent sides.

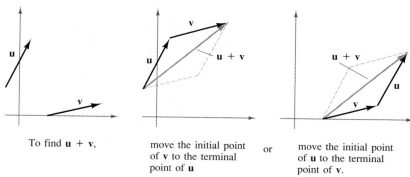

To find $\mathbf{u} + \mathbf{v}$,   move the initial point   or   move the initial point
of **v** to the terminal   of **u** to the terminal
point of **u**   point of **v**.

FIGURE 11.7

Figure 11.8 shows the equivalence of the geometric and algebraic definitions of vector addition and scalar multiplication. The right-most portion of the figure gives a geometric interpretation of $\mathbf{u} - \mathbf{v}$.

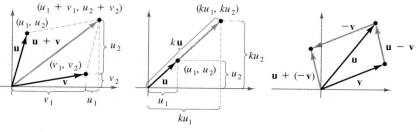

Vector Addition   Scalar Multiplication   Vector Subtraction

FIGURE 11.8

WILLIAM ROWAN HAMILTON

Some of the earliest work with vectors was done by the Irish mathematician William Rowan Hamilton (1805–1865). Hamilton spent many years developing a system of vector-like quantities called quaternions. Although Hamilton was convinced of the benefits of quaternions, the operations he defined did not produce good models for physical phenomena. It wasn't until the latter half of the nineteenth century that the Scottish physicist James Maxwell (1831–1879) restructured Hamilton's quaternions in a form useful for representing physical quantities such as force, velocity, and acceleration.

EXAMPLE 3   Vector Operations

Given $\mathbf{v} = \langle -2, 5 \rangle$ and $\mathbf{w} = \langle 3, 4 \rangle$, find the following vectors.

a. $\dfrac{1}{2}\mathbf{v}$ b. $\mathbf{w} - \mathbf{v}$ c. $\mathbf{v} + 2\mathbf{w}$

Solution

a. $\dfrac{1}{2}\mathbf{v} = \left\langle \dfrac{1}{2}(-2), \dfrac{1}{2}(5) \right\rangle = \left\langle -1, \dfrac{5}{2} \right\rangle$

b. $\mathbf{w} - \mathbf{v} = \langle w_1 - v_1, w_2 - v_2 \rangle = \langle 3 - (-2), 4 - 5 \rangle = \langle 5, -1 \rangle$

c. Using $2\mathbf{w} = \langle 6, 8 \rangle$, you have

$$\mathbf{v} + 2\mathbf{w} = \langle -2, 5 \rangle + \langle 6, 8 \rangle = \langle -2 + 6, 5 + 8 \rangle = \langle 4, 13 \rangle.$$

Vector addition and scalar multiplication share many properties of ordinary arithmetic, as shown in the following theorem.

THEOREM 11.1   Properties of Vector Operations

Let $\mathbf{u}$, $\mathbf{v}$, and $\mathbf{w}$ be vectors in the plane, and let c and d be scalars.

1. $\mathbf{u} + \mathbf{v} = \mathbf{v} + \mathbf{u}$ Commutative property
2. $(\mathbf{u} + \mathbf{v}) + \mathbf{w} = \mathbf{u} + (\mathbf{v} + \mathbf{w})$ Associative property
3. $\mathbf{u} + \mathbf{0} = \mathbf{u}$
4. $\mathbf{u} + (-\mathbf{u}) = \mathbf{0}$
5. $c(d\mathbf{u}) = (cd)\mathbf{u}$
6. $(c + d)\mathbf{u} = c\mathbf{u} + d\mathbf{u}$ Distributive property
7. $c(\mathbf{u} + \mathbf{v}) = c\mathbf{u} + c\mathbf{v}$ Distributive property
8. $1(\mathbf{u}) = \mathbf{u}, \; 0(\mathbf{u}) = \mathbf{0}$

Proof   The proof of the *associative property* of vector addition follows the associative property of addition of real numbers.

$$
\begin{aligned}
(\mathbf{u} + \mathbf{v}) + \mathbf{w} &= [\langle u_1, u_2 \rangle + \langle v_1, v_2 \rangle] + \langle w_1, w_2 \rangle \\
&= \langle u_1 + v_1, u_2 + v_2 \rangle + \langle w_1, w_2 \rangle \\
&= \langle (u_1 + v_1) + w_1, (u_2 + v_2) + w_2 \rangle \\
&= \langle u_1 + (v_1 + w_1), u_2 + (v_2 + w_2) \rangle \\
&= \langle u_1, u_2 \rangle + \langle v_1 + w_1, v_2 + w_2 \rangle = \mathbf{u} + (\mathbf{v} + \mathbf{w})
\end{aligned}
$$

Similarly, the proof of the following distributive property depends on the distributive property of real numbers.

$$
\begin{aligned}
(c + d)\mathbf{u} &= (c + d)\langle u_1, u_2 \rangle \\
&= \langle (c + d)u_1, (c + d)u_2 \rangle \\
&= \langle cu_1 + du_1, cu_2 + du_2 \rangle \\
&= \langle cu_1, cu_2 \rangle + \langle du_1, du_2 \rangle = c\mathbf{u} + d\mathbf{u}
\end{aligned}
$$

The other properties can be proved in a similar manner.

Any set of vectors (with an accompanying set of scalars) that satisfies the eight properties given in Theorem 11.1 is a **vector space.** The eight properties are the *vector space axioms.* Thus, this theorem states that the set of vectors in the plane (with the set of real numbers) forms a vector space. You will study vector spaces in detail if you take a course in *linear algebra.*

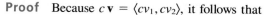

THEOREM 11.2   Length of a Scalar Multiple

Let **v** be a vector and c be a scalar. Then
$$\| c\,\mathbf{v} \| = |c|\,\|\mathbf{v}\|$$
where $|c|$ is the absolute value of c.

Proof   Because $c\,\mathbf{v} = \langle cv_1, cv_2 \rangle$, it follows that
$$
\begin{aligned}
\| c\,\mathbf{v} \| = \| \langle cv_1, cv_2 \rangle \| &= \sqrt{(cv_1)^2 + (cv_2)^2} \\
&= \sqrt{c^2 v_1{}^2 + c^2 v_2{}^2} \\
&= \sqrt{c^2(v_1{}^2 + v_2{}^2)} \\
&= |c|\sqrt{v_1{}^2 + v_2{}^2} \\
&= |c|\,\|\mathbf{v}\|.
\end{aligned}
$$

In many applications of vectors it is useful to find a unit vector that has the same direction as a given vector. The following theorem gives a procedure for doing this.

THEOREM 11.3   Unit Vector in the Direction of v

If **v** is a nonzero vector in the plane, then the vector
$$\mathbf{u} = \frac{\mathbf{v}}{\|\mathbf{v}\|} = \frac{1}{\|\mathbf{v}\|}\mathbf{v}$$
and has length 1 and the same direction as **v**.

Proof   Because $1/\|\mathbf{v}\|$ is positive and $\mathbf{u} = (1/\|\mathbf{v}\|)\mathbf{v}$, you can conclude that **u** has the same direciton as **v**. To see that $\|\mathbf{u}\| = 1$, note that
$$
\begin{aligned}
\|\mathbf{u}\| &= \left\| \left(\frac{1}{\|\mathbf{v}\|}\right)\mathbf{v} \right\| \\
&= \left| \frac{1}{\|\mathbf{v}\|} \right| \|\mathbf{v}\| \\
&= \frac{1}{\|\mathbf{v}\|} \|\mathbf{v}\| = 1.
\end{aligned}
$$
Thus, **u** has length 1 and the same direction as **v**.

In Theorem 11.3, **u** is called a **unit vector in the direction of v.** The process of multiplying **v** by $1/\|\mathbf{v}\|$ to get a unit vector is called **normalization of v.**

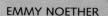

EMMY NOETHER

One person who contributed to our knowledge of axiomatic systems was the German mathematician Emmy Noether (1882–1935). Noether is generally recognized as the leading woman mathematician in recent history.

FOR FURTHER INFORMATION
For more information on Emmy Noether, see the article "Emmy Noether, Greatest Woman Mathematician" by Clark Kimberling in the March, 1982 issue of *Mathematics Teacher.*

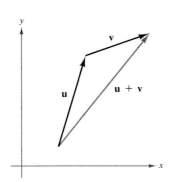

FIGURE 11.9
Triangle inequality

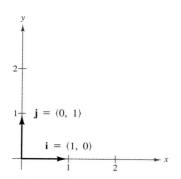

FIGURE 11.10
Standard unit vectors **i** and **j**.

EXAMPLE 4   Finding a Unit Vector

Find a unit vector in the direction of $\mathbf{v} = \langle -2, 5 \rangle$ and verify that the result has length 1.

Solution   From Theorem 11.3, the unit vector in the direction of **v** is

$$\frac{\mathbf{v}}{\|\mathbf{v}\|} = \frac{\langle -2, 5 \rangle}{\sqrt{(-2)^2 + (5)^2}} = \frac{1}{\sqrt{29}} \langle -2, 5 \rangle = \left\langle \frac{-2}{\sqrt{29}}, \frac{5}{\sqrt{29}} \right\rangle.$$

This vector has length 1, because

$$\sqrt{\left(\frac{-2}{\sqrt{29}}\right)^2 + \left(\frac{5}{\sqrt{29}}\right)^2} = \sqrt{\frac{4}{29} + \frac{25}{29}} = \sqrt{\frac{29}{29}} = 1.$$

Generally, the length of the sum of two vectors is not equal to the sum of their lengths. To see this, consider the vectors **u** and **v** as shown in Figure 11.9. By considering **u** and **v** as two sides of a triangle, you can see that the length of the third side is $\|\mathbf{u} + \mathbf{v}\|$, and you have

$$\|\mathbf{u} + \mathbf{v}\| \le \|\mathbf{u}\| + \|\mathbf{v}\|.$$

Equality occurs only if the vectors **u** and **v** have the *same* direction. This result is called the **Triangle Inequality** for vectors. (You are asked to prove this in Exercise 60, Section 11.3.)

Standard Unit Vectors

The unit vectors $\langle 1, 0 \rangle$ and $\langle 0, 1 \rangle$ are called the **standard unit vectors** in the plane and are denoted by

$$\mathbf{i} = \langle 1, 0 \rangle \quad \text{and} \quad \mathbf{j} = \langle 0, 1 \rangle \qquad \text{Standard unit vectors}$$

as shown in Figure 11.10. These vectors can be used to represent any vector, as follows.

$$\mathbf{v} = \langle v_1, v_2 \rangle = \langle v_1, 0 \rangle + \langle 0, v_2 \rangle = v_1 \langle 1, 0 \rangle + v_2 \langle 0, 1 \rangle = v_1 \mathbf{i} + v_2 \mathbf{j}$$

The vector $\mathbf{v} = v_1 \mathbf{i} + v_2 \mathbf{j}$ is called a **linear combination** of **i** and **j**. The scalars v_1 and v_2 are called the **horizontal** and **vertical components of v**, respectively.

EXAMPLE 5   Writing a Vector as a Linear Combination of Unit Vectors

Let **u** be the vector with initial point $(2, -5)$ and terminal point $(-1, 3)$, and let $\mathbf{v} = 2\mathbf{i} - \mathbf{j}$. Write each of the following vectors as a linear combination of the standard unit vectors **i** and **j**.

a. u   **b. w** $= 2\mathbf{u} - 3\mathbf{v}$

Solution

a. $\mathbf{u} = \langle q_1 - p_1, q_2 - p_2 \rangle = \langle -1 - 2, 3 - (-5) \rangle$
$$= \langle -3, 8 \rangle = -3\mathbf{i} + 8\mathbf{j}$$

b. $\mathbf{w} = 2\mathbf{u} - 3\mathbf{v} = 2(-3\mathbf{i} + 8\mathbf{j}) - 3(2\mathbf{i} - \mathbf{j})$
$$= -6\mathbf{i} + 16\mathbf{j} - 6\mathbf{i} + 3\mathbf{j} = -12\mathbf{i} + 19\mathbf{j}$$

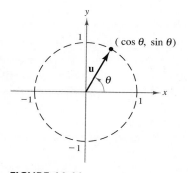

FIGURE 11.11
The angle θ from the positive x-axis to the vector **u**.

If **u** is a unit vector such that θ is the angle (measured counterclockwise) from the positive x-axis to **u**, then the terminal point of **u** lies on the unit circle, and you have

$$\mathbf{u} = \langle \cos\theta, \sin\theta \rangle = \cos\theta\,\mathbf{i} + \sin\theta\,\mathbf{j} \qquad \text{Unit vector}$$

as shown in Figure 11.11. Moreover, it follows that any other nonzero vector **v** making an angle θ with the positive x-axis has the same direction as **u**, and you can write

$$\mathbf{v} = \|\mathbf{v}\|\,\langle \cos\theta, \sin\theta \rangle = \|\mathbf{v}\|\cos\theta\,\mathbf{i} + \|\mathbf{v}\|\sin\theta\,\mathbf{j}.$$

EXAMPLE 6   Writing a Vector of Given Length and Direction

The vector **v** has a length of 3 and makes an angle of $30° = \pi/6$ with the positive x-axis. Write **v** as a linear combination of the unit vectors **i** and **j**.

Solution   Because the angle between **v** and the positive x-axis is $\theta = \pi/3$, you can write the following.

$$\mathbf{v} = \|\mathbf{v}\|\cos\theta\,\mathbf{i} + \|\mathbf{v}\|\sin\theta\,\mathbf{j} = 3\cos\frac{\pi}{6}\mathbf{i} + 3\sin\frac{\pi}{6}\mathbf{j}$$

$$= \frac{3\sqrt{3}}{2}\mathbf{i} + \frac{3}{2}\mathbf{j}$$

Applications of Vectors

There are many applications of vectors in physics and engineering. We conclude this section by considering two examples.

EXAMPLE 7   Finding the Resultant Force

Two tugboats are pushing an ocean liner, as shown in Figure 11.12. Each boat is exerting a force of 400 pounds. What is the resultant force on the ocean liner?

Solution   Using Figure 11.12, you can represent the forces exerted by the first and second tugboats as

$$\mathbf{F}_1 = 400\langle \cos 20°, \sin 20° \rangle$$
$$= 400\cos(20°)\mathbf{i} + 400\sin(20°)\mathbf{j}$$
$$\mathbf{F}_2 = 400\langle \cos(-20°), \sin(-20°) \rangle$$
$$= 400\cos(20°)\mathbf{i} - 400\sin(20°)\mathbf{j}.$$

To obtain the resultant force on the ocean liner, add these two forces.

$$\mathbf{F} = \mathbf{F}_1 + \mathbf{F}_2$$
$$= 400\cos(20°)\mathbf{i} + 400\sin(20°)\mathbf{j} + 400\cos(20°)\mathbf{i} - 400\sin(20°)\mathbf{j}$$
$$= 800\cos(20°)\mathbf{i}$$
$$\approx 752\mathbf{i}$$

Thus, the resultant force on the ocean liner is approximately 752 pounds in the direction of the positive x-axis.

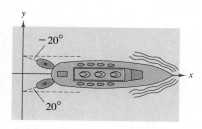

FIGURE 11.12
The resultant force on the ocean liner is approximately 752 pounds in the positive x-direction.

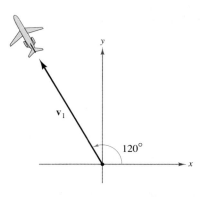

v_1

$120°$

Direction without wind

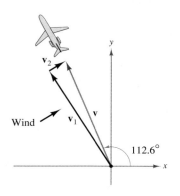

Wind v_1 v_2 v

$112.6°$

Direction with wind

FIGURE 11.13

EXAMPLE 8   Finding a Velocity

An airplane is traveling at a fixed altitude with a negligible wind factor. The plane is headed N 30° W (which means 30° west of north) at a speed of 500 miles per hour, as shown in Figure 11.13. As the plane reaches a certain point, it encounters wind with a velocity of 70 miles per hour in the direction E 45° N. What is the resultant speed and direction of the plane?

Solution   Using Figure 11.13, you can represent the velocity of the plane by the vector

$$\mathbf{v}_1 = 500\cos(120°)\mathbf{i} + 500\sin(120°)\mathbf{j}.$$

The velocity of the wind is represented by the vector

$$\mathbf{v}_2 = 70\cos(45°)\mathbf{i} + 70\sin(45°)\mathbf{j}.$$

The resultant velocity of the plane is

$$\begin{aligned}\mathbf{v} &= \mathbf{v}_1 + \mathbf{v}_2 \\ &= 500\cos(120°)\mathbf{i} + 500\sin(120°)\mathbf{j} + 70\cos(45°)\mathbf{i} + 70\sin(45°)\mathbf{j} \\ &\approx -200.5\mathbf{i} + 482.5\mathbf{j}.\end{aligned}$$

To find the speed and direction, write $\mathbf{v} = \|\mathbf{v}\|(\cos\theta\,\mathbf{i} + \sin\theta\,\mathbf{j})$. Because

$$\|\mathbf{v}\| \approx \sqrt{(-200.5)^2 + (482.5)^2} \approx 522.5$$

you can write

$$\mathbf{v} \approx 522.5\left(\frac{-200.5}{522.5}\mathbf{i} + \frac{482.5}{522.5}\mathbf{j}\right) \approx 522.5[\cos(112.6°)\mathbf{i} + \sin(112.6°)\mathbf{j}].$$

Therefore, the speed of the plane, as altered by the wind, is approximately 522.5 miles per hour in a flight path that makes an angle of 112.6° with the positive x-axis.

EXERCISES for Section 11.1

In Exercises 1–4, (a) find the component form of the vector **v** and (b) sketch the vector with its initial point at the origin.

1.

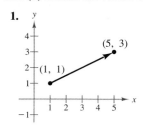

2.

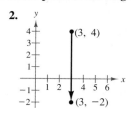

3.

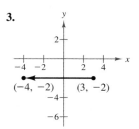

4.

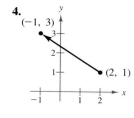

In Exercises 5–12, the initial and terminal points of a vector **v** are given. (a) Sketch the given directed line segment, (b) write the vector in component form, and (c) sketch the vector with its initial point at the origin.

	Initial point	*Terminal point*
5.	(1, 2)	(5, 5)
6.	(3, −5)	(4, 7)
7.	(10, 2)	(6, −1)
8.	(0, −4)	(−5, −1)
9.	(6, 2)	(6, 6)
10.	(7, −1)	(−3, −1)
11.	$(\frac{3}{2}, \frac{4}{3})$	$(\frac{1}{2}, 3)$
12.	(0.12, 0.60)	(0.84, 1.25)

In Exercises 13 and 14, sketch the scalar multiple of v.

13. $\mathbf{v} = \langle 2, 3\rangle$

    a. $2\mathbf{v}$ **b.** $-3\mathbf{v}$ **c.** $\frac{7}{2}\mathbf{v}$ **d.** $\frac{2}{3}\mathbf{v}$

14. $\mathbf{v} = \langle -1, 5 \rangle$

    a. $4\mathbf{v}$ **b.** $-\frac{1}{2}\mathbf{v}$ **c.** $0\mathbf{v}$ **d.** $-6\mathbf{v}$

In Exercises 15–20, find the vector v, where u = $\langle 2, -1 \rangle$ and w = $\langle 1, 2 \rangle$. Illustrate the indicated vector operations geometrically.

15. $\mathbf{v} = \frac{3}{2}\mathbf{u}$ **16.** $\mathbf{v} = \mathbf{u} + \mathbf{w}$

17. $\mathbf{v} = \mathbf{u} + 2\mathbf{w}$ **18.** $\mathbf{v} = -\mathbf{u} + \mathbf{w}$

19. $\mathbf{v} = \frac{1}{2}(3\mathbf{u} + \mathbf{w})$ **20.** $\mathbf{v} = \mathbf{u} - 2\mathbf{w}$

In Exercises 21–26, find a and b such that v = au + bw, where u = $\langle 1, 2 \rangle$ and w = $\langle 1, -1 \rangle$.

21. $\mathbf{v} = \langle 2, 1 \rangle$ **22.** $\mathbf{v} = \langle 0, 3 \rangle$

23. $\mathbf{v} = \langle 3, 0 \rangle$ **24.** $\mathbf{v} = \langle 3, 3 \rangle$

25. $\mathbf{v} = \langle 1, 1 \rangle$ **26.** $\mathbf{v} = \langle -1, 7 \rangle$

In Exercises 27 and 28, the vector v and its initial point are given. Find the terminal point.

27. $\mathbf{v} = \langle -1, 3 \rangle$, initial point $(4, 2)$

28. $\mathbf{v} = \langle 4, -9 \rangle$, initial point $(3, 2)$

In Exercises 29–34, find the magnitude of v.

29. $\mathbf{v} = \langle 4, 3 \rangle$ **30.** $\mathbf{v} = \langle 12, -5 \rangle$

31. $\mathbf{v} = 6\mathbf{i} - 5\mathbf{j}$ **32.** $\mathbf{v} = -10\mathbf{i} + 3\mathbf{j}$

33. $\mathbf{v} = 4\mathbf{j}$ **34.** $\mathbf{v} = \mathbf{i} - \mathbf{j}$

In Exercises 35–38, find the following.

  a. $\|\mathbf{u}\|$ **b.** $\|\mathbf{v}\|$ **c.** $\|\mathbf{u} + \mathbf{v}\|$

  d. $\left\|\dfrac{\mathbf{u}}{\|\mathbf{u}\|}\right\|$ **e.** $\left\|\dfrac{\mathbf{v}}{\|\mathbf{v}\|}\right\|$ **f.** $\left\|\dfrac{\mathbf{u} + \mathbf{v}}{\|\mathbf{u} + \mathbf{v}\|}\right\|$

35. $\mathbf{u} = \langle 1, -1 \rangle$ **36.** $\mathbf{u} = \langle 0, 1 \rangle$
    $\mathbf{v} = \langle -1, 2 \rangle$ $\mathbf{v} = \langle 3, -3 \rangle$

37. $\mathbf{u} = \langle 1, \frac{1}{2} \rangle$ **38.** $\mathbf{u} = \langle 2, -4 \rangle$
    $\mathbf{v} = \langle 2, 3 \rangle$ $\mathbf{v} = \langle 5, 5 \rangle$

In Exercises 39 and 40, demonstrate the triangle inequality using the vectors u and v.

39. $\mathbf{u} = \langle 2, 1 \rangle$ **40.** $\mathbf{u} = \langle -3, 2 \rangle$
    $\mathbf{v} = \langle 5, 4 \rangle$ $\mathbf{v} = \langle 1, -2 \rangle$

In Exercises 41–44, find the vector v with the given magnitude and the same direction as u.

Magnitude	Direction
41. $\|\mathbf{v}\| = 4$	$\mathbf{u} = \langle 1, 1 \rangle$
42. $\|\mathbf{v}\| = 4$	$\mathbf{u} = \langle -1, 1 \rangle$
43. $\|\mathbf{v}\| = 2$	$\mathbf{u} = \langle \sqrt{3}, 3 \rangle$
44. $\|\mathbf{v}\| = 3$	$\mathbf{u} = \langle 0, 3 \rangle$

In Exercises 45–48, find a unit vector (a) parallel to the graph of $f(x)$ at the indicated point, and (b) normal to the graph of $f(x)$ at the indicated point.

Function	Point
45. $f(x) = x^3$	$(1, 1)$
46. $f(x) = x^3$	$(-2, -8)$
47. $f(x) = \sqrt{25 - x^2}$	$(3, 4)$
48. $f(x) = \tan x$	$\left(\dfrac{\pi}{4}, 1\right)$

In Exercises 49–52, find the component form of v given its magnitude and the angle it makes with the positive x-axis.

Magnitude	Angle
49. $\|\mathbf{v}\| = 3$	$\theta = 0°$
50. $\|\mathbf{v}\| = 1$	$\theta = 45°$
51. $\|\mathbf{v}\| = 2$	$\theta = 150°$
52. $\|\mathbf{v}\| = 1$	$\theta = 3.5°$

In Exercises 53–56, find the component form of u + v given the magnitudes of u and v and the angles that u and v make with the positive x-axis.

53. $\|\mathbf{u}\| = 1, \theta_{\mathbf{u}} = 0°$
    $\|\mathbf{v}\| = 3, \theta_{\mathbf{v}} = 45°$

54. $\|\mathbf{u}\| = 4, \theta_{\mathbf{u}} = 0°$
    $\|\mathbf{v}\| = 2, \theta_{\mathbf{v}} = 60°$

55. $\|\mathbf{u}\| = 2, \theta_{\mathbf{u}} = 4$
    $\|\mathbf{v}\| = 1, \theta_{\mathbf{v}} = 2$

56. $\|\mathbf{u}\| = 5, \theta_{\mathbf{u}} = -0.5$
    $\|\mathbf{v}\| = 5, \theta_{\mathbf{v}} = 0.5$

In Exercises 57 and 58, find the component form of v given the magnitudes of u and u + v and the angles that u and u + v make with the positive x-axis.

57. $\|\mathbf{u}\| = 1, \theta = 45°$ **58.** $\|\mathbf{u}\| = 4, \theta = 30°$
    $\|\mathbf{u} + \mathbf{v}\| = \sqrt{2}, \theta = 90°$ $\|\mathbf{u} + \mathbf{v}\| = 6, \theta = 120°$

C **In Exercises 59 and 60, use a computer algebra system to find the magnitude and direction of the resultant of the vectors.**

59.   **60.**

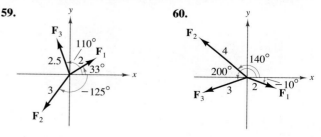

*A **C** indicates an exercise in which you are instructed to use graphing technology or a symbolic computer algebra system. The solutions of other exercises may also be facilitated by appropriate technology.

61. *Resultant Force*   Forces with magnitudes of 35 and 50 pounds act on a hook (see figure). The angle between the two forces is 30°. Find the direction and magnitude of the resultant (vector sum) of these two forces.

62. *Resultant Force*   Forces with magnitudes of 500 and 200 pounds act on a machine part at angles of 30° and −45°, respectively, with the *x*-axis (see figure). Find the direction and magnitude of the resultant (vector sum) of these forces.

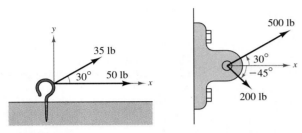

FIGURE FOR 61   **FIGURE FOR 62**

63. *Resultant Force*   Three forces with magnitudes of 75, 100, and 125 pounds act on an object at angles of 30°, 45°, and 120°, respectively, with the positive *x*-axis. Find the direction and magnitude of the resultant of these forces.

64. *Resultant Force*   Three forces with magnitudes of 70, 40, and 60 pounds act on an object at angles of −30°, 45°, and 135°, respectively, with the positive *x*-axis. Find the direction and magnitude of the resultant of these forces.

65. *Tether Ball*   A tether ball weighing 1 pound is pulled outward from the pole by a horizontal force **u** until the rope makes a 30° angle with the pole (see figure). Determine the resulting tension in the rope and the magnitude of **u**.

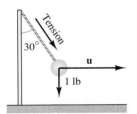

FIGURE FOR 65

66. *Barge Towing*   A loaded barge is being towed by two tugboats, and the magnitude of the resultant is 6000 pounds directed along the axis of the barge. Find the tension in the tow lines if they each make a 20° angle with the axis of the barge.

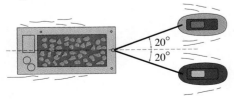

FIGURE FOR 66

67. *Shared Load*   To carry a 100-pound cylindrical weight, two workers lift on the ends of short ropes tied to an eyelet on the top center of the cylinder. One rope makes a 20° angle away from the vertical and the other a 30° angle (see figure).
   a. Find the tension in each rope if the resultant force is vertical.
   b. Find the vertical component of each worker's force.

68. *Navigation*   An airplane is headed 32° north of west. Its speed with respect to the air is 580 miles per hour. The wind at the plane's altitude is from the southwest at 60 miles per hour (see figure). What is the true direction of the plane, and what is its speed with respect to the ground?

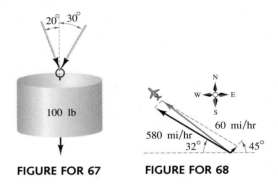 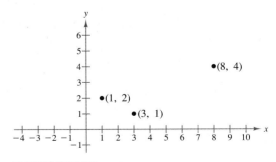

FIGURE FOR 67   **FIGURE FOR 68**

69. *Navigation*   A plane flies at a constant ground speed of 450 miles per hour due east and encounters a 50 mile per hour wind from the northwest. Find the air speed and compass direction that will allow the plane to maintain its ground speed and eastward direction.

70. *Projectile Motion*   A gun with a muzzle velocity of 1200 feet per second is fired at an angle of 6° with the horizontal. Find the vertical and horizontal components of the velocity.

71. Three vertices of a parallelogram are (1, 2), (3, 1), and (8, 4). Find the three possible fourth vertices (see figure).

FIGURE FOR 71

72. Use vectors to find the points of trisection of the line segment with endpoints (1, 2) and (7, 5).

73. If $\mathbf{F}_1 + \mathbf{F}_2 + \mathbf{F}_3 = \mathbf{0}$, find T_2 and T_3.

$\mathbf{F}_1 = -3600\mathbf{j}$

$\mathbf{F}_2 = T_2(\cos 35°\mathbf{i} - \sin 35°\mathbf{j})$

$\mathbf{F}_3 = T_3(\cos 92°\mathbf{i} + \sin 92°\mathbf{j})$

74. Prove that the vectors

$\mathbf{u} = (\cos\theta)\mathbf{i} - (\sin\theta)\mathbf{j}$

and

$\mathbf{v} = (\sin\theta)\mathbf{i} + (\cos\theta)\mathbf{j}$

are unit vectors for any angle θ.

75. Using vectors, prove that the line segment joining the midpoints of two sides of a triangle is parallel to, and one-half the length of, the third side.

76. Using vectors, prove that the diagonals of a parallelogram bisect each other.

True or False   In Exercises 77–82, determine whether the statement is true or false. If it is false, explain why or give an example that shows it is false.

77. If $\mathbf{u}$ and $\mathbf{v}$ have the same magnitude and direction, then $\mathbf{u} = \mathbf{v}$.

78. If $\mathbf{u}$ is a unit vector in the direction of $\mathbf{v}$, then $\mathbf{v} = \|\mathbf{v}\|\,\mathbf{u}$.

79. If $\mathbf{u} = a\mathbf{i} + b\mathbf{j}$ is a unit vector, then $a^2 + b^2 = 1$.

80. If $\mathbf{v} = a\mathbf{i} + b\mathbf{j} = \mathbf{0}$, then $a = -b$.

81. If $a = b$, then $\|a\mathbf{i} + b\mathbf{j}\| = \sqrt{2}a$.

82. If $\mathbf{u}$ and $\mathbf{v}$ have the same magnitude but opposite directions, then $\mathbf{u} + \mathbf{v} = \mathbf{0}$.

83. Prove that the vector $\mathbf{w} = \|\mathbf{u}\|\,\mathbf{v} + \|\mathbf{v}\|\,\mathbf{u}$ bisects the angle between $\mathbf{u}$ and $\mathbf{v}$.

11.2

Coordinates in Space • Vectors in Space • Applications

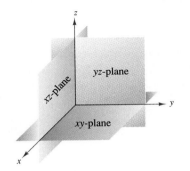

FIGURE 11.14
The three-dimensional
coordinate system.

Coordinates in Space

Up to this point in the text, we have been primarily concerned with the two-dimensional coordinate system. Much of the remaining part of your study of calculus will involve the three-dimensional coordinate system.

Before extending the concept of a vector to three dimensions, we introduce the **three-dimensional coordinate system.** You can construct this system by passing a z-axis perpendicular to both the x- and y-axes at the origin. Figure 11.14 shows the positive portion of each coordinate axis. Taken as pairs, the axes determine three **coordinate planes:** the **xy-plane,** the **xz-plane,** and the **yz-plane.** These three coordinate planes separate three-space into eight **octants.** The first octant is the one for which all three coordinates are positive. In this three-dimensional system, a point P in space is determined by an ordered triple (x, y, z), where x, y, and z are as follows.

$$x = \text{directed distance from } yz\text{-plane to } P$$
$$y = \text{directed distance from } xz\text{-plane to } P$$
$$z = \text{directed distance from } xy\text{-plane to } P$$

Several points are shown in Figure 11.15.

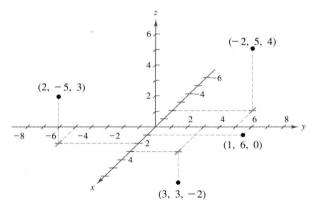

FIGURE 11.15
Points in the three-dimensional coordinate system are represented by ordered triples.

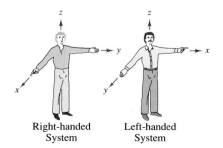

Right-handed
System   Left-handed
System

FIGURE 11.16

A three-dimensional coordinate system can have either a **left-handed** or a **right-handed** orientation. To determine the orientation of a system, imagine that you are standing at the origin, with your arms pointing in the direction of the positive x- and y-axes, and with the z-axis pointing up, as shown in Figure 11.16. The system is right-handed or left-handed, depending on which hand points along the x-axis. In this text we work exclusively with the right-handed system.

Many of the formulas established for the two-dimensional coordinate system can be extended to three dimensions. For example, to find the distance between two points in space, you can use the Pythagorean Theorem twice, as shown in Figure 11.17. By doing this, you will obtain the formula for the distance between the points (x_1, y_1, z_1) and (x_2, y_2, z_2).

$$d = \sqrt{(x_2 - x_1)^2 + (y_2 - y_1)^2 + (z_2 - z_1)^2}$$ Distance Formula

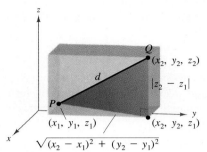

FIGURE 11.17
The distance between two points in space.

EXAMPLE 1   Finding the Distance Between Two Points in Space

The distance between the points $(2, -1, 3)$ and $(1, 0, -2)$ is

$$d = \sqrt{(1 - 2)^2 + (0 + 1)^2 + (-2 - 3)^2}$$
$$= \sqrt{1 + 1 + 25} = \sqrt{27} = 3\sqrt{3}.$$

A **sphere** with center at (x_0, y_0, z_0) and radius r is defined as the set of all points (x, y, z) such that the distance between (x, y, z) and (x_0, y_0, z_0) is r. You can use the Distance Formula to find the **standard equation of a sphere** of radius r, centered at (x_0, y_0, z_0). If (x, y, z) is an arbitrary point on the sphere, then the equation of the sphere is

$$(x - x_0)^2 + (y - y_0)^2 + (z - z_0)^2 = r^2$$ Equation of a sphere

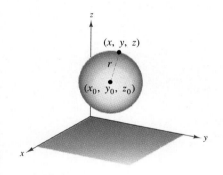

FIGURE 11.18

as shown in Figure 11.18. Moreover, the midpoint of the line segment joining the points (x_1, y_1, z_1) and (x_2, y_2, z_2) has coordinates

$$\left(\frac{x_1 + x_2}{2}, \frac{y_1 + y_2}{2}, \frac{z_1 + z_2}{2} \right).$$ Midpoint Rule

The following example makes use of both of these formulas.

EXAMPLE 2   Finding the Equation of a Sphere

Find the standard equation for the sphere that has the points $(5, -2, 3)$ and $(0, 4, -3)$ as endpoints of a diameter.

Solution   By the Midpoint Rule, the center of the sphere is

$$\left(\frac{5 + 0}{2}, \frac{-2 + 4}{2}, \frac{3 - 3}{2} \right) = \left(\frac{5}{2}, 1, 0 \right).$$

By the Distance Formula, the radius is

$$r = \sqrt{\left(0 - \frac{5}{2} \right)^2 + (4 - 1)^2 + (-3 - 0)^2} = \sqrt{\frac{97}{4}} = \frac{\sqrt{97}}{2}.$$

Therefore, the standard equation of the sphere is

$$\left(x - \frac{5}{2} \right)^2 + (y - 1)^2 + (z - 0)^2 = \frac{97}{4}.$$

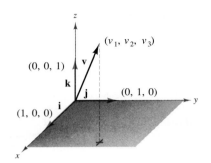

FIGURE 11.19
The standard unit vectors in space.

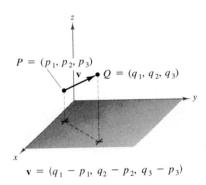

$v = \langle q_1 - p_1, q_2 - p_2, q_3 - p_3 \rangle$

FIGURE 11.20

Vectors in Space

In space, vectors are denoted by ordered triples $\mathbf{v} = \langle v_1, v_2, v_3 \rangle$. The **zero vector** is denoted by $\mathbf{0} = \langle 0, 0, 0 \rangle$. Using the unit vectors $\mathbf{i} = \langle 1, 0, 0 \rangle$, $\mathbf{j} = \langle 0, 1, 0 \rangle$, and $\mathbf{k} = \langle 0, 0, 1 \rangle$ in the direction of the positive z-axis, the **standard unit vector notation** for $\mathbf{v}$ is

$$\mathbf{v} = v_1 \mathbf{i} + v_2 \mathbf{j} + v_3 \mathbf{k}$$

as shown in Figure 11.19. If $\mathbf{v}$ is represented by the directed line segment from $P = (p_1, p_2, p_3)$ to $Q = (q_1, q_2, q_3)$, as shown in Figure 11.20, then the component form of $\mathbf{v}$ is given by subtracting the coordinates of the initial point from the coordinates of the terminal point, as follows.

$$\mathbf{v} = \langle v_1, v_2, v_3 \rangle = \langle q_1 - p_1, q_2 - p_2, q_3 - p_3 \rangle$$

Vectors in Space

Let $\mathbf{u} = \langle u_1, u_2, u_3 \rangle$ and $\mathbf{v} = \langle v_1, v_2, v_3 \rangle$ be vectors in space and let c be a scalar.

1. *Equality of Vectors:* $\mathbf{u} = \mathbf{v}$ if and only if $u_1 = v_1$, $u_2 = v_2$, and $u_3 = v_3$.
2. *Component Form:* If $\mathbf{v}$ is represented by the directed line segment from $P = (p_1, p_2, p_3)$ to $Q = (q_1, q_2, q_3)$ then
   $$\mathbf{v} = \langle v_1, v_2, v_3 \rangle = \langle q_1 - p_1, q_2 - p_2, q_3 - p_3 \rangle.$$
3. *Length:* $\| \mathbf{v} \| = \sqrt{v_1^2 + v_2^2 + v_3^2}$
4. *Unit Vector in the Direction of* $\mathbf{v}$: $\dfrac{\mathbf{v}}{\| \mathbf{v} \|} = \left(\dfrac{1}{\| \mathbf{v} \|} \right) \langle v_1, v_2, v_3 \rangle$, $\mathbf{v} \neq \mathbf{0}$
5. *Vector Addition:* $\mathbf{v} + \mathbf{u} = \langle v_1 + u_1, v_2 + u_2, v_3 + u_3 \rangle$
6. *Scalar Multiplication:* $c\mathbf{v} = \langle cv_1, cv_2, cv_3 \rangle$

REMARK The properties of vector addition and scalar multiplication given in Theorem 11.1 are also valid for vectors in space.

EXAMPLE 3   Finding the Component Form of a Vector in Space

Find the component form and length of the vector $\mathbf{v}$ having initial point $(-2, 3, 1)$ and terminal point $(0, -4, 4)$. Then find a unit vector in the direction of $\mathbf{v}$.

Solution   The component form of $\mathbf{v}$ is

$$\mathbf{v} = \langle q_1 - p_1, q_2 - p_2, q_3 - p_3 \rangle = \langle 0 - (-2), -4 - 3, 4 - 1 \rangle$$
$$= \langle 2, -7, 3 \rangle$$

which implies that its length is

$$\| \mathbf{v} \| = \sqrt{(2)^2 + (-7)^2 + (3)^2} = \sqrt{62}.$$

The unit vector in the direction of $\mathbf{v}$ is

$$\mathbf{u} = \frac{\mathbf{v}}{\| \mathbf{v} \|} = \frac{1}{\sqrt{62}} \langle 2, -7, 3 \rangle.$$

Recall from the definition of scalar multiplication that positive scalar multiples of a nonzero vector **v** have the same direction as **v**, whereas negative multiples have the direction opposite that of **v**. In general, two nonzero vectors **u** and **v** are **parallel** if there is some scalar c such that $\mathbf{u} = c\mathbf{v}$.

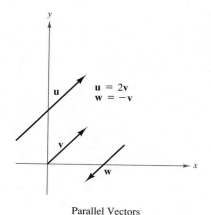

u = 2**v**
w = −**v**

Parallel Vectors

FIGURE 11.21

Definition of Parallel Vectors

Two nonzero vectors **u** and **v** are **parallel** if there is some scalar c such that $\mathbf{u} = c\mathbf{v}$.

For example, in Figure 11.21, the vectors **u**, **v**, and **w** are parallel because $\mathbf{u} = 2\mathbf{v}$ and $\mathbf{w} = -\mathbf{v}$.

EXAMPLE 4   Parallel Vectors

Vector **w** has initial point $(2, -1, 3)$ and terminal point $(-4, 7, 5)$. Which of the following vectors is parallel to **w**?

a. $\mathbf{u} = \langle 3, -4, -1 \rangle$ **b.** $\mathbf{v} = \langle 12, -16, 4 \rangle$

Solution   Begin by writing **w** in component form.

$$\mathbf{w} = \langle -4 - 2, 7 - (-1), 5 - 3 \rangle = \langle -6, 8, 2 \rangle$$

a. Because $\mathbf{u} = \langle 3, -4, -1 \rangle = -\frac{1}{2}\langle -6, 8, 2 \rangle = -\frac{1}{2}\mathbf{w}$, you can conclude that **u** *is* parallel to **w**.

b. In this case, you want to find a scalar c such that

$$\langle 12, -16, 4 \rangle = c\langle -6, 8, 2 \rangle.$$

However, when you equate corresponding components, you obtain $c = -2$ for the first two components and $c = 2$ for the third. Hence, the equation has no solution, and the vectors are *not* parallel.

EXAMPLE 5   Using Vectors to Determine Collinear Points

Determine whether the points $P = (1, -2, 3)$, $Q = (2, 1, 0)$, and $R = (4, 7, -6)$ lie on the same line.

Solution   The component forms of $\vec{PQ}$ and $\vec{PR}$ are

$$\vec{PQ} = \langle 2 - 1, 1 - (-2), 0 - 3 \rangle = \langle 1, 3, -3 \rangle$$

and

$$\vec{PR} = \langle 4 - 1, 7 - (-2), -6 - 3 \rangle = \langle 3, 9, -9 \rangle.$$

These two vectors have a common initial point. Hence, P, Q, and R lie on the same line if and only if $\vec{PQ}$ and $\vec{PR}$ are parallel—which they are because $\vec{PR} = 3\vec{PQ}$, as shown in Figure 11.22.

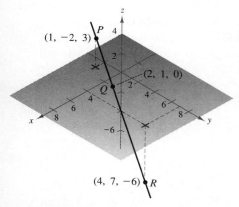

FIGURE 11.22
The points P, Q, and R lie on the same line.

EXAMPLE 6   Standard Unit Vector Notation

a. Write the vector $\mathbf{v} = 4\mathbf{i} - 5\mathbf{k}$ in component form.
b. Find the terminal point of the vector $\mathbf{v} = 7\mathbf{i} - \mathbf{j} + 3\mathbf{k}$, given that the initial point is $P = (-2, 3, 5)$.

Solution

a. Because $\mathbf{j}$ is missing, its component is 0 and

$$\mathbf{v} = 4\mathbf{i} - 5\mathbf{k} = \langle 4, 0, -5 \rangle.$$

b. You need to find $Q = (q_1, q_2, q_3)$ such that $\mathbf{v} = \overrightarrow{PQ} = 7\mathbf{i} - \mathbf{j} + 3\mathbf{k}$. This implies that $q_1 - (-2) = 7$, $q_2 - 3 = -1$, and $q_3 - 5 = 3$. The solution of these three equations is $q_1 = 5$, $q_2 = 2$, and $q_3 = 8$. Therefore, $Q = (5, 2, 8)$. ▬

Applications

EXAMPLE 7   Measuring Force

A television camera weighing 120 pounds is supported by a tripod, as shown in Figure 11.23. Represent the force exerted on each leg of the tripod as a vector. (Assume that the weight is distributed equally among the three legs.)

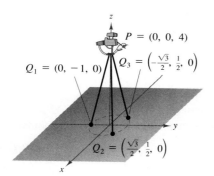

FIGURE 11.23

Solution   Let the vectors $\mathbf{F}_1$, $\mathbf{F}_2$, and $\mathbf{F}_3$ represent the forces exerted on the three legs. From Figure 11.23, you can determine the directions of $\mathbf{F}_1$, $\mathbf{F}_2$, and $\mathbf{F}_3$ to be as follows.

$$\overrightarrow{PQ_1} = \langle 0 - 0, -1 - 0, 0 - 4 \rangle = \langle 0, -1, -4 \rangle$$

$$\overrightarrow{PQ_2} = \left\langle \frac{\sqrt{3}}{2} - 0, \frac{1}{2} - 0, 0 - 4 \right\rangle = \left\langle \frac{\sqrt{3}}{2}, \frac{1}{2}, -4 \right\rangle$$

$$\overrightarrow{PQ_3} = \left\langle -\frac{\sqrt{3}}{2} - 0, \frac{1}{2} - 0, 0 - 4 \right\rangle = \left\langle -\frac{\sqrt{3}}{2}, \frac{1}{2}, -4 \right\rangle$$

Because each leg has the same length, and the total force is distributed equally among the three legs, you know that $\| \mathbf{F}_1 \| = \| \mathbf{F}_2 \| = \| \mathbf{F}_3 \|$. Hence, there exists a constant c such that

$$\mathbf{F}_1 = c\langle 0, -1, -4 \rangle, \qquad \mathbf{F}_2 = c\left\langle \frac{\sqrt{3}}{2}, \frac{1}{2}, -4 \right\rangle, \qquad \mathbf{F}_3 = c\left\langle -\frac{\sqrt{3}}{2}, \frac{1}{2}, -4 \right\rangle.$$

Let the total force exerted by the object be given by $\mathbf{F} = -120\mathbf{k}$. Then, using the fact that

$$\mathbf{F} = \mathbf{F}_1 + \mathbf{F}_2 + \mathbf{F}_3$$

you can conclude that $\mathbf{F}_1$, $\mathbf{F}_2$, and $\mathbf{F}_3$ each has a vertical component of -40. This implies that $c(-4) = -40$ and $c = 10$. Therefore, the forces exerted on the legs can be represented by

$$\mathbf{F}_1 = \langle 0, -10, -40 \rangle, \qquad \mathbf{F}_2 = \langle 5\sqrt{3}, 5, -40 \rangle, \qquad \mathbf{F}_3 = \langle -5\sqrt{3}, 5, -40 \rangle.$$

▬

EXERCISES for Section 11.2

In Exercises 1–4, plot the points on the same three-dimensional coordinate system.

1. a. $(2, 1, 3)$ **b.** $(-1, 2, 1)$

2. a. $(3, -2, 5)$ **b.** $\left(\frac{3}{2}, 4, -2\right)$

3. a. $(5, -2, 2)$ **b.** $(5, -2, -2)$

4. a. $(0, 4, -5)$ **b.** $(4, 0, 5)$

In Exercises 5–8, find the lengths of the triangle with the indicated vertices, and determine whether the triangle is a right triangle, an isosceles triangle, or neither.

5. $(0, 0, 0), (2, 2, 1), (2, -4, 4)$

6. $(5, 3, 4), (7, 1, 3), (3, 5, 3)$

7. $(1, -3, -2), (5, -1, 2), (-1, 1, 2)$

8. $(5, 0, 0), (0, 2, 0), (0, 0, -3)$

In Exercises 9 and 10, find the coordinates of the midpoint of the line segment joining the points.

9. $(5, -9, 7), (-2, 3, 3)$ **10.** $(4, 0, -6), (8, 8, 20)$

In Exercises 11–14, find the general form of the equation of the sphere.

11. Center: $(0, 2, 5)$ **12.** Center: $(4, -1, 1)$
Radius: 2   Radius: 5

13. Endpoints of a diameter: $(2, 0, 0), (0, 6, 0)$

14. Center: $(-2, 1, 1)$, tangent to the xy-coordinate plane

In Exercises 15–18, find the center and radius of the sphere.

15. $x^2 + y^2 + z^2 - 2x + 6y + 8z + 1 = 0$

16. $x^2 + y^2 + z^2 + 9x - 2y + 10z + 19 = 0$

17. $9x^2 + 9y^2 + 9z^2 - 6x + 18y + 1 = 0$

18. $4x^2 + 4y^2 + 4z^2 - 4x - 32y + 8z + 33 = 0$

In Exercises 19–22, (a) find the component form of the vector v and (b) sketch the vector with its initial point at the origin.

19.

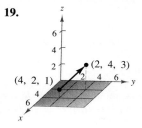

$(2, 4, 3)$
$(4, 2, 1)$

20.

$(4, 0, 3)$ $(0, 5, 1)$

21.

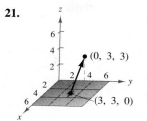

$(0, 3, 3)$
$(3, 3, 0)$

22.

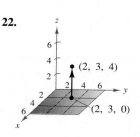

$(2, 3, 4)$
$(2, 3, 0)$

In Exercises 23 and 24, the initial and terminal points of a vector v are given. (a) Sketch the directed line segment, (b) find the component form of the vector, and (c) sketch the vector with its initial point at the origin.

23. Initial point: $(-1, 2, 3)$
Terminal point: $(3, 3, 4)$

24. Initial point: $(2, -1, -2)$
Terminal point: $(-4, 3, 7)$

In Exercises 25 and 26, sketch each scalar multiple of v.

25. $\mathbf{v} = \langle 1, 2, 2 \rangle$
    a. $2\mathbf{v}$ **b.** $-\mathbf{v}$ **c.** $\frac{3}{2}\mathbf{v}$ **d.** $0\mathbf{v}$

26. $\mathbf{v} = \langle 2, -2, 1 \rangle$
    a. $-\mathbf{v}$ **b.** $2\mathbf{v}$ **c.** $\frac{1}{2}\mathbf{v}$ **d.** $\frac{5}{2}\mathbf{v}$

In Exercises 27–32, find the vector z, given $\mathbf{u} = \langle 1, 2, 3 \rangle$, $\mathbf{v} = \langle 2, 2, -1 \rangle$, and $\mathbf{w} = \langle 4, 0, -4 \rangle$.

27. $\mathbf{z} = \mathbf{u} - \mathbf{v}$ **28.** $\mathbf{z} = \mathbf{u} - \mathbf{v} + 2\mathbf{w}$

29. $\mathbf{z} = 2\mathbf{u} + 4\mathbf{v} - \mathbf{w}$ **30.** $\mathbf{z} = 5\mathbf{u} - 3\mathbf{v} - \frac{1}{2}\mathbf{w}$

31. $2\mathbf{z} - 3\mathbf{u} = \mathbf{w}$ **32.** $2\mathbf{u} + \mathbf{v} - \mathbf{w} + 3\mathbf{z} = \mathbf{0}$

In Exercises 33–36, determine which of the vectors are parallel to z.

33. $\mathbf{z} = \langle 3, 2, -5 \rangle$
    a. $\langle -6, -4, 10 \rangle$ **b.** $\langle 2, \frac{4}{3}, -\frac{10}{3} \rangle$
    c. $\langle 6, 4, 10 \rangle$ **d.** $\langle 1, -4, 2 \rangle$

34. $\mathbf{z} = \frac{1}{2}\mathbf{i} - \frac{2}{3}\mathbf{j} + \frac{3}{4}\mathbf{k}$
    a. $6\mathbf{i} - 4\mathbf{j} + 9\mathbf{k}$ **b.** $-\mathbf{i} + \frac{4}{3}\mathbf{j} - \frac{3}{2}\mathbf{k}$
    c. $12\mathbf{i} + 9\mathbf{k}$ **d.** $\frac{3}{4}\mathbf{i} - \mathbf{j} + \frac{9}{8}\mathbf{k}$

35. z has initial point $(1, -1, 3)$ and terminal point $(-2, 3, 5)$.
    a. $-6\mathbf{i} + 8\mathbf{j} + 4\mathbf{k}$ **b.** $4\mathbf{j} + 2\mathbf{k}$

36. z has initial point $(3, 2, -1)$ and terminal point $(-1, -3, 5)$.
    a. $\langle 0, 5, -6 \rangle$ **b.** $\langle 8, 10, -12 \rangle$

In Exercises 37–40, use vectors to determine whether the given points lie in a straight line.

37. $(0, -2, -5), (3, 4, 4), (2, 2, 1)$

38. $(1, -1, 5), (0, -1, 6), (3, -1, 3)$

39. $(1, 2, 4), (2, 5, 0), (0, 1, 5)$

40. $(0, 0, 0), (1, 3, -2), (2, -6, 4)$

In Exercises 41 and 42, use vectors to show that the points form the vertices of a parallelogram.

41. (2, 9, 1), (3, 11, 4), (0, 10, 2), (1, 12, 5)

42. (1, 1, −3), (9, −1, 2), (11, 2, 1), (3, 4, −4)

In Exercises 43 and 44, the vector v and its initial point are given. Find the terminal point.

43. $\mathbf{v} = \langle 3, -5, 6 \rangle$
Initial point: (0, 6, 2)

44. $\mathbf{v} = \langle 0, \frac{1}{2}, -\frac{1}{3} \rangle$
Initial point: $\left(3, 0, -\frac{2}{3} \right)$

In Exercises 45–50, find the magnitude of v.

45. $\mathbf{v} = \langle 0, 0, 0 \rangle$ **46.** $\mathbf{v} = \langle 1, 0, 3 \rangle$

47. $\mathbf{v} = \mathbf{i} - 2\mathbf{j} - 3\mathbf{k}$ **48.** $\mathbf{v} = -4\mathbf{i} + 3\mathbf{j} + 7\mathbf{k}$

49. Initial point of **v**: (1, −3, 4)
Terminal point of **v**: (1, 0, −1)

50. Initial point of **v**: (0, −1, 0)
Terminal point of **v**: (1, 2, −2)

In Exercises 51–54, find a unit vector (a) in the direction of u and (b) in the direction opposite that of u.

51. $\mathbf{u} = \langle 2, -1, 2 \rangle$ **52.** $\mathbf{u} = \langle 6, 0, 8 \rangle$

53. $\mathbf{u} = \langle 3, 2, -5 \rangle$ **54.** $\mathbf{u} = \langle 8, 0, 0 \rangle$

C | **In Exercises 55–58, use a computer algebra system to determine the specified quantity where $\mathbf{u} = \langle -1, 3, 4 \rangle$ and $\mathbf{v} = \langle 5, 4.5, -6 \rangle$.**

55. $6\mathbf{u} - 4\mathbf{v}$ **56.** $2\mathbf{u} + \frac{5}{2}\mathbf{v}$

57. $\| \mathbf{u} + \mathbf{v} \|$ **58.** $\dfrac{\mathbf{v}}{\| \mathbf{v} \|}$

In Exercises 59 and 60, determine the values of c that satisfy the equation. Let $\mathbf{u} = \mathbf{i} + 2\mathbf{j} + 3\mathbf{k}$ and $\mathbf{v} = 2\mathbf{i} + 2\mathbf{j} - \mathbf{k}$.

59. $\| c\mathbf{v} \| = 5$ **60.** $\| c\mathbf{u} \| = 3$

In Exercises 61 and 62, use vectors to find the point that lies two-thirds of the way from P to Q.

61. $P = (4, 3, 0)$, $Q = (1, -3, 3)$

62. $P = (1, 2, 5)$, $Q = (6, 8, 2)$

In Exercises 63 and 64, sketch the vector v and write its component form.

63. **v** lies in the yz-plane, has magnitude 2, and makes an angle of 30° with the positive y-axis.

64. **v** lies in the xz-plane, has magnitude 5, and makes an angle of 45° with the positive z-axis.

65. Let $\mathbf{u} = \mathbf{i} + \mathbf{j}$, $\mathbf{v} = \mathbf{j} + \mathbf{k}$, and $\mathbf{w} = a\mathbf{u} + b\mathbf{v}$.
   a. Sketch **u** and **v**.
   b. If $\mathbf{w} = \mathbf{0}$, show that a and b must both be 0.
   c. Find a and b such that $\mathbf{w} = \mathbf{i} + 2\mathbf{j} + \mathbf{k}$.
   d. Show that no choice of a and b yields $\mathbf{w} = \mathbf{i} + 2\mathbf{j} + 3\mathbf{k}$.

66. The initial and terminal points of the vector **v** are (x_1, y_1, z_1) and (x, y, z), respectively. Describe the set of all points (x, y, z) such that $\| \mathbf{v} \| = 4$.

67. *Diagonal of a Cube*   Find the component form of the unit vector **v** in the direction of the diagonal of the cube shown in the accompanying figure.

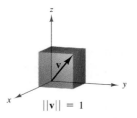

$\|\mathbf{v}\| = 1$ **FIGURE FOR 67**

68. *Tower Guy Wire*   The guy wire to a 100-foot tower has a tension of 550 pounds. Using the distances shown in the figure, write the component form of the vector **F** respresenting the tension in the wire.

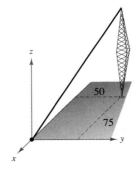

FIGURE FOR 68

69. *Light Installation*   The lights in an auditorium are 25-pound discs of radius 18 inches. Each disc is supported by three equally spaced 48-inch wires to the ceiling (see figure). Find the tension in each wire.

48 in.

18 in.   **FIGURE FOR 69**

70. *Light Installation*   Repeat Exercise 69 using r_0 inches as the radius of each light fixture. Determine the limit of the tension of each wire as $r_0 \rightarrow 48^-$.

71. *Load Supports* Find the tension in each of the supporting cables in the accompanying figure if the weight of the crate is 500 newtons.

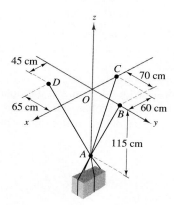

FIGURE FOR 71

72. *Building Construction* A precast concrete wall is temporarily kept in its vertical position by ropes (see figure). Find the total force exerted on the pin at position A if the tensions in AB and AC are 420 and 650 pounds, respectively.

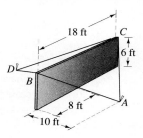

FIGURE FOR 72

73. Write an equation whose graph consists of the set of points $P = (x, y, z)$ that are twice as far from $A = (0, -1, 1)$ as from $B = (1, 2, 0)$.

The Dot Product

So far you have studied two operations with vectors—vector addition and multiplication by a scalar—each of which yields another vector. In this section you will study a third vector operation, called the **dot product.** This product yields a scalar, rather than a vector.

Definition of Dot Product

The **dot product** of $\mathbf{u} = \langle u_1, u_2 \rangle$ and $\mathbf{v} = \langle v_1, v_2 \rangle$ is

$$\mathbf{u} \cdot \mathbf{v} = u_1 v_1 + u_2 v_2.$$

The **dot product** of $\mathbf{u} = \langle u_1, u_2, u_3 \rangle$ and $\mathbf{v} = \langle v_1, v_2, v_3 \rangle$ is

$$\mathbf{u} \cdot \mathbf{v} = u_1 v_1 + u_2 v_2 + u_3 v_3.$$

REMARK The dot product of two vectors is also called the **inner product** (or scalar product) of two vectors.

THEOREM 11.4 Properties of the Dot Product

Let $\mathbf{u}$, $\mathbf{v}$, and $\mathbf{w}$ be vectors in the plane or in space and let c be a scalar.

1. $\mathbf{u} \cdot \mathbf{v} = \mathbf{v} \cdot \mathbf{u}$ Commutative property
2. $\mathbf{u} \cdot (\mathbf{v} + \mathbf{w}) = \mathbf{u} \cdot \mathbf{v} + \mathbf{u} \cdot \mathbf{w}$ Distributive property
3. $c(\mathbf{u} \cdot \mathbf{v}) = c\mathbf{u} \cdot \mathbf{v} = \mathbf{u} \cdot c\mathbf{v}$
4. $\mathbf{0} \cdot \mathbf{v} = 0$
5. $\mathbf{v} \cdot \mathbf{v} = \| \mathbf{v} \|^2$

Proof To prove the first property, let $\mathbf{u} = \langle u_1, u_2, u_3 \rangle$ and $\mathbf{v} = \langle v_1, v_2, v_3 \rangle$. Then

$$\mathbf{u} \cdot \mathbf{v} = u_1 v_1 + u_2 v_2 + u_3 v_3$$
$$= v_1 u_1 + v_2 u_2 + v_3 u_3$$
$$= \mathbf{v} \cdot \mathbf{u}.$$

For the fifth property, let $\mathbf{v} = \langle v_1, v_2, v_3 \rangle$. Then

$$\mathbf{v} \cdot \mathbf{v} = v_1^2 + v_2^2 + v_3^2$$
$$= \left(\sqrt{v_1^2 + v_2^2 + v_3^2} \right)^2 = \| \mathbf{v} \|^2.$$

Proofs of the other properties are left to you.

EXAMPLE 1 Finding Dot Products

Given $\mathbf{u} = \langle 2, -2 \rangle$, $\mathbf{v} = \langle 5, 8 \rangle$, and $\mathbf{w} = \langle -4, 3 \rangle$, find the following.

a. $\mathbf{u} \cdot \mathbf{v}$ **b.** $(\mathbf{u} \cdot \mathbf{v})\mathbf{w}$ **c.** $\mathbf{u} \cdot (2\mathbf{v})$ **d.** $\|\mathbf{w}\|^2$

Solution

a. $\mathbf{u} \cdot \mathbf{v} = \langle 2, -2 \rangle \cdot \langle 5, 8 \rangle = 2(5) + (-2)(8) = -6$

b. $(\mathbf{u} \cdot \mathbf{v})\mathbf{w} = -6\langle -4, 3 \rangle = \langle 24, -18 \rangle$

c. $\mathbf{u} \cdot (2\mathbf{v}) = 2(\mathbf{u} \cdot \mathbf{v}) = 2(-6) = -12$

d. $\|\mathbf{w}\|^2 = \mathbf{w} \cdot \mathbf{w} = \langle -4, 3 \rangle \cdot \langle -4, 3 \rangle = (-4)(-4) + (3)(3) = 25$

Notice that the result of part b is a *vector* quantity, whereas the results of the other three parts are *scalar* quantities.

Angle Between Two Vectors

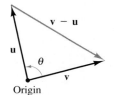

FIGURE 11.24
The angle between two vectors.

The **angle between two nonzero vectors** is the angle θ, $0 \le \theta \le \pi$, between their respective standard position vectors, as shown in Figure 11.24. The next theorem shows how to find this angle using the dot product. (Note that we do not define the angle between the zero vector and another vector.)

THEOREM 11.5 Angle Between Two Vectors

If θ is the angle between two nonzero vectors $\mathbf{u}$ and $\mathbf{v}$, then

$$\cos \theta = \frac{\mathbf{u} \cdot \mathbf{v}}{\|\mathbf{u}\| \|\mathbf{v}\|}.$$

Proof Consider the triangle determined by vectors $\mathbf{u}$, $\mathbf{v}$, and $\mathbf{v} - \mathbf{u}$, as shown in Figure 11.24. By the Law of Cosines, you can write

$$\|\mathbf{v} - \mathbf{u}\|^2 = \|\mathbf{u}\|^2 + \|\mathbf{v}\|^2 - 2\|\mathbf{u}\| \|\mathbf{v}\| \cos \theta.$$

Using the properties of the dot product, the left side can be rewritten as

$$
\begin{aligned}
\|\mathbf{v} - \mathbf{u}\|^2 &= (\mathbf{v} - \mathbf{u}) \cdot (\mathbf{v} - \mathbf{u}) \\
&= (\mathbf{v} - \mathbf{u}) \cdot \mathbf{v} - (\mathbf{v} - \mathbf{u}) \cdot \mathbf{u} \\
&= \mathbf{v} \cdot \mathbf{v} - \mathbf{u} \cdot \mathbf{v} - \mathbf{v} \cdot \mathbf{u} + \mathbf{u} \cdot \mathbf{u} \\
&= \|\mathbf{v}\|^2 - 2\mathbf{u} \cdot \mathbf{v} + \|\mathbf{u}\|^2
\end{aligned}
$$

and substitution back into the Law of Cosines yields

$$
\begin{aligned}
\|\mathbf{v}\|^2 - 2\mathbf{u} \cdot \mathbf{v} + \|\mathbf{u}\|^2 &= \|\mathbf{u}\|^2 + \|\mathbf{v}\|^2 - 2\|\mathbf{u}\| \|\mathbf{v}\| \cos \theta \\
-2\mathbf{u} \cdot \mathbf{v} &= -2\|\mathbf{u}\| \|\mathbf{v}\| \cos \theta \\
\cos \theta &= \frac{\mathbf{u} \cdot \mathbf{v}}{\|\mathbf{u}\| \|\mathbf{v}\|}.
\end{aligned}
$$

If the angle between two vectors is known, then rewriting Theorem 11.5 in the form

$$\mathbf{u} \cdot \mathbf{v} = \|\mathbf{u}\| \, \|\mathbf{v}\| \cos \theta$$ Alternative form of dot product

produces an alternative way to calculate the dot product. From this form, you can see that because $\|\mathbf{u}\|$ and $\|\mathbf{v}\|$ are always positive, $\mathbf{u} \cdot \mathbf{v}$ and $\cos \theta$ will always have the same sign. Figure 11.25 shows the five possible orientations of two vectors.

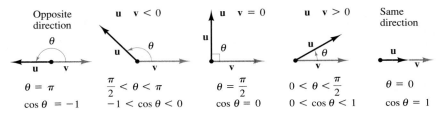

Opposite direction	$\mathbf{u} \cdot \mathbf{v} < 0$	$\mathbf{u} \cdot \mathbf{v} = 0$	$\mathbf{u} \cdot \mathbf{v} > 0$	Same direction
$\theta = \pi$	$\dfrac{\pi}{2} < \theta < \pi$	$\theta = \dfrac{\pi}{2}$	$0 < \theta < \dfrac{\pi}{2}$	$\theta = 0$
$\cos \theta = -1$	$-1 < \cos \theta < 0$	$\cos \theta = 0$	$0 < \cos \theta < 1$	$\cos \theta = 1$

FIGURE 11.25

Definition of Orthogonal Vectors

The vectors $\mathbf{u}$ and $\mathbf{v}$ are **orthogonal** if $\mathbf{u} \cdot \mathbf{v} = 0$.

REMARK   The terms "perpendicular," "orthogonal," and "normal" all mean essentially the same thing—meeting at right angles. However, we usually say that two vectors are *orthogonal*, two lines or planes are *perpendicular*, and a vector is *normal* to a given line or plane.

From this definition, it follows that the zero vector is orthogonal to every vector $\mathbf{u}$, because $\mathbf{0} \cdot \mathbf{u} = 0$. Moreover, for $0 \leq \theta \leq \pi$, you know that $\cos \theta = 0$ if and only if $\theta = \pi/2$. Thus, you can use Theorem 11.5 to conclude that two *nonzero* vectors are orthogonal if and only if the angle between them is $\pi/2$.

EXAMPLE 2   Finding the Angle Between Two Vectors

For $\mathbf{u} = \langle 3, -1, 2 \rangle$, $\mathbf{v} = \langle -4, 0, 2 \rangle$, $\mathbf{w} = \langle 1, -1, -2 \rangle$, and $\mathbf{z} = \langle 2, 0, -1 \rangle$, find the angles between the following pairs of vectors.

a. $\mathbf{u}$ and $\mathbf{v}$ **b.** $\mathbf{u}$ and $\mathbf{w}$ **c.** $\mathbf{v}$ and $\mathbf{z}$

Solution

a. $\cos \theta = \dfrac{\mathbf{u} \cdot \mathbf{v}}{\|\mathbf{u}\| \, \|\mathbf{v}\|} = \dfrac{-12 + 4}{\sqrt{14}\sqrt{20}} = \dfrac{-8}{2\sqrt{14}\sqrt{5}} = \dfrac{-4}{\sqrt{70}}$

Because $\mathbf{u} \cdot \mathbf{v} < 0$, $\theta = \arccos \dfrac{-4}{\sqrt{70}} \approx 2.069$ radians.

b. $\cos \theta = \dfrac{\mathbf{u} \cdot \mathbf{w}}{\|\mathbf{u}\| \, \|\mathbf{w}\|} = \dfrac{3 + 1 - 4}{\sqrt{14}\sqrt{6}} = \dfrac{0}{\sqrt{84}} = 0$

Because $\mathbf{u} \cdot \mathbf{w} = 0$, $\mathbf{u}$ and $\mathbf{w}$ are *orthogonal*. Furthermore, $\theta = \pi/2$.

c. $\cos \theta = \dfrac{\mathbf{v} \cdot \mathbf{z}}{\|\mathbf{v}\| \, \|\mathbf{z}\|} = \dfrac{-8 + 0 - 2}{\sqrt{20}\sqrt{5}} = \dfrac{-10}{\sqrt{100}} = -1$

Consequently, $\theta = \pi$.

Direction Cosines

For a vector in the plane, you have seen that it is convenient to measure direction in terms of the angle, measured counterclockwise, *from* the positive *x*-axis to the vector. In space it is more convenient to measure direction in terms of the angles *between* the nonzero vector **v** and the three unit vectors **i**, **j**, and **k**, as shown in Figure 11.26. The angles α, β, and γ are the **direction angles of v**, and $\cos\alpha$, $\cos\beta$, and $\cos\gamma$ are the **direction cosines of v**. Because

$$\mathbf{v}\cdot\mathbf{i} = \|\mathbf{v}\|\,\|\mathbf{i}\|\cos\alpha = \|\mathbf{v}\|\cos\alpha$$

and

$$\mathbf{v}\cdot\mathbf{i} = \langle v_1, v_2, v_3\rangle\cdot\langle 1, 0, 0\rangle = v_1$$

it follows that $\cos\alpha = v_1/\|\mathbf{v}\|$. By similar reasoning with the unit vectors **j** and **k**, you have

$$\cos\alpha = \frac{v_1}{\|\mathbf{v}\|} \qquad \alpha \text{ is angle between } \mathbf{v} \text{ and } \mathbf{i}$$

$$\cos\beta = \frac{v_2}{\|\mathbf{v}\|} \qquad \beta \text{ is angle between } \mathbf{v} \text{ and } \mathbf{j}$$

$$\cos\gamma = \frac{v_3}{\|\mathbf{v}\|}. \qquad \gamma \text{ is angle between } \mathbf{v} \text{ and } \mathbf{k}$$

Consequently, any nonzero vector **v** in space has the normalized form

$$\frac{\mathbf{v}}{\|\mathbf{v}\|} = \frac{v_1}{\|\mathbf{v}\|}\mathbf{i} + \frac{v_2}{\|\mathbf{v}\|}\mathbf{j} + \frac{v_3}{\|\mathbf{v}\|}\mathbf{k} = \cos\alpha\,\mathbf{i} + \cos\beta\,\mathbf{j} + \cos\gamma\,\mathbf{k}$$

and because $\mathbf{v}/\|\mathbf{v}\|$ is a unit vector, it follows that

$$\cos^2\alpha + \cos^2\beta + \cos^2\gamma = 1.$$

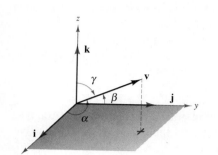

FIGURE 11.26
Direction angles

EXAMPLE 3   Finding Direction Angles

Find the direction cosines and angles for the vector $\mathbf{v} = 2\mathbf{i} + 3\mathbf{j} + 4\mathbf{k}$, and show that $\cos^2\alpha + \cos^2\beta + \cos^2\gamma = 1$.

Solution   Because $\|\mathbf{v}\| = \sqrt{2^2 + 3^2 + 4^2} = \sqrt{29}$, you can write the following.

$$\cos\alpha = \frac{v_1}{\|\mathbf{v}\|} = \frac{2}{\sqrt{29}} \qquad \longrightarrow \qquad \alpha \approx 68.2°$$

$$\cos\beta = \frac{v_2}{\|\mathbf{v}\|} = \frac{3}{\sqrt{29}} \qquad \longrightarrow \qquad \beta \approx 56.1°$$

$$\cos\gamma = \frac{v_3}{\|\mathbf{v}\|} = \frac{4}{\sqrt{29}} \qquad \longrightarrow \qquad \gamma \approx 42.0°$$

Furthermore, the sum of the squares of the direction cosines is

$$\cos^2\alpha + \cos^2\beta + \cos^2\gamma = \frac{4}{29} + \frac{9}{29} + \frac{16}{29}$$

$$= \frac{29}{29}$$

$$= 1.$$

(See Figure 11.27.)

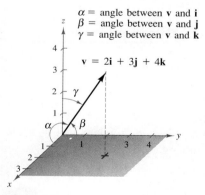

α = angle between **v** and **i**
β = angle between **v** and **j**
γ = angle between **v** and **k**

$\mathbf{v} = 2\mathbf{i} + 3\mathbf{j} + 4\mathbf{k}$

FIGURE 11.27
The direction angles of **v**.

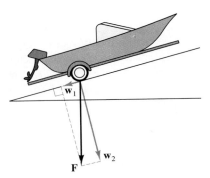

FIGURE 11.28
The force due to gravity pulls the boat against the ramp and down the ramp.

Projections and Vector Components

You have already seen applications in which two vectors are added to produce a resultant vector. Many applications in physics and engineering pose the reverse problem—decomposing a given vector into the sum of two **vector components.** To see the usefulness of this procedure, we look at a physical example.

Consider a boat on an inclined ramp, as shown in Figure 11.28. The force **F** due to gravity pulls the boat *down* the ramp and *against* the ramp. These two forces, $\mathbf{w}_1$ and $\mathbf{w}_2$, are orthogonal—they are called the vector components of **F**.

$$\mathbf{F} = \mathbf{w}_1 + \mathbf{w}_2 \qquad \text{Vector components of } \mathbf{F}$$

The forces $\mathbf{w}_1$ and $\mathbf{w}_2$ help you analyze the effect of gravity on the boat. For example, $\mathbf{w}_1$ indicates the force necessary to keep the boat from rolling down the ramp, whereas $\mathbf{w}_2$ indicates the force that the tires must withstand.

Definition of Projection and Vector Components

Let **u** and **v** be nonzero vectors. Moreover, let $\mathbf{u} = \mathbf{w}_1 + \mathbf{w}_2$, where $\mathbf{w}_1$ is parallel to **v** and $\mathbf{w}_2$ is orthogonal to **v**, as shown in Figure 11.29.

1. $\mathbf{w}_1$ is called the **projection of u onto v** or the **vector component of u along v**, and is denoted by $\mathbf{w}_1 = \text{proj}_\mathbf{v}\,\mathbf{u}$.
2. $\mathbf{w}_2 = \mathbf{u} - \mathbf{w}_1$ is called the **vector component of u orthogonal to v.**

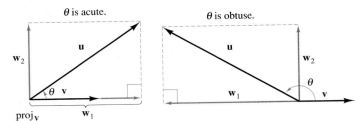

θ is acute.   θ is obtuse.

FIGURE 11.29
$\mathbf{w}_1 = \text{proj}_\mathbf{v}\,\mathbf{u} = $ projection of **u** onto **v** = vector component of **u** along **v**.

$\mathbf{w}_2 = $ vector component of **u** orthogonal to **v**.

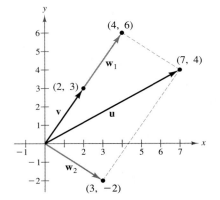

FIGURE 11.30
$\mathbf{u} = \mathbf{w}_1 + \mathbf{w}_2$

EXAMPLE 4   Finding a Vector Component of u Orthogonal to v

Find the vector component of $\mathbf{u} = \langle 7, 4 \rangle$ that is orthogonal to $\mathbf{v} = \langle 2, 3 \rangle$, given that $\mathbf{w}_1 = \langle 4, 6 \rangle$ and

$$\mathbf{u} = \langle 7, 4 \rangle = \mathbf{w}_1 + \mathbf{w}_2.$$

Solution   Because $\mathbf{u} = \mathbf{w}_1 + \mathbf{w}_2$, where $\mathbf{w}_1$ is parallel to **v**, it follows that $\mathbf{w}_2$ is the vector component of **u** orthogonal to **v**. Thus, you have

$$\mathbf{w}_2 = \mathbf{u} - \mathbf{w}_1 = \langle 7, 4 \rangle - \langle 4, 6 \rangle = \langle 3, -2 \rangle.$$

Check to see that $\mathbf{w}_2$ is orthogonal to **v**, as shown in Figure 11.30.

From Example 4, you can see that it is easy to find the vector component $\mathbf{w}_2$ once you have found the projection, $\mathbf{w}_1$, of $\mathbf{u}$ onto $\mathbf{v}$. To find this projection, use the dot product, as indicated in the next theorem.

THEOREM 11.6   Projection Using the Dot Product

If $\mathbf{u}$ and $\mathbf{v}$ are nonzero vectors, then the projection of $\mathbf{u}$ onto $\mathbf{v}$ is given by

$$\text{proj}_\mathbf{v} \mathbf{u} = \left(\frac{\mathbf{u} \cdot \mathbf{v}}{\| \mathbf{v} \|^2} \right) \mathbf{v}.$$

Proof   From Figure 11.29, let $\mathbf{w}_1 = \text{proj}_\mathbf{v} \mathbf{u}$. Because $\mathbf{w}_1$ is a scalar multiple of $\mathbf{v}$, you can write

$$\mathbf{u} = \mathbf{w}_1 + \mathbf{w}_2 = c\,\mathbf{v} + \mathbf{w}_2.$$

Taking the dot product of both sides with $\mathbf{v}$ produces

$$\mathbf{u} \cdot \mathbf{v} = (c\,\mathbf{v} + \mathbf{w}_2) \cdot \mathbf{v}$$
$$= c\,\mathbf{v} \cdot \mathbf{v} + \mathbf{w}_2 \cdot \mathbf{v}$$
$$= c \| \mathbf{v} \|^2 + \mathbf{w}_2 \cdot \mathbf{v}.$$

Because $\mathbf{w}_2$ and $\mathbf{v}$ are orthogonal, it follows that $\mathbf{w}_2 \cdot \mathbf{v} = 0$ and you have

$$\mathbf{u} \cdot \mathbf{v} = c \| \mathbf{v} \|^2 \quad \rightarrow \quad c = \frac{\mathbf{u} \cdot \mathbf{v}}{\| \mathbf{v} \|^2}.$$

Therefore, you can write $\mathbf{w}_1$ as

$$\mathbf{w}_1 = \left(\frac{\mathbf{u} \cdot \mathbf{v}}{\| \mathbf{v} \|^2} \right) \mathbf{v}.$$

The projection of $\mathbf{u}$ onto $\mathbf{v}$ can be written as a scalar multiple of a unit vector in the direction of $\mathbf{v}$. That is,

$$\left(\frac{\mathbf{u} \cdot \mathbf{v}}{\| \mathbf{v} \|^2} \right) \mathbf{v} = \left(\frac{\mathbf{u} \cdot \mathbf{v}}{\| \mathbf{v} \|} \right) \frac{\mathbf{v}}{\| \mathbf{v} \|} = (k) \frac{\mathbf{v}}{\| \mathbf{v} \|}.$$

The scalar k is called the **component of $\mathbf{u}$ in the direction of $\mathbf{v}$**. Thus,

$$k = \frac{\mathbf{u} \cdot \mathbf{v}}{\| \mathbf{v} \|} = \| \mathbf{u} \| \cos\theta. \qquad \text{Component of } \mathbf{u} \text{ in the direction of } \mathbf{v}$$

REMARK   Note the distinction between the terms "component" and "vector component." For example, using the standard unit vectors with $\mathbf{u} = u_1\mathbf{i} + u_2\mathbf{j}$, you have

u_1 is the *component* of $\mathbf{u}$ in the direction of $\mathbf{i}$

and

$u_1\mathbf{i}$ is the *vector component* in the direction of $\mathbf{i}$.

EXAMPLE 5   Decomposing a Vector into Vector Components

Find the projection of **u** onto **v** and the vector component of **u** orthogonal to **v** for the vectors

$$\mathbf{u} = 3\mathbf{i} - 5\mathbf{j} + 2\mathbf{k} \quad \text{and} \quad \mathbf{v} = 7\mathbf{i} + \mathbf{j} - 2\mathbf{k}.$$

Solution   The projection of **u** onto **v** is

$$\mathbf{w}_1 = \left(\frac{\mathbf{u} \cdot \mathbf{v}}{\|\mathbf{v}\|^2}\right)\mathbf{v} = \left(\frac{12}{54}\right)(7\mathbf{i} + \mathbf{j} - 2\mathbf{k}) = \frac{14}{9}\mathbf{i} + \frac{2}{9}\mathbf{j} - \frac{4}{9}\mathbf{k}.$$

The vector component of **u** orthogonal to **v** is the vector

$$\mathbf{w}_2 = \mathbf{u} - \mathbf{w}_1$$

$$= (3\mathbf{i} - 5\mathbf{j} + 2\mathbf{k}) - \left(\frac{14}{9}\mathbf{i} + \frac{2}{9}\mathbf{j} - \frac{4}{9}\mathbf{k}\right)$$

$$= \frac{13}{9}\mathbf{i} - \frac{47}{9}\mathbf{j} + \frac{22}{9}\mathbf{k}.$$

(See Figure 11.31.)

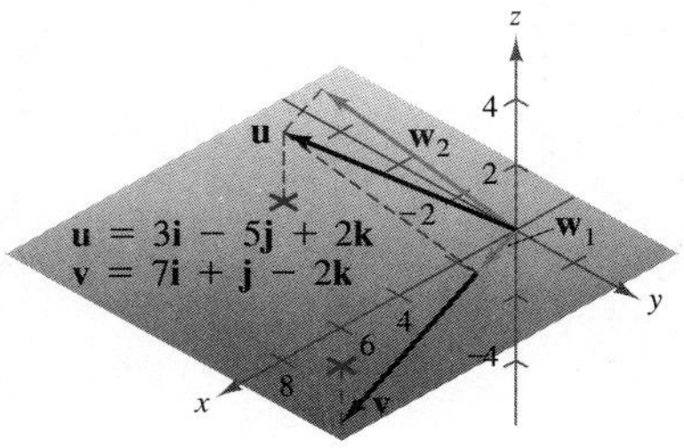

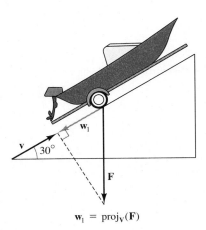

FIGURE 11.31
$\mathbf{u} = \mathbf{w}_1 + \mathbf{w}_2$

In the next example, we return to the problem involving the boat and the ramp to see how we can use vector components in a physical problem.

EXAMPLE 6   Finding a Force

A 600-pound boat sits on a ramp inclined at 30°, as shown in Figure 11.32. What force is required to keep the boat from rolling down the ramp?

Solution   Because the force due to gravity is vertical and downward, you can represent the gravitational force by the vector

$$\mathbf{F} = -600\mathbf{j}.$$

To find the force required to keep the boat from rolling down the ramp, we project **F** onto a unit vector **v** in the direction of the ramp, as follows.

$$\mathbf{v} = \cos 30°\,\mathbf{i} + \sin 30°\,\mathbf{j} = \frac{\sqrt{3}}{2}\mathbf{i} + \frac{1}{2}\mathbf{j} \qquad \text{Unit vector along ramp}$$

Therefore, the projection of **F** onto **v** is given by

$$\mathbf{w}_1 = \text{proj}_\mathbf{v}\,\mathbf{F} = \left(\frac{\mathbf{F} \cdot \mathbf{v}}{\|\mathbf{v}\|^2}\right)\mathbf{v}$$

$$= (\mathbf{F} \cdot \mathbf{v})\mathbf{v} = (-600)\left(\frac{1}{2}\right)\mathbf{v}$$

$$= -300\left(\frac{\sqrt{3}}{2}\mathbf{i} + \frac{1}{2}\mathbf{j}\right).$$

The magnitude of this force is 300, and therefore a force of 300 pounds is required to keep the boat from rolling down the ramp.

$\mathbf{w}_1 = \text{proj}_\mathbf{v}(\mathbf{F})$

FIGURE 11.32

Work

The work W done by a constant force $\mathbf{F}$ acting along the lines of motion of an object is given by

$$W = \text{(magnitude of force)(distance)}$$

$$= \|\mathbf{F}\|\,\|\overrightarrow{PQ}\|$$

as shown in Figure 11.33(a). If the constant force $\mathbf{F}$ is not directed along the line of motion, then you can see from Figure 11.33(b) that the work W done by the force is

$$W = \|\text{proj}_{\overrightarrow{PQ}}\mathbf{F}\|\,\|\overrightarrow{PQ}\|$$

$$= (\cos\theta)\,\|\mathbf{F}\|\,\|\overrightarrow{PQ}\|$$

$$= \mathbf{F}\cdot\overrightarrow{PQ}.$$

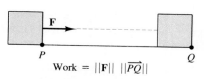

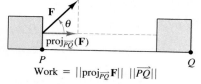

(a) Force acts along the line of motion.

(b) Force acts at angle θ with the line of motion.

FIGURE 11.33

We summarize this notion of work in the following definition.

Definition of Work

The work W done by a constant force $\mathbf{F}$ as its point of application moves along the vector $\overrightarrow{PQ}$ is given by either of the following.

1. $W = \|\text{proj}_{\overrightarrow{PQ}}\mathbf{F}\|\,\|\overrightarrow{PQ}\|$ Projection form

2. $W = \mathbf{F}\cdot\overrightarrow{PQ}$ Dot product form

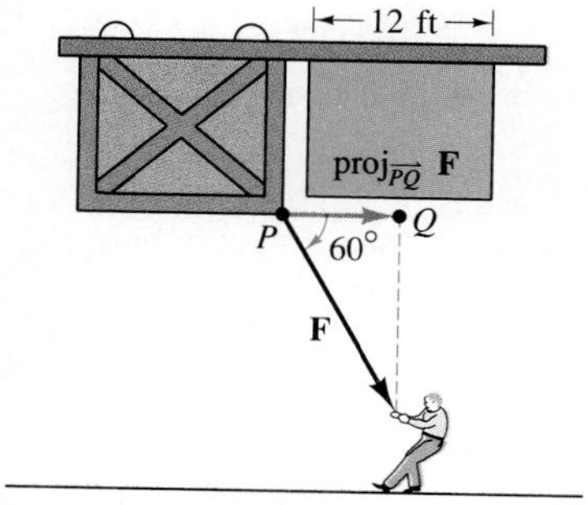

EXAMPLE 7   Finding Work

To close a sliding door, a person pulls on a rope with a constant force of 50 pounds at a constant angle of 60°, as shown in Figure 11.34. Find the work done in moving the door 12 feet to its closed position.

Solution   Using a projection, you can calculate the work as follows.

$$W = \|\text{proj}_{\overrightarrow{PQ}}\mathbf{F}\|\,\|\overrightarrow{PQ}\|$$

$$= \cos(60°)\,\|\mathbf{F}\|\,\|\overrightarrow{PQ}\|$$

$$= \frac{1}{2}(50)(12)$$

$$= 300 \text{ ft}\cdot\text{lb}$$

FIGURE 11.34

EXERCISES for Section 11.3

In Exercises 1–6, find (a) $\mathbf{u} \cdot \mathbf{v}$, (b) $\mathbf{u} \cdot \mathbf{u}$, (c) $\|\mathbf{u}\|^2$, (d) $(\mathbf{u} \cdot \mathbf{v})\mathbf{v}$, and (e) $\mathbf{u} \cdot (2\mathbf{v})$.

1. $\mathbf{u} = \langle 3, 4 \rangle$
   $\mathbf{v} = \langle 2, -3 \rangle$

2. $\mathbf{u} = \langle 5, 12 \rangle$
   $\mathbf{v} = \langle -3, 2 \rangle$

3. $\mathbf{u} = \langle 2, -3, 4 \rangle$
   $\mathbf{v} = \langle 0, 6, 5 \rangle$

4. $\mathbf{u} = \mathbf{i}$
   $\mathbf{v} = \mathbf{i}$

5. $\mathbf{u} = 2\mathbf{i} - \mathbf{j} + \mathbf{k}$
   $\mathbf{v} = \mathbf{i} - \mathbf{k}$

6. $\mathbf{u} = 2\mathbf{i} + \mathbf{j} - 2\mathbf{k}$
   $\mathbf{v} = \mathbf{i} - 3\mathbf{j} + 2\mathbf{k}$

7. *Revenue* The vector $\mathbf{u} = \langle 3240, 1450, 2235 \rangle$ gives the number of units for products X, Y, and Z. The vector $\mathbf{v} = \langle 2.22, 1.85, 3.25 \rangle$ gives the price (in dollars) per unit for each product. Find the dot product $\mathbf{u} \cdot \mathbf{v}$, and explain what information it gives.

8. If $\mathbf{u} \cdot \mathbf{v} = \mathbf{u} \cdot \mathbf{w}$ and $\mathbf{u} \neq 0$, then is it true that $\mathbf{v} = \mathbf{w}$? If it is false, explain why or give an example that shows it is false.

In Exercises 9 and 10, find $\mathbf{u} \cdot \mathbf{v}$.

9. $\|\mathbf{u}\| = 8$, $\|\mathbf{v}\| = 5$, and the angle between $\mathbf{u}$ and $\mathbf{v}$ is $\pi/3$.

10. $\|\mathbf{u}\| = 40$, $\|\mathbf{v}\| = 25$, and the angle between $\mathbf{u}$ and $\mathbf{v}$ is $5\pi/6$.

In Exercises 11–18, find the angle θ between the given vectors.

11. $\mathbf{u} = \langle 1, 1 \rangle$
    $\mathbf{v} = \langle 2, -2 \rangle$

12. $\mathbf{u} = \langle 3, 1 \rangle$
    $\mathbf{v} = \langle 2, -1 \rangle$

13. $\mathbf{u} = 3\mathbf{i} + \mathbf{j}$
    $\mathbf{v} = -2\mathbf{i} + 4\mathbf{j}$

14. $\mathbf{u} = \cos\left(\dfrac{\pi}{6}\right)\mathbf{i} + \sin\left(\dfrac{\pi}{6}\right)\mathbf{j}$
    $\mathbf{v} = \cos\left(\dfrac{3\pi}{4}\right)\mathbf{i} + \sin\left(\dfrac{3\pi}{4}\right)\mathbf{j}$

15. $\mathbf{u} = \langle 1, 1, 1 \rangle$
    $\mathbf{v} = \langle 2, 1, -1 \rangle$

16. $\mathbf{u} = 2\mathbf{i} + 3\mathbf{j} + \mathbf{k}$
    $\mathbf{v} = -3\mathbf{i} + 2\mathbf{j}$

17. $\mathbf{u} = 3\mathbf{i} + 4\mathbf{j}$
    $\mathbf{v} = -2\mathbf{j} + 3\mathbf{k}$

18. $\mathbf{u} = 2\mathbf{i} - 3\mathbf{j} + \mathbf{k}$
    $\mathbf{v} = \mathbf{i} - 2\mathbf{j} + \mathbf{k}$

In Exercises 19–26, determine whether u and v are orthogonal or parallel, or neither.

19. $\mathbf{u} = \langle 4, 0 \rangle$
    $\mathbf{v} = \langle 1, 1 \rangle$

20. $\mathbf{u} = \langle 2, 18 \rangle$
    $\mathbf{v} = \langle \frac{3}{2}, -\frac{1}{6} \rangle$

21. $\mathbf{u} = \langle 4, 3 \rangle$
    $\mathbf{v} = \langle \frac{1}{2}, -\frac{2}{3} \rangle$

22. $\mathbf{u} = -\frac{1}{3}(\mathbf{i} - 2\mathbf{j})$
    $\mathbf{v} = 2\mathbf{i} - 4\mathbf{j}$

23. $\mathbf{u} = \mathbf{j} + 6\mathbf{k}$
    $\mathbf{v} = \mathbf{i} - 2\mathbf{j} - \mathbf{k}$

24. $\mathbf{u} = -2\mathbf{i} + 3\mathbf{j} - \mathbf{k}$
    $\mathbf{v} = 2\mathbf{i} + \mathbf{j} - \mathbf{k}$

25. $\mathbf{u} = \langle 2, -3, 1 \rangle$
    $\mathbf{v} = \langle -1, -1, -1 \rangle$

26. $\mathbf{u} = \langle \cos\theta, \sin\theta, -1 \rangle$
    $\mathbf{v} = \langle \sin\theta, -\cos\theta, 0 \rangle$

27. Use vectors to prove that the diagonals of a rhombus are perpendicular.

28. Consider a regular tetrahedron with vertices $(0, 0, 0)$, $(k, k, 0)$, $(k, 0, k)$, and $(0, k, k)$, where k is a positive real number.
    a. Sketch the graph of the tetrahedron.
    b. Find the length of each edge.
    c. Use the dot product to find the angle between any two edges.
    d. Find the angle between the line segments from the centroid $(k/2, k/2, k/2)$ to two vertices. This is the *bond angle* for a molecule such as CH_4 or $PbCl_4$, where the structure of the molecule is a tetrahedron.

29. What is known about θ, the angle between two nonzero vectors $\mathbf{u}$ and $\mathbf{v}$, if
    a. $\mathbf{u} \cdot \mathbf{v} = 0$?   b. $\mathbf{u} \cdot \mathbf{v} > 0$?   c. $\mathbf{u} \cdot \mathbf{v} < 0$?

30. If $\mathbf{u}$ and $\mathbf{v}$ are orthogonal to $\mathbf{w}$, then is it true that $\mathbf{u} + \mathbf{v}$ is orthogonal to $\mathbf{w}$? If it is true, prove it. Otherwise explain why it is false or give an example that shows it is false.

In Exercises 31–34, find the direction cosines of u and demonstrate that the sum of the squares of the direction cosines is 1.

31. $\mathbf{u} = \mathbf{i} + 2\mathbf{j} + 2\mathbf{k}$

32. $\mathbf{u} = 3\mathbf{i} - \mathbf{j} + 5\mathbf{k}$

33. $\mathbf{u} = \langle 0, 6, -4 \rangle$

34. $\mathbf{u} = \langle a, b, c \rangle$

C In Exercises 35 and 36, use a computer algebra system or write a computer program to determine the magnitude and direction angles of the resultant of forces F_1 and F_2. The magnitude and terminal point of each vector is given. Assume that the initial point of the vectors is at the origin.

Vector	Magnitude	Terminal point
35. F_1	50 lb	$(10, 5, 3)$
F_2	80 lb	$(12, 7, -5)$
36. F_1	300 N	$(-20, -10, 5)$
F_2	100 N	$(5, 15, 0)$

37. Find the angle between the diagonal of a cube and one of its edges.

38. Find the angle between the diagonal of a cube and the diagonal of one of its sides.

39. *Load-Supporting Cables* A load is supported by three cables, as shown in the accompanying figure. Find the direction angles of the load supporting cable OA.

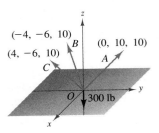

FIGURE FOR 39

40. Determine the weight of the load in Exercise 39 if the tension in the cable *OA* is 200 newtons.

In Exercises 41–48, (a) find the projection of u onto v, and (b) find the vector component of u orthogonal to v.

41. $\mathbf{u} = \langle 2, 3 \rangle$
$\mathbf{v} = \langle 5, 1 \rangle$

42. $\mathbf{u} = \langle 2, -3 \rangle$
$\mathbf{v} = \langle 3, 2 \rangle$

43. $\mathbf{u} = \langle 2, 1, 2 \rangle$
$\mathbf{v} = \langle 0, 3, 4 \rangle$

44. $\mathbf{u} = \langle 0, 4, 1 \rangle$
$\mathbf{v} = \langle 0, 2, 3 \rangle$

45. $\mathbf{u} = \langle 1, 1, 1 \rangle$
$\mathbf{v} = \langle -2, -1, 1 \rangle$

46. $\mathbf{u} = \langle -2, -1, 1 \rangle$
$\mathbf{v} = \langle 1, 1, 1 \rangle$

47. $\mathbf{u} = \langle 5, -4, 3 \rangle$
$\mathbf{v} = \langle 1, 0, 0 \rangle$

48. $\mathbf{u} = \langle 5, -4, 3 \rangle$
$\mathbf{v} = \langle 0, 1, 0 \rangle$

49. *Braking Load*   A truck with a gross weight of 32,000 pounds is parked on a 15° slope (see figure). Assuming that the only force to overcome is the force due to gravity,
a. find the force required to keep the truck from rolling down the hill.
b. find the force perpendicular to the hill.

50. *Load-Supporting Cables*   Find the magnitude of the projection of the load-supporting cable *OA* onto the positive *z*-axis as shown in the figure.

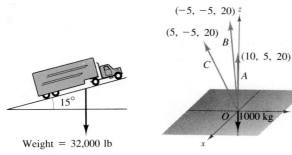

FIGURE FOR 49

Weight = 32,000 lb

FIGURE FOR 50

$(-5, -5, 20)$ z
$(5, -5, 20)$
B
$(10, 5, 20)$
C
A
O 1000 kg y
x

51. What can be said about the vectors **u** and **v** if
a. the projection of **u** onto **v** equals **u**?
b. the projection of **u** onto **v** equals **0**?

52. If the projection of **u** onto **v** has the same magnitude as the projection of **v** onto **u**, then is it true that $\|\mathbf{u}\| = \|\mathbf{v}\|$?

53. *Work*   An object is pulled 10 feet across a floor, using a force of 85 pounds. Find the work done if the direction of the force is 60° above the horizontal (see figure).

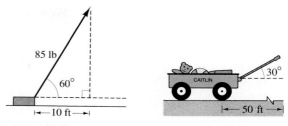

85 lb

60°

|← 10 ft →|

FIGURE FOR 53

30°

CAITLIN

|← 50 ft →|

FIGURE FOR 54

54. *Work*   A toy wagon is pulled by exerting a force of 15 pounds on a handle that makes a 30° angle with the horizontal. Find the work done in pulling the wagon 50 feet (see figure).

Work   **In Exercises 55 and 56, find the work done in moving a particle from *P* to *Q* if the magnitude and direction of the force is given by v.**

55. $P = (0, 0, 0)$, $Q = (4, 7, 5)$, $\mathbf{v} = \langle 1, 4, 8 \rangle$

56. $P = (1, 3, 0)$, $Q = (-3, 5, 10)$, $\mathbf{v} = -2\mathbf{i} + 3\mathbf{j} + 6\mathbf{k}$

57. Prove properties 2, 3, and 4 of Theorem 11.4.

58. Prove that

$$\|\mathbf{u} - \mathbf{v}\|^2 = \|\mathbf{u}\|^2 + \|\mathbf{v}\|^2 - 2\mathbf{u} \cdot \mathbf{v}.$$

59. Prove the **Cauchy-Schwarz Inequality**

$$\|\mathbf{u} \cdot \mathbf{v}\| \le \|\mathbf{u}\| \, \|\mathbf{v}\|.$$

60. Prove the triangle inequality

$$\|\mathbf{u} + \mathbf{v}\| \le \|\mathbf{u}\| + \|\mathbf{v}\|.$$

[*Hint:* Use the result of Exercise 59 and the fact that $\|\mathbf{u} + \mathbf{v}\|^2 = (\mathbf{u} + \mathbf{v}) \cdot (\mathbf{u} + \mathbf{v})$.]

61. Consider the vectors $\mathbf{u} = \langle \cos \alpha, \sin \alpha, 0 \rangle$ and $\mathbf{v} = \langle \cos \beta, \sin \beta, 0 \rangle$, where $\alpha > \beta$. Find the dot product of the vectors and use the result to prove the identity

$$\cos(\alpha - \beta) = \cos \alpha \cos \beta + \sin \alpha \sin \beta.$$

62. Consider the two curves $y_1 = x^2$ and $y_2 = x^{1/3}$. Find unit tangent vectors to each curve at their points of intersection. Find the angles between the curves at their points of intersection.

The Cross Product

Many applications in physics, engineering, and geometry involve finding a vector in space that is orthogonal to two given vectors. In this section you will study a product that will yield such a vector. It is called the **cross product,** and it is most conveniently defined and calculated using the standard unit vector form.

> **Definition of Cross Product of Two Vectors in Space**
>
> Let $\mathbf{u} = u_1\mathbf{i} + u_2\mathbf{j} + u_3\mathbf{k}$ and $\mathbf{v} = v_1\mathbf{i} + v_2\mathbf{j} + v_3\mathbf{k}$ be vectors in space. The **cross product** of $\mathbf{u}$ and $\mathbf{v}$ is the vector
>
> $$\mathbf{u} \times \mathbf{v} = (u_2v_3 - u_3v_2)\mathbf{i} - (u_1v_3 - u_3v_1)\mathbf{j} + (u_1v_2 - u_2v_1)\mathbf{k}.$$

REMARK   Be sure you see that this definition applies only to three-dimensional vectors. The cross product is not defined for two-dimensional vectors.

A convenient way to calculate $\mathbf{u} \times \mathbf{v}$ is to use the following *determinant form* with cofactor expansion. (This 3×3 determinant form is used simply to help remember the formula for the cross product—it is technically not a determinant, because the entries of the corresponding matrix are not all real numbers.)

$$\mathbf{u} \times \mathbf{v} = \begin{vmatrix} \mathbf{i} & \mathbf{j} & \mathbf{k} \\ u_1 & u_2 & u_3 \\ v_1 & v_2 & v_3 \end{vmatrix} \begin{matrix} \leftarrow \text{Put ``}\mathbf{u}\text{'' in Row 2} \\ \leftarrow \text{Put ``}\mathbf{v}\text{'' in Row 3} \end{matrix}$$

$$= \begin{vmatrix} \mathbf{i} & \mathbf{j} & \mathbf{k} \\ u_1 & u_2 & u_3 \\ v_1 & v_2 & v_3 \end{vmatrix} \mathbf{i} - \begin{vmatrix} \mathbf{i} & \mathbf{j} & \mathbf{k} \\ u_1 & u_2 & u_3 \\ v_1 & v_2 & v_3 \end{vmatrix} \mathbf{j} + \begin{vmatrix} \mathbf{i} & \mathbf{j} & \mathbf{k} \\ u_1 & u_2 & u_3 \\ v_1 & v_2 & v_3 \end{vmatrix} \mathbf{k}$$

$$= \begin{vmatrix} u_2 & u_3 \\ v_2 & v_3 \end{vmatrix} \mathbf{i} - \begin{vmatrix} u_1 & u_3 \\ v_1 & v_3 \end{vmatrix} \mathbf{j} + \begin{vmatrix} u_1 & u_2 \\ v_1 & v_2 \end{vmatrix} \mathbf{k}$$

$$= (u_2v_3 - u_3v_2)\mathbf{i} - (u_1v_3 - u_3v_1)\mathbf{j} + (u_1v_2 - u_2v_1)\mathbf{k}$$

Note the minus sign in front of the **j**-component. Each of the three 2×2 determinants can be evaluated by using the following diagonal pattern.

$$\begin{vmatrix} a & b \\ c & d \end{vmatrix} = ad - bc$$

EXAMPLE 1 Finding the Cross Product

Given $\mathbf{u} = \mathbf{i} - 2\mathbf{j} + \mathbf{k}$ and $\mathbf{v} = 3\mathbf{i} + \mathbf{j} - 2\mathbf{k}$, find the following.

a. $\mathbf{u} \times \mathbf{v}$ b. $\mathbf{v} \times \mathbf{u}$ c. $\mathbf{v} \times \mathbf{v}$

Solution

a. $\mathbf{u} \times \mathbf{v} = \begin{vmatrix} \mathbf{i} & \mathbf{j} & \mathbf{k} \\ 1 & -2 & 1 \\ 3 & 1 & -2 \end{vmatrix} = \begin{vmatrix} -2 & 1 \\ 1 & -2 \end{vmatrix} \mathbf{i} - \begin{vmatrix} 1 & 1 \\ 3 & -2 \end{vmatrix} \mathbf{j} + \begin{vmatrix} 1 & -2 \\ 3 & 1 \end{vmatrix} \mathbf{k}$

$$= (4 - 1)\mathbf{i} - (-2 - 3)\mathbf{j} + (1 + 6)\mathbf{k}$$
$$= 3\mathbf{i} + 5\mathbf{j} + 7\mathbf{k}$$

b. $\mathbf{v} \times \mathbf{u} = \begin{vmatrix} \mathbf{i} & \mathbf{j} & \mathbf{k} \\ 3 & 1 & -2 \\ 1 & -2 & 1 \end{vmatrix} = \begin{vmatrix} 1 & -2 \\ -2 & 1 \end{vmatrix} \mathbf{i} - \begin{vmatrix} 3 & -2 \\ 1 & 1 \end{vmatrix} \mathbf{j} + \begin{vmatrix} 3 & 1 \\ 1 & -2 \end{vmatrix} \mathbf{k}$

$$= (1 - 4)\mathbf{i} - (3 + 2)\mathbf{j} + (-6 - 1)\mathbf{k}$$
$$= -3\mathbf{i} - 5\mathbf{j} - 7\mathbf{k}$$

Note that this result is the negative of that in part a.

c. $\mathbf{v} \times \mathbf{v} = \begin{vmatrix} \mathbf{i} & \mathbf{j} & \mathbf{k} \\ 3 & 1 & -2 \\ 3 & 1 & -2 \end{vmatrix} = \mathbf{0}$

The results obtained in Example 1 suggest some interesting *algebraic* properties of the cross product. For instance, $\mathbf{u} \times \mathbf{v} = -(\mathbf{v} \times \mathbf{u})$ and $\mathbf{v} \times \mathbf{v} = \mathbf{0}$. These properties, and several others, are summarized in the following theorem.

THEOREM 11.7 Algebraic Properties of the Cross Product

Let $\mathbf{u}$, $\mathbf{v}$, and $\mathbf{w}$ be vectors in space and let c be a scalar.

1. $\mathbf{u} \times \mathbf{v} = -(\mathbf{v} \times \mathbf{u})$
2. $\mathbf{u} \times (\mathbf{v} + \mathbf{w}) = (\mathbf{u} \times \mathbf{v}) + (\mathbf{u} \times \mathbf{w})$
3. $c(\mathbf{u} \times \mathbf{v}) = (c\mathbf{u}) \times \mathbf{v} = \mathbf{u} \times (c\mathbf{v})$
4. $\mathbf{u} \times \mathbf{0} = \mathbf{0} \times \mathbf{u} = \mathbf{0}$
5. $\mathbf{u} \times \mathbf{u} = \mathbf{0}$
6. $\mathbf{u} \cdot (\mathbf{v} \times \mathbf{w}) = (\mathbf{u} \times \mathbf{v}) \cdot \mathbf{w}$

Proof To prove the first property, let $\mathbf{u} = u_1\mathbf{i} + u_2\mathbf{j} + u_3\mathbf{k}$ and $v_1\mathbf{i} + v_2\mathbf{j} + v_3\mathbf{k}$. Then,

$$\mathbf{u} \times \mathbf{v} = (u_2 v_3 - u_3 v_2)\mathbf{i} - (u_1 v_3 - u_3 v_1)\mathbf{j} + (u_1 v_2 - u_2 v_1)\mathbf{k}$$

and

$$\mathbf{v} \times \mathbf{u} = (v_2 u_3 - v_3 u_2)\mathbf{i} - (v_1 u_3 - v_3 u_1)\mathbf{j} + (v_1 u_2 - v_2 u_1)\mathbf{k}$$

which implies that $\mathbf{u} \times \mathbf{v} = -(\mathbf{v} \times \mathbf{u})$. Proofs of properties 2, 3, 5, and 6 are left as exercises (see Exercises 39–42).

Note that the first property listed in Theorem 11.7 indicates that the cross product is *not commutative.* In particular, this property indicates that the vectors $\mathbf{u} \times \mathbf{v}$ and $\mathbf{v} \times \mathbf{u}$ have equal lengths but opposite directions. The following theorem lists some other *geometric* properties of the cross product of two vectors.

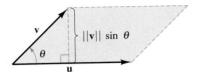

FIGURE 11.35
The vectors **u** and **v** form adjacent sides of a parallelogram.

THEOREM 11.8   Geometric Properties of the Cross Product

Let **u** and **v** be nonzero vectors in space, and let θ be the angle between **u** and **v**.

1. $\mathbf{u} \times \mathbf{v}$ is orthogonal to both **u** and **v**.
2. $\|\mathbf{u} \times \mathbf{v}\| = \|\mathbf{u}\|\,\|\mathbf{v}\| \sin\theta$.
3. $\mathbf{u} \times \mathbf{v} = \mathbf{0}$ if and only if **u** and **v** are scalar multiples of each other.
4. $\|\mathbf{u} \times \mathbf{v}\| =$ area of parallelogram having **u** and **v** as adjacent sides.

Proof   To prove the second property, note that because $\cos\theta = (\mathbf{u} \cdot \mathbf{v})/(\|\mathbf{u}\|\,\|\mathbf{v}\|)$, it follows that

$$\|\mathbf{u}\|\,\|\mathbf{v}\|\sin\theta = \|\mathbf{u}\|\,\|\mathbf{v}\|\sqrt{1 - \cos^2\theta}$$

$$= \|\mathbf{u}\|\,\|\mathbf{v}\|\sqrt{1 - \frac{(\mathbf{u} \cdot \mathbf{v})^2}{\|\mathbf{u}\|^2\|\mathbf{v}\|^2}}$$

$$= \sqrt{\|\mathbf{u}\|^2\|\mathbf{v}\|^2 - (\mathbf{u} \cdot \mathbf{v})^2}$$

$$= \sqrt{(u_1^2 + u_2^2 + u_3^2)(v_1^2 + v_2^2 + v_3^2) - (u_1v_1 + u_2v_2 + u_3v_3)^2}$$

$$= \sqrt{(u_2v_3 - u_3v_2)^2 + (u_1v_3 - u_3v_1)^2 + (u_1v_2 - u_2v_1)^2}$$

$$= \|\mathbf{u} \times \mathbf{v}\|.$$

To prove the fourth property, refer to Figure 11.35, which is a parallelogram having **v** and **u** as adjacent sides. Because the height of the parallelogram is $\|\mathbf{v}\|\sin\theta$, the area is

$$\text{Area} = (\text{base})(\text{height}) = \|\mathbf{u}\|\,\|\mathbf{v}\|\sin\theta = \|\mathbf{u} \times \mathbf{v}\|.$$

Proofs of the first and third properties are left as exercises (see Exercises 43 and 44.)

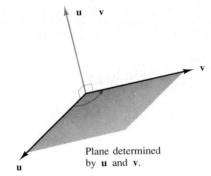

Plane determined by **u** and **v**.

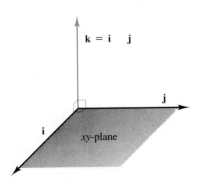

FIGURE 11.36
Right-handed systems

REMARK   It follows from the first two properties listed in Theorem 11.8 that if **n** is a unit vector orthogonal to both **u** and **v**, then

$$\mathbf{u} \times \mathbf{v} = \pm\big(\|\mathbf{u}\|\,\|\mathbf{v}\|\sin\theta\big)\mathbf{n}.$$

Both $\mathbf{u} \times \mathbf{v}$ and $\mathbf{v} \times \mathbf{u}$ are perpendicular to the plane determined by **u** and **v**. One way to remember the orientation of the vectors **u**, **v**, and $\mathbf{u} \times \mathbf{v}$ is to compare them with the unit vectors **i**, **j**, and $\mathbf{k} = \mathbf{i} \times \mathbf{j}$, as shown in Figure 11.36. The three vectors **u**, **v**, and $\mathbf{u} \times \mathbf{v}$ form a *right-handed system,* whereas the three vectors **u**, **v**, and $\mathbf{v} \times \mathbf{u}$ form a *left-handed system.*

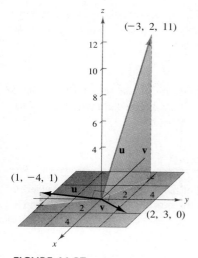

FIGURE 11.37
The vector $\mathbf{u} \times \mathbf{v}$ is orthogonal to both $\mathbf{u}$ and $\mathbf{v}$.

EXAMPLE 2   Using the Cross Product

Find a unit vector that is orthogonal to both

$$\mathbf{u} = \mathbf{i} - 4\mathbf{j} + \mathbf{k} \quad \text{and} \quad \mathbf{v} = 2\mathbf{i} + 3\mathbf{j}.$$

Solution   The cross product $\mathbf{u} \times \mathbf{v}$, as shown in Figure 11.37, is orthogonal to both $\mathbf{u}$ and $\mathbf{v}$.

$$\mathbf{u} \times \mathbf{v} = \begin{vmatrix} \mathbf{i} & \mathbf{j} & \mathbf{k} \\ 1 & -4 & 1 \\ 2 & 3 & 0 \end{vmatrix}$$

$$= -3\mathbf{i} + 2\mathbf{j} + 11\mathbf{k}$$

Because $\|\mathbf{u} \times \mathbf{v}\| = \sqrt{(-3)^2 + 2^2 + 11^2} = \sqrt{134}$, a unit vector orthogonal to both $\mathbf{u}$ and $\mathbf{v}$ is

$$\frac{\mathbf{u} \times \mathbf{v}}{\|\mathbf{u} \times \mathbf{v}\|} = -\frac{3}{\sqrt{134}}\mathbf{i} + \frac{2}{\sqrt{134}}\mathbf{j} + \frac{11}{\sqrt{134}}\mathbf{k}.$$

REMARK   In Example 2, note that you could have used the cross product $\mathbf{v} \times \mathbf{u}$ to form a unit vector that is orthogonal to both $\mathbf{u}$ and $\mathbf{v}$. With that choice, you would have obtained the negative of the unit vector found in the example.

EXAMPLE 3   Geometric Application of the Cross Product

Show that the quadrilateral with vertices at the following points is a parallelogram, and find its area.

$$A = (5, 2, 0) \qquad B = (2, 6, 1)$$
$$C = (2, 4, 7) \qquad D = (5, 0, 6)$$

Solution   From Figure 11.38 you can see that the sides of the quadrilateral correspond to the following four vectors.

$$\overrightarrow{AB} = -3\mathbf{i} + 4\mathbf{j} + \mathbf{k} \qquad \overrightarrow{CD} = 3\mathbf{i} - 4\mathbf{j} - \mathbf{k} = -\overrightarrow{AB}$$
$$\overrightarrow{AD} = 0\mathbf{i} - 2\mathbf{j} + 6\mathbf{k} \qquad \overrightarrow{CB} = 0\mathbf{i} + 2\mathbf{j} - 6\mathbf{k} = -\overrightarrow{AD}$$

Thus, $\overrightarrow{AB}$ is parallel to $\overrightarrow{CD}$ and $\overrightarrow{AD}$ is parallel to $\overrightarrow{CB}$, and you can conclude that the quadrilateral is a parallelogram with $\overrightarrow{AB}$ and $\overrightarrow{AD}$ as adjacent sides. Moreover, because

$$\overrightarrow{AB} \times \overrightarrow{AD} = \begin{vmatrix} \mathbf{i} & \mathbf{j} & \mathbf{k} \\ -3 & 4 & 1 \\ 0 & -2 & 6 \end{vmatrix}$$

$$= 26\mathbf{i} + 18\mathbf{j} + 6\mathbf{k}$$

the area of the parallelogram is

$$\|\overrightarrow{AB} \times \overrightarrow{AD}\| = \sqrt{1036} \approx 32.19.$$

Is the parallelogram a rectangle? You can tell whether it is by finding the angle between the vectors $\overrightarrow{AB}$ and $\overrightarrow{AD}$.

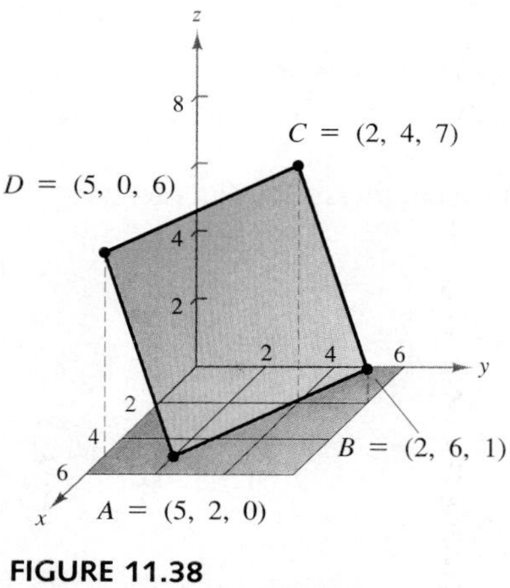

FIGURE 11.38
The area of the parallelogram is approximately 32.19.

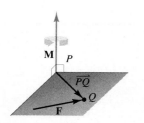

FIGURE 11.39
The moment of **F** about P.

In physics, the cross product can be used to measure **torque**—the **moment M of a force F about a point P,** as shown in Figure 11.39. If the point of application of the force is Q, then the moment of **F** about P is given by

$$\mathbf{M} = \overrightarrow{PQ} \times \mathbf{F}.$$

The magnitude of the moment **M** measures the tendency of the vector $\overrightarrow{PQ}$ to rotate counterclockwise (using the right-hand rule) about an axis directed along the vector **M.**

EXAMPLE 4 An Application of the Cross Product

A vertical force of 50 pounds is applied to the end of a 1-foot lever that is attached to an axle at point P, as shown in Figure 11.40. Find the moment of this force about the point P when $\theta = 60°$.

Solution If you represent the 50-pound force as $\mathbf{F} = -50\mathbf{k}$ and the lever as

$$\overrightarrow{PQ} = \cos(60°)\mathbf{j} + \sin(60°)\mathbf{k} = \frac{1}{2}\mathbf{j} + \frac{\sqrt{3}}{2}\mathbf{k}$$

then the moment of **F** about P is given by

$$\mathbf{M} = \overrightarrow{PQ} \times \mathbf{F} = \begin{vmatrix} \mathbf{i} & \mathbf{j} & \mathbf{k} \\ 0 & \dfrac{1}{2} & \dfrac{\sqrt{3}}{2} \\ 0 & 0 & -50 \end{vmatrix} = -25\mathbf{i}.$$

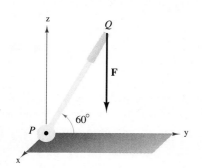

FIGURE 11.40
A vertical force of 50 pounds is applied at point Q.

The magnitude of this moment is 25 foot-pounds.

REMARK In Example 4, note that the moment (the tendency of the lever to rotate about its axle) is dependent upon the angle θ. When $\theta = \pi/2$, the moment is **0**. The moment is greatest when $\theta = 0$.

The Triple Scalar Product

For vectors **u**, **v**, and **w** in space, the dot product of **u** and **v** × **w**

$$\mathbf{u} \cdot (\mathbf{v} \times \mathbf{w})$$

is called the **triple scalar product.** The proof of this theorem is left as an exercise (see Exercise 47).

REMARK The value of a determinant is multiplied by -1 if two rows are interchanged. After two such interchanges, the value of the determinant will be unchanged. Thus, the following triple scalar products are equivalent.

$\mathbf{u} \cdot (\mathbf{v} \times \mathbf{w})$

$= \mathbf{v} \cdot (\mathbf{w} \times \mathbf{u})$

$= \mathbf{w} \cdot (\mathbf{u} \times \mathbf{v})$

THEOREM 11.9 The Triple Scalar Product

For $\mathbf{u} = u_1\mathbf{i} + u_2\mathbf{j} + u_3\mathbf{k}$, $\mathbf{v} = v_1\mathbf{i} + v_2\mathbf{j} + v_3\mathbf{k}$, and $\mathbf{w} = w_1\mathbf{i} + w_2\mathbf{j} + w_3\mathbf{k}$, the triple scalar product is given by

$$\mathbf{u} \cdot (\mathbf{v} \times \mathbf{w}) = \begin{vmatrix} u_1 & u_2 & u_3 \\ v_1 & v_2 & v_3 \\ w_1 & w_2 & w_3 \end{vmatrix}$$

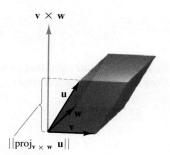

FIGURE 11.41
Area of base $= \|\mathbf{v} \times \mathbf{w}\|$
Volume of
parallelepiped $= |\mathbf{u} \cdot (\mathbf{v} \times \mathbf{w})|$

If the vectors $\mathbf{u}$, $\mathbf{v}$, and $\mathbf{w}$ do not lie in the same plane, then the triple scalar product $\mathbf{u} \cdot (\mathbf{v} \times \mathbf{w})$ can be used to determine the volume of the parallelepiped with $\mathbf{u}$, $\mathbf{v}$, and $\mathbf{w}$ as adjacent sides, as shown in Figure 11.41. This is established in the following theorem.

THEOREM 11.10   Geometric Property of Triple Scalar Product

The volume of V of a parallelepiped with vectors $\mathbf{u}$, $\mathbf{v}$, and $\mathbf{w}$ as adjacent sides is given by

$$V = |\mathbf{u} \cdot (\mathbf{v} \times \mathbf{w})|.$$

Proof   In Figure 11.41, note that

$$\|\mathbf{v} \times \mathbf{w}\| = \text{area of base}$$

and

$$\|\text{proj}_{\mathbf{v} \times \mathbf{w}} \mathbf{u}\| = \text{height of a parallelepiped}.$$

Therefore, the volume is

$$
\begin{aligned}
V = (\text{height})(\text{area of base}) &= \|\text{proj}_{\mathbf{v} \times \mathbf{w}} \mathbf{u}\| \, \|\mathbf{v} \times \mathbf{w}\| \\
&= \left| \frac{\mathbf{u} \cdot (\mathbf{v} \times \mathbf{w})}{\|\mathbf{v} \times \mathbf{w}\|} \right| \|\mathbf{v} \times \mathbf{w}\| \\
&= |\mathbf{u} \cdot (\mathbf{v} \times \mathbf{w})|.
\end{aligned}
$$

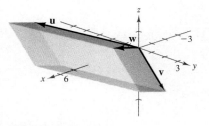

FIGURE 11.42
The parallelepiped has a volume of 36.

EXAMPLE 5   Volume by the Triple Scalar Product

Find the volume of the parallelepiped having $\mathbf{u} = 3\mathbf{i} - 5\mathbf{j} + \mathbf{k}$, $\mathbf{v} = 2\mathbf{j} - 2\mathbf{k}$, and $\mathbf{w} = 3\mathbf{i} + \mathbf{j} + \mathbf{k}$ as adjacent edges (see Figure 11.42).

Solution   By Theorem 11.10, you have

$$
\begin{aligned}
V &= |\mathbf{u} \cdot (\mathbf{v} \times \mathbf{w})| \\
&= \begin{vmatrix} 3 & -5 & 1 \\ 0 & 2 & -2 \\ 3 & 1 & 1 \end{vmatrix} \\
&= 3 \begin{vmatrix} 2 & -2 \\ 1 & 1 \end{vmatrix} - (-5) \begin{vmatrix} 0 & -2 \\ 3 & 1 \end{vmatrix} + (1) \begin{vmatrix} 0 & 2 \\ 3 & 1 \end{vmatrix} \\
&= 3(4) + 5(6) + 1(-6) \\
&= 36.
\end{aligned}
$$

A natural consequence of Theorem 11.10 is that the volume of the parallelepiped is 0 if and only if the three vectors are coplanar. That is, if the vectors $\mathbf{u} = \langle u_1, u_2, u_3 \rangle$, $\mathbf{v} = \langle v_1, v_2, v_3 \rangle$, and $\mathbf{w} = \langle w_1, w_2, w_3 \rangle$ have the same initial point, then they lie in the same plane if and only if

$$\mathbf{u} \cdot (\mathbf{v} \times \mathbf{w}) = \begin{vmatrix} u_1 & u_2 & u_3 \\ v_1 & v_2 & v_3 \\ w_1 & w_2 & w_3 \end{vmatrix} = 0.$$

EXERCISES for Section 11.4

TECHNOLOGY
Laboratory Guide
Lab 11.4

In Exercises 1–6, find the cross product of unit vectors and sketch your result.

1. $\mathbf{j} \times \mathbf{i}$ **2.** $\mathbf{i} \times \mathbf{j}$

3. $\mathbf{j} \times \mathbf{k}$ **4.** $\mathbf{k} \times \mathbf{j}$

5. $\mathbf{i} \times \mathbf{k}$ **6.** $\mathbf{k} \times \mathbf{i}$

In Exercises 7–12, find $\mathbf{u} \times \mathbf{v}$ and show that it is orthogonal to both $\mathbf{u}$ and $\mathbf{v}$.

7. $\mathbf{u} = \langle 2, -3, 1 \rangle$ **8.** $\mathbf{u} = \langle -1, 1, 2 \rangle$
$\mathbf{v} = \langle 1, -2, 1 \rangle$ $\mathbf{v} = \langle 0, 1, 0 \rangle$

9. $\mathbf{u} = \langle 12, -3, 0 \rangle$ **10.** $\mathbf{u} = \langle -10, 0, 6 \rangle$
$\mathbf{v} = \langle -2, 5, 0 \rangle$ $\mathbf{v} = \langle 7, 0, 0 \rangle$

11. $\mathbf{u} = \mathbf{i} + \mathbf{j} + \mathbf{k}$ **12.** $\mathbf{u} = \mathbf{j} + 6\mathbf{k}$
$\mathbf{v} = 2\mathbf{i} + \mathbf{j} - \mathbf{k}$ $\mathbf{v} = \mathbf{i} - 2\mathbf{j} + \mathbf{k}$

C **In Exercises 13–16, use a computer algebra system to find $\mathbf{u} \times \mathbf{v}$ and a unit vector orthogonal to $\mathbf{u}$ and $\mathbf{v}$.**

13. $\mathbf{u} = \langle 4, -3.5, 7 \rangle$ **14.** $\mathbf{u} = \langle -8, -6, 4 \rangle$
$\mathbf{v} = \langle -1, 8, 4 \rangle$ $\mathbf{v} = \langle 10, -12, -2 \rangle$

15. $\mathbf{u} = -3\mathbf{i} + 2\mathbf{j} - 5\mathbf{k}$ **16.** $\mathbf{u} = \frac{2}{3}\mathbf{k}$
$\mathbf{v} = \frac{1}{2}\mathbf{i} - \frac{3}{4}\mathbf{j} + \frac{1}{10}\mathbf{k}$ $\mathbf{v} = \frac{1}{2}\mathbf{i} + 6\mathbf{k}$

In Exercises 17–20, find the area of the parallelogram that has the vectors as adjacent sides.

17. $\mathbf{u} = \mathbf{j}$ **18.** $\mathbf{u} = \mathbf{i} + \mathbf{j} + \mathbf{k}$
$\mathbf{v} = \mathbf{j} + \mathbf{k}$ $\mathbf{v} = \mathbf{j} + \mathbf{k}$

19. $\mathbf{u} = \langle 3, 2, -1 \rangle$ **20.** $\mathbf{u} = \langle 2, -1, 0 \rangle$
$\mathbf{v} = \langle 1, 2, 3 \rangle$ $\mathbf{v} = \langle -1, 2, 0 \rangle$

In Execises 21 and 22, verify that the points are the vertices of a parallelogram and find its area.

21. $(1, 1, 1), (2, 3, 4), (6, 5, 2), (7, 7, 5)$

22. $(2, -1, 1), (5, 1, 4), (0, 1, 1), (3, 3, 4)$

In Exercises 23–26, find the area of the triangle with the given vertices. ($\frac{1}{2} \| \mathbf{u} \times \mathbf{v} \|$ is the area of the triangle having $\mathbf{u}$ and $\mathbf{v}$ as adjacent sides.)

23. $(0, 0, 0), (1, 2, 3), (-3, 0, 0)$

24. $(2, -3, 4), (0, 1, 2), (-1, 2, 0)$

25. $(1, 3, 5), (3, 3, 0), (-2, 0, 5)$

26. $(1, 2, 0), (-2, 1, 0), (0, 0, 0)$

In Exercises 27–30, find $\mathbf{u} \cdot (\mathbf{v} \times \mathbf{w})$.

27. $\mathbf{u} = \mathbf{i}$ **28.** $\mathbf{u} = \langle 1, 1, 1 \rangle$
$\mathbf{v} = \mathbf{j}$ $\mathbf{v} = \langle 2, 1, 0 \rangle$
$\mathbf{w} = \mathbf{k}$ $\mathbf{w} = \langle 0, 0, 1 \rangle$

29. $\mathbf{u} = \langle 2, 0, 1 \rangle$ **30.** $\mathbf{u} = \langle 2, 0, 0 \rangle$
$\mathbf{v} = \langle 0, 3, 0 \rangle$ $\mathbf{v} = \langle 1, 1, 1 \rangle$
$\mathbf{w} = \langle 0, 0, 1 \rangle$ $\mathbf{w} = \langle 0, 2, 2 \rangle$

In Exercises 31 and 32, use the triple scalar product to find the volume of the parallelepiped having adjacent edges $\mathbf{u}$, $\mathbf{v}$, and $\mathbf{w}$ (see figures).

31. $\mathbf{u} = \mathbf{i} + \mathbf{j}$ **32.** $\mathbf{u} = \langle 1, 3, 1 \rangle$
$\mathbf{v} = \mathbf{j} + \mathbf{k}$ $\mathbf{v} = \langle 0, 5, 5 \rangle$
$\mathbf{w} = \mathbf{i} + \mathbf{k}$ $\mathbf{w} = \langle 4, 0, 4 \rangle$

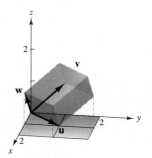 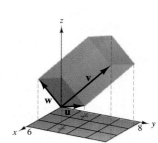

FIGURE FOR 31   **FIGURE FOR 32**

In Exercises 33 and 34, find the volume of the parallelepiped with the given vertices (see figures).

33. $(0, 0, 0), (3, 0, 0), (0, 5, 1), (3, 5, 1), (2, 0, 5), (5, 0, 5),$
$(2, 5, 6), (5, 5, 6)$

34. $(0, 0, 0), (1, 1, 0), (1, 0, 2), (0, 1, 1), (2, 1, 2), (1, 1, 3),$
$(1, 2, 1), (2, 2, 3)$

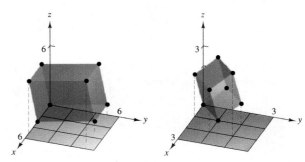

FIGURE FOR 33   **FIGURE FOR 34**

35. *Torque* A child applies the brakes on a bicycle by applying a downward force of 20 pounds on the pedal when the crank makes a 40° angle with the horizontal (see figure). Find the torque at P if the crank is 6 inches in length.

FIGURE FOR 35

36. *Torque*   Both the magnitude and direction of the force on a crankshaft change as the crankshaft rotates. Find the torque on the crankshaft using the position and data shown in the figure.

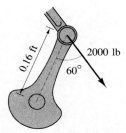

2000 lb

0.16 ft

60°

FIGURE FOR 36

37. *Torque*   A force of 200 pounds acts on the bracket shown in the figure.
   a. Determine the vector $\overrightarrow{AB}$ and the vector $\mathbf{F}$ representing the force. ($\mathbf{F}$ will be in terms of θ.)
   b. Find the magnitude of the moment about A by evaluating $\|\overrightarrow{AB} \times \mathbf{F}\|$.
   c. Use the result of part b to determine the magnitude of the moment when $\theta = 30°$.
   d. Use the result of part b to determine the angle θ when the magnitude of the moment is maximum.

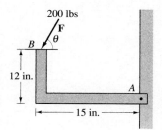

200 lbs

F

θ

B

12 in.

A

15 in.

FIGURE FOR 37

38. *Torque*   A force of 60 pounds acts on the pipe wrench shown in the figure.
   a. Find the magnitude of the moment about O by evaluating $\|\overrightarrow{OA} \times \mathbf{F}\|$. (The result will be a function of θ.)
   b. Use the result of part a to determine the magnitude of the moment when $\theta = 45°$.
   c. Use the result of part a to determine the angle θ when the magnitude of the moment is maximum. Is the answer what you expected? Why or why not?

In Exercises 39–46, prove the property of the cross product.

39. $\mathbf{u} \times (\mathbf{v} + \mathbf{w}) = (\mathbf{u} \times \mathbf{v}) + (\mathbf{u} \times \mathbf{w})$

40. $(c\,\mathbf{u}) \times \mathbf{v} = c(\mathbf{u} \times \mathbf{v})$

41. $\mathbf{u} \times \mathbf{u} = \mathbf{0}$

42. $\mathbf{u} \cdot (\mathbf{v} \times \mathbf{w}) = (\mathbf{u} \times \mathbf{v}) \cdot \mathbf{w}$

43. $\mathbf{u} \times \mathbf{v}$ is orthogonal to both $\mathbf{u}$ and $\mathbf{v}$.

44. $\mathbf{u} \times \mathbf{v} = \mathbf{0}$ if and only if $\mathbf{u}$ and $\mathbf{v}$ are scalar multiples of each other.

45. $\|\mathbf{u} \times \mathbf{v}\| = \|\mathbf{u}\|\,\|\mathbf{v}\|$ if $\mathbf{u}$ and $\mathbf{v}$ are orthogonal.

46. $\mathbf{u} \times (\mathbf{v} \times \mathbf{w}) = (\mathbf{u} \cdot \mathbf{w})\mathbf{v} - (\mathbf{u} \cdot \mathbf{v})\mathbf{w}$

47. Prove Theorem 11.9.

48. Consider the vectors $\mathbf{u} = \langle \cos \alpha, \sin \alpha, 0 \rangle$ and $\mathbf{v} = \langle \cos \beta, \sin \beta, 0 \rangle$, where $\alpha > \beta$. Find the cross product of the vectors and use the result to prove the identity

$$\sin(\alpha - \beta) = \sin \alpha \cos \beta - \cos \alpha \sin \beta.$$

49. *Essay*   Read the article "Tooth Tables: Solution of a Dental Problem by Vector Algebra" by Gary Hosler Meisters in the November, 1982 issue of *Mathematics Magazine*. Then write a paragraph explaining how vectors and vector algebra can be used in the construction of dental inlays.

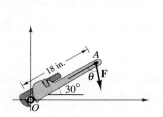

A

18 in.

θ

F

30°

O

FIGURE FOR 38

11.5 Lines in Space • Planes in Space • Sketching Planes in Space • Distances Between Points, Planes, and Lines

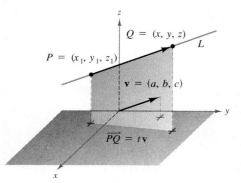

FIGURE 11.43
A line has direction vector **v**.

Lines in Space

In the plane, *slope* is used to determine an equation of a line. In space, it is more convenient to use *vectors* to determine the equation of a line.

In Figure 11.43, consider the line L through the point $P = (x_1, y_1, z_1)$ and parallel to the vector $\mathbf{v} = \langle a, b, c \rangle$. The vector $\mathbf{v}$ is the **direction vector** for the line L, and a, b, and c are the **direction numbers.** One way of describing the line L is to say that it consists of all points $Q = (x, y, z)$ for which the vector $\overrightarrow{PQ}$ is parallel to $\mathbf{v}$. This means that $\overrightarrow{PQ}$ is a scalar multiple of $\mathbf{v}$, and you can write $\overrightarrow{PQ} = t\mathbf{v}$, where t is a scalar.

$$\overrightarrow{PQ} = \langle x - x_1, y - y_1, z - z_1 \rangle = \langle at, bt, ct \rangle = t\mathbf{v}$$

By equating corresponding components, you can obtain the **parametric equations** of a line in space.

THEOREM 11.11 Parametric Equations of a Line in Space

A line L parallel to the vector $\mathbf{v} = \langle a, b, c \rangle$ and passing through the point $P = (x_1, y_1, z_1)$ is represented by the **parametric equations**

$$x = x_1 + at, \qquad y = y_1 + bt, \qquad z = z_1 + ct.$$

If the direction numbers a, b, and c are all nonzero, then you can eliminate the parameter t to obtain the **symmetric equations** of a line.

$$\frac{x - x_1}{a} = \frac{y - y_1}{b} = \frac{z - z_1}{c} \qquad \text{Symmetric equations}$$

EXAMPLE 1 Finding Parametric and Symmetric Equations

Find parametric and symmetric equations of the line L that passes through the point $(1, -2, 4)$ and is parallel to $\mathbf{v} = \langle 2, 4, -4 \rangle$.

Solution To find a set of parametric equations of the line, use the coordinates $x_1 = 1$, $y_1 = -2$, and $z_1 = 4$ and direction numbers $a = 2$, $b = 4$, and $c = -4$ (see Figure 11.44).

$$x = 1 + 2t, \qquad y = -2 + 4t, \qquad z = 4 - 4t \qquad \text{Parametric equations}$$

Because a, b, and c are all nonzero, a set of symmetric equations is

$$\frac{x - 1}{2} = \frac{y + 2}{4} = \frac{z - 4}{-4}. \qquad \text{Symmetric equations}$$

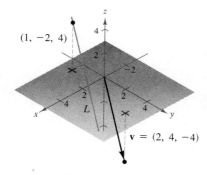

FIGURE 11.44
The vector **v** is parallel to the line.

Neither the parametric equations nor the symmetric equations of a given line are unique. For instance, in Example 1, by letting $t = 1$ in the parametric equations you would obtain the point $(3, 2, 0)$. Using this point with the direction numbers $a = 2$, $b = 4$, and $c = -4$ produces the parametric equations

$$x = 3 + 2t, \qquad y = 2 + 4t, \qquad z = -4t.$$

EXAMPLE 2 Parametric Equations of a Line Through Two Points

Find a set of parametric equations of the line that passes through the points $(-2, 1, 0)$ and $(1, 3, 5)$.

Solution   Begin by letting $P = (-2, 1, 0)$ and $Q = (1, 3, 5)$. Then a direction vector for the line passing through P and Q is given by

$$\mathbf{v} = \overrightarrow{PQ} = \langle 1 - (-2), 3 - 1, 5 - 0 \rangle = \langle 3, 2, 5 \rangle = \langle a, b, c \rangle.$$

Using the direction numbers $a = 3$, $b = 2$, and $c = 5$, with the point $P = (-2, 1, 0)$, you can obtain the parametric equations

$$x = -2 + 3t, \qquad y = 1 + 2t, \qquad z = 5t.$$

Planes in Space

You have seen how an equation of a line in space can be obtained from a point on the line and a vector *parallel* to it. You will now see that an equation of a plane in space can be obtained from a point in the plane and a vector *normal* (perpendicular) to it.

Consider the plane containing the point $P = (x_1, y_1, z_1)$ and having a nonzero normal vector $\mathbf{n} = \langle a, b, c \rangle$, as shown in Figure 11.45. This plane consists of all points $Q = (x, y, z)$ for which vector $\overrightarrow{PQ}$ is orthogonal to $\mathbf{n}$. Using the dot product, you can write the following.

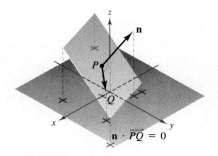

FIGURE 11.45
The normal vector $\mathbf{n}$ is orthogonal to each vector $\overrightarrow{PQ}$ in the plane.

$$\mathbf{n} \cdot \overrightarrow{PQ} = 0$$
$$\langle a, b, c \rangle \cdot \langle x - x_1, y - y_1, z - z_1 \rangle = 0$$
$$a(x - x_1) + b(y - y_1) + c(z - z_1) = 0$$

The third equation of the plane is said to be in **standard form.**

THEOREM 11.12   Standard Equation of a Plane in Space

The plane containing the point (x_1, y_1, z_1) and having a normal vector $\mathbf{n} = \langle a, b, c \rangle$ can be represented, in **standard form,** by the equation
$$a(x - x_1) + b(y - y_1) + c(z - z_1) = 0.$$

By regrouping terms, you obtain the **general form** of the equation of a plane in space,

$$ax + by + cz + d = 0.$$

Given the general form of the equation of a plane, it is easy to find a normal vector to the plane. Simply use the coefficients of x, y, and z and write $\mathbf{n} = \langle a, b, c \rangle$.

EXAMPLE 3   Finding an Equation of a Plane in Three-Space

Find the general equation of the plane containing the points $(2, 1, 1)$, $(0, 4, 1)$, and $(-2, 1, 4)$.

Solution   To apply Theorem 11.12, you need a point in the plane and a vector that is normal to the plane. There are three choices for the point, but no normal vector is given. To obtain a normal vector, use the cross product of vectors $\mathbf{u}$ and $\mathbf{v}$ extending from the point $(2, 1, 1)$ to the points $(0, 4, 1)$ and $(-2, 1, 4)$, as shown in Figure 11.46. The component forms of $\mathbf{u}$ and $\mathbf{v}$ are

$$\mathbf{u} = \langle 0 - 2, 4 - 1, 1 - 1 \rangle = \langle -2, 3, 0 \rangle$$
$$\mathbf{v} = \langle -2 - 2, 1 - 1, 4 - 1 \rangle = \langle -4, 0, 3 \rangle$$

and it follows that

$$\mathbf{n} = \mathbf{u} \times \mathbf{v} = \begin{vmatrix} \mathbf{i} & \mathbf{j} & \mathbf{k} \\ -2 & 3 & 0 \\ -4 & 0 & 3 \end{vmatrix}$$
$$= 9\mathbf{i} + 6\mathbf{j} + 12\mathbf{k}$$
$$= \langle a, b, c \rangle$$

is normal to the given plane. Using the direction numbers for $\mathbf{n}$ and the point $(x_1, y_1, z_1) = (2, 1, 1)$, you can determine an equation of the plane to be

$$a(x - x_1) + b(y - y_1) + c(z - z_1) = 0$$
$$9(x - 2) + 6(y - 1) + 12(z - 1) = 0 \qquad \text{Standard form}$$
$$9x + 6y + 12z - 36 = 0$$
$$3x + 2y + 4z - 12 = 0. \qquad \text{General form}$$

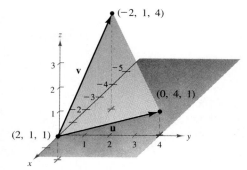

FIGURE 11.46
A plane determined by **u** and **v**.

REMARK   In Example 3, check to see that each of the three points satisfies the equation $3x + 2y + 4z - 12 = 0$.

Two distinct planes in three-space either are parallel or intersect in a line. If they intersect, you can determine the angle between them from the angle between their normal vectors, as shown in Figure 11.47. Specifically, if vectors $\mathbf{n}_1$ and $\mathbf{n}_2$ are normal to two intersecting planes, then the angle θ between the normal vectors is equal to the angle between the two planes and is given by

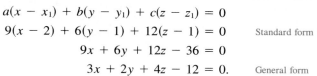

$$\cos \theta = \frac{|\mathbf{n}_1 \cdot \mathbf{n}_2|}{\|\mathbf{n}_1\| \|\mathbf{n}_2\|}. \qquad \text{Angle between two planes}$$

Consequently, two planes with normal vectors $\mathbf{n}_1$ and $\mathbf{n}_2$ are

1. *perpendicular* if $\mathbf{n}_1 \cdot \mathbf{n}_2 = 0$.
2. *parallel* if $\mathbf{n}_1$ is a scalar multiple of $\mathbf{n}_2$.

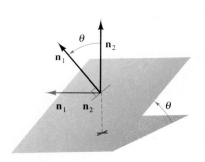

FIGURE 11.47
The angle between two planes.

EXAMPLE 4   Finding the Line of Intersection of Two Planes

Find the angle between the two planes given by

$$x - 2y + z = 0 \qquad \text{Equation for Plane 1}$$
$$2x + 3y - 2z = 0 \qquad \text{Equation for Plane 2}$$

and find parametric equations of their line of intersection (see Figure 11.48).

Solution   The normal vectors for the planes are $\mathbf{n}_1 = \langle 1, -2, 1 \rangle$ and $\mathbf{n}_2 = \langle 2, 3, -2 \rangle$. Consequently, the angle between the two planes is determined as follows.

$$\cos\theta = \frac{|\mathbf{n}_1 \cdot \mathbf{n}_2|}{\|\mathbf{n}_1\|\,\|\mathbf{n}_2\|} \qquad \text{Cosine of angle between } \mathbf{n}_1 \text{ and } \mathbf{n}_2$$

$$= \frac{|-6|}{\sqrt{6}\sqrt{17}}$$

$$= \frac{6}{\sqrt{102}}$$

$$\approx 0.59409 \qquad \theta \approx \arccos 0.59409$$

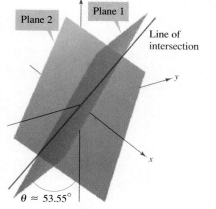

FIGURE 11.48
The angle between the planes is approximately 53.55°.

This implies that the angle between the two planes is $\theta \approx 53.55°$. You can find the line of intersection of the two planes by simultaneously solving the two linear equations representing the planes. One way to do this is to multiply the first equation by -2 and add the result to the second equation.

$$x - 2y + z = 0 \quad \rightarrow \quad -2x + 4y - 2z = 0$$
$$\underline{2x + 3y - 2z = 0 \qquad\qquad 2x + 3y - 2z = 0}$$
$$7y - 4z = 0 \quad \rightarrow \quad y = \frac{4z}{7}$$

Substituting $y = 4z/7$ back into one of the original equations, you can determine that $x = z/7$. Finally, by letting $t = z/7$, you obtain the parametric equations

$$x = t, \qquad y = 4t, \qquad z = 7t \qquad \text{Line of intersection}$$

which indicate that 1, 4, and 7 are direction numbers for the line of intersection.

Note that the direction numbers in Example 4 can be obtained from the cross product of the two normal vectors as follows.

$$\mathbf{n}_1 \times \mathbf{n}_2 = \begin{vmatrix} \mathbf{i} & \mathbf{j} & \mathbf{k} \\ 1 & -2 & 1 \\ 2 & 3 & -2 \end{vmatrix}$$

$$= \begin{vmatrix} -2 & 1 \\ 3 & -2 \end{vmatrix} \mathbf{i} - \begin{vmatrix} 1 & 1 \\ 2 & -2 \end{vmatrix} \mathbf{j} + \begin{vmatrix} 1 & -2 \\ 2 & 3 \end{vmatrix} \mathbf{k}$$

$$= \mathbf{i} + 4\mathbf{j} + 7\mathbf{k}$$

This means that the line of intersection of the two planes is parallel to the cross product of their normal vectors.

Sketching Planes in Space

If a plane in space intersects one of the coordinate planes, we call the line of intersection the **trace** of the given plane in the coordinate plane. To sketch a plane in space, it is helpful to find its points of intersection with the coordinate axes and its traces in the coordinate planes. For example, consider the plane given by

$$3x + 2y + 4z = 12. \qquad \text{Equation of plane}$$

We find the xy-trace by letting $z = 0$ and sketching the line

$$3x + 2y = 12 \qquad xy\text{-trace}$$

in the xy-plane. This line intersects the x-axis at $(4, 0, 0)$ and the y-axis at $(0, 6, 0)$. In Figure 11.49, we continue this process by finding the yz-trace and the xz-trace, and then shading in the triangular region lying in the first octant.

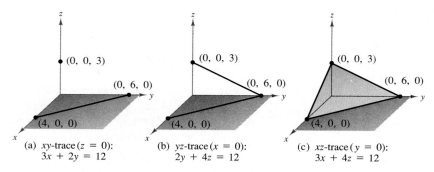

(a) xy-trace $(z = 0)$:
$\quad 3x + 2y = 12$

(b) yz-trace $(x = 0)$:
$\quad 2y + 4z = 12$

(c) xz-trace $(y = 0)$:
$\quad 3x + 4z = 12$

FIGURE 11.49
Traces of the plane:
$3x + 2y + 4z = 12$.

If the equation of a plane has a missing variable such as $2x + z = 1$, then the plane must be *parallel to the axis* represented by the missing variable, as shown in Figure 11.50. If two variables are missing from the equation of a plane, then it is *parallel to the coordinate plane* represented by the missing variables, as shown in Figure 11.51.

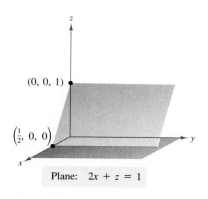

Plane: $2x + z = 1$

FIGURE 11.50

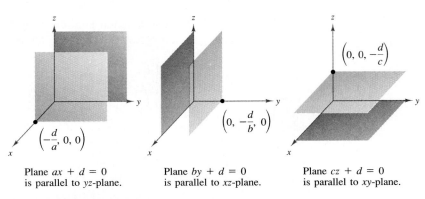

Plane $ax + d = 0$
is parallel to yz-plane.

Plane $by + d = 0$
is parallel to xz-plane.

Plane $cz + d = 0$
is parallel to xy-plane.

FIGURE 11.51

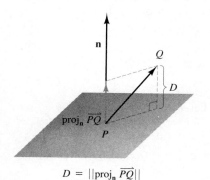

$$D = \|\text{proj}_\mathbf{n}\, \overrightarrow{PQ}\|$$

FIGURE 11.52
The distance between a point
and a plane.

Distances Between Points, Planes, and Lines

We conclude this section with a discussion of two basic types of distance problems in space.

1. Finding the distance between a point and a plane
2. Finding the distance between a point and a line

The solutions of these problems illustrate the versatility and usefulness of vectors in coordinate geometry—the first problem uses the *dot product* of two vectors, and the second problem uses the *cross product*.

The distance D between a point Q and a plane is the length of the shortest line segment connecting Q to the plane, as shown in Figure 11.52. If P is *any* point in the plane, you can find this distance by projecting the vector $\overrightarrow{PQ}$ onto the normal vector $\mathbf{n}$. The length of this projection is the desired distance.

> **THEOREM 11.13   Distance Between a Point and a Plane**
>
> The distance between a plane and a point Q (not in the plane) is
>
> $$D = \|\text{proj}_\mathbf{n}\, \overrightarrow{PQ}\| = \frac{|\overrightarrow{PQ} \cdot \mathbf{n}|}{\|\mathbf{n}\|}$$
>
> where P is a point in the plane and $\mathbf{n}$ is normal to the plane.

To find a point in the plane given by $ax + by + cz + d = 0$ $(a \neq 0)$, let $y = 0$ and $z = 0$. Then, from the equation $ax + d = 0$, you can conclude that the point $(-d/a, 0, 0)$ lies in the plane.

EXAMPLE 5   Finding the Distance Between a Point and a Plane

Find the distance between the point $Q = (1, 5, -4)$ and the plane given by $3x - y + 2z = 6$.

REMARK   The choice of the point P in Example 5 is arbitrary. Try choosing a different point to verify that you obtain the same distance.

Solution   You know that $\mathbf{n} = \langle 3, -1, 2 \rangle$ is normal to the given plane. To find a point in the plane, let $y = 0$ and $z = 0$, and obtain the point $P = (2, 0, 0)$. The vector from P to Q is given by

$$\overrightarrow{PQ} = \langle 1 - 2, 5 - 0, -4 - 0 \rangle$$
$$= \langle -1, 5, -4 \rangle.$$

Using the distance formula (given in Theorem 11.13) produces

$$D = \frac{|\overrightarrow{PQ} \cdot \mathbf{n}|}{\|\mathbf{n}\|} = \frac{|\langle -1, 5, -4 \rangle \cdot \langle 3, -1, 2 \rangle|}{\sqrt{9 + 1 + 4}}$$
$$= \frac{|-3 - 5 - 8|}{\sqrt{14}}$$
$$= \frac{16}{\sqrt{14}}.$$

From Theorem 11.13, you can determine that the distance between the point $Q = (x_0, y_0, z_0)$ and the plane given by $ax + by + cz + d = 0$ is

$$D = \frac{|a(x_0 - x_1) + b(y_0 - y_1) + c(z_0 - z_1)|}{\sqrt{a^2 + b^2 + c^2}}$$

$$D = \frac{|ax_0 + by_0 + cz_0 + d|}{\sqrt{a^2 + b^2 + c^2}} \qquad \text{Distance between point and plane}$$

where $P = (x_1, y_1, z_1)$ is a point on the plane and $d = -(ax_1 + by_1 + cz_1)$.

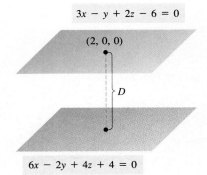

$3x - y + 2z - 6 = 0$

$(2, 0, 0)$

D

$6x - 2y + 4z + 4 = 0$

FIGURE 11.53
The distance between the parallel planes is approximately 2.14.

EXAMPLE 6 Finding the Distance Between Two Parallel Planes

Find the distance between the two parallel planes given by

$$3x - y + 2z - 6 = 0 \quad \text{and} \quad 6x - 2y + 4z + 4 = 0.$$

Solution The two planes are shown in Figure 11.53. To find the distance between the planes, choose a point in the first plane, say $(x_0, y_0, z_0) = (2, 0, 0)$. Then, from the second plane, you can determine that $a = 6, b = -2, c = 4$, and $d = 4$, and conclude that the distance is

$$\begin{aligned} D &= \frac{|ax_0 + by_0 + cz_0 + d|}{\sqrt{a^2 + b^2 + c^2}} \\ &= \frac{|6(2) + (-2)(0) + (4)(0) + 4|}{\sqrt{6^2 + (-2)^2 + 4^2}} = \frac{16}{\sqrt{56}} = \frac{8}{\sqrt{14}} \approx 2.14. \end{aligned}$$

The formula for the distance between a point and a line in space resembles that for the distance between a point and a plane—except that you replace the dot product by the cross product and replace the normal vector $\mathbf{n}$ by a direction vector for the given line.

> ### THEOREM 11.14 Distance Between a Point and a Line in Space
>
> The distance between a point Q and a line in space is given by
>
> $$D = \frac{\|\vec{PQ} \times \mathbf{u}\|}{\|\mathbf{u}\|}$$
>
> where $\mathbf{u}$ is the direction vector for the line and P is a point on the line.

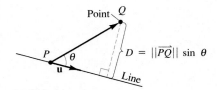

Point Q

P

θ

$\mathbf{u}$

$D = \|\vec{PQ}\| \sin\theta$

Line

FIGURE 11.54
The distance between a point and a line.

Proof In Figure 11.54, let D be the distance between the point Q and the given line. Then $D = \|\vec{PQ}\| \sin\theta$, where θ is the angle between $\mathbf{u}$ and $\vec{PQ}$. By Theorem 11.8, you have

$$\|\mathbf{u}\| \|\vec{PQ}\| \sin\theta = \|\mathbf{u} \times \vec{PQ}\| = \|\vec{PQ} \times \mathbf{u}\|.$$

Consequently,

$$D = \|\vec{PQ}\| \sin\theta = \frac{\|\vec{PQ} \times \mathbf{u}\|}{\|\mathbf{u}\|}.$$

EXAMPLE 7   Finding the Distance Between a Point and a Line

Find the distance between the point $Q = (3, -1, 4)$ and the line given by

$$x = -2 + 3t, \quad y = -2t, \quad \text{and} \quad z = 1 + 4t.$$

Solution   Using the direction numbers 3, -2, and 4, you know that the direction vector for the line is

$\mathbf{u} = \langle 3, -2, 4 \rangle.$ Direction vector for line

To find a point on the line, let $t = 0$ and obtain

$P = (-2, 0, 1).$ Point on the line

Thus,

$$\vec{PQ} = \langle 3 - (-2), -1 - 0, 4 - 1 \rangle = \langle 5, -1, 3 \rangle$$

and you can form the cross product

$$\vec{PQ} \times \mathbf{u} = \begin{vmatrix} \mathbf{i} & \mathbf{j} & \mathbf{k} \\ 5 & -1 & 3 \\ 3 & -2 & 4 \end{vmatrix} = 2\mathbf{i} - 11\mathbf{j} - 7\mathbf{k} = \langle 2, -11, -7 \rangle.$$

Finally, using Theorem 11.14, you can find the distance to be

$$D = \frac{\|\vec{PQ} \times \mathbf{u}\|}{\|\mathbf{u}\|} = \frac{\sqrt{174}}{\sqrt{29}} = \sqrt{6} \approx 2.45.$$

(See Figure 11.55.)

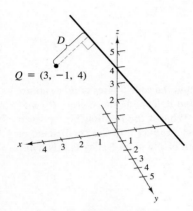

FIGURE 11.55
The distance between the point
Q and the line is $\sqrt{6} \approx 2.45$.

EXERCISES for Section 11.5

TECHNOLOGY
Laboratory Guide
Lab 11.5

1. The figure shows the line given by

$$x = 1 + 3t, \quad y = 2 - t, \quad \text{and} \quad z = 2 + 5t.$$

a. Draw an arrow on the line to indicate its orientation.
b. Find the coordinates of two points P and Q on the line. Determine the vector $\vec{PQ}$. What is the relationship of the components of the vector with the coefficients of t in the parametric equations? Why is this true?
c. Determine the coordinates of the point where the line intersects the xz-plane.

2. The figure shows the line given by

$$x = 2 - 3t, \quad y = 2, \quad \text{and} \quad z = 1 - t.$$

a. Draw an arrow on the line to indicate its orientation.
b. Find the coordinates of two points P and Q on the line. Determine the vector $\vec{PQ}$. What is the relationship of the components of the vector with the coefficients of t in the parametric equations? Why is this true?

c. Determine the coordinates of the point where the line intersects the xy-plane.
d. Does the line intersect the xz-coordinate plane? Explain why or why not.

FIGURE FOR 1

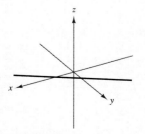

FIGURE FOR 2

In Exercises 3–8, find a set of (a) parametric equations and (b) symmetric equations of the line through the point and parallel to the specified vector or line. (For each line, express the direction numbers as integers.)

Point	Parallel to
3. $(0, 0, 0)$	$\mathbf{v} = \langle 1, 2, 3 \rangle$
4. $(0, 0, 0)$	$\mathbf{v} = \langle -2, \frac{5}{2}, 1 \rangle$
5. $(-2, 0, 3)$	$\mathbf{v} = 2\mathbf{i} + 4\mathbf{j} - 2\mathbf{k}$
6. $(-2, 0, 3)$	$\mathbf{v} = 6\mathbf{i} + 3\mathbf{j}$
7. $(1, 0, 1)$	$x = 3 + 3t$
	$y = 5 - 2t$
	$z = -7 + t$
8. $(-3, 5, 4)$	$\dfrac{x - 1}{3} = \dfrac{y + 1}{-2} = z - 3$

In Exercises 9 and 10, find a set of (a) parametric equations and (b) symmetric equations of the line through the two points. (For each line, express the direction numbers as integers.)

9. $(5, -3, -2), \left(-\frac{2}{3}, \frac{2}{3}, 1\right)$

10. $(1, 0, 1), (1, 3, -2)$

In Exercises 11 and 12, find a set of parametric equations of the line.

11. The line passes through the point $(2, 3, 4)$ and is parallel to the xz-plane and the yz-plane.

12. The line passes through the point $(2, 3, 4)$ and is perpendicular to the plane given by $3x + 2y - z = 6$.

In Exercises 13 and 14, determine which of the points lie on the line L.

13. The line L passes through the point $(-2, 3, 1)$ and is parallel to the vector $\mathbf{v} = 4\mathbf{i} - \mathbf{k}$.
a. $(2, 3, 0)$ **b.** $(-6, 3, 2)$
c. $(2, 1, 0)$ **d.** $(6, 3, -2)$

14. The line L passes through the points $(2, 0, -3)$ and $(4, 2, -2)$.
a. $(4, 1, -2)$ **b.** $\left(\frac{5}{2}, \frac{1}{2}, -\frac{11}{4}\right)$
c. $(-1, -3, -4)$ **d.** $(0, -2, -4)$

In Exercises 15–18, determine whether the lines intersect, and if so, find the point of intersection and the cosine of the angle of intersection.

15. $x = 4t + 2$ $x = 2s + 2$
     $y = 3$ $y = 2s + 3$
     $z = -t + 1$ $z = s + 1$

16. $x = -3t + 1$ $x = 3s + 1$
     $y = 4t + 1$ $y = 2s + 4$
     $z = 2t + 4$ $z = -s + 1$

17. $\dfrac{x}{3} = \dfrac{y - 2}{-1} = z + 1$

$\dfrac{x - 1}{4} = y + 2 = \dfrac{z + 3}{-3}$

18. $\dfrac{x - 2}{-3} = \dfrac{y - 2}{6} = z - 3$

$\dfrac{x - 3}{2} = y + 5 = \dfrac{z + 2}{4}$

C In Exercises 19 and 20, use a computer algebra system to graph the pair of intersecting lines and find the point of intersection.

19. $x = 2t + 3$ $x = -2s + 7$
     $y = 5t - 2$ $y = s + 8$
     $z = -t + 1$ $z = 2s - 1$

20. $x = 2t - 1$ $x = -5s - 12$
     $y = -4t + 10$ $y = 3s + 11$
     $z = t$ $z = -2s - 4$

In Exercises 21 and 22, (a) find the coordinates of three points P, Q, and R in the plane, and determine the vectors $\overrightarrow{PQ}$ and $\overrightarrow{PR}$ and (b) find $\overrightarrow{PQ} \times \overrightarrow{PR}$. What is the relationship between the components of the cross product and the coefficients of the variables in the equation of the plane? Why is this true?

21.   **22.**

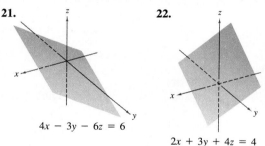

$4x - 3y - 6z = 6$

$2x + 3y + 4z = 4$

In Exercises 23–28, find an equation of the plane passing through the point and perpendicular to the specified vector or line.

Point	Perpendicular to
23. $(2, 1, 2)$	$\mathbf{n} = \mathbf{i}$
24. $(1, 0, -3)$	$\mathbf{n} = \mathbf{k}$
25. $(3, 2, 2)$	$\mathbf{n} = 2\mathbf{i} + 3\mathbf{j} - \mathbf{k}$
26. $(0, 0, 0)$	$\mathbf{n} = -3\mathbf{i} + 2\mathbf{k}$
27. $(0, 0, 6)$	$x = 1 - t, y = 2 + t, z = 4 - 2t$
28. $(3, 2, 2)$	$\dfrac{x - 1}{4} = y + 2 = \dfrac{z + 3}{-3}$

In Exercises 29–40, find an equation of the plane.

29. The plane passes through the points $(0, 0, 0)$, $(1, 2, 3)$, and $(-2, 3, 3)$.

30. The plane passes through the points $(1, 2, -3)$, $(2, 3, 1)$, and $(0, -2, -1)$.

31. The plane passes through the points $(1, 2, 3)$, $(3, 2, 1)$, and $(-1, -2, 2)$.

32. The plane passes through the point $(1, 2, 3)$ and is parallel to the yz-plane.

33. The plane passes through the point $(1, 2, 3)$ and is parallel to the xy-plane.

34. The plane contains the y-axis and makes an angle of $\pi/6$ with the positive x-axis.

35. The plane contains lines given by

$$\frac{x-1}{-2} = y - 4 = z$$

and

$$\frac{x-2}{-3} = \frac{y-1}{4} = \frac{z-2}{-1}.$$

36. The plane passes through the point $(2, 2, 1)$ and contains the line given by

$$\frac{x}{2} = \frac{y-4}{-1} = z.$$

37. The plane passes through the points $(2, 2, 1)$ and $(-1, 1, -1)$ and is perpendicular to the plane $2x - 3y + z = 3$.

38. The plane passes through the points $(3, 2, 1)$ and $(3, 1, -5)$ and is perpendicular to the plane $6x + 7y + 2z = 10$.

39. The plane passes through the points $(1, -2, -1)$ and $(2, 5, 6)$ and is parallel to the x-axis.

40. The plane passes through the points $(4, 2, 1)$ and $(-3, 5, 7)$ and is parallel to the z-axis.

In Exercises 41–46, determine whether the planes are parallel or orthogonal, or neither. If they are neither parallel nor orthogonal, find the angle of intersection.

41. $5x - 3y + z = 4$
$x + 4y + 7z = 1$

42. $3x + y - 4z = 3$
$-9x - 3y + 12z = 4$

43. $x - 3y + 6z = 4$
$5x + y - z = 4$

44. $3x + 2y - z = 7$
$x - 4y + 2z = 0$

45. $x - 5y - z = 1$
$5x - 25y - 5z = -3$

46. $2x - z = 1$
$4x + y + 8z = 10$

In Exercises 47–52, mark the intercepts and sketch a graph of the plane.

47. $4x + 2y + 6z = 12$

48. $3x + 6y + 2z = 6$

49. $2x - y + 3z = 4$

50. $2x - y + z = 4$

51. $y + z = 5$

52. $x + 2y = 4$

C **In Exercises 53–56, use a computer algebra system to obtain a graph of the plane.**

53. $2x + y - z = 6$

54. $x - 3z = 3$

55. $-5x + 4y - 6z + 8 = 0$

56. $2.1x - 4.7y - z + 3 = 0$

In Exercises 57 and 58, find a set of parametric equations for the line of intersection of the planes.

57. $3x + 2y - z = 7$
$x - 4y + 2z = 0$

58. $x - 3y + 6z = 4$
$5x + y - z = 4$

In Exercises 59–62, find the point of intersection (if any) of the plane and the line. Also determine whether the line lies in the plane.

59. $2x - 2y + z = 12$

$$x - \frac{1}{2} = \frac{y + (3/2)}{-1} = \frac{z+1}{2}$$

60. $2x + 3y = -5$

$$\frac{x-1}{4} = \frac{y}{2} = \frac{z-3}{6}$$

61. $2x + 3y = 10$

$$\frac{x-1}{3} = \frac{y+1}{-2} = z - 3$$

62. $5x + 3y = 17$

$$\frac{x-4}{2} = \frac{y+1}{-3} = \frac{z+2}{5}$$

In Exercises 63 and 64, find the distance between the point and the line.

63. $(10, 3, -2)$
$x = 4t - 2$
$y = 3$
$z = -t + 1$

64. $(4, 1, -2)$
$x = 2t + 2$
$y = 2t$
$z = t - 3$

In Exercises 65 and 66, find the distance between the point and the plane.

65. $(0, 0, 0)$
$2x + 3y + z = 12$

66. $(1, 2, 3)$
$2x - y + z = 4$

In Exercises 67 and 68, find the distance between the planes.

67. $x - 3y + 4z = 10$
$x - 3y + 4z = 6$

68. $2x - 4z = 4$
$2x - 4z = 10$

In Exercises 69 and 70, find the distance between the two skew lines (lines that are neither parallel nor intersecting).

69. $x = \frac{y}{2} = \frac{z}{3}$ $\frac{x-1}{-1} = y - 4 = z + 1$

70. $x = 3t$ $x = 4s + 1$
$y = -t + 2$ $y = s - 2$
$z = t - 1$ $z = -3s - 3$

71. a. Describe and find an equation for the surface generated by all points (x, y, z) that are four units from the point $(3, -2, 5)$.
 b. Describe and find an equation for the surface generated by all points (x, y, z) that are four units from the plane $4x - 3y + z = 10$.

72. Consider the two nonzero vectors **u** and **v**. Describe the geometric figure generated by the terminal points of the following vectors where s and t represent all real numbers.
 a. $t\mathbf{v}$ **b.** $\mathbf{u} + t\mathbf{v}$ **c.** $s\mathbf{u} + t\mathbf{v}$

73. *Mechanical Design*   A chute at the top of the grain elevator of a combine has the purpose of funneling the grain into a bin (see figure). Find the angle between two adjacent sides.

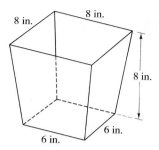

FIGURE FOR 73

74. If a_1, b_1, c_1 and a_2, b_2, c_2 are two sets of direction numbers for the same line, show that there exists a scalar d such that $a_1 = a_2 d$, $b_1 = b_2 d$, and $c_1 = c_2 d$.

True or False   **In Exercises 75 and 76, determine whether the statement is true or false. If it is false, explain why or give an example that shows it is false.**

75. If $\mathbf{v} = a_1 \mathbf{i} + b_1 \mathbf{j} + c_1 \mathbf{k}$ is any vector in the plane given by $a_2 x + b_2 y + c_2 z + d_2 = 0$, then $a_1 a_2 + b_1 b_2 + c_1 c_2 = 0$.

76. Every pair of lines in space are either intersecting or parallel.

77. Consider the plane that passes through the points P, R, and S. Show that the distance from a point Q to this plane is

$$\text{Distance} = \frac{|\mathbf{u} \cdot (\mathbf{v} \times \mathbf{w})|}{\|\mathbf{u} \times \mathbf{v}\|}$$

where $\mathbf{u} = \overrightarrow{PR}$, $\mathbf{v} = \overrightarrow{PS}$, and $\mathbf{w} = \overrightarrow{PQ}$.

78. Show that the distance between the parallel planes $ax + by + cz + d_1 = 0$ and $ax + by + cz + d_2 = 0$ is

$$\text{Distance} = \frac{|d_1 - d_2|}{\sqrt{a^2 + b^2 + c^2}}.$$

79. Prove that any two nonintersecting lines in space lie in parallel planes.

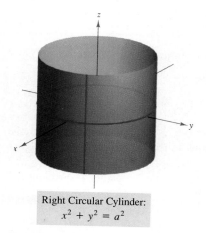

Right Circular Cylinder:
$x^2 + y^2 = a^2$

FIGURE 11.56
Rulings are parallel to z-axis.

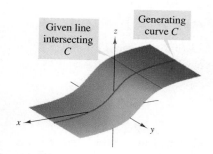

FIGURE 11.57
Cylinder: Rulings intersect C and
are parallel to the given line.

SECTION 11.6 Surfaces in Space

Cylindrical Surfaces • Quadric Surfaces • Surfaces of Revolution

Cylindrical Surfaces

The first five sections of this chapter contained the vector portion of the preliminary work necessary to study vector calculus and the calculus of space. In this and the next section, you will study surfaces in space and alternative coordinate systems for space. You have already studied two special types of surfaces.

1. **Spheres** $(x - x_0)^2 + (y - y_0)^2 + (z - z_0)^2 = r^2$ Section 11.2
2. **Planes** $ax + by + cz + d = 0$ Section 11.5

A third type of surface in space is called a **cylindrical surface,** or simply a **cylinder.** To define a cylinder, consider the familiar right circular cylinder shown in Figure 11.56. You can imagine that this cylinder is generated by a vertical line moving around the circle $x^2 + y^2 = a^2$ in the xy-plane. This circle is called a **generating curve** for the cylinder, as indicated in the following definition.

Definition of a Cylinder

Let C be a curve in a plane and let L be a line not in a parallel plane. The set of all lines parallel to L and intersecting C is called a **cylinder.** C is called the **generating curve** (or **directrix**) of the cylinder, and the parallel lines are called **rulings.**

REMARK Without loss of generality, you can assume that C lies in one of the three coordinate planes. Moreover, in this text we restrict the discussion to *right* cylinders—cylinders whose rulings are perpendicular to the coordinate plane containing C, as shown in Figure 11.57.

For the right circular cylinder shown in Figure 11.56, the equation of the generating curve is

$$x^2 + y^2 = a^2.$$ Equation of generating curve in xy-plane

To find an equation for the cylinder, note that you can generate any one of the rulings by fixing the values of x and y and then allowing z to take on all real values. In this sense the value of z is arbitrary and is, therefore, not included in the equation. In other words, the equation of this cylinder is simply the equation of its generating curve.

$$x^2 + y^2 = a^2$$ Equation of cylinder in space

EXAMPLE 1   Sketching a Cylinder

Sketch the surfaces represented by the following equations.

a. $z = y^2$ **b.** $z = \sin x, \qquad 0 \le x \le 2\pi$

Solution

a. The graph is a cylinder whose generating curve, $z = y^2$, is a parabola in the yz-plane. The rulings of the cylinder are parallel to the x-axis, as shown in Figure 11.58.

b. The graph is a cylinder generated by the sine curve in the xz-plane. The rulings are parallel to the y-axis, as shown in Figure 11.59.

Quadric Surfaces

The fourth basic type of surface in space is a **quadric surface.** Quadric surfaces are the three-dimensional analogs of conic sections.

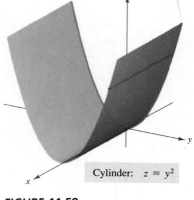

Generating curve C lies in yz-plane.

Cylinder: $z = y^2$

FIGURE 11.58
Rulings are parallel to x-axis.

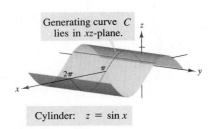

Generating curve C lies in xz-plane.

Cylinder: $z = \sin x$

FIGURE 11.59
Rulings are parallel to y-axis.

The intersection of a surface with a plane is called the **trace of the surface** in the plane. To visualize a surface in space, it is helpful to determine its traces in some well-chosen planes. The traces of quadric surfaces are conics. These traces, together with the **standard form** of the equation of each quadric surface, are shown in Table 11.1.

In Table 11.1, only one of several orientations of each quadric surface is shown. If the surface is oriented along a different axis, then its standard equation will change accordingly, as illustrated in Examples 2 and 3. The fact that the two types of paraboloids have one variable raised to the first power can be helpful in classifying quadric surfaces. The other four types of basic quadric surfaces have equations that are of *second degree* in all three variables.

TABLE 11.1 Quadric Surfaces

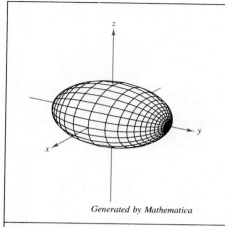

Generated by Mathematica

Ellipsoid

$$\frac{x^2}{a^2} + \frac{y^2}{b^2} + \frac{z^2}{c^2} = 1$$

Trace	Plane
Ellipse	Parallel to xy-plane
Ellipse	Parallel to xz-plane
Ellipse	Parallel to yz-plane

The surface is a sphere if $a = b = c \neq 0$.

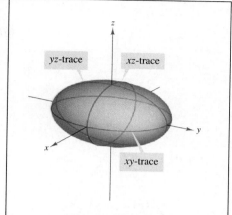

Hyperboloid of One Sheet

$$\frac{x^2}{a^2} + \frac{y^2}{b^2} - \frac{z^2}{c^2} = 1$$

Trace	Plane
Ellipse	Parallel to xy-plane
Hyperbola	Parallel to xz-plane
Hyperbola	Parallel to yz-plane

The axis of the hyperboloid corresponds to the variable whose coefficient is negative.

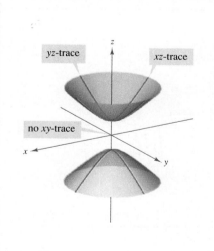

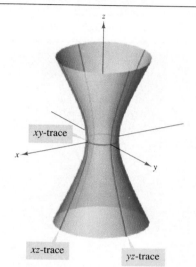

Generated by Mathematica

Hyperboloid of Two Sheets

$$\frac{z^2}{c^2} - \frac{x^2}{a^2} - \frac{y^2}{b^2} = 1$$

Trace	Plane
Ellipse	Parallel to xy-plane
Hyperbola	Parallel to xz-plane
Hyperbola	Parallel to yz-plane

The axis of the hyperboloid corresponds to the variable whose coefficient is positive. There is no trace in the coordinate plane perpendicular to this axis.

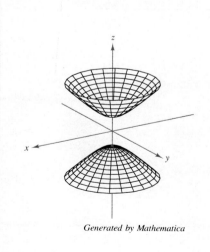

Generated by Mathematica

TABLE 11.1 **(Continued)**

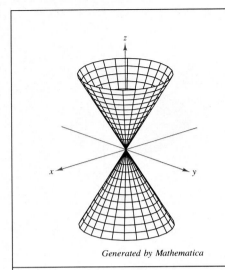 *Generated by Mathematica*	**Elliptic Cone** $$\frac{x^2}{a^2} + \frac{y^2}{b^2} - \frac{z^2}{c^2} = 0$$	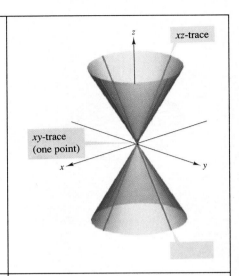

Trace	Plane
Ellipse	Parallel to xy-plane
Hyperbola	Parallel to xz-plane
Hyperbola	Parallel to yz-plane

The axis of the cone corresponds to the variable whose coefficient is negative. The traces in the coordinate planes parallel to this axis are intersecting lines.

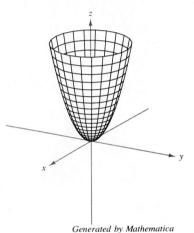 *Generated by Mathematica*	**Elliptic Paraboloid** $$z = \frac{x^2}{a^2} + \frac{y^2}{b^2}$$	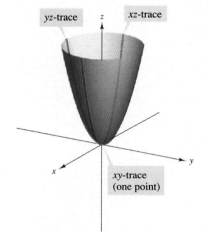

Trace	Plane
Ellipse	Parallel to xy-plane
Parabola	Parallel to xz-plane
Parabola	Parallel to yz-plane

The axis of the paraboloid corresponds to the variable raised to the first power.

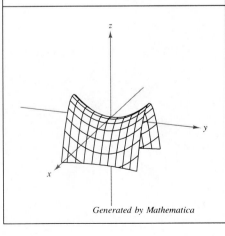 *Generated by Mathematica*	**Hyperbolic Paraboloid** $$z = \frac{y^2}{b^2} - \frac{x^2}{a^2}$$	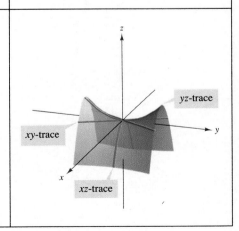

Trace	Plane
Hyperbola	Parallel to xy-plane
Parabola	Parallel to xz-plane
Parabola	Parallel to yz-plane

The axis of the paraboloid corresponds to the variable raised to the first power.

To classify a quadric surface, begin by writing the surface in standard form. Then, determine several traces taken in the coordinate planes *or* taken in planes that are parallel to the coordinate planes.

EXAMPLE 2 Sketching a Quadric Surface

Classify and sketch the surface given by $4x^2 - 3y^2 + 12z^2 + 12 = 0$.

Solution Begin by writing the given equation in standard form.

$$4x^2 - 3y^2 + 12z^2 + 12 = 0 \qquad \text{Given equation}$$

$$\frac{x^2}{-3} + \frac{y^2}{4} - z^2 - 1 = 0 \qquad \text{Divide by } -12$$

$$\frac{y^2}{4} - \frac{x^2}{3} - \frac{z^2}{1} = 1 \qquad \text{Standard form}$$

From Table 11.1, you can conclude that the surface is a hyperboloid of two sheets with the y-axis as its axis. To sketch the graph of this surface, it helps to find the traces in the coordinate planes.

xy-trace $(z = 0)$	$\dfrac{y^2}{4} - \dfrac{x^2}{3} = 1$	Hyperbola
xz-trace $(y = 0)$	$\dfrac{x^2}{3} + \dfrac{z^2}{1} = -1$	No trace
yz-trace $(x = 0)$	$\dfrac{y^2}{4} - \dfrac{z^2}{1} = 1$	Hyperbola

The graph is shown in Figure 11.60.

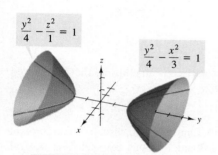

$$\frac{y^2}{4} - \frac{z^2}{1} = 1$$

$$\frac{y^2}{4} - \frac{x^2}{3} = 1$$

Hyperboloid of Two Sheets:
$$\frac{y^2}{4} - \frac{x^2}{3} - z^2 = 1$$

FIGURE 11.60

EXAMPLE 3 Sketching a Quadric Surface

Classify and sketch the surface given by $x - y^2 - 4z^2 = 0$.

Solution Because x is raised only to the first power, the surface is a paraboloid. The axis of the paraboloid is the x-axis. In the standard form, the equation is

$$x = y^2 + 4z^2. \qquad \text{Standard form}$$

Some convenient traces are as follows.

xy-trace $(z = 0)$	$x = y^2$	Parabola
xz-trace $(y = 0)$	$x = 4z^2$	Parabola
parallel to yz-plane $(x = 4)$	$\dfrac{y^2}{4} + \dfrac{z^2}{1} = 1$	Ellipse

Thus, the surface is an *elliptic* paraboloid, as shown in Figure 11.61.

Some second-degree equations in x, y, and z do not represent quadric surfaces. For instance, the graph of

$$x^2 + y^2 + z^2 = 0$$

is a single point, and the graph of

$$x^2 + y^2 = 1$$

is a right circular cylinder.

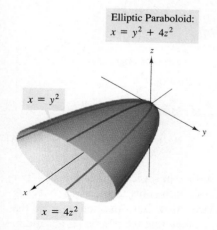

Elliptic Paraboloid:
$$x = y^2 + 4z^2$$

$x = y^2$

$x = 4z^2$

FIGURE 11.61

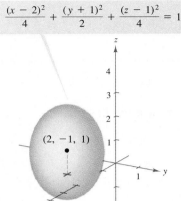

$$\frac{(x-2)^2}{4} + \frac{(y+1)^2}{2} + \frac{(z-1)^2}{4} = 1$$

FIGURE 11.62
An Ellipsoid centered at
$(2, -1, 1)$.

For a quadric surface not centered at the origin, you can form the standard equation by completing the square, as demonstrated in Example 4.

EXAMPLE 4   A Quadric Surface Not Centered at the Origin

Classify and sketch the surface given by

$$x^2 + 2y^2 + z^2 - 4x + 4y - 2z + 3 = 0.$$

Solution   Completing the square for each variable produces the following.

$$(x^2 - 4x + \quad) + 2(y^2 + 2y + \quad) + (z^2 - 2z + \quad) = -3$$
$$(x^2 - 4x + 4) + 2(y^2 + 2y + 1) + (z^2 - 2z + 1) = -3 + 4 + 2 + 1$$
$$(x - 2)^2 + 2(y + 1)^2 + (z - 1)^2 = 4$$
$$\frac{(x - 2)^2}{4} + \frac{(y + 1)^2}{2} + \frac{(z - 1)^2}{4} = 1$$

From this equation, you can see that the quadric surface is an ellipsoid that is centered at $(2, -1, 1)$. Its graph is shown in Figure 11.62.

TECHNOLOGY   A computer graphing utility can help you visualize a surface in space.* Most such utilities create three-dimensional illusions by sketching several traces of the surface and then applying a "hidden-line" routine that blocks out portions of the surface that lie behind other portions of the surface. Figure 11.63 shows two different quadric surfaces that were generated by a computer.

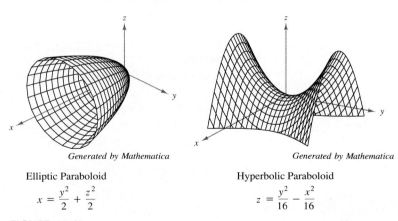

Generated by Mathematica   *Generated by Mathematica*

Elliptic Paraboloid   Hyperbolic Paraboloid

$$x = \frac{y^2}{2} + \frac{z^2}{2}$$ $$z = \frac{y^2}{16} - \frac{x^2}{16}$$

FIGURE 11.63

Using a computer to sketch the graph of a surface in space requires practice. For one thing, you must know enough about the surface to be able to specify a "viewing box" that gives a representative view of the surface. Also, you can often improve the view of a surface by rotating the axis. For instance, note that the elliptic paraboloid in Figure 11.63 is seen from a line of sight that is "higher" than the line of sight used to view the hyperbolic paraboloid.

* Some 3-D graphing utilities require surfaces to be entered with parametric equations. For a discussion of this technique, see Section 15.5.

Surfaces of Revolution

The fifth special type of surface we will study is called a **surface of revolution.** In Section 6.4 we looked at a method for finding the *area* of such a surface. We now look at a procedure for finding its *equation.*

Consider the graph of the **radius function**

$$y = r(z) \qquad \text{Generating curve}$$

in the *yz*-plane. If this graph is revolved about the *z*-axis, it forms a surface of revolution, as shown in Figure 11.64. The trace of the surface in the plane $z = z_0$ is a circle whose radius is $r(z_0)$ and whose equation is

$$x^2 + y^2 = [r(z_0)]^2. \qquad \text{Circular trace in plane} \quad z = z_0$$

Replacing z_0 by z produces an equation that is valid for all values of z. In a similar manner we can obtain equations for surfaces of revolution for the other two axes, and we summarize the results as follows.

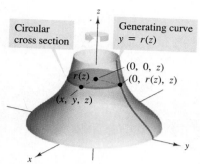

FIGURE 11.64
A surface of revolution.

Surface of Revolution

If the graph of a radius function r is revolved about one of the coordinate axes, then the equation of the resulting surface of revolution has one of the following forms.

1. **Revolved about the x-axis** $y^2 + z^2 = [r(x)]^2$
2. **Revolved about the y-axis** $x^2 + z^2 = [r(y)]^2$
3. **Revolved about the z-axis** $x^2 + y^2 = [r(z)]^2$

EXAMPLE 5   Finding an Equation for a Surface of Revolution

a. An equation for the surface of revolution formed by revolving the graph of $y = 1/z$ about the *z*-axis is

$$x^2 + y^2 = [r(z)]^2 = \left(\frac{1}{z}\right)^2$$

b. To find an equation for the surface formed by revolving the graph of $9x^2 = y^3$ about the *y*-axis, solve for x in terms of y to obtain

$$x = \frac{1}{3}y^{3/2} = r(y). \qquad \text{Radius function}$$

Thus, the equation for this surface is

$$x^2 + z^2 = [r(y)]^2 \qquad \text{Revolved about the } y\text{-axis}$$

$$x^2 + z^2 = \left(\frac{1}{3}y^{3/2}\right)^2 \qquad \text{Substitute } \tfrac{1}{3}y^{3/2} \text{ for } r(y)$$

$$x^2 + z^2 = \frac{1}{9}y^3. \qquad \text{Equation of surface}$$

The graph is shown in Figure 11.65.

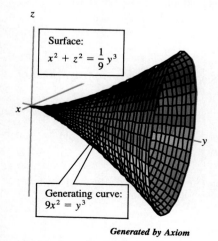

Surface:
$x^2 + z^2 = \frac{1}{9}y^3$

Generating curve:
$9x^2 = y^3$

Generated by Axiom

FIGURE 11.65

The generating curve for a surface of revolution is not unique. For instance, the surface

$$x^2 + z^2 = e^{-2y}$$

can be formed by revolving either the graph of $x = e^{-y}$ about the y-axis or the graph of $z = e^{-y}$ about the y-axis, as shown in Figure 11.66.

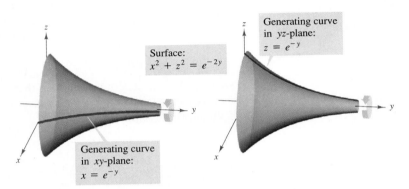

FIGURE 11.66

EXAMPLE 6   Finding a Generating Curve for a Surface of Revolution

Find a generating curve and the axis of revolution for the surface given by $x^2 + 3y^2 + z^2 = 9$.

Solution   You now know that the equation has one of the following forms.

$$x^2 + y^2 = [r(z)]^2 \qquad \text{Revolved about } z\text{-axis}$$
$$y^2 + z^2 = [r(x)]^2 \qquad \text{Revolved about } x\text{-axis}$$
$$x^2 + z^2 = [r(y)]^2 \qquad \text{Revolved about } y\text{-axis}$$

Because the coefficients of x^2 and z^2 are equal, you should choose the third form and write

$$x^2 + z^2 = 9 - 3y^2.$$

The y-axis is the axis of revolution. You can choose a generating curve from either of the following traces.

$$x^2 = 9 - 3y^2 \qquad \text{Trace in } xy\text{-plane}$$
$$z^2 = 9 - 3y^2 \qquad \text{Trace in } yz\text{-plane}$$

For example, using the first trace, the generating curve is the semiellipse given by

$$x = \sqrt{9 - 3y^2}. \qquad \text{Generating curve}$$

The graph of this surface is shown in Figure 11.67.

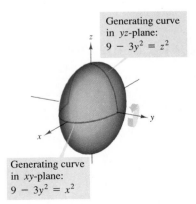

FIGURE 11.67

EXERCISES for Section 11.6

TECHNOLOGY
Laboratory Guide
Lab 11.6

In Exercises 1–6, match the equation with its graph. [The graphs are labeled (a), (b), (c), (d), (e), and (f).]

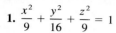

1. $\dfrac{x^2}{9} + \dfrac{y^2}{16} + \dfrac{z^2}{9} = 1$

2. $15x^2 - 4y^2 + 15z^2 = -4$

3. $4x^2 - y^2 + 4z^2 = 4$ **4.** $y^2 = 4x^2 + 9z^2$

5. $4x^2 - 4y + z^2 = 0$ **6.** $4x^2 - y^2 + 4z = 0$

(a)

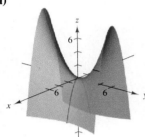

(b)

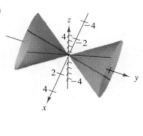

(c)

 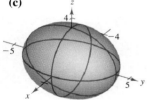

(d)

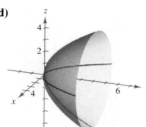

(e)

 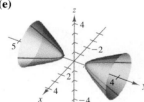

(f)

In Exercises 7–16, describe and sketch each surface.

7. $z = 3$ 　　　　　　　**8.** $x = 4$

9. $y^2 + z^2 = 9$ 　　　　**10.** $x^2 + z^2 = 16$

11. $x^2 - y = 0$ 　　　　**12.** $y^2 + z = 4$

13. $4x^2 + y^2 = 4$ 　　　**14.** $y^2 - z^2 = 4$

15. $z - \sin y = 0$ 　　　**16.** $z - e^y = 0$

17. The four figures are graphs of the quadric surface

$$z = x^2 + y^2.$$

Match each of the four graphs with the point in space from which the paraboloid is viewed. The four points are $(0, 0, 20)$, $(0, 20, 0)$, $(20, 0, 0)$, and $(10, 10, 20)$.

(a)

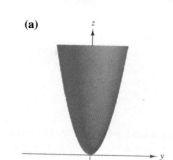

(b)

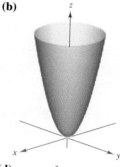

(c)

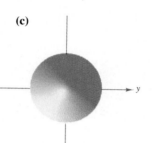

(d)

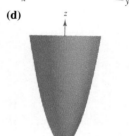

C **18** Use a graphing utility to sketch three views of the equation

$$y^2 + z^2 = 4$$

with views from the points
a. $(10, 0, 0)$ 　　**b.** $(0, 10, 0)$ 　　**c.** $(10, 10, 10)$.

In Exercises 19–30, identify and sketch the given quadric surface.

19. $x^2 + \dfrac{y^2}{4} + z^2 = 1$ 　　**20.** $\dfrac{x^2}{9} + \dfrac{y^2}{16} + \dfrac{z^2}{16} = 1$

21. $16x^2 - y^2 + 16z^2 = 4$ 　　**22.** $z^2 - x^2 - \dfrac{y^2}{4} = 1$

23. $x^2 - y + z^2 = 0$ 　　**24.** $z = 4x^2 + y^2$

25. $x^2 - y^2 + z = 0$ 　　**26.** $3z = -y^2 + x^2$

27. $z^2 = x^2 + \dfrac{y^2}{4}$ 　　**28.** $x^2 = 2y^2 + 2z^2$

29. $16x^2 + 9y^2 + 16z^2 - 32x - 36y + 36 = 0$

30. $4x^2 + y^2 - 4z^2 - 16x - 6y - 16z + 9 = 0$

C In Exercises 31–38, use a computer algebra system to obtain a graph of the surface. Identify the surface as a cylinder, quadric surface, or surface of revolution. (*Hint:* It may be necessary to solve for z and acquire two equations to graph.)

31. $z = 2 \sin x$ 　　　　**32.** $z = x^2 + 0.5y^2$

33. $x^2 + z^2 = \left(\dfrac{2}{y}\right)^2$ 　　**34.** $x^2 + y^2 = e^{-z}$

35. $z^2 = x^2 + 4y^2$ 　　　**36.** $4y = x^2 + z^2$

37. $4x^2 - y^2 + 4z^2 = -16$ **38.** $9x^2 + 4y^2 - 8z^2 = 72$

In Exercises 39–42, sketch the region bounded by the graphs of the equations.

39. $z = 2\sqrt{x^2 + y^2}, z = 2$

40. $z = \sqrt{4 - x^2}, y = \sqrt{4 - x^2}, x = 0, y = 0, z = 0$

41. $x^2 + y^2 = 1, x + z = 2, z = 0$

42. $z = \sqrt{4 - x^2 - y^2}, y = 2z, z = 0$

In Exercises 43–48, find an equation for the surface of revolution generated by revolving the curve in the specified coordinate plane about the given axis.

Equation of curve	Coordinate plane	Axis of revolution
43. $z^2 = 4y$	yz-plane	y-axis
44. $z = 2y$	yz-plane	y-axis
45. $z = 2y$	yz-plane	z-axis
46. $2z = \sqrt{4 - x^2}$	xz-plane	x-axis
47. $xy = 2$	xy-plane	x-axis
48. $z = \ln y$	yz-plane	z-axis

In Exercises 49 and 50, find an equation of a generating curve given the equation of its surface of revolution.

49. $x^2 + y^2 - 2z = 0$ **50.** $x^2 + z^2 = \sin^2 y$

In Exercises 51 and 52, use the Shell Method to find the volume of the solid below the surface of revolution and above the xy-coordinate plane.

51. The curve $z = 4x - x^2$ in the xz-plane is revolved about the z-axis.

52. The curve $z = \sin y$ $(0 \leq y \leq \pi)$ in the yz-plane is revolved about the z-axis.

In Exercises 53 and 54, analyze the trace when the surface given by

$$z = \frac{x^2}{2} + \frac{y^2}{4}$$

is intersected by the planes.

53. Find the length of the major and minor axes and the coordinates of the foci of the ellipse generated when the surface is intersected by the planes given by
a. $z = 2$.   **b.** $z = 8$.

54. Find the coordinates of the focus of the parabola formed when the surface is intersected by the planes given by
a. $y = 4$.   **b.** $x = 2$.

55. *Shape of the Earth* Because of the forces caused by its rotation, the earth is an oblate ellipsoid rather than a sphere. The equatorial radius is 3963 miles and the polar radius is 3942 miles. Find an equation of the ellipsoid. (Assume that the center of the earth is at the origin and the trace formed by the plane $z = 0$ corresponds to the equator.)

56. *Satellite Antenna* A satellite receiving dish is a paraboloid with the dimensions shown in the figure. Find the equation of the generating curve in the yz-plane and find the corresponding equation of the surface of revolution.

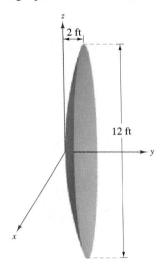

FIGURE FOR 56

57. *Inside or Outside* Three classic "topological" surfaces are shown below. The sphere and torus have both an "inside" and an "outside." Does the Klein bottle have both an inside and an outside? Explain.

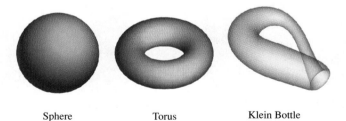

Sphere   Torus   Klein Bottle

FIGURE FOR 57

58. Determine the intersection of the hyperbolic paraboloid $z = y^2/b^2 - x^2/a^2$ with the plane $bx + ay - z = 0$. (Assume $a, b > 0$.)

Cylindrical and Spherical Coordinates

11.7   Cylindrical Coordinates • Spherical Coordinates

Cylindrical Coordinates

You have already seen that some two-dimensional graphs are easier to represent in polar coordinates than in rectangular coordinates. A similar situation exists for surfaces in space. In this section, you will study two alternative space-coordinate systems. The first, the **cylindrical coordinate system,** is an extension of polar coordinates to space.

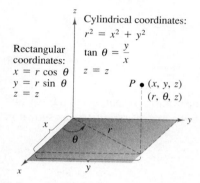

Cylindrical coordinates:
$$r^2 = x^2 + y^2$$
$$\tan \theta = \frac{y}{x}$$
$$z = z$$

Rectangular coordinates:
$$x = r \cos \theta$$
$$y = r \sin \theta$$
$$z = z$$

$P \bullet (x, y, z)$
(r, θ, z)

FIGURE 11.68

The Cylindrical Coordinate System

In a **cylindrical coordinate system,** a point P in space is represented by an ordered triple (r, θ, z).

1. (r, θ) is a polar representation of the projection of P in the xy-plane.
2. z is the directed distance from (r, θ) to P.

To convert from rectangular to cylindrical coordinates (or vice versa), use the conversion guidelines for polar coordinates, as illustrated in Figure 11.68.

Cylindrical to rectangular

$$x = r \cos \theta, \; y = r \sin \theta, \; z = z$$

Rectangular to cylindrical

$$r^2 = x^2 + y^2, \; \tan \theta = \frac{y}{x}, \; z = z$$

The point $(0, 0, 0)$ is called the **pole.** Moreover, because the representation of a point in the polar coordinate system is not unique, it follows that the representation in the cylindrical coordinate system is also not unique.

EXAMPLE 1   Changing from Cylindrical to Rectangular Coordinates

Express the point $(r, \theta, z) = (4, 5\pi/6, 3)$ in rectangular coordinates.

Solution   Using the *cylindrical-to-rectangular* conversion equations produces

$$x = 4 \cos \frac{5\pi}{6} = 4 \left(-\frac{\sqrt{3}}{2} \right) = -2\sqrt{3}$$

$$y = 4 \sin \frac{5\pi}{6} = 4 \left(\frac{1}{2} \right) = 2$$

$$z = 3.$$

Thus, in rectangular coordinates, the point is $(x, y, z) = \left(-2\sqrt{3}, 2, 3 \right)$, as shown in Figure 11.69.

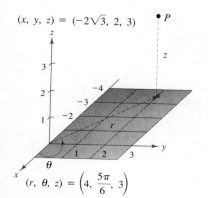

$(x, y, z) = (-2\sqrt{3}, 2, 3)$ $\bullet P$

$(r, \theta, z) = \left(4, \frac{5\pi}{6}, 3 \right)$

FIGURE 11.69

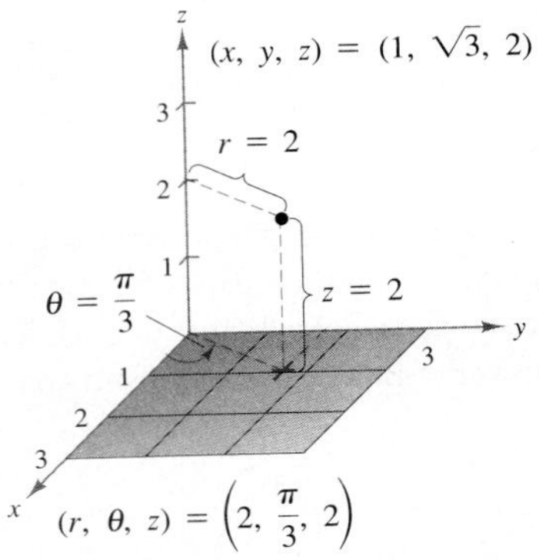

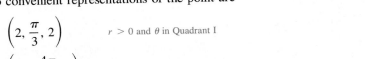

FIGURE 11.70

EXAMPLE 2   **Changing from Rectangular to Cylindrical Coordinates**

Express the point $(x, y, z) = \left(1, \sqrt{3}, 2\right)$ in cylindrical coordinates.

Solution   Use the rectangular-to-cylindrical conversion equations.

$$r = \pm\sqrt{1 + 3} = \pm 2$$

$$\tan\theta = \sqrt{3} \quad \longrightarrow \quad \theta = \arctan\left(\sqrt{3}\right) + n\pi = \frac{\pi}{3} + n\pi$$

$$z = 2$$

You have two choices for r and infinitely many choices for θ. As shown in Figure 11.70, two convenient representations of the point are

$$\left(2, \frac{\pi}{3}, 2\right) \qquad r > 0 \text{ and } \theta \text{ in Quadrant I}$$

$$\left(-2, \frac{4\pi}{3}, 2\right). \qquad r < 0 \text{ and } \theta \text{ in Quadrant III}$$

Cylindrical coordinates are especially convenient for representing cylindrical surfaces and surfaces of revolution with the z-axis as the axis of symmetry, as shown in Figure 11.71.

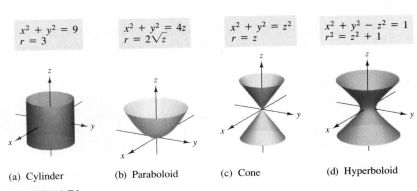

$x^2 + y^2 = 9$
$r = 3$

$x^2 + y^2 = 4z$
$r = 2\sqrt{z}$

$x^2 + y^2 = z^2$
$r = z$

$x^2 + y^2 - z^2 = 1$
$r^2 = z^2 + 1$

(a) Cylinder   (b) Paraboloid   (c) Cone   (d) Hyperboloid

FIGURE 11.71

Vertical planes containing the z-axis and horizontal planes also have simple cylindrical coordinate equations, as shown in Figure 11.72.

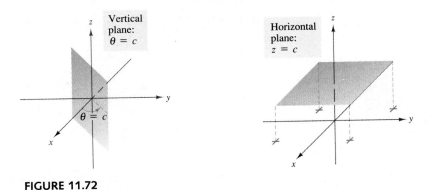

Vertical plane: $\theta = c$

$\theta = c$

Horizontal plane: $z = c$

FIGURE 11.72

EXAMPLE 3 Rectangular-to-Cylindrical Conversion

Find equations in cylindrical coordinates for the surfaces whose rectangular equations are as follows.

a. $x^2 + y^2 = 4z^2$ **b.** $y^2 = x$

Rectangular
coordinates:
$x^2 + y^2 = 4z^2$

Cylindrical
coordinates:
$r = \pm 2z$

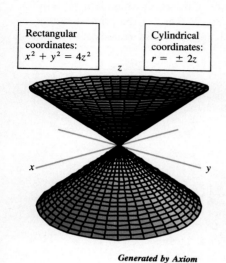

Generated by Axiom

FIGURE 11.73

Solution

a. From the previous section, you know that the graph $x^2 + y^2 = 4z^2$ is a "double-napped" cone with its axis along the z-axis, as shown in Figure 11.73. If you replace $x^2 + y^2$ by r^2, the equation in cylindrical coordinates is

$$x^2 + y^2 + 4z^2. \qquad \text{Rectangular coordinate equation}$$
$$r^2 = 4z^2. \qquad \text{Cylindrical coordinate equation}$$

The equation $r = 2z$ represents the top half of the cone, and the equation $r = -2z$ represents the bottom half of the cone.

b. The graph of the surface $y^2 = x$ is a parabolic cylinder with rulings parallel to the z-axis, as shown in Figure 11.74. By replacing y^2 by $r^2 \sin^2 \theta$ and x by $r \cos \theta$, you obtain the following equation in cylindrical coordinates.

Rectangular
coordinates:
$y^2 = x$

Cylindrical
coordinates:
$r = \csc \theta \cot \theta$

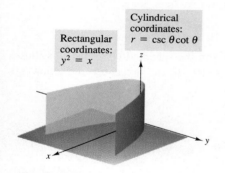

FIGURE 11.74

$$y^2 = x \qquad \text{Rectangular equation}$$
$$r^2 \sin^2 \theta = r \cos \theta \qquad \text{Substitute } r\sin\theta \text{ for } y \text{ and } r\cos\theta \text{ for } x$$
$$r(r \sin^2 \theta - \cos \theta) = 0 \qquad \text{Collect terms and factor}$$
$$r \sin^2 \theta - \cos \theta = 0 \qquad \text{Divide both sides by } r$$
$$r = \frac{\cos \theta}{\sin^2 \theta} \qquad \text{Solve for } r$$
$$r = \csc \theta \cot \theta \qquad \text{Cylindrical equation}$$

Note that this equation includes a point for which $r = 0$, so nothing was lost by dividing both sides by the factor r.

EXAMPLE 4 Cylindrical-to-Rectangular Conversion

Find a rectangular equation for the graph represented by the cylindrical equation $r^2 \cos 2\theta + z^2 + 1 = 0$.

Cylindrical coordinates:
$r^2 \cos 2\theta + z^2 + 1 = 0$

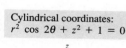

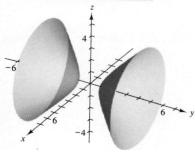

Rectangular
coordinates:
$y^2 - x^2 - z^2 = 1$

FIGURE 11.75

Solution

$$r^2 \cos 2\theta + z^2 + 1 = 0 \qquad \text{Cylindrical equation}$$
$$r^2(\cos^2 \theta - \sin^2 \theta) + z^2 + 1 = 0 \qquad \text{Trigonometric identity}$$
$$r^2 \cos^2 \theta - r^2 \sin^2 \theta + z^2 = -1$$
$$x^2 - y^2 + z^2 = -1 \qquad \text{Replace } r\cos\theta \text{ by } x \text{ and } r\sin\theta \text{ by } y$$
$$y^2 - x^2 - z^2 = 1 \qquad \text{Rectangular equation}$$

which is a hyperboloid of two sheets whose axis lies along the y-axis, as shown in Figure 11.75.

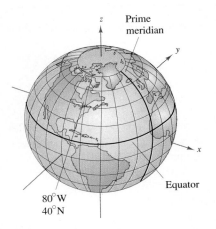

80°W
40°N

FIGURE 11.76

Spherical Coordinates

In the **spherical coordinate system,** each point is represented by an ordered triple— the first coordinate is a distance, and the second and third coordinates are angles. This system is similar to the latitude-longitude system used to identify points on the surface of the earth. For example, the point on the surface of the earth whose latitude is 40° N (north of the equator) and whose longitude is 80° W (west of the prime meridan) is shown in Figure 11.76. Assuming that the earth is spherical with a radius of 4000 miles, you would label this point as

$$(4000, -80°, 50°)$$

Radius ←   80° clockwise   → 50° down from
from prime   North Pole
meridian

The Spherical Coordinate System

In a **spherical coordinate system,** a point P in space is represented by an ordered triple (ρ, θ, ϕ).

1. ρ is the distance between P and the origin, $\rho \geq 0$.
2. θ is the same angle used in cylindrical coordinates.
3. ϕ is the angle *between* the positive z-axis and the line segment $\overrightarrow{OP}$, $0 \leq \phi \leq \pi$.

Note that the first and third coordinates, ρ and ϕ, are nonnegative. ρ is the lowercase Greek letter rho, and ϕ is the lowercase Greek letter phi.

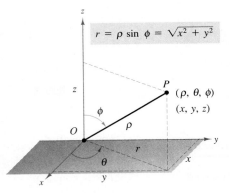

FIGURE 11.77
Spherical coordinates

The relationship between the rectangular and the spherical coordinates is illustrated in Figure 11.77. To convert from one system to the other, use the following conversion equations.

Spherical to rectangular

$$x = \rho \sin \phi \cos \theta, \qquad y = \rho \sin \phi \sin \theta, \qquad z = \rho \cos \phi$$

Rectangular to spherical

$$\rho^2 = x^2 + y^2 + z^2, \qquad \tan \theta = \frac{y}{x}, \qquad \phi = \arccos\left(\frac{z}{\sqrt{x^2 + y^2 + z^2}}\right)$$

To change coordinates between the cylindrical and spherical systems, use the following conversion equations.

Spherical to cylindrical

$$r^2 = \rho^2 \sin^2 \phi, \qquad \theta = \theta, \qquad z = \rho \cos \phi$$

Cylindrical to spherical

$$\rho = \sqrt{r^2 + z^2}, \qquad \theta = \theta, \qquad \phi = \arccos\left(\frac{z}{\sqrt{r^2 + z^2}}\right)$$

The spherical coordinate system is useful primarily for surfaces in space that have a *point* or *center* of symmetry. For example, Figure 11.78 shows three surfaces with simple spherical equations.

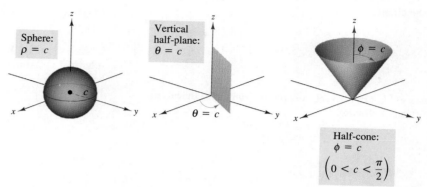

FIGURE 11.78

EXAMPLE 5   Rectangular-to-Spherical Conversion

Find an equation in spherical coordinates for the surfaces represented by the following rectangular coordinate equations.

a. Cone $x^2 + y^2 = z^2$ **b. Sphere** $x^2 + y^2 + z^2 - 4z = 0$

Solution

a. Making the appropriate replacements for x, y, and z in the given equation yields the following.

$$x^2 + y^2 = z^2$$
$$\rho^2 \sin^2 \phi \cos^2 \theta + \rho^2 \sin^2 \phi \sin^2 \theta = \rho^2 \cos^2 \phi$$
$$\rho^2 \sin^2 \phi (\cos^2 \theta + \sin^2 \theta) = \rho^2 \cos^2 \phi$$
$$\rho^2 \sin^2 \phi = \rho^2 \cos^2 \phi$$
$$\frac{\sin^2 \phi}{\cos^2 \phi} = 1 \qquad \rho \geq 0$$
$$\tan^2 \phi = 1 \qquad \phi = \pi/4 \text{ or } \phi = 3\pi/4$$

The equation $\phi = \pi/4$ represents the *upper* half-cone, and the equation $\phi = 3\pi/4$ represents the *lower* half-cone.

b. Because $\rho^2 = x^2 + y^2 + z^2$ and $z = \rho \cos \phi$, the given equation has the following spherical form.

$$\rho^2 - 4\rho \cos \phi = 0 \qquad \longrightarrow \qquad \rho(\rho - 4 \cos \phi) = 0$$

Temporarily discarding the possibility that $\rho = 0$, we have the spherical equation

$$\rho - 4 \cos \phi = 0 \quad \text{or} \quad \rho = 4 \cos \phi.$$

Note that the solution set for this equation includes a point for which $\rho = 0$, so nothing is lost by discarding the factor ρ. The sphere represented by the equation $\rho = 4 \cos \phi$ is shown in Figure 11.79.

Rectangular:
$x^2 + y^2 + z^2 - 4z = 0$

Spherical:
$\rho = 4 \cos \phi$

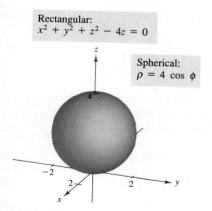

FIGURE 11.79

EXERCISES for Section 11.7

In Exercises 1–6, convert the point from rectangular to cylindrical coordinates.

1. $(0, 5, 1)$ **2.** $\left(2\sqrt{2}, -2\sqrt{2}, 4\right)$

3. $\left(1, \sqrt{3}, 4\right)$ **4.** $\left(\sqrt{3}, -1, 2\right)$

5. $(2, -2, -4)$ **6.** $(-3, 2, -1)$

In Exercises 7–12, convert the point from cylindrical to rectangular coordinates.

7. $(5, 0, 2)$ **8.** $\left(4, \dfrac{\pi}{2}, -2\right)$

9. $\left(2, \dfrac{\pi}{3}, 2\right)$ **10.** $\left(3, -\dfrac{\pi}{4}, 1\right)$

11. $\left(4, \dfrac{7\pi}{6}, 3\right)$ **12.** $\left(1, \dfrac{3\pi}{2}, 1\right)$

In Exercises 13–20, find an equation in rectangular coordinates for the equation in cylindrical coordinates, and sketch its graph.

13. $r = 2$ **14.** $z = 2$

15. $\theta = \dfrac{\pi}{6}$ **16.** $r = \dfrac{z}{2}$

17. $r = 2\sin\theta$ **18.** $r = 2\cos\theta$

19. $r^2 + z^2 = 4$ **20.** $z = r^2\sin^2\theta$

In Exercises 21–26, convert the point from rectangular to spherical coordinates.

21. $(4, 0, 0)$ **22.** $(1, 1, 1)$

23. $\left(-2, 2\sqrt{3}, 4\right)$ **24.** $\left(2, 2, 4\sqrt{2}\right)$

25. $\left(\sqrt{3}, 1, 2\sqrt{3}\right)$ **26.** $(-4, 0, 0)$

In Exercises 27–32, convert the point from spherical to rectangular coordinates.

27. $\left(4, \dfrac{\pi}{6}, \dfrac{\pi}{4}\right)$ **28.** $\left(12, \dfrac{3\pi}{4}, \dfrac{\pi}{9}\right)$

29. $\left(12, -\dfrac{\pi}{4}, 0\right)$ **30.** $\left(9, \dfrac{\pi}{4}, \pi\right)$

31. $\left(5, \dfrac{\pi}{4}, \dfrac{3\pi}{4}\right)$ **32.** $\left(6, \pi, \dfrac{\pi}{2}\right)$

In Exercises 33–40, find an equation in rectangular coordinates for the equation in spherical coordinates, and sketch its graph.

33. $\rho = 2$ **34.** $\theta = \dfrac{3\pi}{4}$

35. $\phi = \dfrac{\pi}{6}$ **36.** $\phi = \dfrac{\pi}{2}$

37. $\rho = 4\cos\phi$ **38.** $\rho = 2\sec\phi$

39. $\rho = \csc\phi$ **40.** $\rho = 4\csc\phi\sec\theta$

In Exercises 41–46, convert the point from cylindrical to spherical coordinates.

41. $\left(4, \dfrac{\pi}{4}, 0\right)$ **42.** $\left(2, \dfrac{2\pi}{3}, -2\right)$

43. $\left(4, -\dfrac{\pi}{6}, 6\right)$ **44.** $\left(-4, \dfrac{\pi}{3}, 4\right)$

45. $(12, \pi, 5)$ **46.** $\left(4, \dfrac{\pi}{2}, 3\right)$

In Exercises 47–52, convert the point from spherical to cylindrical coordinates.

47. $\left(10, \dfrac{\pi}{6}, \dfrac{\pi}{2}\right)$ **48.** $\left(4, \dfrac{\pi}{18}, \dfrac{\pi}{2}\right)$

49. $\left(6, -\dfrac{\pi}{6}, \dfrac{\pi}{3}\right)$ **50.** $\left(5, -\dfrac{5\pi}{6}, \pi\right)$

51. $\left(8, \dfrac{7\pi}{6}, \dfrac{\pi}{6}\right)$ **52.** $\left(7, \dfrac{\pi}{4}, \dfrac{3\pi}{4}\right)$

C In Exercises 53–58, use a computer algebra system or write a computer program to convert the coordinates of a point from one system to another among the rectangular, cylindrical, and spherical coordinate systems. Use the computer to complete the following table.

	Rectangular	Cylindrical	Spherical
53.	$(4, 6, 3)$		
54.	$(6, -2, -3)$		
55.		$\left(5, \dfrac{\pi}{9}, 8\right)$	
56.		$(10, -0.75, 6)$	
57.			$\left(20, \dfrac{2\pi}{3}, \dfrac{\pi}{4}\right)$
58.			$(7.5, 0.25, 1)$

In Exercises 59–64, match the equation (expressed in terms of cylindrical or spherical coordinates) with its graph. [The graphs are labeled (a), (b), (c), (d), (e), and (f).]

59. $r = 5$ **60.** $\theta = \dfrac{\pi}{4}$

61. $\rho = 5$ **62.** $\phi = \dfrac{\pi}{4}$

63. $r^2 = z$

(a)

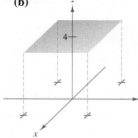

64. $\rho = 4\sec\phi$

(b)

(c)

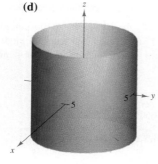

(d)

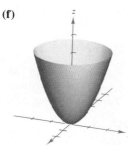

(e)

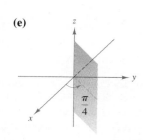

(f)

In Exercises 65–72, convert the rectangular equation to (a) cylindrical coordinates and (b) spherical coordinates.

65. $x^2 + y^2 + z^2 = 16$

66. $4(x^2 + y^2) = z^2$

67. $x^2 + y^2 + z^2 - 2z = 0$

68. $x^2 + y^2 = z$

69. $x^2 + y^2 = 4y$

70. $x^2 + y^2 = 16$

71. $x^2 - y^2 = 9$

72. $y = 4$

In Exercises 73–76, sketch the solid that has the given description in cylindrical coordinates.

73. $0 \le \theta \le \pi/2,\ 0 \le r \le 2,\ 0 \le z \le 4$

74. $-\pi/2 \le \theta \le \pi/2,\ 0 \le r \le 3,\ 0 \le z \le r\cos\theta$

75. $0 \le \theta \le 2\pi,\ 0 \le r \le a,\ r \le z \le a$

76. $0 \le \theta \le 2\pi,\ 2 \le r \le 4,\ z^2 \le -r^2 + 6r - 8$

In Exercises 77 and 78, sketch the solid that has the given description in spherical coordinates.

77. $0 \le \theta \le 2\pi,\ 0 \le \phi \le \pi/6,\ 0 \le \rho \le a\sec\phi$

78. $0 \le \theta \le 2\pi,\ \pi/4 \le \phi \le \pi/2,\ 0 \le \rho \le 1$

In Exercises 79–82, find inequalities that describe the solid, and state the coordinate system used. Position the solid on the coordinate system you choose so that the inequalities are as simple as possible.

79. A cube with each edge 10 centimeters long

80. A cylindrical shell 8 feet long with an inside diameter of 0.75 inch and an outside diameter of 1.25 inches

81. A spherical shell with inside and outside radii of 4 and 6 inches, respectively

82. The solid that remains after a hole 1 inch in diameter is drilled through the center of a sphere 6 inches in diameter

83. *Latitude and Longitude* Los Angeles is located at 34.05° north latitude and 118.24° west longitude, and Rio de Janeiro, Brazil is located at 22.90° south latitude and 43.22° west longitude (see figure). Assume that the earth is spherical with a radius of 4000 miles.
   a. Find the spherical coordinates for the location of each city.
   b. Find the rectangular coordinates for the location of each city.
   c. Find the angle (in radians) between the vectors from the center of the earth to each city.
   d. Find the great-circle distance s between the cities. [*Hint:* $s = r\theta$]

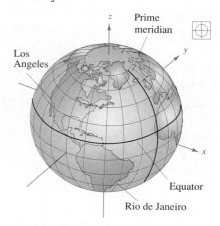

FIGURE FOR 83

84. Repeat Exercise 83 for the cities of Boston, located at 42.36° north latitude and 71.06° west longitude, and Honolulu, located at 21.31° north latitude and 157.86° west longitude.

85. Identify the curve of intersection of the surfaces (in cylindrical coordinates) $z = \sin\theta$ and $r = 1$.

REVIEW EXERCISES for Chapter 11

In Exercises 1 and 2, let $\mathbf{u} = \overrightarrow{PQ}$ and $\mathbf{v} = \overrightarrow{PR}$, and find (a) the component forms of u and v, (b) the magnitude of v, (c) u · v, (d) 2u + v, and (e) the vector component of u in the direction of v, and (f) the vector component of u orthogonal to v.

1. $P = (1, 2)$, $Q = (4, 1)$, $R = (5, 4)$

2. $P = (-2, -1)$, $Q = (5, -1)$, $R = (2, 4)$

In Exercises 3 and 4, let $\mathbf{u} = \overrightarrow{PQ}$ and $\mathbf{v} = \overrightarrow{PR}$, and find (a) the component forms of u and v, (b) u · v, (c) u × v, (d) an equation of the plane containing P, Q, and R, and (e) a set of parametric equations of the line through P and Q.

3. $P = (5, 0, 0)$, $Q = (4, 4, 0)$, $R = (2, 0, 6)$

4. $P = (2, -1, 3)$, $Q = (0, 5, 1)$, $R = (5, 5, 0)$

In Exercises 5 and 6, determine if the vectors are orthogonal or parallel, or neither.

5. $\langle -4, 3, -6 \rangle$
   $\langle 16, -12, 24 \rangle$

6. $\langle 7, -2, 3 \rangle$
   $\langle -1, 4, 5 \rangle$

In Exercises 7–10, find the angle θ between the vectors u and v.

7. $\mathbf{u} = 5\left[\cos\left(\dfrac{3\pi}{4}\right)\mathbf{i} + \sin\left(\dfrac{3\pi}{4}\right)\mathbf{j}\right]$
   $\mathbf{v} = 2\left[\cos\left(\dfrac{2\pi}{3}\right)\mathbf{i} + \sin\left(\dfrac{2\pi}{3}\right)\mathbf{j}\right]$

8. $\mathbf{u} = \langle 4, -1, 5 \rangle$
   $\mathbf{v} = \langle 3, 2, -2 \rangle$

9. $\mathbf{u} = \langle 10, -5, 15 \rangle$
   $\mathbf{v} = \langle -2, 1, -3 \rangle$

10. $\mathbf{u} = \langle 1, 0, -3 \rangle$
    $\mathbf{v} = \langle 2, -2, 1 \rangle$

In Exercises 11–14, find the component form of u.

11. The angle, measured counterclockwise, from the positive x-axis to u is 135°, and $\|\mathbf{u}\| = 4$.

12. The angle between u and the positive x-axis is 180°, and $\|\mathbf{u}\| = 8$.

13. u is perpendicular to the plane $x - 3y + 4z = 0$, and $\|\mathbf{u}\| = 3$.

14. u is a unit vector perpendicular to the lines
    $x = 4 - t$ $x = -3 + 7s$
    $y = 3 + 2t$ $y = -2 + s$
    $z = 1 + 5t$ $z = 1 + 2s.$

In Exercises 15–24, let $\mathbf{u} = \langle 3, -2, 1 \rangle$, $\mathbf{v} = \langle 2, -4, -3 \rangle$, and $\mathbf{w} = \langle -1, 2, 2 \rangle$.

15. Find $\|\mathbf{u}\|$.

16. Find the angle between u and v.

17. Show that $\mathbf{u} \cdot \mathbf{u} = \|\mathbf{u}\|^2$.

18. Determine a unit vector perpendicular to the plane containing v and w.

19. Determine the projection of w onto u.

20. Show that $\mathbf{u} \times \mathbf{v} = -(\mathbf{v} \times \mathbf{u})$.

21. Show that $\mathbf{u} \cdot (\mathbf{v} + \mathbf{w}) = \mathbf{u} \cdot \mathbf{v} + \mathbf{u} \cdot \mathbf{w}$.

22. Show that $\mathbf{u} \times (\mathbf{v} + \mathbf{w}) = (\mathbf{u} \times \mathbf{v}) + (\mathbf{u} \times \mathbf{w})$.

23. Find the volume of the solid whose edges are u, v, and w.

24. Find the work done in moving an object along the vector u, if the applied force is w.

25. *Load Supports*   Find the tension in each of the supporting cables shown in the figure.

26. *Equilibrium*   A 100-pound collar slides on a frictionless vertical rod (see figure). Find the distance y for which the system is in equilibrium if the counterweight weighs 120 pounds.

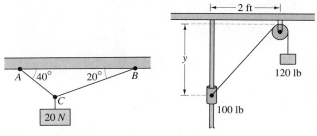

FIGURE FOR 25   **FIGURE FOR 26**

27. *Minimum Length*   In a manufacturing process, an electric hoist lifts 500-pound ingots (see figure). Find the shortest cable connecting points P, O, and Q that can be used if the tension in the cable cannot exceed 750 pounds. (Assume that O is at the midpoint of the cable.)

28. *Torque*   The specifications for a tractor state that the torque on a bolt with head size $\frac{7}{8}$ inch cannot exceed 200 foot-pounds. Determine the maximum force $\|\mathbf{F}\|$ that can be applied to the wrench in the figure.

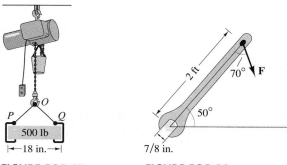

FIGURE FOR 27   **FIGURE FOR 28**

In Exercises 29–32, find (a) a set of parametric equations for the given line, and (b) a set of symmetric equations for the given line.

29. The line passes through $(1, 2, 3)$ and is perpendicular to the xz-coordinate plane.

30. The line passes through $(1, 2, 3)$ and is parallel to the line given by $x = y = z$.

31. The line is the intersection of the planes given by

$$3x - 3y - 7z = -4$$

and

$$x - y + 2z = 3.$$

32. The line passes through the point $(0, 1, 4)$ and is perpendicular to $\mathbf{u} = \langle 2, -5, 1 \rangle$ and $\mathbf{v} = \langle -3, 1, 4 \rangle$.

In Exercises 33–36, find an equation of the plane.

33. The plane passes through the point $(1, 2, 3)$ and is orthogonal to the line given by $x = y = z$.

34. The plane passes through the point $(4, 2, 1)$ and is parallel to the yz-coordinate plane.

35. The plane contains the lines

$$\frac{x - 1}{-2} = y = z + 1$$

$$\frac{x + 1}{-2} = y - 1 = z - 2.$$

36. The plane passes through the points $(-3, -4, 2)$, $(-3, 4, 1)$, and $(1, 1, -2)$.

In Exercises 37 and 38, find the distance from the point to the plane.

37. $(1, 0, 2)$
$2x - 3y + 6z = 6$

38. $(0, 0, 0)$
$4x - 7y + z = 2$

In Exercises 39 and 40, find the distance between the parallel planes.

39. $5x - 3y + z = 2$
$5x - 3y + z = -3$

40. $3x - 2y - z = -1$
$6x + 4y - 2z = 1$

In Exercises 41 and 42, find the distance between the two skew lines.

41. $\dfrac{x}{1} = \dfrac{y}{2} + \dfrac{z}{3}$

$\dfrac{x + 1}{-1} = \dfrac{y}{3} = \dfrac{z + 2}{2}$

42. $x - 4 = \dfrac{y - 3}{-1} = \dfrac{z - 7}{3}$

$\dfrac{x + 3}{-5} = \dfrac{y - 7}{2} = \dfrac{z + 5}{-6}$

In Exercises 43–52, sketch a graph of the specified surface.

43. $x + 2y + 3z = 6$

44. $y = z^2$

45. $y = \frac{1}{2}z$

46. $y = \cos z$

47. $x^2 + z^2 = 4$

48. $x^2 + y^2 + z^2 - 2x + 4y - 6z + 5 = 0$

49. $16x^2 + 16y^2 - 9z^2 = 0$

50. $\dfrac{x^2}{16} + \dfrac{y^2}{9} + z^2 = 1$

51. $\dfrac{x^2}{16} - \dfrac{y^2}{9} + z^2 = -1$

52. $\dfrac{x^2}{25} + \dfrac{y^2}{4} - \dfrac{z^2}{100} = 1$

C **In Exercises 53–56, use a computer algebra system to graph the surface. (*Hint:* It may be necessary to solve for z and acquire two equations to graph.)**

53. $z = y^2 - 4x^2$

54. $z = 4y^2 - x^3$

55. $z = e^{-x/2} \sin y$

56. $\dfrac{x^2}{16} + \dfrac{y^2}{9} - z^2 = 1$

57. *Machine Design* The top of a rubber bushing designed to absorb vibrations in an automobile is the surface of revolution generated by revolving the curve $z = \frac{1}{2}y^2 + 1 (0 \le y \le 2)$ in the yz-plane about the z-axis (see figure).

  a. Find an equation for the surface of revolution.

  b. If all measurements are in centimeters and the bushing is set on the xy-plane, use the Shell Method to find its volume.

  c. Suppose the bushing has a hole of diameter 1 cm through its center and parallel to the axis of revolution. Find the volume of rubber in the bushing.

58. *Machine Design* A tractor fuel tank has the shape and dimensions shown in the figure. In fabricating the tank, it is necessary to know the angle between two adjacent sides. Find the angle.

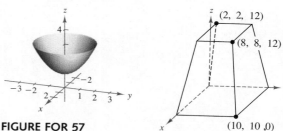

FIGURE FOR 57

FIGURE FOR 58

In Exercises 59 and 60, convert the given point from rectangular coordinates to (a) cylindrical coordinates and (b) spherical coordinates.

59. $\left(-2\sqrt{2}, \ 2\sqrt{2}, \ 2 \right)$

60. $\left(\dfrac{\sqrt{3}}{4}, \ \dfrac{3}{4}, \ \dfrac{3\sqrt{3}}{2} \right)$

In Exercises 61 and 62, find an equation of the given surface in (a) cylindrical coordinates and (b) spherical coordinates.

61. $x^2 - y^2 = 2z$

62. $x^2 + y^2 + z^2 = 16$

In Exercises 63 and 64, find an equation in rectangular coordinates for the equation in cylindrical coordinates.

63. $r^2(\cos^2 \theta - \sin^2 \theta) + z^2 = 1$

64. $r^2 = 16z$

In Exercises 65 and 66, find an equation in rectangular coordinates for the equation in spherical coordinates.

65. $\rho = \csc \phi$

66. $\rho = 5$

Chapter 12

Vector-Valued
Functions

12.1
Space Curves and Vector-Valued Functions • Limits and Continuity

REMARK Technically, a curve in the plane or in space consists of a collection of points *and* the defining parametric equations. Two different curves can have the same graph. For instance, each of the curves given by $\mathbf{r} = \sin t\,\mathbf{i} + \cos t\,\mathbf{j}$ and $\mathbf{r} = \sin t^2\,\mathbf{i} + \cos t^2\,\mathbf{j}$ has the unit circle as its graph, but these equations do not represent the same curve—because the circle is traced out in different ways on the graphs.

Space Curves and Vector-Valued Functions

In Section 10.1, a *plane curve* was defined as the set of ordered pairs $(f(t), g(t))$ together with their defining parametric equations

$$x = f(t) \quad \text{and} \quad y = g(t)$$

where f and g are continuous functions of t on an interval I. This definition can be extended naturally to three-dimensional space as follows. A **space curve** C is the set of all ordered triples $(f(t), g(t), h(t))$ together with their defining parametric equations

$$x = f(t), \quad y = g(t), \quad \text{and} \quad z = h(t)$$

where f, g, and h are continuous functions of t on an interval I.

Before looking at examples of space curves, we introduce a new type of function, called a **vector-valued function**, that maps real numbers onto vectors.

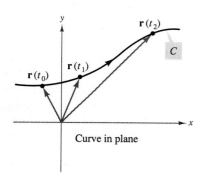

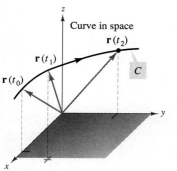

FIGURE 12.1
Curve C is traced out by the terminal point of position vector $\mathbf{r}(t)$.

Definition of a Vector-Valued Function

A function of the form

$$\mathbf{r}(t) = f(t)\mathbf{i} + g(t)\mathbf{j} \qquad \text{Plane}$$

or

$$\mathbf{r}(t) = f(t)\mathbf{i} + g(t)\mathbf{j} + h(t)\mathbf{k} \qquad \text{Space}$$

is a **vector-valued function**, where the **component functions** f, g, and h are real-valued functions of the parameter t. Vector-valued functions are sometimes denoted as $\mathbf{r}(t) = \langle f(t), g(t) \rangle$ or $\mathbf{r}(t) = \langle f(t), g(t), h(t) \rangle$.

REMARK Note the distinction between the vector-valued function $\mathbf{r}$ and the real-valued functions f, g, and h. All are functions of the real variable t, but $\mathbf{r}(t)$ is a vector, whereas $f(t)$, $g(t)$, and $h(t)$ are real numbers (for each specific value of t).

Vector-valued functions serve dual roles in the representation of curves. By letting the parameter t represent time, you can use a vector-valued function to represent *motion* along a curve. Or, in the more general case, you can use a vector-valued function to *trace the graph* of a curve. In either case, the terminal point of the position vector $\mathbf{r}(t)$ coincides with the point (x, y) or (x, y, z) on the curve given by the parametric equations, as shown in Figure 12.1. The arrowhead on the curve indicates the curve's *orientation* by pointing in the direction of increasing values of t.

◀ *The angle at which a roadway should be banked so that no lateral frictional force is exerted on an automobile's tires is discussed in Section 12.3, Exercise 44.*

Unless stated otherwise, the **domain** of a vector-valued function **r** is considered to be the intersection of the domains of the component functions f, g, and h. For instance, the domain of

$$\mathbf{r}(t) = (\ln t)\mathbf{i} + \sqrt{1 - t}\,\mathbf{j} + t\,\mathbf{k}$$

is the interval $(0, 1]$.

EXAMPLE 1   Sketching a Plane Curve

Sketch the plane curve represented by the vector-valued function

$$\mathbf{r}(t) = 2\cos t\,\mathbf{i} - 3\sin t\,\mathbf{j}, \qquad 0 \le t \le 2\pi.$$

Solution   From the position vector $\mathbf{r}(t)$, you can write the parametric equations $x = 2\cos t$ and $y = -3\sin t$. Solving for $\cos t$ and $\sin t$ and using the identity $\cos^2 t + \sin^2 t = 1$ produce the rectangular equation

$$\frac{x^2}{2^2} + \frac{y^2}{3^2} = 1.$$

The graph of this rectangular equation is the ellipse shown in Figure 12.2. Note that the curve has a *clockwise* orientation. That is, as t increases from 0 to 2π, the position vector $\mathbf{r}(t)$ moves clockwise, and its terminal point traces the ellipse.

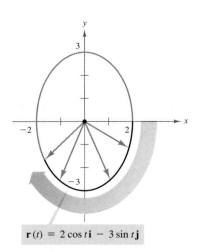

$\mathbf{r}(t) = 2\cos t\,\mathbf{i} - 3\sin t\,\mathbf{j}$

FIGURE 12.2
The ellipse is traced clockwise as the parameter t increases from 0 to 2π.

EXAMPLE 2   Sketching a Space Curve

Sketch the space curve represented by the vector-valued function

$$\mathbf{r}(t) = 4\cos t\,\mathbf{i} + 4\sin t\,\mathbf{j} + t\,\mathbf{k}, \qquad 0 \le t \le 4\pi.$$

Solution   From the first two parametric equations $x = 4\cos t$ and $y = 4\sin t$, you can obtain

$$x^2 + y^2 = 16.$$

This means that the curve lies on a right circular cylinder of radius 4, centered about the z-axis. To locate the curve on this cylinder, you can use the third parametric equation $z = t$. In Figure 12.3, note that as t increases from 0 to 4π the point (x, y, z) spirals up the cylinder to produce a **helix.**

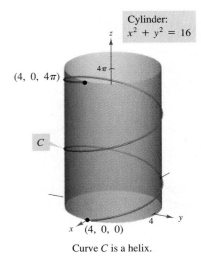

Curve C is a helix.

FIGURE 12.3
At t increases from 0 to 4π, two spirals on the helix are traced out.

In Examples 1 and 2, you were given a vector-valued function and asked to sketch the corresponding curve. The next two examples concern the reverse problem—finding a vector-valued function to represent a given graph. Of course, if the graph is described parametrically, then representation by a vector-valued function is straightforward. For instance, to represent the line in space given by

$$x = 2 + t, \quad y = 3t, \quad \text{and} \quad z = 4 - t$$

you can simply use the vector-valued function given by

$$\mathbf{r}(t) = (2 + t)\mathbf{i} + 3t\,\mathbf{j} + (4 - t)\mathbf{k}.$$

If a set of parametric equations for the graph is not given, then the problem of representing the graph by a vector-valued function boils down to finding a set of parametric equations.

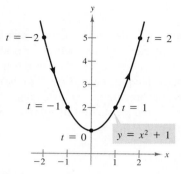

FIGURE 12.4
There are many ways to parametrize this graph. One way is to let $x = t$.

EXAMPLE 3   Representing a Graph by a Vector-Valued Function

Represent the parabola given by $y = x^2 + 1$ by a vector-valued function.

Solution   Although there are many ways to choose the parameter t, a natural choice is to let $x = t$. Then $y = t^2 + 1$ and you have $\mathbf{r}(t) = t\mathbf{i} + (t^2 + 1)\mathbf{j}$. Note in Figure 12.4 the orientation produced by this particular choice of parameter. Had you chosen $x = -t$ as the parameter, the curve would have been oriented in the opposite direction.

In the next example, you can see how to represent a graph in space that is defined as the intersection of two surfaces in space.

EXAMPLE 4   Representing a Graph by a Vector-Valued Function

Sketch the graph represented by the intersection of the semiellipsoid

$$\frac{x^2}{12} + \frac{y^2}{24} + \frac{z^2}{4} = 1, \qquad z \geq 0$$

and the parabolic cylinder $y = x^2$. Then, find a vector-valued function to represent the graph.

Solution   The intersection of the two surfaces is shown in Figure 12.5. As in Example 3, a natural choice of parameter is $x = t$. For this choice, you can use the given equation $y = x^2$ to obtain $y = t^2$. Then, it follows that

$$\frac{z^2}{4} = 1 - \frac{x^2}{12} - \frac{y^2}{24} = 1 - \frac{t^2}{12} - \frac{t^4}{24} = \frac{24 - 2t^2 - t^4}{24}.$$

Because the curve lies above the xy-plane, you should choose the positive square root for z and obtain the following parametric equations.

$$x = t, \quad y = t^2, \quad \text{and} \quad z = \sqrt{\frac{24 - 2t^2 - t^4}{6}}$$

The resulting vector-valued function is

$$\mathbf{r}(t) = t\mathbf{i} + t^2\mathbf{j} + \sqrt{\frac{24 - 2t^2 - t^4}{6}}\,\mathbf{k}, \qquad -2 \leq t \leq 2.$$

From the points $(-2, 4, 0)$ and $(2, 4, 0)$ shown in Figure 12.5, you can see that the curve is traced as t increases from -2 to 2.

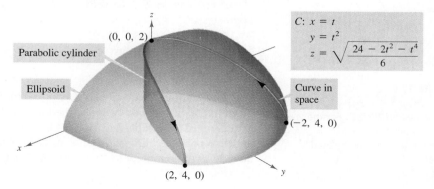

FIGURE 12.5
The curve C is the intersection of the semiellipsoid and the parabolic cylinder.

Limits and Continuity

Many techniques and definitions used in the calculus of real-valued functions can be applied to vector-valued functions. For instance, you can add and subtract vector-valued functions, multiply a vector-valued function by a scalar, take the limit of a vector-valued function, differentiate a vector-valued function, and so on. The basic approach is to capitalize on the linearity of vector operations by extending the definitions on a component-by-component basis. For example, to add or subtract two vector-valued functions (in the plane), you can write

$$\mathbf{r}_1(t) + \mathbf{r}_2(t) = [f_1(t)\mathbf{i} + g_1(t)\mathbf{j}] + [f_2(t)\mathbf{i} + g_2(t)\mathbf{j}] \qquad \text{Sum}$$
$$= [f_1(t) + f_2(t)]\mathbf{i} + [g_1(t) + g_2(t)]\mathbf{j}$$
$$\mathbf{r}_1(t) - \mathbf{r}_2(t) = [f_1(t)\mathbf{i} + g_1(t)\mathbf{j}] - [f_2(t)\mathbf{i} + g_2(t)\mathbf{j}] \qquad \text{Difference}$$
$$= [f_1(t) - f_2(t)]\mathbf{i} + [g_1(t) - g_2(t)]\mathbf{j}.$$

Similarly, to multiply a vector-valued function by a scalar, you can write

$$c\,\mathbf{r}(t) = c[f_1(t)\mathbf{i} + g_1(t)\mathbf{j}] \qquad \text{Scalar multiple}$$
$$= c f_1(t)\mathbf{i} + c g_1(t)\mathbf{j}.$$

This component-by-component extension of operations with real-valued functions to vector-valued functions is further illustrated in the following definition of the limit of a vector-valued function.

Definition of the Limit of a Vector-Valued Function

1. If $\mathbf{r}$ is a vector-valued function such that $\mathbf{r}(t) = f(t)\mathbf{i} + g(t)\mathbf{j}$, then

$$\lim_{t \to a}\mathbf{r}(t) = \left[\lim_{t \to a}f(t)\right]\mathbf{i} + \left[\lim_{t \to a}g(t)\right]\mathbf{j} \qquad \text{Plane}$$

provided f and g have limits as $t \to a$.

2. If $\mathbf{r}$ is a vector-valued function such that $\mathbf{r}(t) = f(t)\mathbf{i} + g(t)\mathbf{j} + h(t)\mathbf{k}$, then

$$\lim_{t \to a}\mathbf{r}(t) = \left[\lim_{t \to a}f(t)\right]\mathbf{i} + \left[\lim_{t \to a}g(t)\right]\mathbf{j} + \left[\lim_{t \to a}h(t)\right]\mathbf{j} \qquad \text{Space}$$

provided f, g, and h have limits as $t \to a$.

If $\mathbf{r}(t)$ approaches the vector $\mathbf{L}$ as $t \to a$, then the length of the vector $\mathbf{r}(t) - \mathbf{L}$ approaches 0. That is,

$$\| \mathbf{r}(t) - \mathbf{L} \| \to 0 \quad \text{as} \quad t \to a.$$

This is illustrated graphically in Figure 12.6. With this definition of the limit of a vector-valued function, you can develop vector versions of most of the limit theorems given in Chapter 1. For example, the limit of the sum of two vector-valued functions is the sum of their individual limits. Also, you can use the orientation of the curve $\mathbf{r}(t)$ to define one-sided limits of vector-valued functions. The following definition extends the notion of continuity to vector-valued functions.

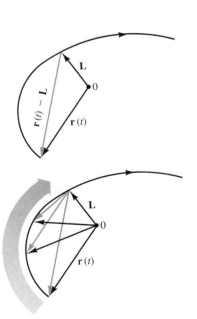

FIGURE 12.6
As t approaches a, $\mathbf{r}(t)$ approaches the limit $\mathbf{L}$. For the limit $\mathbf{L}$ to exist, it is not necessary that $\mathbf{r}(a)$ be defined or that $\mathbf{r}(a)$ be equal to $\mathbf{L}$.

Definition of Continuity of a Vector-Valued Function

A vector-valued function $\mathbf{r}$ is **continuous at the point** given by $t = a$ if the limit of $\mathbf{r}(t)$ exists as $t \rightarrow a$ and

$$\lim_{t \to a} \mathbf{r}(t) = \mathbf{r}(a).$$

A vector-valued function $\mathbf{r}$ is **continuous on an interval** I if it is continuous at every point in the interval.

From this definition, it follows that a vector-valued function is continuous at $t = a$ if and only if each of its component functions is continuous at $t = a$.

EXAMPLE 5   Continuity of Vector-Valued Functions

Discuss the continuity of the vector-valued function given by

$$\mathbf{r}(t) = t\mathbf{i} + a\mathbf{j} + (a^2 - t^2)\mathbf{k}, \qquad a \text{ is a constant}$$

at $t = 0$.

Solution   As t approaches 0, the limit is

$$
\begin{aligned}
\lim_{t \to 0} \mathbf{r}(t) &= \left[\lim_{t \to 0} t \right]\mathbf{i} + \left[\lim_{t \to 0} a \right]\mathbf{j} + \left[\lim_{t \to 0}(a^2 - t^2) \right]\mathbf{k} \\
&= 0\mathbf{i} + a\mathbf{j} + a^2\mathbf{k} \\
&= a\mathbf{j} + a^2\mathbf{k}.
\end{aligned}
$$

Because

$$\mathbf{r}(0) = (0)\mathbf{i} + (a)\mathbf{j} + (a^2)\mathbf{k} = a\mathbf{j} + a^2\mathbf{k}$$

you can conclude that $\mathbf{r}$ is continuous at $t = 0$. By similar reasoning, you can conclude that the vector-valued function $\mathbf{r}$ is continuous at all real-number values of t.

For each value of a, the curve represented by the vector-valued function in Example 5

$$\mathbf{r}(t) = t\mathbf{i} + a\mathbf{j} + (a^2 - t^2)\mathbf{k}, \qquad a \text{ is a constant}$$

is a parabola. You can think of each parabola as the intersection of the vertical plane $y = a$ and the hyperbolic paraboloid $y^2 - x^2 = z$, as shown in Figure 12.7.

TECHNOLOGY   Almost any type of three-dimensional sketch is difficult to do by hand, but sketching curves in space is especially difficult. The problem is in trying to create the illusion of three dimensions. Computer graphing utilities use a variety of techniques to add "three-dimensionality" to sketches of space curves—one way is to show the curve on a surface, as in Figure 12.7.

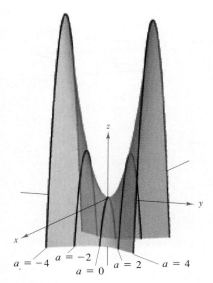

$a = -4 \quad a = -2 \quad a = 0 \quad a = 2 \quad a = 4$

FIGURE 12.7

For each value of a, the curve represented by $\mathbf{r}(t) = t\mathbf{i} + a\mathbf{j} + (a^2 - t^2)\mathbf{k}$ is a parabola.

EXERCISES for Section 12.1

In Exercises 1–8, find the domain of the vector-valued function.

1. $\mathbf{r}(t) = 5t\,\mathbf{i} - 4t\,\mathbf{j} - \dfrac{1}{t}\mathbf{k}$

2. $\mathbf{r}(t) = \sqrt{4 - t^2}\,\mathbf{i} + t^2\,\mathbf{j} - 6t\,\mathbf{k}$

3. $\mathbf{r}(t) = \ln t\,\mathbf{i} - e^t\,\mathbf{j} - t\,\mathbf{k}$

4. $\mathbf{r}(t) = \sin t\,\mathbf{i} + 4\cos t\,\mathbf{j} + t\,\mathbf{k}$

5. $\mathbf{r}(t) = \mathbf{F}(t) + \mathbf{G}(t)$ where

$\mathbf{F}(t) = \cos t\,\mathbf{i} - \sin t\,\mathbf{j} + \sqrt{t}\,\mathbf{k}$

and

$\mathbf{G}(t) = \cos t\,\mathbf{i} + \sin t\,\mathbf{j}.$

6. $\mathbf{r}(t) = \mathbf{F}(t) - \mathbf{G}(t)$ where

$\mathbf{F}(t) = \ln t\,\mathbf{i} + 5t\,\mathbf{j} - 3t^2\,\mathbf{k}$

and

$\mathbf{G}(t) = \mathbf{i} + 4t\,\mathbf{j} - 3t^2\,\mathbf{k}.$

7. $\mathbf{r}(t) = \mathbf{F}(t) \times \mathbf{G}(t)$ where

$\mathbf{F}(t) = \sin t\,\mathbf{i} + \cos t\,\mathbf{j}$

and

$\mathbf{G}(t) = \sin t\,\mathbf{j} + \cos t\,\mathbf{k}.$

8. $\mathbf{r}(t) = \mathbf{F}(t) \times \mathbf{G}(t)$ where

$\mathbf{F}(t) = t^3\,\mathbf{i} - t\,\mathbf{j} + t\,\mathbf{k}$

and

$\mathbf{G}(t) = \sqrt[3]{t}\,\mathbf{i} + \dfrac{1}{t+1}\mathbf{j} + (t + 2)\mathbf{k}.$

In Exercises 9 and 10, find $\|\mathbf{r}(t)\|$.

9. $\mathbf{r}(t) = \sin 3t\,\mathbf{i} + \cos 3t\,\mathbf{j} + t\,\mathbf{k}$

10. $\mathbf{r}(t) = \sqrt{t}\,\mathbf{i} + 3t\,\mathbf{j} - 4t\,\mathbf{k}$

In Exercises 11–14, match the equation with its graph. [The graphs are labeled (a), (b), (c), and (d).]

11. $\mathbf{r}(t) = t\,\mathbf{i} + 2t\,\mathbf{j} + t^2\,\mathbf{k}, \quad -2 \le t \le 2$

12. $\mathbf{r}(t) = \cos(\pi t)\mathbf{i} + \sin(\pi t)\mathbf{j} + t^2\,\mathbf{k}, \quad -1 \le t \le 1$

13. $\mathbf{r}(t) = t\,\mathbf{i} + t^2\,\mathbf{j} + e^{0.75t}\,\mathbf{k}, \quad -2 \le t \le 2$

14. $\mathbf{r}(t) = t\,\mathbf{i} + \ln t\,\mathbf{j} + \dfrac{2t}{3}\mathbf{k}, \quad 0.1 \le t \le 5$

(a)   **(b)**

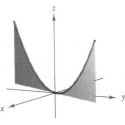

(c)   **(d)**

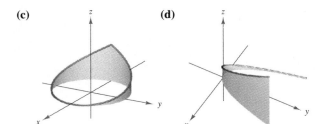

15. The four figures below are graphs of the vector-valued function

$\mathbf{r}(t) = 4\cos t\,\mathbf{i} + 4\sin t\,\mathbf{j} + \dfrac{t}{4}\mathbf{k}.$

Match the four graphs with the point in space from which the helix is viewed. The four points are $(0, 0, 20)$, $(20, 0, 0)$, $(-20, 0, 0)$, and $(10, 20, 10)$.

(a)   **(b)**

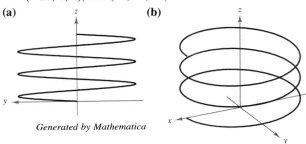

Generated by Mathematica

Generated by Mathematica

(c)   **(d)**

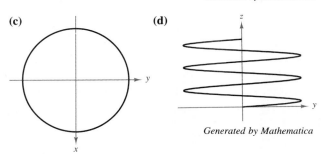

Generated by Mathematica

Generated by Mathematica

16. Sketch three graphs of the vector-valued function

$\mathbf{r}(t) = t\,\mathbf{i} + t\,\mathbf{j} + 2\mathbf{k}$

with views from the points
a. $(0, 0, 20)$ **b.** $(10, 0, 0)$ **c.** $(5, 5, 5)$.

In Exercises 17–26, sketch the curve represented by the vector-valued function and give the orientation of the curve.

17. $\mathbf{r}(t) = 3t\,\mathbf{i} + (t - 1)\mathbf{j}$

18. $\mathbf{r}(t) = 2\cos t\,\mathbf{i} + 2\sin t\,\mathbf{j}$

19. $\mathbf{r}(t) = (-t + 1)\mathbf{i} + (4t + 2)\mathbf{j} + (2t + 3)\mathbf{k}$

20. $\mathbf{r}(t) = t\,\mathbf{i} + (2t - 5)\mathbf{j} + 3t\,\mathbf{k}$

21. $\mathbf{r}(t) = 2\cos t\,\mathbf{i} + 2\sin t\,\mathbf{j} + t\,\mathbf{k}$

22. $\mathbf{r}(t) = 3\cos t\,\mathbf{i} + 4\sin t\,\mathbf{j} + \dfrac{t}{2}\mathbf{k}$

23. $\mathbf{r}(t) = 2\sin t\,\mathbf{i} + 2\cos t\,\mathbf{j} + e^{-t}\mathbf{k}$

24. $\mathbf{r}(t) = t\,\mathbf{i} + t^2\,\mathbf{j} + \dfrac{3t}{2}\mathbf{k}$

25. $\mathbf{r}(t) = \left\langle t, t^2, \frac{2}{3}t^3 \right\rangle$

26. $\mathbf{r}(t) = \langle \cos t + t\sin t, \sin t - t\cos t, t \rangle$

C In Exercises 27–30, use a computer algebra system to identify the common curve.

27. $\mathbf{r}(t) = -\dfrac{1}{2}t^2\mathbf{i} + t\,\mathbf{j} - \dfrac{\sqrt{3}}{2}t^2\mathbf{k}$

28. $\mathbf{r}(t) = t\,\mathbf{i} - \dfrac{\sqrt{3}}{2}t^2\mathbf{j} + \dfrac{1}{2}t^2\mathbf{k}$

29. $\mathbf{r}(t) = \sin t\,\mathbf{i} + \left(\dfrac{\sqrt{3}}{2}\cos t - \dfrac{1}{2}t \right)\mathbf{j} + \left(\dfrac{1}{2}\cos t + \dfrac{\sqrt{3}}{2} \right)\mathbf{k}$

30. $\mathbf{r}(t) = -\sqrt{2}\sin t\,\mathbf{i} + 2\cos t\,\mathbf{j} + \sqrt{2}\sin t\,\mathbf{k}$

In Exercises 31–34, represent the plane curve by a vector-valued function. (There are many correct answers.)

31. $y = 4 - x$ **32.** $y = 4 - x^2$

33. $x^2 + y^2 = 25$ **34.** $\dfrac{x^2}{25} + \dfrac{y^2}{16} = 1$

In Exercises 35–42, sketch the space curve represented by the intersection of the surfaces. Then, represent the curve by a vector-valued function using the given parameter.

Surfaces	Parameter
35. $z = x^2 + y^2,\ x + y = 0$	$x = t$
36. $z = x^2 + y^2,\ z = 4$	$x = 2\cos t$
37. $x^2 + y^2 = 4,\ z = x^2$	$x = 2\sin t$
38. $4x^2 + y^2 + 4z^2 = 16,\ x = y^2$	$y = t$
39. $x^2 + y^2 + z^2 = 4,\ x + z = 2$	$x = 1 + \sin t$
40. $x^2 + y^2 + z^2 = 10,\ x + y = 4$	$x = 2 + \sin t$
41. $x^2 + z^2 = 4,\ y^2 + z^2 = 4$ (first octant)	$x = t$
42. $x^2 + y^2 + z^2 = 16,\ xy = 4$ (first octant)	$x = t$

In Exercises 43–48, evaluate the limit.

43. $\displaystyle \lim_{t \to 2} \left(t\,\mathbf{i} + \dfrac{t^2 - 4}{t^2 - 2t}\mathbf{j} + \dfrac{1}{t}\mathbf{k} \right)$

44. $\displaystyle \lim_{t \to 0} \left(e^t\mathbf{i} + \dfrac{\sin t}{t}\mathbf{j} + e^{-t}\mathbf{k} \right)$

45. $\displaystyle \lim_{t \to 0} \left(t^2\mathbf{i} + 3t\,\mathbf{j} + \dfrac{1 - \cos t}{t}\mathbf{k} \right)$

46. $\displaystyle \lim_{t \to 1} \left(\sqrt{t}\,\mathbf{i} + \dfrac{\ln t}{t^2 - 1}\mathbf{j} + 2t^2\mathbf{k} \right)$

47. $\displaystyle \lim_{t \to 0} \left(\dfrac{1}{t}\mathbf{i} + \cos t\,\mathbf{j} + \sin t\,\mathbf{k} \right)$

48. $\displaystyle \lim_{t \to \infty} \left(e^{-t}\mathbf{i} + \dfrac{1}{t}\mathbf{j} + \dfrac{t}{t^2 + 1}\mathbf{k} \right)$

In Exercises 49–54, determine the interval(s) on which the vector-valued function is continuous.

49. $\mathbf{r}(t) = t\,\mathbf{i} + \dfrac{1}{t}\mathbf{j}$

50. $\mathbf{r}(t) = \sqrt{t}\,\mathbf{i} + \sqrt{t - 1}\,\mathbf{j}$

51. $\mathbf{r}(t) = t\,\mathbf{i} + \arcsin t\,\mathbf{j} + (t - 1)\mathbf{k}$

52. $\mathbf{r}(t) = \sin t\,\mathbf{i} + \cos t\,\mathbf{j} + \ln t\,\mathbf{k}$

53. $\mathbf{r}(t) = \langle e^{-t}, t^2, \tan t \rangle$

54. $\mathbf{r}(t) = \left\langle 8, \sqrt{t}, \sqrt[3]{t} \right\rangle$

55. Let $\mathbf{r}(t)$ and $\mathbf{u}(t)$ be vector-valued functions whose limits exist as $t \to c$. Prove that
$$\lim_{t \to c}[\mathbf{r}(t) \times \mathbf{u}(t)] = \lim_{t \to c}\mathbf{r}(t) \times \lim_{t \to c}\mathbf{u}(t).$$

56. Let $\mathbf{r}(t)$ and $\mathbf{u}(t)$ be vector-valued functions whose limits exist as $t \to c$. Prove that
$$\lim_{t \to c}[\mathbf{r}(t) \cdot \mathbf{u}(t)] = \lim_{t \to c}\mathbf{r}(t) \cdot \lim_{t \to c}\mathbf{u}(t).$$

57. Prove that if $\mathbf{r}$ is a vector-valued function that is continuous at c, then $\|\mathbf{r}\|$ is continuous at c.

58. Verify that the converse of Exercise 57 is not true by finding a vector-valued function $\mathbf{r}$ such that $\|\mathbf{r}\|$ is continuous at c but $\mathbf{r}$ is not continuous at c.

True or False   In Exercises 59 and 60, determine whether the statement is true or false. If it is false, explain why or give an example that shows it is false.

59. If f, g, and h are first-degree polynomial functions, then the curve given by $x = f(t)$, $y = g(t)$, $z = h(t)$ is a line.

60. If the curve given by $x = f(t)$, $y = g(t)$, $z = h(t)$ is a line, then f, g, and h are first-degree polynomial functions of t.

A *C* indicates an exercise in which you are instructed to use graphing technology or a symbolic computer algebra system. The solutions of other exercises may also be facilitated by appropriate technology.

12.2   Differentiation of Vector-Valued Functions • Integration of Vector-Valued Functions

Differentiation of Vector-Valued Functions

In Sections 12.3–12.5, you will study several important applications involving the calculus of vector-valued functions. In preparation for that study, this section is devoted to the mechanics of differentiation and integration of vector-valued functions.

The definition of the derivative of a vector-valued function parallels that given for real-valued functions.

Definition of the Derivative of a Vector-Valued Function

The **derivative of a vector-valued function r** is defined by

$$\mathbf{r}'(t) = \lim_{\Delta t \to 0} \frac{\mathbf{r}(t + \Delta t) - \mathbf{r}(t)}{\Delta t}$$

for all t for which the limit exists. If $\mathbf{r}'(c)$ exists, then **r** is **differentiable** at c. If $\mathbf{r}'(c)$ exists for all c in an open interval I, then **r** is **differentiable** on the interval I. Differentiability of vector-valued functions can be extended to closed intervals by considering one-sided limits.

REMARK   In addition to $\mathbf{r}'(t)$, other notations for the derivative of a vector-valued function are

$$D_t[\mathbf{r}(t)], \frac{d}{dt}[\mathbf{r}(t)], \quad \text{and} \quad \frac{d\mathbf{r}}{dt}.$$

Differentiation of vector-valued functions can be done on a *component-by-component basis*. To see why this is true, consider the function given by $\mathbf{r}(t) = f(t)\mathbf{i} + g(t)\mathbf{j}$. Applying the definition of the derivative produces the following.

$$\mathbf{r}'(t) = \lim_{\Delta t \to 0} \frac{\mathbf{r}(t + \Delta t) - \mathbf{r}(t)}{\Delta t}$$

$$= \lim_{\Delta t \to 0} \frac{f(t + \Delta t)\mathbf{i} + g(t + \Delta t)\mathbf{j} - f(t)\mathbf{i} - g(t)\mathbf{j}}{\Delta t}$$

$$= \lim_{\Delta t \to 0} \left\{ \left[\frac{f(t + \Delta t) - f(t)}{\Delta t} \right]\mathbf{i} + \left[\frac{g(t + \Delta t) - g(t)}{\Delta t} \right]\mathbf{j} \right\}$$

$$= \left\{ \lim_{\Delta t \to 0} \left[\frac{f(t + \Delta t) - f(t)}{\Delta t} \right] \right\}\mathbf{i} + \left\{ \lim_{\Delta t \to 0} \left[\frac{g(t + \Delta t) - g(t)}{\Delta t} \right] \right\}\mathbf{j}$$

$$= f'(t)\mathbf{i} + g'(t)\mathbf{j}$$

This important result is listed in the following theorem. Note that the derivative of the vector-valued function **r** is itself a vector-valued function. (A geometric interpretation of the derivative of a vector-valued function is discussed in the next section.)

> **THEOREM 12.1   Differentiation of Vector-Valued Functions**
>
> 1. If $\mathbf{r}(t) = f(t)\mathbf{i} + g(t)\mathbf{j}$, where f and g are differentiable functions of t, then
> $\mathbf{r}'(t) = f'(t)\mathbf{i} + g'(t)\mathbf{j}$.   Plane
> 2. If $\mathbf{r}(t) = f(t)\mathbf{i} + g(t)\mathbf{j} + h(t)\mathbf{k}$, where f, g, and h are differentiable functions of t, then
> $\mathbf{r}'(t) = f'(t)\mathbf{i} + g'(t)\mathbf{j} + h'(t)\mathbf{k}$.   Space

EXAMPLE 1   Differentiation of Vector-Valued Functions

Find the derivative of each of the following vector-valued functions.

a. $\mathbf{r}(t) = t^2\mathbf{i} - 4\mathbf{j}$ **b.** $\mathbf{r}(t) = \dfrac{1}{t}\mathbf{i} + \ln t\,\mathbf{j} + e^{2t}\mathbf{k}$

Solution   Differentiating on a component-by-component basis produces the following.

a. $\mathbf{r}'(t) = 2t\,\mathbf{i} - 0\mathbf{j} = 2t\,\mathbf{i}$

b. $\mathbf{r}'(t) = -\dfrac{1}{t^2}\mathbf{i} + \dfrac{1}{t}\mathbf{j} + 2e^{2t}\mathbf{k}$

Higher-order derivatives of vector-valued functions are obtained by successive differentiation of each component function.

EXAMPLE 2   Higher-Order Differentiation

For the vector-valued function given by $\mathbf{r}(t) = \cos t\,\mathbf{i} + \sin t\,\mathbf{j} + 2t\,\mathbf{k}$, find the following.

a. $\mathbf{r}'(t)$ **b.** $\mathbf{r}''(t)$ **c.** $\mathbf{r}'(t)\cdot\mathbf{r}''(t)$ **d.** $\mathbf{r}'(t) \times \mathbf{r}''(t)$

Solution

a. $\mathbf{r}'(t) = -\sin t\,\mathbf{i} + \cos t\,\mathbf{j} + 2\mathbf{k}$

b. $\mathbf{r}''(t) = -\cos t\,\mathbf{i} - \sin t\,\mathbf{j} + 0\mathbf{k} = -\cos t\,\mathbf{i} - \sin t\,\mathbf{j}$

c. $\mathbf{r}'(t)\cdot\mathbf{r}''(t) = \sin t\cos t - \sin t\cos t = 0$

d. $\mathbf{r}'(t) \times \mathbf{r}''(t) = \begin{vmatrix} \mathbf{i} & \mathbf{j} & \mathbf{k} \\ -\sin t & \cos t & 2 \\ -\cos t & -\sin t & 0 \end{vmatrix}$

$$= \begin{vmatrix} \cos t & 2 \\ -\sin t & 0 \end{vmatrix}\mathbf{i} - \begin{vmatrix} -\sin t & 2 \\ -\cos t & 0 \end{vmatrix}\mathbf{j} + \begin{vmatrix} -\sin t & \cos t \\ -\cos t & -\sin t \end{vmatrix}\mathbf{k}$$

$$= 2\sin t\,\mathbf{i} - 2\cos t\,\mathbf{j} + \mathbf{k}$$

Note that the dot product in part c is a *real-valued* function, not a vector-valued function.

The curve represented by the vector-valued function

$$\mathbf{r}(t) = f(t)\mathbf{i} + g(t)\mathbf{j} + h(t)\mathbf{k}$$

is **smooth on an open interval** I if f', g', and h' are continuous on I and $\mathbf{r}'(t) \neq \mathbf{0}$ for any value of t in the interval I.

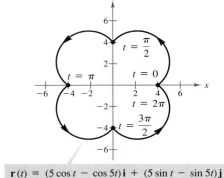

$\mathbf{r}(t) = (5\cos t - \cos 5t)\mathbf{i} + (5\sin t - \sin 5t)\mathbf{j}$

FIGURE 12.8
The epicycloid is not smooth at the points where it intersects the axes.

EXAMPLE 3   Finding Intervals on Which a Curve is Smooth

Find the intervals on which the epicycloid C given by

$$\mathbf{r}(t) = (5\cos t - \cos 5t)\mathbf{i} + (5\sin t - \sin 5t)\mathbf{j}, \qquad 0 \le t \le 2\pi$$

is smooth.

Solution   The derivative of $\mathbf{r}$ is

$$\mathbf{r}'(t) = (-5\sin t + 5\sin 5t)\mathbf{i} + (5\cos t - 5\cos 5t)\mathbf{j}.$$

In the interval $[0, 2\pi]$, the only values of t for which $\mathbf{r}'(t) = 0\mathbf{i} + 0\mathbf{j}$ are $t = 0$, $\pi/2$, π, $3\pi/2$, and 2π. Therefore, you can conclude that C is smooth in the intervals

$$\left(0, \frac{\pi}{2}\right), \quad \left(\frac{\pi}{2}, \pi\right), \quad \left(\pi, \frac{3\pi}{2}\right), \quad \text{and} \quad \left(\frac{3\pi}{2}, 2\pi\right)$$

as shown in Figure 12.8.

REMARK   In Figure 12.8, note that the curve is not smooth at points at which the curve makes an abrupt change in direction—such points are called **cusps** or **nodes.**

Most of the differentiation rules in Chapter 2 have counterparts for vector-valued functions, and several are listed in the following theorem. Note that the theorem contains three versions of "product rules." Property 3 gives the derivative of the product of a real-valued function f and a vector-valued function $\mathbf{r}$. Property 4 gives the derivative of the dot product of two vector-valued functions, and Property 5 gives the derivative of the cross product of two vector-valued functions, (in space). (Property 5 applies only to three-dimensional vector-valued functions, because the cross product is not defined for two-dimensional vectors.)

THEOREM 12.2   Properties of the Derivative

Let $\mathbf{r}$ and $\mathbf{u}$ be differentiable vector-valued functions of t, let f be a differentiable real-valued function of t, and let c be a scalar.

1. $D_t[c\,\mathbf{r}(t)] = c\,\mathbf{r}'(t)$
2. $D_t[\mathbf{r}(t) \pm \mathbf{u}(t)] = \mathbf{r}'(t) \pm \mathbf{u}'(t)$
3. $D_t[f(t)\mathbf{r}(t)] = f(t)\mathbf{r}'(t) + f'(t)\mathbf{r}(t)$
4. $D_t[\mathbf{r}(t) \cdot \mathbf{u}(t)] = \mathbf{r}(t) \cdot \mathbf{u}'(t) + \mathbf{r}'(t) \cdot \mathbf{u}(t)$
5. $D_t[\mathbf{r}(t) \times \mathbf{u}(t)] = \mathbf{r}(t) \times \mathbf{u}'(t) + \mathbf{r}'(t) \times \mathbf{u}(t)$
6. $D_t[\mathbf{r}(f(t))] = \mathbf{r}'(f(t))f'(t)$
7. If $\mathbf{r}(t) \cdot \mathbf{r}(t) = c$, then $\mathbf{r}(t) \cdot \mathbf{r}'(t) = 0$.

Proof   To prove the fourth property, let

$$\mathbf{r}(t) = f_1(t)\mathbf{i} + g_1(t)\mathbf{j} \quad \text{and} \quad \mathbf{u}(t) = f_2(t)\mathbf{i} + g_2(t)\mathbf{j}$$

where f_i and g_i are differentiable functions of t. Then,

$$\mathbf{r}(t) \cdot \mathbf{u}(t) = f_1(t)f_2(t) + g_1(t)g_2(t)$$

and it follows that

$$\begin{aligned} D_t[\mathbf{r}(t) \cdot \mathbf{u}(t)] &= f_1(t)f_2'(t) + f_1'(t)f_2(t) + g_1(t)g_2'(t) + g_1'(t)g_2(t) \\ &= [f_1(t)f_2'(t) + g_1(t)g_2'(t)] + [f_1'(t)f_2(t) + g_1'(t)g_2(t)] \\ &= \mathbf{r}(t) \cdot \mathbf{u}'(t) + \mathbf{r}'(t) \cdot \mathbf{u}(t). \end{aligned}$$

Proofs of the other properties are left as exercises (see Exercises 45–49 and Exercise 52).

EXAMPLE 4   Using Properties of the Derivative

For the vector-valued functions given by

$$\mathbf{r}(t) = \frac{1}{t}\mathbf{i} - \mathbf{j} + (\ln t)\mathbf{k} \quad \text{and} \quad \mathbf{u}(t) = t^2\mathbf{i} - 2t\mathbf{j} + \mathbf{k}$$

find

a. $D_t[\mathbf{r}(t) \cdot \mathbf{u}(t)]$.   **b.** $D_t[\mathbf{u}(t) \times \mathbf{u}'(t)]$.

Solution

a. Because $\mathbf{r}'(t) = -\dfrac{1}{t^2}\mathbf{i} + \dfrac{1}{t}\mathbf{k}$ and $\mathbf{u}'(t) = 2t\mathbf{i} - 2\mathbf{j}$, you have

$$\begin{aligned} D_t[\mathbf{r}(t) \cdot \mathbf{u}(t)] &= \mathbf{r}(t) \cdot \mathbf{u}'(t) + \mathbf{r}'(t) \cdot \mathbf{u}(t) \\ &= \left(\frac{1}{t}\mathbf{i} - \mathbf{j} + \ln t\,\mathbf{k}\right) \cdot (2t\mathbf{i} - 2\mathbf{j}) \\ &\quad + \left(-\frac{1}{t^2}\mathbf{i} + \frac{1}{t}\mathbf{k}\right) \cdot (t^2\mathbf{i} - 2t\mathbf{j} + \mathbf{k}) \\ &= 2 + 2 + (-1) + \frac{1}{t} \\ &= 3 + \frac{1}{t}. \end{aligned}$$

b. Because $\mathbf{u}'(t) = 2t\mathbf{i} - 2\mathbf{j}$ and $\mathbf{u}''(t) = 2\mathbf{i}$, you have

$$\begin{aligned} D_t[\mathbf{u}(t) \times \mathbf{u}'(t)] &= [\mathbf{u}(t) \times \mathbf{u}''(t)] + [\mathbf{u}'(t) \times \mathbf{u}'(t)] \\ &= \begin{vmatrix} \mathbf{i} & \mathbf{j} & \mathbf{k} \\ t^2 & -2t & 1 \\ 2 & 0 & 0 \end{vmatrix} + \mathbf{0} \\ &= \begin{vmatrix} -2t & 1 \\ 0 & 0 \end{vmatrix}\mathbf{i} - \begin{vmatrix} t^2 & 1 \\ 2 & 0 \end{vmatrix}\mathbf{j} + \begin{vmatrix} t^2 & -2t \\ 2 & 0 \end{vmatrix}\mathbf{k} \\ &= 0\mathbf{i} - (-2)\mathbf{j} + 4t\,\mathbf{k} \\ &= 2\mathbf{j} + 4t\,\mathbf{k}. \end{aligned}$$

REMARK   Try reworking parts a and b in Example 4 by first forming the dot and cross products and then differentiating to see that you obtain the same results.

Integration of Vector-Valued Functions

The following definition is a natural consequence of the definition of the derivative of a vector-valued function.

Definition of Integration of Vector-Valued Functions

1. If $\mathbf{r}(t) = f(t)\mathbf{i} + g(t)\mathbf{j}$, where f and g are continuous on $[a, b]$, then the **indefinite integral (antiderivative)** of $\mathbf{r}$ is

$$\int \mathbf{r}(t)\,dt = \left[\int f(t)\,dt\right]\mathbf{i} + \left[\int g(t)\,dt\right]\mathbf{j} \qquad \text{Plane}$$

and its **definite integral** over the interval $a \leq t \leq b$ is

$$\int_a^b \mathbf{r}(t)\,dt = \left[\int_a^b f(t)\,dt\right]\mathbf{i} + \left[\int_a^b g(t)\,dt\right]\mathbf{j}.$$

2. If $\mathbf{r}(t) = f(t)\mathbf{i} + g(t)\mathbf{j} + h(t)\mathbf{k}$, where f, g, and h are continuous on $[a, b]$, then the **indefinite integral (antiderivative)** of $\mathbf{r}$ is

$$\int \mathbf{r}(t)\,dt = \left[\int f(t)\,dt\right]\mathbf{i} + \left[\int g(t)\,dt\right]\mathbf{j} + \left[\int h(t)\,dt\right]\mathbf{k} \qquad \text{Space}$$

and its **definite integral** over the interval $a \leq t \leq b$ is

$$\int_a^b \mathbf{r}(t)\,dt = \left[\int_a^b f(t)\,dt\right]\mathbf{i} + \left[\int_a^b g(t)\,dt\right]\mathbf{j} + \left[\int_a^b h(t)\,dt\right]\mathbf{k}.$$

The antiderivative of a vector-valued function is a family of vector-valued functions all differing by a constant vector $\mathbf{C}$. For instance, if $\mathbf{r}(t)$ is a three-dimensional vector-valued function, then for the indefinite integral $\int \mathbf{r}(t)\,dt$, you obtain three constants of integration

$$\int f(t)\,dt = F(t) + C_1, \quad \int g(t)\,dt = G(t) + C_2, \quad \int h(t)\,dt = H(t) + C_3$$

where $F'(t) = f(t)$, $G'(t) = g(t)$, and $H'(t) = h(t)$. These three *scalar* constants produce one *vector* constant of integration,

$$\begin{aligned}
\int \mathbf{r}(t)\,dt &= [F(t) + C_1]\mathbf{i} + [G(t) + C_2]\mathbf{j} + [H(t) + C_3]\mathbf{k} \\
&= [F(t)\mathbf{i} + G(t)\mathbf{j} + H(t)\mathbf{k}] + [C_1\mathbf{i} + C_2\mathbf{j} + C_3\mathbf{k}] \\
&= \mathbf{R}(t) + \mathbf{C}
\end{aligned}$$

where $\mathbf{R}'(t) = \mathbf{r}(t)$.

EXAMPLE 5   Integrating a Vector-Valued Function

Evaluate the indefinite integral

$$\int (t\,\mathbf{i} + 3\mathbf{j})\,dt.$$

Solution   Integrating on a component-by-component basis produces

$$\int (t\,\mathbf{i} + 3\mathbf{j})\,dt = \frac{t^2}{2}\mathbf{i} + 3t\,\mathbf{j} + \mathbf{C}.$$

Example 6 shows how to evaluate the definite integral of a vector-valued function.

EXAMPLE 6   Definite Integral of a Vector-Valued Function

Evaluate the integral

$$\int_0^1 \mathbf{r}(t)\, dt = \int_0^1 \left(\sqrt[3]{t}\, \mathbf{i} + \frac{1}{t+1}\mathbf{j} + e^{-t}\mathbf{k} \right) dt.$$

Solution

$$\int_0^1 \mathbf{r}(t)\, dt = \left(\int_0^1 t^{1/3}\, dt \right)\mathbf{i} + \left(\int_0^1 \frac{1}{t+1}\, dt \right)\mathbf{j} + \left(\int_0^1 e^{-t}\, dt \right)\mathbf{k}$$

$$= \left[\left(\frac{3}{4} \right) t^{4/3} \right]_0^1 \mathbf{i} + \left[\ln|t+1| \right]_0^1 \mathbf{j} + \left[-e^{-t} \right]_0^1 \mathbf{k}$$

$$= \frac{3}{4}\mathbf{i} + (\ln 2)\mathbf{j} + \left(1 - \frac{1}{e} \right)\mathbf{k}$$

As with real-valued functions, you can narrow the family of antiderivatives of a vector-valued function $\mathbf{r}'$ down to a single antiderivative by imposing an initial condition on the vector-valued function $\mathbf{r}$. This is demonstrated in the next example.

EXAMPLE 7   The Antiderivative of a Vector-Valued Function

Find the antiderivative of

$$\mathbf{r}'(t) = \cos 2t\, \mathbf{i} - 2 \sin t\, \mathbf{j} + \frac{1}{1+t^2}\mathbf{k}$$

that satisfies the initial condition $\mathbf{r}(0) = 3\mathbf{i} - 2\mathbf{j} + \mathbf{k}$.

Solution

$$\mathbf{r}(t) = \int \mathbf{r}'(t)\, dt$$

$$= \left(\int \cos 2t\, dt \right)\mathbf{i} + \left(\int -2 \sin t\, dt \right)\mathbf{j} + \left(\int \frac{1}{1+t^2}\, dt \right)\mathbf{k}$$

$$= \left(\frac{1}{2} \sin 2t + C_1 \right)\mathbf{i} + (2 \cos t + C_2)\mathbf{j} + (\arctan t + C_3)\mathbf{k}$$

Letting $t = 0$ and using the fact that $\mathbf{r}(0) = 3\mathbf{i} - 2\mathbf{j} + \mathbf{k}$, you have

$$\mathbf{r}(0) = (0 + C_1)\mathbf{i} + (2 + C_2)\mathbf{j} + (0 + C_3)\mathbf{k}$$
$$= 3\mathbf{i} + (-2)\mathbf{j} + \mathbf{k}.$$

Equating corresponding components produces

$$C_1 = 3, \quad 2 + C_2 = -2, \quad \text{and} \quad C_3 = 1.$$

Thus, the antiderivative that satisfies the given initial condition is

$$\mathbf{r}(t) = \left(\frac{1}{2} \sin 2t + 3 \right)\mathbf{i} + (2 \cos t - 4)\mathbf{j} + (\arctan t + 1)\mathbf{k}.$$

EXERCISES for Section 12.2

TECHNOLOGY
Laboratory Guide
Lab 12.2

In Exercises 1–4, (a) sketch the plane curve represented by the vector-valued function and (b) sketch the vectors $\mathbf{r}(t_0)$ and $\mathbf{r}'(t_0)$ for the specified value of t_0. Position the vectors so that the initial point of $\mathbf{r}(t_0)$ is at the origin and the initial point of $\mathbf{r}'(t_0)$ is at the terminal point of $\mathbf{r}(t_0)$.

1. $\mathbf{r}(t) = t^2\mathbf{i} + t\mathbf{j}$ $t_0 = 2$

2. $\mathbf{r}(t) = t\mathbf{i} + t^3\mathbf{j}$ $t_0 = 1$

3. $\mathbf{r}(t) = \cos t\,\mathbf{i} + \sin t\,\mathbf{j}$ $t_0 = \dfrac{\pi}{2}$

4. $\mathbf{r}(t) = t^2\mathbf{i} + \dfrac{1}{t}\mathbf{j}$ $t_0 = 2$

5. Consider the vector-valued function $\mathbf{r}(t) = t\mathbf{i} + t^2\mathbf{j}$.
   a. Sketch the graph of $\mathbf{r}(t)$.
   b. Sketch the vectors $\mathbf{r}(\frac{1}{4})$, $\mathbf{r}(\frac{1}{2})$, and $\mathbf{r}(\frac{1}{2}) - \mathbf{r}(\frac{1}{4})$ on the graph in part a.
   c. Compare the vector $\mathbf{r}'(\frac{1}{4})$ with the vector
   $$\frac{\mathbf{r}(\frac{1}{2}) - \mathbf{r}(\frac{1}{4})}{\frac{1}{2} - \frac{1}{4}}.$$

6. Consider the vector-valued function $\mathbf{r}(t) = t\mathbf{i} + (4 - t^2)\mathbf{j}$.
   a. Sketch the graph of $\mathbf{r}(t)$.
   b. Sketch the vectors $\mathbf{r}(1)$, $\mathbf{r}(1.25)$, and $\mathbf{r}(1.25) - \mathbf{r}(1)$ on the graph in part a.
   c. Compare the vector $\mathbf{r}'(1)$ with the vector
   $$\frac{\mathbf{r}(1.25) - \mathbf{r}(1)}{1.25 - 1}.$$

In Exercises 7 and 8, (a) sketch the space curve represented by the vector-valued function. (b) sketch the vectors $\mathbf{r}(t_0)$ and $\mathbf{r}'(t_0)$ for the specified value of t_0.

7. $\mathbf{r}(t) = 2\cos t\,\mathbf{i} + 2\sin t\,\mathbf{j} + t\mathbf{k}$, $t_0 = \dfrac{3\pi}{2}$

8. $\mathbf{r}(t) = t\mathbf{i} + t^2\mathbf{j} + \frac{3}{2}\mathbf{k}$, $t_0 = 2$

In Exercises 9 and 10, a vector-valued function and its graph are given. The graph also shows the unit vectors $\mathbf{r}'(t_0)/\|\mathbf{r}'(t_0)\|$ and $\mathbf{r}''(t_0)/\|\mathbf{r}''(t_0)\|$. Find these two unit vectors and identify them on the graph.

9. $\mathbf{r}(t) = \cos(\pi t)\mathbf{i} + \sin(\pi t)\mathbf{j} + t^2\mathbf{k}$, $t_0 = -\frac{1}{4}$

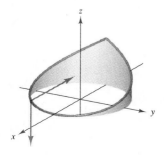

10. $\mathbf{r}(t) = t\mathbf{i} + t^2\mathbf{j} + e^{0.75t}\mathbf{k}$, $t_0 = \frac{1}{4}$

In Exercises 11–18, find $\mathbf{r}'(t)$.

11. $\mathbf{r}(t) = 6t\mathbf{i} - 7t^2\mathbf{j} + t^3\mathbf{k}$

12. $\mathbf{r}(t) = \dfrac{1}{t}\mathbf{i} + 16t\mathbf{j} + \dfrac{t^2}{2}\mathbf{k}$

13. $\mathbf{r}(t) = a\cos^3 t\,\mathbf{i} + a\sin^3 t\,\mathbf{j} + \mathbf{k}$

14. $\mathbf{r}(t) = \sqrt{t}\,\mathbf{i} + t\sqrt{t}\,\mathbf{j} + \ln t\,\mathbf{k}$

15. $\mathbf{r}(t) = e^{-t}\mathbf{i} + 4\mathbf{j}$

16. $\mathbf{r}(t) = \langle \sin t - t\cos t,\ \cos t + t\sin t,\ t^2 \rangle$

17. $\mathbf{r}(t) = \langle t\sin t,\ t\cos t,\ t \rangle$

18. $\mathbf{r}(t) = \langle \arcsin t,\ \arccos t,\ 0 \rangle$

In Exercises 19 and 20, find the following.
   a. $\mathbf{r}'(t)$ b. $\mathbf{r}''(t)$
   c. $D_t[\mathbf{r}(t) \cdot \mathbf{u}(t)]$ d. $D_t[3\mathbf{r}(t) - \mathbf{u}(t)]$
   e. $D_t[\mathbf{r}(t) \times \mathbf{u}(t)]$ f. $D_t[\|\mathbf{r}(t)\|]$, $t > 0$

19. $\mathbf{r}(t) = t\mathbf{i} + 3t\mathbf{j} + t^2\mathbf{k}$
   $\mathbf{u}(t) = 4t\mathbf{i} + t^2\mathbf{j} + t^3\mathbf{k}$

20. $\mathbf{r}(t) = t^2\mathbf{i} + \sin t\,\mathbf{j} + \cos t\,\mathbf{k}$
   $\mathbf{u}(t) = \dfrac{1}{t^2}\mathbf{i} + \sin t\,\mathbf{j} + \cos t\,\mathbf{k}$

In Exercises 21–26, find the open interval(s) on which the curve given by the vector-valued function is smooth.

21. $\mathbf{r}(t) = t^2\mathbf{i} + t^3\mathbf{j}$

22. $\mathbf{r}(t) = \dfrac{1}{t-1}\mathbf{i} + 3t\mathbf{j}$

23. $\mathbf{r}(\theta) = 2\cos^3\theta\,\mathbf{i} + 3\sin^3\theta\,\mathbf{j}$

24. $\mathbf{r}(\theta) = (\theta + \sin\theta)\mathbf{i} + (1 - \cos\theta)\mathbf{j}$

25. $\mathbf{r}(\theta) = (\theta - 2\sin\theta)\mathbf{i} + (1 - 2\cos\theta)\mathbf{j}$

26. $\mathbf{r}(t) = \dfrac{3t}{1 + t^3}\mathbf{i} + \dfrac{3t^2}{1 + t^3}\mathbf{j}$

In Exercises 27–34, evaluate the indefinite integral.

27. $\displaystyle\int (2t\mathbf{i} + \mathbf{j} + \mathbf{k})\,dt$

28. $\displaystyle\int (3t^2\mathbf{i} + 4t\mathbf{j} - 8t^3\mathbf{k})\,dt$

29. $\int \left(\dfrac{1}{t}\mathbf{i} + \mathbf{j} - t^{3/2}\mathbf{k} \right) dt$

30. $\int \left[(2t - 1)\mathbf{i} + 4t^3\mathbf{j} + 3\sqrt{t}\,\mathbf{k} \right] dt$

31. $\int (e^t\mathbf{i} + \sin t\,\mathbf{j} + \cos t\,\mathbf{k}) \, dt$

32. $\int \left(\ln t\,\mathbf{i} + \dfrac{1}{t}\mathbf{j} + \mathbf{k} \right) dt$

33. $\int \left(\sec^2 t\,\mathbf{i} + \dfrac{1}{1 + t^2}\mathbf{j} \right) dt$

34. $\int (e^{-t}\sin t\,\mathbf{i} + e^{-t}\cos t\,\mathbf{j}) \, dt$

In Exercises 35–40, find r(t) for the given conditions.

35. $\mathbf{r}'(t) = 4e^{2t}\mathbf{i} + 3e^t\mathbf{j}$
     $\mathbf{r}(0) = 2\mathbf{i}$

36. $\mathbf{r}'(t) = 2t\mathbf{j} + \sqrt{t}\,\mathbf{k}$
     $\mathbf{r}(0) = \mathbf{i} + \mathbf{j}$

37. $\mathbf{r}''(t) = -32\mathbf{j}$
     $\mathbf{r}'(0) = 600\sqrt{3}\mathbf{i} + 600\mathbf{j}$
     $\mathbf{r}(0) = \mathbf{0}$

38. $\mathbf{r}''(t) = -4\cos t\,\mathbf{j} - 3\sin 5\mathbf{k}$
     $\mathbf{r}'(0) = 3\mathbf{k}$
     $\mathbf{r}(0) = 4\mathbf{j}$

39. $\mathbf{r}'(t) = te^{-t^2}\mathbf{i} - e^{-t}\mathbf{j} + \mathbf{k}$
     $\mathbf{r}(0) = \frac{1}{2}\mathbf{i} - \mathbf{j} + \mathbf{k}$

40. $\mathbf{r}'(t) = \dfrac{1}{1 + t^2}\mathbf{i} + \dfrac{1}{t^2}\mathbf{j} + \dfrac{1}{t}\mathbf{k}$
     $\mathbf{r}(1) = 2\mathbf{i}$

In Exercises 41–44, evaluate the definite integral.

41. $\displaystyle\int_0^1 (8t\mathbf{i} + t\mathbf{j} - \mathbf{k}) \, dt$

42. $\displaystyle\int_{-1}^1 \left(t\mathbf{i} + t^3\mathbf{j} + \sqrt[3]{t}\,\mathbf{k} \right) dt$

43. $\displaystyle\int_0^{\pi/2} [(a\cos t)\mathbf{i} + (a\sin t)\mathbf{j} + \mathbf{k}] \, dt$

44. $\displaystyle\int_0^3 (e^t\mathbf{i} + te^t\mathbf{k}) \, dt$

In Exercises 45–52, prove the given property. In each case, assume that r, u, and v are differentiable vector-valued functions of t, f is a differentiable real-valued function of t, and c is a scalar.

45. $D_t[c\,\mathbf{r}(t)] = c\,\mathbf{r}'(t)$

46. $D_t[\mathbf{r}(t) \pm \mathbf{u}(t)] = \mathbf{r}'(t) \pm \mathbf{u}'(t)$

47. $D_t[f(t)\mathbf{r}(t)] = f(t)\mathbf{r}'(t) + f'(t)\mathbf{r}(t)$

48. $D_t[\mathbf{r}(t) \times \mathbf{u}(t)] = [\mathbf{r}(t) \times \mathbf{u}'(t)] + [\mathbf{r}'(t) \times \mathbf{u}(t)]$

49. $D_t[\mathbf{r}(f(t))] = \mathbf{r}'(f(t))f'(t)$

50. $D_t[\mathbf{r}(t) \times \mathbf{r}'(t)] = \mathbf{r}(t) \times \mathbf{r}''(t)$

51. $D_t[\mathbf{r}(t) \cdot (\mathbf{u}(t) \times \mathbf{v}(t))]$
     $= \mathbf{r}'(t) \cdot [\mathbf{u}(t) \times \mathbf{v}(t)] + \mathbf{r}(t) \cdot [\mathbf{u}'(t) \times \mathbf{v}(t)] +$
     $\quad \mathbf{r}(t) \cdot [\mathbf{u}(t) \times \mathbf{v}'(t)]$

52. If $\mathbf{r}(t) \cdot \mathbf{r}(t)$ is a constant, then $\mathbf{r}(t) \cdot \mathbf{r}'(t) = 0$.

True or False   **In Exercises 53 and 54, determine whether the statement is true or false. If it is false, explain why or give an example that shows it is false.**

53. $\dfrac{d}{dt}\big[\|\mathbf{r}(t)\| \big] = \|\mathbf{r}'(t)\|$

54. If $\mathbf{r}$ and $\mathbf{u}$ are differentiable vector-valued functions of t, then
     $D_t[\mathbf{r}(t) \cdot \mathbf{u}(t)] = \mathbf{r}'(t) \cdot \mathbf{u}'(t)$.

12.3

Velocity and Acceleration • Projectile Motion

Velocity and Acceleration

You are now ready to combine your study of parametric equations, curves, vectors, and vector-valued functions to form a model for motion along a curve. We begin by looking at the motion of an object in the plane. (The motion of an object in space could be developed similarly.)

As an object moves along a curve in the plane, the coordinates x and y of its center of mass are both functions of time t. Rather than using f and g to represent these two functions, it is convenient to write

$$x = x(t) \quad \text{and} \quad y = y(t).$$

Thus, the position vector $\mathbf{r}(t)$ takes the form

$$\mathbf{r}(t) = x(t)\mathbf{i} + y(t)\mathbf{j}. \qquad \text{Position vector}$$

The beauty of this vector model for representing motion is that you can use the first and second derivatives of the vector-valued function $\mathbf{r}$ to find the object's velocity and acceleration. (Recall from the previous chapter that velocity and acceleration are both vector quantities having magnitude and direction.)

To find the velocity and acceleration vectors at a given time t, consider a point

$$Q = (x(t + \Delta t), y(t + \Delta t))$$

that is approaching the point

$$P = (x(t), y(t))$$

along the curve C given by

$$\mathbf{r}(t) = x(t)\mathbf{i} + y(t)\mathbf{j}$$

as shown in Figure 12.9. As $\Delta t \to 0$, the direction of the vector $\overrightarrow{PQ}$ (denoted by $\Delta\mathbf{r}$) approaches the *direction of motion* at the time t.

$$\Delta\mathbf{r} = \mathbf{r}(t + \Delta t) - \mathbf{r}(t)$$

$$\frac{\Delta\mathbf{r}}{\Delta t} = \frac{\mathbf{r}(t + \Delta t) - \mathbf{r}(t)}{\Delta t}$$

$$\lim_{\Delta t \to 0} \frac{\Delta\mathbf{r}}{\Delta t} = \lim_{\Delta t \to 0} \frac{\mathbf{r}(t + \Delta t) - \mathbf{r}(t)}{\Delta t}$$

If this limit exists (and is not equal to the zero vector), it is defined to be the **tangent vector** to the curve at the point P. Note that this is the same limit used to define $\mathbf{r}'(t)$. Thus, the direction of $\mathbf{r}'(t)$ gives the direction of motion at time t. Moreover, the magnitude of the vector $\mathbf{r}'(t)$

$$\|\mathbf{r}'(t)\| = \|x'(t)\mathbf{i} + y'(t)\mathbf{j}\|$$

$$= \sqrt{[x'(t)]^2 + [y'(t)]^2}$$

gives the **speed** of the object at time t. Similarly, you can use $\mathbf{r}''(t)$ to represent acceleration, as indicated in the following definition.

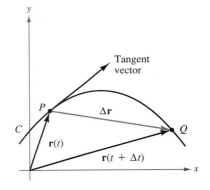

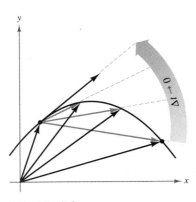

FIGURE 12.9

As $\Delta t \to 0$, $\dfrac{\Delta\mathbf{r}}{\Delta t}$ approaches tangent vector.

Definition of Velocity and Acceleration

If x and y are twice-differentiable functions of t, and $\mathbf{r}$ is a vector-valued function given by $\mathbf{r}(t) = x(t)\mathbf{i} + y(t)\mathbf{j}$, then the velocity vector, acceleration vector, and speed at time t are as follows.

$$\text{Velocity} = \mathbf{v}(t) \quad = \mathbf{r}'(t) \quad = x'(t)\mathbf{i} + y'(t)\mathbf{j}$$
$$\text{Acceleration} = \mathbf{a}(t) \quad = \mathbf{r}''(t) \quad = x''(t)\mathbf{i} + y''(t)\mathbf{j}$$
$$\text{Speed} = \| \mathbf{v}(t) \| = \| \mathbf{r}'(t) \| = \sqrt{[x'(t)]^2 + [y'(t)]^2}$$

For motion along a space curve, the definitions are similar. That is, if $\mathbf{r}(t) = x(t)\mathbf{i} + y(t)\mathbf{j} + z(t)\mathbf{k}$, then you have

$$\text{Velocity} = \mathbf{v}(t) \quad = \mathbf{r}'(t) \quad = x'(t)\mathbf{i} + y'(t)\mathbf{j} + z'(t)\mathbf{k}$$
$$\text{Acceleration} = \mathbf{a}(t) \quad = \mathbf{r}''(t) \quad = x''(t)\mathbf{i} + y''(t)\mathbf{j} + z''(t)\mathbf{k}$$
$$\text{Speed} = \| \mathbf{v}(t) \| = \| \mathbf{r}'(t) \| = \sqrt{[x'(t)]^2 + [y'(t)]^2 + [z'(t)]^2}.$$

EXAMPLE 1   Finding Velocity and Acceleration Along a Plane Curve

REMARK In Example 1, note that the velocity and acceleration vectors are orthogonal at any point in time. This is characteristic of motion at a constant speed. (See Exercise 47.)

Find the velocity vector, speed, and acceleration vector of a particle that moves along the plane curve C described by

$$\mathbf{r}(t) = 2 \sin \frac{t}{2}\mathbf{i} + 2 \cos \frac{t}{2}\mathbf{j}. \qquad \text{Position vector}$$

Solution The velocity vector is

$$\mathbf{v}(t) = \mathbf{r}'(t) = \cos \frac{t}{2}\mathbf{i} - \sin \frac{t}{2}\mathbf{j}. \qquad \text{Velocity vector}$$

The speed (at any time) is

$$\| \mathbf{r}'(t) \| = \sqrt{\cos^2 \frac{t}{2} + \sin^2 \frac{t}{2}} = 1. \qquad \text{Speed}$$

The acceleration vector is

$$\mathbf{a}(t) = \mathbf{r}''(t) = -\frac{1}{2} \sin \frac{t}{2}\mathbf{i} - \frac{1}{2} \cos \frac{t}{2}\mathbf{j}. \qquad \text{Acceleration vector}$$

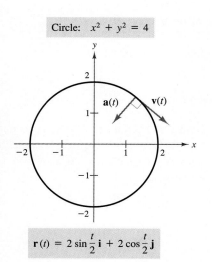

Circle: $x^2 + y^2 = 4$

$$\mathbf{r}(t) = 2 \sin \frac{t}{2}\mathbf{i} + 2 \cos \frac{t}{2}\mathbf{j}$$

FIGURE 12.10
The particle moves around the circle at constant speed.

The parametric equations for the curve in Example 1 are $x = 2 \sin(t/2)$ and $y = 2 \cos(t/2)$. By eliminating the parameter t, you can obtain the rectangular equation

$$x^2 + y^2 = 4. \qquad \text{Rectangular equation}$$

Thus, the curve is a circle of radius 2 centered at the origin, as shown in Figure 12.10. Because the velocity vector

$$\mathbf{v}(t) = \cos \frac{t}{2}\mathbf{i} - \sin \frac{t}{2}\mathbf{j}$$

has a constant magnitude but a changing direction as t increases, the particle moves around the circle at a constant speed.

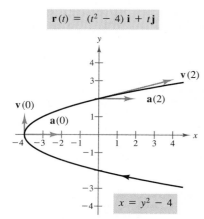

$$\mathbf{r}(t) = (t^2 - 4)\,\mathbf{i} + t\mathbf{j}$$

$$x = y^2 - 4$$

FIGURE 12.11
At each point on the curve, the acceleration vector points to the right.

EXAMPLE 2 Sketching Velocity and Acceleration Vectors in the Plane

Sketch the path of an object moving along the plane curve given by

$$\mathbf{r}(t) = (t^2 - 4)\mathbf{i} + t\,\mathbf{j} \qquad \text{Position vector}$$

and find the velocity and acceleration vectors when $t = 0$ and $t = 2$.

Solution Using the parametric equations $x = t^2 - 4$ and $y = t$, you can determine that the curve is a parabola given by $x = y^2 - 4$, as shown in Figure 12.11. The velocity vector (at any time) is

$$\mathbf{v}(t) = \mathbf{r}'(t) = 2t\,\mathbf{i} + \mathbf{j} \qquad \text{Velocity vector}$$

and the acceleration vector (at any time) is

$$\mathbf{a}(t) = \mathbf{r}''(t) = 2\,\mathbf{i}. \qquad \text{Acceleration vector}$$

When $t = 0$, the velocity and acceleration vectors are given by

$$\mathbf{v}(0) = 2(0)\mathbf{i} + \mathbf{j} = \mathbf{j} \quad \text{and} \quad \mathbf{a}(0) = 2\mathbf{i}.$$

When $t = 2$, the velocity and acceleration vectors are given by

$$\mathbf{v}(2) = 2(2)\mathbf{i} + \mathbf{j} = 4\mathbf{i} + \mathbf{j}\,\dot{} \ \text{and} \quad \mathbf{a}(2) = 2\mathbf{i}.$$

For the object moving along the path shown in Figure 12.11, note that the acceleration vector is constant (it has a magnitude of 2 and points to the right). This implies that the speed of the object is decreasing as the object moves toward the vertex of the parabola, and the speed is increasing as the object moves away from the vertex of the parabola.

This type of motion is *not* characteristic of comets that travel on parabolic paths through our solar system. For such comets, the acceleration vector always points to the origin (the sun), which implies that the comet's speed increases as it approaches the vertex of the path and decreases as it moves away from the vertex. (See Figure 12.12.)

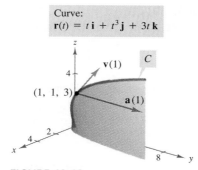

FIGURE 12.12
At each point in the comet's orbit, the acceleration vector points toward the sun.

EXAMPLE 3 Sketching Velocity and Acceleration Vectors in Space

Sketch the path of an object moving along the space curve C given by

$$\mathbf{r}(t) = t\,\mathbf{i} + t^3\,\mathbf{j} + 3t\,\mathbf{k}, \qquad t \geq 0 \qquad \text{Position vector}$$

and find the velocity and acceleration vectors when $t = 1$.

Solution Using the parametric equations $x = t$ and $y = t^3$, you can determine that the path of the object lies on the cubic cylinder given by $y = x^3$. Moreover, because $z = 3t$, the object starts at $(0, 0, 0)$ and moves upward as t increases, as shown in Figure 12.13. Because $\mathbf{r}(t) = t\mathbf{i} + t^3\mathbf{j} + 3t\mathbf{k}$, you have

$$\mathbf{v}(t) = \mathbf{r}'(t) = \mathbf{i} + 3t^2\mathbf{j} + 3\mathbf{k} \qquad \text{Velocity vector}$$

and

$$\mathbf{a}(t) = \mathbf{r}''(t) = 6t\,\mathbf{j}. \qquad \text{Acceleration vector}$$

When $t = 1$, the velocity and acceleration vectors are given by

$$\mathbf{v}(1) = \mathbf{r}'(1) = \mathbf{i} + 3\mathbf{j} + 3\mathbf{k} \quad \text{and} \quad \mathbf{a}(1) = \mathbf{r}''(1) = 6\mathbf{j}.$$

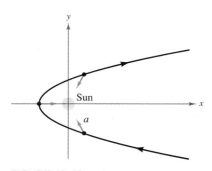

Curve:
$$\mathbf{r}(t) = t\,\mathbf{i} + t^3\,\mathbf{j} + 3t\,\mathbf{k}$$

FIGURE 12.13

So far in this section, we have concentrated on finding the velocity and acceleration by differentiating the position function. Many practical applications involve the reverse problem—finding the position function for a given velocity or acceleration. This is demonstrated in the next example.

EXAMPLE 4   Finding a Position Function by Integration

An object starts from rest at the point $P = (1, 2, 0)$ and moves with an acceleration of

$$\mathbf{a}(t) = \mathbf{j} + 2\mathbf{k} \qquad \text{Acceleration vector}$$

where $\| \mathbf{a}(t) \|$ is measured in feet per second per second. Find the location of the object after $t = 2$ seconds.

Solution   From the description of the object's motion, you can deduce the following *initial conditions*. Because the object starts from rest, you have

$$\mathbf{v}(0) = \mathbf{0}.$$

Moreover, because the object starts at the point $(x, y, z) = (1, 2, 0)$, you have

$$\mathbf{r}(0) = x(0)\mathbf{i} + y(0)\mathbf{j} + z(0)\mathbf{k} = 1\mathbf{i} + 2\mathbf{j} + 0\mathbf{k} = \mathbf{i} + 2\mathbf{j}.$$

To find the position function, you should integrate twice, each time using one of the initial conditions to solve for the constant of integration. The velocity vector is

$$\mathbf{v}(t) = \int \mathbf{a}(t)\, dt = \int (\mathbf{j} + 2\mathbf{k})\, dt = t\mathbf{j} + 2t\mathbf{k} + \mathbf{C}$$

where $\mathbf{C} = C_1\mathbf{i} + C_2\mathbf{j} + C_3\mathbf{k}$. Letting $t = 0$ and applying the initial condition $\mathbf{v}(0) = \mathbf{0}$, you obtain

$$\mathbf{v}(0) = C_1\mathbf{i} + C_2\mathbf{j} + C_3\mathbf{k} = \mathbf{0} \quad \longrightarrow \quad C_1 = C_2 = C_3 = 0.$$

Thus, the *velocity* at any time t is

$$\mathbf{v}(t) = t\mathbf{j} + 2t\mathbf{k}. \qquad \text{Velocity vector}$$

Integrating once more produces

$$\mathbf{r}(t) = \int \mathbf{v}(t)\, dt = \int (t\mathbf{j} + 2t\mathbf{k})\, dt = \frac{t^2}{2}\mathbf{j} + t^2\mathbf{k} + \mathbf{C}$$

where $\mathbf{C} = C_4\mathbf{i} + C_5\mathbf{j} + C_6\mathbf{k}$. Letting $t = 0$ and applying the initial condition $\mathbf{r}(0) = \mathbf{i} + 2\mathbf{j}$, you have

$$\mathbf{r}(0) = C_4\mathbf{i} + C_5\mathbf{j} + C_6\mathbf{k} = \mathbf{i} + 2\mathbf{j} \quad \longrightarrow \quad C_4 = 1, \, C_5 = 2, \, C_6 = 0.$$

Thus, the *position* vector is

$$\mathbf{r}(t) = \mathbf{i} + \left(\frac{t^2}{2} + 2 \right)\mathbf{j} + t^2\mathbf{k}. \qquad \text{Position vector}$$

The location of the object after 2 seconds is given by $\mathbf{r}(2) = \mathbf{i} + 4\mathbf{j} + 4\mathbf{k}$, as shown in Figure 12.14.

Curve:
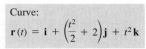

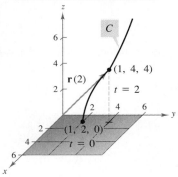

FIGURE 12.14
The object takes two seconds to move from the point $(1, 2, 0)$ to the point $(1, 4, 4)$.

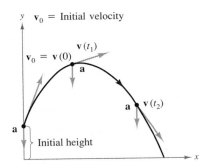

FIGURE 12.15
The parabolic path of a projectile.

Projectile Motion

We now have the machinery to derive the parametric equations for the path of a projectile. We assume that gravity is the only force acting on the projectile after it is launched. Hence, the motion occurs in a vertical plane, which we represent by the xy-coordinate system with the origin as a point on the earth's surface, as shown in Figure 12.15. For a projectile of mass m, the force due to gravity is

$$\mathbf{F} = -mg\,\mathbf{j} \qquad\qquad \text{Force due to gravity}$$

where the gravitational constant $g = 32$ feet per second per second, or 9.81 meters per second per second. By **Newton's Second Law of Motion,** this same force produces an acceleration $\mathbf{a} = \mathbf{a}(t)$, and satisfies the equation $\mathbf{F} = m\,\mathbf{a}$. Consequently, the acceleration of the projectile is given by $m\,\mathbf{a} = -mg\,\mathbf{j}$, which implies that

$$\mathbf{a} = -g\,\mathbf{j}. \qquad\qquad \text{Acceleration of projectile}$$

EXAMPLE 5   Derivation of the Position Function for a Projectile

A projectile of mass m is launched from an initial position $\mathbf{r}_0$ with an initial velocity $\mathbf{v}_0$. Find its position vector as a function of time.

Solution   Begin with the acceleration $\mathbf{a}(t) = -g\,\mathbf{j}$ and integrate twice.

$$\mathbf{v}(t) = \int \mathbf{a}(t)\,dt = \int -g\,\mathbf{j}\,dt = -gt\,\mathbf{j} + \mathbf{C}_1$$

$$\mathbf{r}(t) = \int \mathbf{v}(t)\,dt = \int (-gt\,\mathbf{j} + \mathbf{C}_1)\,dt = -\frac{1}{2}gt^2\,\mathbf{j} + \mathbf{C}_1 t + \mathbf{C}_2$$

You can use the facts that $\mathbf{v}(0) = \mathbf{v}_0$ and $\mathbf{r}(0) = \mathbf{r}_0$ to solve for the constant vectors $\mathbf{C}_1$ and $\mathbf{C}_2$. Doing this produces $\mathbf{C}_1 = \mathbf{v}_0$ and $\mathbf{C}_2 = \mathbf{r}_0$. Therefore, the position vector is

$$\mathbf{r}(t) = -\frac{1}{2}gt^2\,\mathbf{j} + t\,\mathbf{v}_0 + \mathbf{r}_0. \qquad \text{Position vector} \qquad \blacksquare$$

In many projectile problems, the constant vectors $\mathbf{r}_0$ and $\mathbf{v}_0$ are not given explicitly. Often you are given the initial height h, the initial speed v_0, and the angle θ at which the projectile is launched, as shown in Figure 12.16. From the given height, you can deduce that

$$\mathbf{r}_0 = h\,\mathbf{j}.$$

Because the speed gives the magnitude of the initial velocity, it follows that $v_0 = \|\mathbf{v}_0\|$ and you can write

$$\mathbf{v}_0 = x\,\mathbf{i} + y\,\mathbf{j} = (\|\mathbf{v}_0\|\cos\theta)\mathbf{i} + (\|\mathbf{v}_0\|\sin\theta)\mathbf{j} = v_0\cos\theta\,\mathbf{i} + v_0\sin\theta\,\mathbf{j}.$$

Thus, the position vector can be written in the form

$$\mathbf{r}(t) = -\frac{1}{2}gt^2\,\mathbf{j} + t\,\mathbf{v}_0 + \mathbf{r}_0 \qquad\qquad \text{Position vector}$$

$$= -\frac{1}{2}gt^2\,\mathbf{j} + tv_0\cos\theta\,\mathbf{i} + tv_0\sin\theta\,\mathbf{j} + h\,\mathbf{j}$$

$$= (v_0\cos\theta)t\,\mathbf{i} + \left[h + (v_0\sin\theta)t - \frac{1}{2}gt^2\right]\mathbf{j}.$$

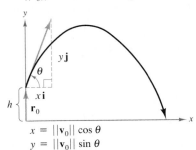

$\|\mathbf{v}_0\| = v_0 = $ initial speed
$\|\mathbf{r}_0\| = h = $ initial height

$x = \|\mathbf{v}_0\|\cos\theta$
$y = \|\mathbf{v}_0\|\sin\theta$

FIGURE 12.16
The initial conditions for a projectile.

> **THEOREM 12.3   Position Function for a Projectile**
>
> Neglecting air resistance, the path of a projectile launched from an initial height h with initial speed v_0 and angle of elevation θ is described by the vector function
>
> $$\mathbf{r}(t) = (v_0 \cos \theta)t\, \mathbf{i} + \left[h + (v_0 \sin \theta)t - \frac{1}{2}gt^2 \right]\mathbf{j}$$
>
> where g is the gravitational constant.

EXAMPLE 6   Describing the Path of a Baseball

A baseball is hit 3 feet above ground at 100 feet per second and at an angle of $\pi/4$ with respect to the ground, as shown in Figure 12.17. Find the maximum height reached by the baseball. Will it clear a 10-foot-high fence located 300 feet from home plate?

Solution   You are given $h = 3$, $v_0 = 100$, and $\theta = \pi/4$. Thus, using $g = 32$ feet per second per second produces

$$\mathbf{r}(t) = \left(100 \cos \frac{\pi}{4} \right) t\, \mathbf{i} + \left[3 + \left(100 \sin \frac{\pi}{4} \right) t - 16t^2 \right]\mathbf{j}$$
$$= (50\sqrt{2}t)\mathbf{i} + (3 + 50\sqrt{2}t - 16t^2)\mathbf{j}$$
$$\mathbf{v}(t) = \mathbf{r}'(t) = 50\sqrt{2}\mathbf{i} + (50\sqrt{2} - 32t)\mathbf{j}.$$

The maximum height occurs when $y'(t) = 50\sqrt{2} - 32t = 0$, which implies that

$$t = \frac{25\sqrt{2}}{16} \approx 2.21 \text{ sec.}$$

Hence, the maximum height reached by the ball is

$$y = 3 + 50\sqrt{2}\left(\frac{25\sqrt{2}}{16} \right) - 16\left(\frac{25\sqrt{2}}{16} \right)^2$$
$$= \frac{649}{8}$$
$$\approx 81 \text{ ft.} \qquad \text{\small Maximum height when } t \approx 2.21$$

The ball is 300 feet from where it was hit when

$$300 = x(t) = 50\sqrt{2}t.$$

Solving this equation for t produces $t = 3\sqrt{2} \approx 4.24$ seconds. At this time, the height of the ball is

$$y = 3 + 50\sqrt{2}(3\sqrt{2}) - 16(3\sqrt{2})^2$$
$$= 303 - 288$$
$$= 15 \text{ ft.} \qquad \text{\small Height when } t \approx 4.24$$

Therefore, the ball clears the 10-foot fence for a home run.

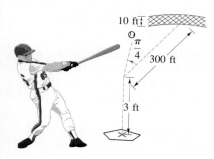

FIGURE 12.17
The batter hits the ball with an initial speed of 100 feet per second.

In Exercises 1–8, the position function r describes the path of an object moving in the *xy*-plane. Sketch a graph of the path and sketch the velocity and acceleration vectors at the given point.

Position function	Point
1. $\mathbf{r}(t) = 3t\,\mathbf{i} + (t - 1)\mathbf{j}$	$(3, 0)$
2. $\mathbf{r}(t) = (6 - t)\mathbf{i} + t\,\mathbf{j}$	$(3, 3)$
3. $\mathbf{r}(t) = t^2\mathbf{i} + t\,\mathbf{j}$	$(4, 2)$
4. $\mathbf{r}(t) = t^3\mathbf{i} + t^2\mathbf{j}$	$(1, 1)$
5. $\mathbf{r}(t) = 2\cos t\,\mathbf{i} + 2\sin t\,\mathbf{j}$	$\left(\sqrt{2}, \sqrt{2}\right)$
6. $\mathbf{r}(t) = 2\cos t\,\mathbf{i} + 3\sin t\,\mathbf{j}$	$(2, 0)$
7. $\mathbf{r}(t) = \langle t - \sin t, 1 - \cos t \rangle$	$(\pi, 2)$
8. $\mathbf{r}(t) = \langle e^{-t}, e^t \rangle$	$(1, 1)$

In Exercises 9–16, the position function r describes the path of an object moving in space. Find the velocity, speed, and acceleration of the object.

9. $\mathbf{r}(t) = t\,\mathbf{i} + (2t - 5)\mathbf{j} + 3t\,\mathbf{k}$

10. $\mathbf{r}(t) = 4t\,\mathbf{i} + 4t\,\mathbf{j} + 2t\,\mathbf{k}$

11. $\mathbf{r}(t) = t\,\mathbf{i} + t^2\mathbf{j} + \dfrac{t^2}{2}\mathbf{k}$

12. $\mathbf{r}(t) = t\,\mathbf{i} + 3t\,\mathbf{j} + \dfrac{t^2}{2}\mathbf{k}$

13. $\mathbf{r}(t) = t\,\mathbf{i} + t\,\mathbf{j} + \sqrt{9 - t^2}\,\mathbf{k}$

14. $\mathbf{r}(t) = t^2\mathbf{i} + t\,\mathbf{j} + 2t^{3/2}\mathbf{k}$

15. $\mathbf{r}(t) = \langle 4t, 3\cos t, 3\sin t \rangle$

16. $\mathbf{r}(t) = \langle e^t\cos t, e^t\sin t, e^t \rangle$

Linear Approximation **In Exercises 17 and 18, the graph of the vector-valued function r(t) and a tangent vector to the graph at $t = t_0$ are given. (a) Find a set of parametric equations for the tangent line to the graph at $t = t_0$ and (b) use the equations for the line to approximate $\mathbf{r}(t_0 + 0.1)$.**

17. $\mathbf{r}(t) = \left\langle t, -t^2, \dfrac{t^3}{4} \right\rangle$, $t_0 = 1$

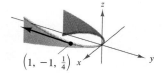

18. $\mathbf{r}(t) = \left\langle t, \sqrt{25 - t^2}, \sqrt{25 - t^2} \right\rangle$, $t_0 = 3$

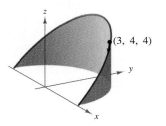

In Exercises 19–22, use the given acceleration function to find the velocity and position functions. Then find the position at time $t = 2$.

19. $\mathbf{a}(t) = \mathbf{i} + \mathbf{j} + \mathbf{k}$
    $\mathbf{v}(0) = \mathbf{0}$
    $\mathbf{r}(0) = \mathbf{0}$

20. $\mathbf{a}(t) = \mathbf{i} + \mathbf{k}$
    $\mathbf{v}(0) = 5\mathbf{j}$
    $\mathbf{r}(0) = \mathbf{0}$

21. $\mathbf{a}(t) = t\,\mathbf{j} + t\,\mathbf{k}$
    $\mathbf{v}(1) = 5\mathbf{j}$
    $\mathbf{r}(1) = \mathbf{0}$

22. $\mathbf{a}(t) = -\cos t\,\mathbf{i} - \sin t\,\mathbf{j}$
    $\mathbf{v}(0) = \mathbf{j} + \mathbf{k}$
    $\mathbf{r}(0) = \mathbf{i}$

Projectile Motion **In Exercises 23–36, use the model for projectile motion and assume there is no air resistance.**

23. Find the vector-valued function for the path of a projectile launched at a height of 10 feet above the ground with an initial velocity of 88 feet per second and at an angle of 30° above the horizontal. Use a graphing utility to sketch the path of the projectile.

24. Determine the maximum height and the range of a projectile fired at a height of 3 feet above the ground with an initial velocity of 900 feet per second and at an angle of 45° above the horizontal.

25. A baseball, hit 3 feet above the ground, leaves the bat at an angle of 45° and is caught by an outfielder 300 feet from home plate. What was the initial speed of the ball, and how high did it rise if it was caught 3 feet above the ground?

26. A baseball player at second base throws the ball 90 feet to the player at first base. The ball is thrown at 50 miles per hour at an angle of 15° above the horizontal. At what height does the first baseman catch the ball if the ball is thrown from a height of 5 feet?

27. The quarterback of a football team releases a pass at a height of 7 feet above the playing field, and the football is caught by a receiver 30 yards directly downfield at a height of 4 feet. The pass is released at an angle of 35° with the horizontal.
  a. Find the speed of the football when it is released.
  b. Find the maximum height of the ball.
  c. Find the time the receiver has to position himself after the quarterback releases the ball.

28. The center-field fence in a ballpark is 10 feet high and 400 feet from home plate. The ball is hit 3 feet above the ground and leaves the bat at a speed of 100 miles per hour. What is the minimum angle if the hit is a home run?

29. A bale ejector consists of two variable-speed belts at the end of a baler. Its purpose is to toss bales into a trailing wagon. In loading the back of the wagon, a bale must be thrown to a position 8 feet above and 16 feet behind the ejector. Find the minimum initial speed of the bale and the corresponding angle at which it must be ejected from the baler.

30. A bomber is flying at an altitude of 30,000 feet with a speed of 540 miles per hour (792 feet per second) (see figure). When should the bomb be released in order to hit the target? (Give your answer in terms of the angle of depression from the plane to the target.) What is the speed of the bomb at the time of impact?

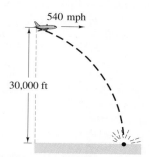

FIGURE FOR 30

31. Find the angle at which an object must be thrown to obtain
  a. the maximum range.
  b. the maximum height.

32. A shot fired from a gun with a muzzle velocity of 1200 feet per second is to hit a target 3000 feet away. Determine the minimum angle of elevation of the gun.

33. A projectile is fired from ground level at an angle of 10° with the horizontal. Find the minimum initial velocity necessary if the projectile is to have a range of 100 feet.

[C] **34.** Use a graphing utility to graph the paths of the projectile for the specified values of θ and v_0. For each case, use the graph to approximate the maximum height and the range of the projectile. (Assume the projectile is launched from ground level.)
  a. $\theta = 10°$, $v_0 = 66$ ft/sec
  b. $\theta = 10°$, $v_0 = 146$ ft/sec
  c. $\theta = 45°$, $v_0 = 66$ ft/sec
  d. $\theta = 45°$, $v_0 = 146$ ft/sec
  e. $\theta = 60°$, $v_0 = 66$ ft/sec
  f. $\theta = 60°$, $v_0 = 146$ ft/sec

35. Eliminate the parameter t from the position function for the motion of a projectile to show that the rectangular equation is

$$y = -\frac{16 \sec^2 \theta}{v_0^2}x^2 + (\tan \theta)x + h.$$

36. The path of a ball is given by the rectangular equation

$$y = x - 0.005x^2.$$

Use the result of Exercise 35 to find the position function. Then find the speed and direction of the ball at the point when it has traveled 60 feet horizontally.

Cycloidal Motion **In Exercises 37 and 38, consider the motion of a point (or particle) on the circumference of a rolling circle. As the circle rolls, it generates the cycloid**

$$\mathbf{r}(t) = b(\omega t - \sin \omega t)\mathbf{i} + b(1 - \cos \omega t)\mathbf{j}$$

where ω is the constant angular velocity of the circle.

37. Find the velocity and acceleration vectors of the particle. Use the results to determine the times that the speed of the particle will be
  a. 0.   **b.** maximum.

38. Find the maximum speed of a point on the circumference of an automobile wheel of radius 1 foot when the automobile is traveling 55 miles per hour. Compare this speed with the speed of the automobile.

Circular Motion **In Exercises 39–42, consider a particle moving on a circular path of radius b described by**

$$\mathbf{r}(t) = b \cos \omega t\,\mathbf{i} + b \sin \omega t\,\mathbf{j}$$

where $\omega = d\theta/dt$ is the constant angular velocity.

39. Find the velocity vector and show that it is orthogonal to $\mathbf{r}(t)$.

40. Show that the speed of the particle is $b\omega$.

41. Find the acceleration vector and show that its direction is always toward the center of the circle.

42. Show that the magnitude of the acceleration vector is $\omega^2 b$.

Circular Motion **In Exercises 43 and 44, use the results of Exercises 39–42.**

43. A stone weighing 1 pound is attached to a 2-foot string and is whirled horizontally (see figure). The string will break under a force of 10 pounds. Find the maximum speed the stone can attain without breaking the string. (Use $\mathbf{F} = m\mathbf{a}$, where $m = \frac{1}{32}$.)

44. A 3000-pound automobile is negotiating a circular interchange of radius 300 feet at 30 miles per hour (see figure). Assuming the roadway to be level, find the force between the tires and the road so that the car stays on the circular path and does not skid. (Use $\mathbf{F} = m\mathbf{a}$, where $m = 3000/32$.) Find the angle at which the roadway should be banked so that no lateral frictional force is exerted on the tires of the automobile.

FIGURE FOR 43   **FIGURE FOR 44**

45. *Throwing a Shot-Put* The path of a shot-put thrown at an angle θ is given by

$$\mathbf{r}(t) = (v_0 \cos\theta)t\,\mathbf{i} + \left[h + (v_0 \sin\theta)t - \tfrac{1}{2}gt^2\right]\mathbf{j}$$

where v_0 is the initial speed, h is the initial height, t is time in seconds, and g is the acceleration due to gravity. Verify that the shot-put will remain in the air for a total of

$$t = \frac{v_0 \sin\theta + \sqrt{v_0^2 \sin^2\theta + 2gh}}{g}\ \text{sec}$$

and will travel a horizontal distance of

$$\frac{v_0^2 \cos\theta}{g}\left(\sin\theta + \sqrt{\sin^2\theta + \frac{2gh}{v_0^2}}\right)\ \text{ft.}$$

46. *Throwing a Shot-Put* A shot-up is thrown from a height of $h = 6$ feet with an initial speed of $v_0 = 45$ feet per second. Find the total time of travel and the total horizontal distance traveled if the shot-put was thrown at an angle of $\theta = 42.5°$ with the horizontal.

47. Prove that if an object is traveling at a constant speed, its velocity and acceleration vectors are orthogonal.

48. Prove that an object moving in a straight line at a constant speed has an acceleration of 0.

49. *Essay* Consider a particle moving on the path $\mathbf{r}_1(t) = x(t)\mathbf{i} + y(t)\mathbf{j} + z(t)\mathbf{k}$. Discuss any changes in the position, velocity, or acceleration of the particle if its position is given by the vector-valued function $\mathbf{r}_2(t) = \mathbf{r}_1(2t)$. Generalize the results for the position function $\mathbf{r}_3(t) = \mathbf{r}_1(\omega t)$.

C A R E E R   I N T E R V I E W

Sarah L. Smith, Ph.D.
Sport Science and
Technology Division
U.S. Olympic Committee
Colorado Springs, CO 80909

As a sports biomechanist, I help elite athletes and their coaches improve technique through the use of video and the principles of physics and human anatomy. To achieve greater distance in the shot put, for example, an athlete's performances are captured on film, and then analyzed to yield shot velocity, angle of release, and release height values. These three factors determine the distance that the shot will travel. Data from multiple trials indicates where adjustments are needed and is compared with the statistics of other world-class performers as well as with mathematical models that suggest optimal technique values.

During my undergraduate program, I took calculus courses to fulfill my math requirements as a physical education major. However, it was not until I was enrolled in a doctoral program that I fully realized how fundamental calculus is to the understanding and application of biomechanics concepts.

Today, in all biomechanical analyses, it is necessary to deal with such measures as linear and angular displacement, velocity, acceleration, force, momentum, and impulse. Whether assisting a decathlete to put the shot farther, a figure skater to complete a triple axel, or a luge athlete to have an excellent start technique, math knowledge and application is a necessary tool.

12.4 Tangent Vectors and Normal Vectors • Tangential and Normal Components of Acceleration

Tangent Vectors and Normal Vectors

In the previous section, you learned that the velocity vector points in the direction of motion. This observation leads to the following definition, which applies to any smooth curve—not just to those for which the parameter represents time.

Definition of Unit Tangent Vector

Let C be a smooth curve represented by $\mathbf{r}$ on an open interval I. The **unit tangent vector** $\mathbf{T}(t)$ at t is defined to be

$$\mathbf{T}(t) = \frac{\mathbf{r}'(t)}{\|\mathbf{r}'(t)\|}, \qquad \mathbf{r}'(t) \neq \mathbf{0}.$$

REMARK   Recall that a curve is *smooth* on an interval if $\mathbf{r}'$ is continuous and nonzero on the interval. Thus, "smoothness" is sufficient to guarantee that a curve has a unit tangent vector.

EXAMPLE 1   Finding the Unit Tangent Vector

Find the unit tangent vector to the curve given by

$$\mathbf{r}(t) = t\mathbf{i} + t^2\mathbf{j}$$

when $t = 1$.

Solution   The derivative of $\mathbf{r}(t)$ is $\mathbf{r}'(t) = \mathbf{i} + 2t\mathbf{j}$. Thus, the unit tangent vector is

$$\mathbf{T}(t) = \frac{\mathbf{r}'(t)}{\|\mathbf{r}'(t)\|} = \frac{1}{\sqrt{1 + 4t^2}}(\mathbf{i} + 2t\mathbf{j}).$$

When $t = 1$, the unit tangent vector is

$$\mathbf{T}(1) = \frac{1}{\sqrt{5}}(\mathbf{i} + 2\mathbf{j})$$

as shown in Figure 12.18.

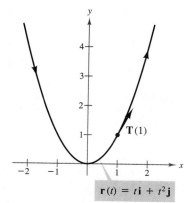

FIGURE 12.18
The direction of the unit tangent vector depends on the orientation of the curve.

$$\mathbf{r}(t) = t\mathbf{i} + t^2\mathbf{j}$$

REMARK   In Example 1, note that the direction of the unit tangent vector depends on the orientation of the curve. For instance, if the parabola in Figure 12.18 were given by $\mathbf{r}(t) = -(t - 2)\mathbf{i} + (t - 2)^2\mathbf{j}$, then $\mathbf{T}(1)$ would still represent the unit tangent vector at the point $(1, 1)$, but it would point in the opposite direction. (Try verifying this.)

The **tangent line to a curve** at a point is the line passing through the point and parallel to the unit tangent vector. In Example 2, the unit tangent vector is used to find the tangent line at a point on a helix.

EXAMPLE 2 Finding the Tangent Line at a Point on a Curve

Find $\mathbf{T}(t)$ and then find a set of parametric equations for the tangent line to the helix given by

$$\mathbf{r}(t) = 2\cos t\,\mathbf{i} + 2\sin t\,\mathbf{j} + t\,\mathbf{k}$$

at the point corresponding to $t = \pi/4$.

Solution The derivative of $\mathbf{r}(t)$ is $\mathbf{r}'(t) = -2\sin t\,\mathbf{i} + 2\cos t\,\mathbf{j} + \mathbf{k}$, which implies that $\|\mathbf{r}'(t)\| = \sqrt{4\sin^2 t + 4\cos^2 t + 1} = \sqrt{5}$. Therefore, the unit tangent vector is

$$\mathbf{T}(t) = \frac{\mathbf{r}'(t)}{\|\mathbf{r}'(t)\|} = \frac{1}{\sqrt{5}}(-2\sin t\,\mathbf{i} + 2\cos t\,\mathbf{j} + \mathbf{k}).$$

When $t = \pi/4$, the unit tangent vector is

$$\mathbf{T}\left(\frac{\pi}{4}\right) = \frac{1}{\sqrt{5}}\left(-2\frac{\sqrt{2}}{2}\mathbf{i} + 2\frac{\sqrt{2}}{2}\mathbf{j} + \mathbf{k}\right)$$

$$= \frac{1}{\sqrt{5}}(-\sqrt{2}\mathbf{i} + \sqrt{2}\mathbf{j} + \mathbf{k}).$$

Using the direction numbers $a = -\sqrt{2}$, $b = \sqrt{2}$, and $c = 1$, and the point $(x_1, y_1, z_1) = (\sqrt{2}, \sqrt{2}, \pi/4)$, you can obtain the following parametric equations (given with parameter s).

$$x = x_1 + as = \sqrt{2} - \sqrt{2}s$$
$$y = y_1 + bs = \sqrt{2} + \sqrt{2}s$$
$$z = z_1 + cs = \frac{\pi}{4} + s$$

This tangent line is shown in Figure 12.19.

In Example 2, there are infinitely many vectors that are orthogonal to the tangent vector $\mathbf{T}(t)$. One of these is the vector $\mathbf{T}'(t)$. This follows from Property 7 of Theorem 12.2. That is,

$$\mathbf{T}(t) \cdot \mathbf{T}(t) = \|\mathbf{T}(t)\|^2 = 1 \quad \rightarrow \quad \mathbf{T}(t) \cdot \mathbf{T}'(t) = 0.$$

By normalizing the vector $\mathbf{T}'(t)$, you obtain a special vector called the **principal unit normal vector**, as indicated in the following definition.

Definition of Principal Unit Normal Vector

Let C be a smooth curve represented by $\mathbf{r}$ on an open interval I. If $\mathbf{T}'(t) \neq \mathbf{0}$, then the **principal unit normal vector** at t is defined to be

$$\mathbf{N}(t) = \frac{\mathbf{T}'(t)}{\|\mathbf{T}'(t)\|}.$$

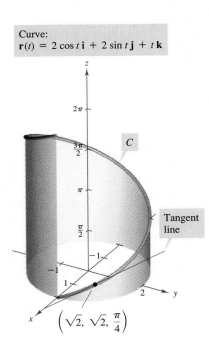

Curve:
$\mathbf{r}(t) = 2\cos t\,\mathbf{i} + 2\sin t\,\mathbf{j} + t\,\mathbf{k}$

$\left(\sqrt{2}, \sqrt{2}, \dfrac{\pi}{4}\right)$

FIGURE 12.19
The tangent line at a point on a curve is determined by the unit tangent at the point.

EXAMPLE 3   Finding the Principal Unit Normal Vector

Find $\mathbf{N}(t)$ and $\mathbf{N}(1)$ for the curve represented by

$$\mathbf{r}(t) = 3t\mathbf{i} + 2t^2\mathbf{j}.$$

Solution   By differentiating, you obtain

$$\mathbf{r}'(t) = 3\mathbf{i} + 4t\mathbf{j} \quad \text{and} \quad \|\mathbf{r}'(t)\| = \sqrt{9 + 16t^2}$$

which implies that the unit tangent vector is

$$\begin{aligned}
\mathbf{T}(t) &= \frac{\mathbf{r}'(t)}{\|\mathbf{r}'(t)\|} \\
&= \frac{1}{\sqrt{9 + 16t^2}}(3\mathbf{i} + 4t\mathbf{j}). \qquad \text{Unit tangent vector}
\end{aligned}$$

Using Theorem 12.2, differentiate $\mathbf{T}(t)$ with respect to t to obtain

$$\begin{aligned}
\mathbf{T}'(t) &= \frac{1}{\sqrt{9 + 16t^2}}(4\mathbf{j}) - \frac{16t}{(9 + 16t^2)^{3/2}}(3\mathbf{i} + 4t\mathbf{j}) \\
&= \frac{12}{(9 + 16t^2)^{3/2}}(-4t\mathbf{i} + 3\mathbf{j}) \\
\|\mathbf{T}'(t)\| &= 12\sqrt{\frac{9 + 16t^2}{(9 + 16t^2)^3}} = \frac{12}{9 + 16t^2}.
\end{aligned}$$

Therefore, the principal unit normal vector is

$$\begin{aligned}
\mathbf{N}(t) &= \frac{\mathbf{T}'(t)}{\|\mathbf{T}'(t)\|} \\
&= \frac{1}{\sqrt{9 + 16t^2}}(-4t\mathbf{i} + 3\mathbf{j}). \qquad \text{Principal unit normal vector}
\end{aligned}$$

When $t = 1$, the principal unit normal vector is

$$\mathbf{N}(1) = \frac{1}{5}(-4\mathbf{i} + 3\mathbf{j})$$

as shown in Figure 12.20.

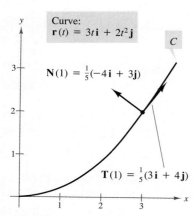

FIGURE 12.20
Principal unit normal vector points toward the concave side of the curve.

Curve:
$\mathbf{r}(t) = 3t\mathbf{i} + 2t^2\mathbf{j}$
$\mathbf{N}(1) = \frac{1}{5}(-4\mathbf{i} + 3\mathbf{j})$
$\mathbf{T}(1) = \frac{1}{5}(3\mathbf{i} + 4\mathbf{j})$

The principal unit normal vector can be difficult to evaluate algebraically. For plane curves, you can simplify the algebra by finding

$$\mathbf{T}(t) = x(t)\mathbf{i} + y(t)\mathbf{j} \qquad \text{Unit tangent vector}$$

and observing that $\mathbf{N}(t)$ must be either

$$\mathbf{N}_1(t) = y(t)\mathbf{i} - x(t)\mathbf{j} \qquad \text{or} \qquad \mathbf{N}_2(t) = -y(t)\mathbf{i} + x(t)\mathbf{j}.$$

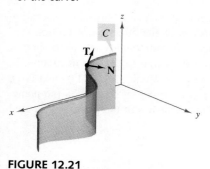

FIGURE 12.21
At any point on a curve, a unit normal vector is orthogonal to the unit tangent vector. The *principal* unit normal vector points in the direction the curve is turning.

Because $\sqrt{[x(t)]^2 + [y(t)]^2} = 1$, it follows that both $\mathbf{N}_1(t)$ and $\mathbf{N}_2(t)$ are unit normal vectors. The *principal* unit normal vector $\mathbf{N}$ is the one that points toward the concave side of the curve, as indicated in Figure 12.20 (see Exercise 43). This also holds for curves in space. That is, for an object moving along a curve C in space, the vector $\mathbf{T}(t)$ points in the direction the object is moving, whereas the vector $\mathbf{N}(t)$ is orthogonal to $\mathbf{T}(t)$ and points in the direction the object is turning, as shown in Figure 12.21.

EXAMPLE 4   Finding the Principal Unit Normal Vector

Find the principal unit normal vector for the helix given by

$$\mathbf{r}(t) = 2\cos t\,\mathbf{i} + 2\sin t\,\mathbf{j} + t\,\mathbf{k}.$$

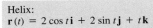

Helix:
$\mathbf{r}(t) = 2\cos t\,\mathbf{i} + 2\sin t\,\mathbf{j} + t\,\mathbf{k}$

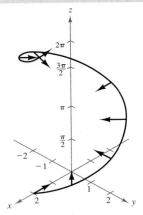

FIGURE 12.22
$\mathbf{N}(t)$ is normal and points toward the z-axis.

Solution   From Example 2, you know that the principal unit tangent vector is

$$\mathbf{T}(t) = \frac{1}{\sqrt{5}}(-2\sin t\,\mathbf{i} + 2\cos t\,\mathbf{j} + \mathbf{k}).$$

Thus, $\mathbf{T}'(t)$ is given by

$$\mathbf{T}'(t) = \frac{1}{\sqrt{5}}(-2\cos t\,\mathbf{i} - 2\sin t\,\mathbf{j}).$$

Because $\|\mathbf{T}'(t)\| = 2/\sqrt{5}$, it follows that the principal unit normal vector is

$$\mathbf{N}(t) = \frac{\mathbf{T}'(t)}{\|\mathbf{T}'(t)\|} = \frac{1}{2}(-2\cos t\,\mathbf{i} - 2\sin t\,\mathbf{j}) = -\cos t\,\mathbf{i} - \sin t\,\mathbf{j}.$$

Note that this vector is horizontal and points toward the z-axis, as shown in Figure 12.22.

Tangential and Normal Components of Acceleration

We now return to the problem of describing the motion of an object along a curve. In the previous section, you saw that for an object traveling at a *constant speed,* the velocity and acceleration vectors are perpendicular. This seems reasonable, because the speed would not be constant if any acceleration were acting in the direction of motion. [You can verify this observation by noting that $\mathbf{r}''(t) \cdot \mathbf{r}'(t) = 0$ if $\|\mathbf{r}'(t)\|$ is a constant. See Property 7 of Theorem 12.2.]

However, for an object traveling at a *variable speed,* the velocity and acceleration vectors are not necessarily perpendicular. For instance, you saw that the acceleration vector for a projectile always points down, regardless of the direction of motion.

In general, part of the acceleration (the tangential component) acts in the line of motion, and part (the normal component) acts perpendicular to the line of motion. In order to determine these two components, you can use the unit vectors $\mathbf{T}(t)$ and $\mathbf{N}(t)$, which serve in much the same way as do $\mathbf{i}$ and $\mathbf{j}$ in representing vectors in the plane. The following theorem states that the acceleration vector lies in the plane determined by $\mathbf{T}(t)$ and $\mathbf{N}(t)$.

THEOREM 12.4   Acceleration Vector

If $\mathbf{r}(t)$ is the position vector for a smooth curve C and $\mathbf{N}(t)$ exists, then the acceleration vector $\mathbf{a}(t)$ lies in the plane determined by $\mathbf{T}(t)$ and $\mathbf{N}(t)$.

Proof   To simplify the notation, we write $\mathbf{T}$ for $\mathbf{T}(t)$, $\mathbf{T}'$ for $\mathbf{T}'(t)$, and so on. Because $\mathbf{T} = \mathbf{r}'/\|\mathbf{r}'\| = \mathbf{v}/\|\mathbf{v}\|$, it follows that

$$\mathbf{v} = \|\mathbf{v}\|\,\mathbf{T}.$$

By differentiating, you obtain

$$\mathbf{a} = \mathbf{v}' = D_t[\|\mathbf{v}\|]\mathbf{T} + \|\mathbf{v}\|\,\mathbf{T}' \qquad \text{Product Rule}$$

$$= D_t[\|\mathbf{v}\|]\mathbf{T} + \|\mathbf{v}\|\,\mathbf{T}'\left(\frac{\|\mathbf{T}'\|}{\|\mathbf{T}'\|}\right)$$

$$= D_t[\|\mathbf{v}\|]\mathbf{T} + \|\mathbf{v}\|\,\|\mathbf{T}'\|\,\mathbf{N}. \qquad \mathbf{N} = \mathbf{T}'/\|\mathbf{T}'\|$$

Because $\mathbf{a}$ is written as a linear combination of $\mathbf{T}$ and $\mathbf{N}$, it must lie in the plane determined by $\mathbf{T}$ and $\mathbf{N}$.

The coefficients of $\mathbf{T}$ and $\mathbf{N}$ in the proof of this theorem are called the **tangential** and **normal components of acceleration** and are denoted by $a_{\mathbf{T}} = D_t[\|\mathbf{v}\|]$ and $a_{\mathbf{N}} = \|\mathbf{v}\|\,\|\mathbf{T}'\|$. Thus, you can write

$$\mathbf{a}(t) = a_{\mathbf{T}}\mathbf{T}(t) + a_{\mathbf{N}}\mathbf{N}(t).$$

The following theorem gives some convenient formulas for $a_{\mathbf{N}}$ and $a_{\mathbf{T}}$.

THEOREM 12.5   Tangential and Normal Components of Acceleration

If $\mathbf{r}(t)$ is the position vector for a smooth curve C [for which $\mathbf{N}(t)$ exists], then the tangential and normal components of acceleration are as follows.

$$a_{\mathbf{T}} = D_t[\|\mathbf{v}\|] = \mathbf{a}\cdot\mathbf{T} = \frac{\mathbf{v}\cdot\mathbf{a}}{\|\mathbf{v}\|}$$

$$a_{\mathbf{N}} = \|\mathbf{v}\|\,\|\mathbf{T}'\| = \mathbf{a}\cdot\mathbf{N} = \frac{\|\mathbf{v}\times\mathbf{a}\|}{\|\mathbf{v}\|} = \sqrt{\|\mathbf{a}\|^2 - a_{\mathbf{T}}^2}$$

Note that $a_{\mathbf{N}} \geq 0$. The normal component of acceleration is also called the **centripetal component of acceleration.**

Proof   Note that $\mathbf{a}$ lies in the plane of $\mathbf{T}$ and $\mathbf{N}$. Thus, you can use Figure 12.23 to conclude that for any time t, the component of the projection of the acceleration vector onto $\mathbf{T}$ is given by $a_{\mathbf{T}} = \mathbf{a}\cdot\mathbf{T}$, and onto $\mathbf{N}$ is given by $a_{\mathbf{N}} = \mathbf{a}\cdot\mathbf{N}$. Moreover, because $\mathbf{a} = \mathbf{v}'$ and $\mathbf{T} = \mathbf{v}/\|\mathbf{v}\|$, you have

$$a_{\mathbf{T}} = \mathbf{a}\cdot\mathbf{T} = \mathbf{T}\cdot\mathbf{a} = \frac{\mathbf{v}}{\|\mathbf{v}\|}\cdot\mathbf{a} = \frac{\mathbf{v}\cdot\mathbf{a}}{\|\mathbf{v}\|}.$$

In Exercises 45 and 46, you are asked to prove the other parts of the theorem.

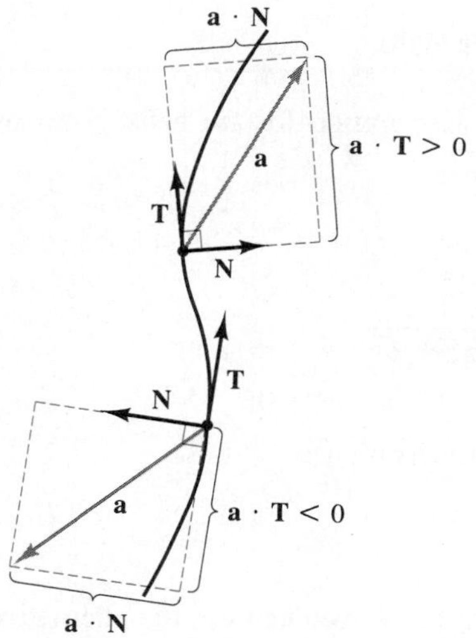

FIGURE 12.23
The tangential and normal components of acceleration are obtained by projecting $\mathbf{a}$ onto $\mathbf{T}$ and $\mathbf{N}$.

REMARK   The formulas from Theorem 12.5, together with several other formulas from this chapter, are summarized on page 825.

EXAMPLE 5 **Tangential and Normal Components of Acceleration**

Find the tangential and normal components of acceleration for the position function given by $\mathbf{r}(t) = 3t\,\mathbf{i} - t\,\mathbf{j} + t^2\mathbf{k}$.

Solution Begin by finding the velocity, speed, and acceleration.

$$\mathbf{v}(t) = \mathbf{r}'(t) = 3\mathbf{i} - \mathbf{j} + 2t\,\mathbf{k}$$
$$\|\mathbf{v}(t)\| = \sqrt{9 + 1 + 4t^2} = \sqrt{10 + 4t^2}$$
$$\mathbf{a}(t) = \mathbf{r}''(t) = 2\mathbf{k}$$

By Theorem 12.5, the tangential component of acceleration is

$$a_{\mathbf{T}} = \frac{\mathbf{v} \cdot \mathbf{a}}{\|\mathbf{v}\|} = \frac{4t}{\sqrt{10 + 4t^2}}$$

and because

$$\mathbf{v} \times \mathbf{a} = \begin{vmatrix} \mathbf{i} & \mathbf{j} & \mathbf{k} \\ 3 & -1 & 2t \\ 0 & 0 & 2 \end{vmatrix} = -2\mathbf{i} - 6\mathbf{j}$$

the normal component of acceleration is

$$a_{\mathbf{N}} = \frac{\|\mathbf{v} \times \mathbf{a}\|}{\|\mathbf{v}\|} = \frac{\sqrt{4 + 36}}{\sqrt{10 + 4t^2}} = \frac{2\sqrt{10}}{\sqrt{10 + 4t^2}}.$$

REMARK In Example 5, you could have used the alternative formula for $a_{\mathbf{N}}$ as follows.

$$a_{\mathbf{N}} = \sqrt{\|\mathbf{a}\|^2 - a_{\mathbf{T}}^2} = \sqrt{(2)^2 - \frac{16t^2}{10 + 4t^2}} = \frac{2\sqrt{10}}{\sqrt{10 + 4t^2}}$$

EXAMPLE 6 **Finding $a_{\mathbf{T}}$ and $a_{\mathbf{N}}$ for a Circular Helix**

Find the tangential and normal components of acceleration for the helix given by $\mathbf{r}(t) = b\cos t\,\mathbf{i} + b\sin t\,\mathbf{j} + ct\,\mathbf{k}$, $b > 0$.

Solution

$$\mathbf{v}(t) = \mathbf{r}'(t) = -b\sin t\,\mathbf{i} + b\cos t\,\mathbf{j} + c\,\mathbf{k}$$
$$\|\mathbf{v}(t)\| = \sqrt{b^2\sin^2 t + b^2\cos^2 t + c^2} = \sqrt{b^2 + c^2}$$
$$\mathbf{a}(t) = \mathbf{r}''(t) = -b\cos t\,\mathbf{i} - b\sin t\,\mathbf{j}$$

By Theorem 12.5, the tangential component of acceleration is

$$a_{\mathbf{T}} = \frac{\mathbf{v} \cdot \mathbf{a}}{\|\mathbf{v}\|} = b^2\sin t\cos t - b^2\sin t\cos t + 0 = 0.$$

Moreover, because $\|\mathbf{a}(t)\| = \sqrt{b^2\cos^2 t + b^2\sin^2 t} = b$, you can use the alternative formula for the normal component of acceleration to obtain

$$a_{\mathbf{N}} = \sqrt{\|\mathbf{a}(t)\|^2 - a_{\mathbf{T}}^2} = \sqrt{b^2 - 0^2} = b.$$

Note that the normal component of acceleration is equal to the magnitude of the acceleration. In other words, because the speed is constant, the acceleration is perpendicular to the velocity (see Figure 12.24).

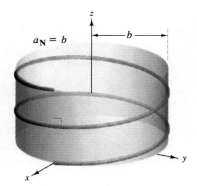

$a_{\mathbf{N}} = b$

FIGURE 12.24
The normal component of acceleration is equal to the radius of the cylinder around which the helix is spiraling.

REMARK The normal component of acceleration is equal to the radius of the cylinder around which the helix is spiraling.

EXAMPLE 7   **Projectile Motion**

The position function for the projectile shown in Figure 12.25 is given by

$$\mathbf{r}(t) = \left(50\sqrt{2}t\right)\mathbf{i} + \left(50\sqrt{2}t - 16t^2\right)\mathbf{j}. \qquad \text{Position vector}$$

Find the tangential component of acceleration when $t = 0$, 1, and $25\sqrt{2}/16$.

Solution

$$\mathbf{v}(t) = 50\sqrt{2}\mathbf{i} + (50\sqrt{2} - 32t)\mathbf{j} \qquad \text{Velocity vector}$$

$$\|\mathbf{v}(t)\| = 2\sqrt{50^2 - 16(50)\sqrt{2}t + 16^2t^2} \qquad \text{Speed}$$

$$\mathbf{a}(t) = -32\mathbf{j} \qquad \text{Acceleration vector}$$

The tangential component of acceleration is

$$a_{\mathbf{T}}(t) = \frac{\mathbf{v}(t) \cdot \mathbf{a}(t)}{\|\mathbf{v}(t)\|}$$

$$= \frac{-32\left(50\sqrt{2} - 32t\right)}{2\sqrt{50^2 - 16(50)\sqrt{2}t + 16^2t^2}}.$$

At the specified times, you have

$$a_{\mathbf{T}}(0) = \frac{-32\left(50\sqrt{2}\right)}{100} = -16\sqrt{2} \approx -22.6$$

$$a_{\mathbf{T}}(1) = \frac{-32\left(50\sqrt{2} - 32\right)}{2\sqrt{50^2 - 16(50)\sqrt{2} + 16^2}} \approx -15.4$$

$$a_{\mathbf{T}}\left(\frac{25\sqrt{2}}{16}\right) = \frac{-32\left(50\sqrt{2} - 50\sqrt{2}\right)}{50\sqrt{2}} = 0.$$

You can see from Figure 12.25 that, at the maximum height, the tangential component is 0. This is reasonable because the direction of motion is horizontal at that point and the tangential component of the acceleration is equal to the horizontal component of the acceleration.

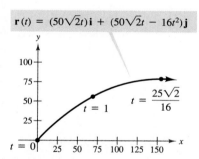

$$\mathbf{r}(t) = (50\sqrt{2}t)\mathbf{i} + (50\sqrt{2}t - 16t^2)\mathbf{j}$$

FIGURE 12.25
The path of a projectile.

In Example 7, the alternative formula for $a_{\mathbf{N}}$ yields the following normal component of acceleration.

$$a_{\mathbf{N}} = \sqrt{\|\mathbf{a}\|^2 - a_{\mathbf{T}}^2} = \sqrt{32^2 - \frac{32^2(50\sqrt{2} - 32t)^2}{4(50^2 - 16(50)\sqrt{2}t + 16^2t^2)}}$$

$$= \frac{32(50)\sqrt{2}}{2\sqrt{50^2 - 16(50)\sqrt{2}t + 16^2t^2}}$$

When $t = 25\sqrt{2}/16$, you can determine that $a_{\mathbf{N}} = 32$, which makes sense because the tangential component is 0 at this point and therefore the entire acceleration is directed downward.

EXERCISES for Section 12.4

In Exercises 1–6, find the unit tangent vector $\mathbf{T}(t)$ and find a set of parametric equations for the line tangent to the space curve at the given point.

Function	Point
1. $\mathbf{r}(t) = t\,\mathbf{i} + t^2\,\mathbf{j} + t\,\mathbf{k}$	$(0,0,0)$
2. $\mathbf{r}(t) = t\,\mathbf{i} + t^2\,\mathbf{j} + \frac{2}{3}\mathbf{k}$	$(1,1,\frac{2}{3})$
3. $\mathbf{r}(t) = 2\cos t\,\mathbf{i} + 2\sin t\,\mathbf{j} + t\,\mathbf{k}$	$(2,0,0)$
4. $\mathbf{r}(t) = \langle t,t,\sqrt{4-t^2}\rangle$	$(1,1,\sqrt{3})$
5. $\mathbf{r}(t) = \langle 2\cos t, 2\sin t, 4\rangle$	$(\sqrt{2},\sqrt{2},4)$
6. $\mathbf{r}(t) = \langle 2\sin t, 2\cos t, 4\sin^2 t\rangle$	$(1,\sqrt{3},1)$

C In Exercises 7 and 8, use a graphing utility to graph the space curve. Then find the tangent vector $\mathbf{T}(t)$ and find a set of parametric equations for the line tangent to the space curve at the given point. Sketch the graph of the line on the space curve.

Function	Point
7. $\mathbf{r}(t) = \langle t, t^2, \frac{2}{3}t^3\rangle$	$(3,9,18)$
8. $\mathbf{r}(t) = 3\cos t\,\mathbf{i} + 4\sin t\,\mathbf{j} + \frac{t}{2}\mathbf{k}$	$\left(0,4,\frac{\pi}{4}\right)$

In Exercises 9–12, find $\mathbf{v}(t)$, $\mathbf{a}(t)$, $\mathbf{T}(t)$, and $\mathbf{N}(t)$ (if it exists) for an object moving along the path given by the vector-valued function $\mathbf{r}(t)$. Use the results to determine the form of the path. Is the speed of the object constant or changing?

9. $\mathbf{r}(t) = 4t\,\mathbf{i}$
10. $\mathbf{r}(t) = 4t\,\mathbf{i} - 2t\,\mathbf{j}$
11. $\mathbf{r}(t) = 4t^2\,\mathbf{i}$
12. $\mathbf{r}(t) = t^2\,\mathbf{j} + \mathbf{k}$

In Exercises 13–18, find $\mathbf{T}(t)$, $\mathbf{N}(t)$, $a_{\mathbf{T}}$, and $a_{\mathbf{N}}$ at the given time t for the plane curve $\mathbf{r}(t)$.

Function	Time
13. $\mathbf{r}(t) = t\,\mathbf{i} + \frac{1}{t}\mathbf{j}$	$t = 1$
14. $\mathbf{r}(t) = t\,\mathbf{i} + t^2\,\mathbf{j}$	$t = 1$
15. $\mathbf{r}(t) = e^t\cos t\,\mathbf{i} + e^t\sin t\,\mathbf{j}$	$t = \frac{\pi}{2}$
16. $\mathbf{r}(t) = a\cos\omega t\,\mathbf{i} + b\sin\omega t\,\mathbf{j}$	$t = 0$
17. $\mathbf{r}(t) = \langle\cos\omega t + \omega t\sin\omega t, \sin\omega t - \omega t\cos\omega t\rangle$	$t = t_0$
18. $\mathbf{r}(t) = \langle\omega t - \sin\omega t, 1 - \cos\omega t\rangle$	$t = t_0$

Circular Motion In Exercises 19–22, consider an object moving according to the position function

$$r(t) = a\cos\omega t\,\mathbf{i} + a\sin\omega t\,\mathbf{j}.$$

19. Find $\mathbf{T}(t)$, $\mathbf{N}(t)$, $a_{\mathbf{T}}$, and $a_{\mathbf{N}}$.

20. Determine the directions of $\mathbf{T}$ and $\mathbf{N}$ relative to the position function $\mathbf{r}$.

21. Determine the speed of the object at any time t and explain its value relative to the value of $a_{\mathbf{T}}$.

22. If the angular velocity ω is halved, by what factor is $a_{\mathbf{N}}$ changed?

In Exercises 23 and 24, sketch the graph of the plane curve represented by the vector-valued function, and, at the point on the curve determined by $\mathbf{r}(t_0)$, sketch the vectors $\mathbf{T}$ and $\mathbf{N}$. Note that $\mathbf{N}$ points toward the concave side of the curve.

Function	Time
23. $\mathbf{r}(t) = t\,\mathbf{i} + \frac{1}{t}\mathbf{j}$	$t_0 = 2$
24. $\mathbf{r}(t) = 2\cos t\,\mathbf{i} + 2\sin t\,\mathbf{j}$	$t_0 = \frac{\pi}{4}$

25. *Motion of a Particle* The figure shows the path of a particle modeled by the vector-valued function

$$\mathbf{r}(t) = \langle\pi t - \sin\pi t, 1 - \cos\pi t\rangle.$$

The figure also shows the vectors $\mathbf{v}(t)/\|\mathbf{v}(t)\|$ and $\mathbf{a}(t)/\|\mathbf{a}(t)\|$ at the specified values of t.
a. Identify the graph and its orientation.
b. Find $a_{\mathbf{T}}$ and $a_{\mathbf{N}}$ at $t = \frac{1}{2}$, $t = 1$, and $t = \frac{3}{2}$.
c. Determine whether the speed of the particle is increasing, decreasing, or maximum at each of the specified values of t. Give reasons for your answers.

26. *Motion of a Particle* The figure shows a particle moving along the involute of a circle modeled by

$$\mathbf{r}(t) = \langle\cos\pi t + \pi t\sin\pi t, \sin\pi t - \pi t\cos\pi t\rangle.$$

It also shows the vectors $\mathbf{v}(t)$ and $\mathbf{a}(t)$ for $t = 1$ and $t = 2$.
a. Find $a_{\mathbf{T}}$ and $a_{\mathbf{N}}$ at $t = 1$ and $t = 2$.
b. Determine whether the speed of the particle is increasing or decreasing at each of the specified values of t. Give reasons for your answers.

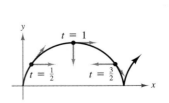

FIGURE FOR 25

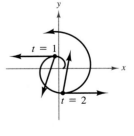

FIGURE FOR 26

In Exercises 27–30, find $T(t)$, $N(t)$, a_T, and a_N at the given time t for the space curve $r(t)$.

Function	Time
27. $r(t) = t\,i + 2t\,j - 3t\,k$	$t = 1$
28. $r(t) = 4t\,i - 4t\,j + 2t\,k$	$t = 2$
29. $r(t) = t\,i + t^2\,j + \dfrac{t^2}{2}\,k$	$t = 1$
30. $r(t) = e^t \cos t\,i + e^t \sin t\,j + e^t\,k$	$t = 0$

C In Exercises 31 and 32, use a graphing utility to graph the space curve. Also find $T(t)$, $N(t)$, a_T, and a_N at the given time t. Sketch $T(t)$ and $N(t)$ on the space curve.

Function	Time
31. $r(t) = 4t\,i + 3\cos t\,j + 3\sin t\,k$	$t = \dfrac{\pi}{2}$
32. $r(t) = t\,i + 3t^2\,j + \dfrac{t^2}{2}\,k$	$t = 2$

Unit Binormal Vector   In Exercises 33 and 34, find the vectors T, N, and B = T × N for the vector-valued function $r(t)$ at the specified value of t (see figures). The vector B is called the unit binormal vector to the curve.

33. $r(t) = 2\cos t\,i + 2\sin t\,j + \dfrac{t}{2}\,k$, $t_0 = \dfrac{\pi}{2}$

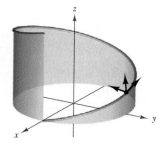

FIGURE FOR 33

34. $r(t) = t\,i + t^2\,j + \dfrac{t^3}{3}\,k$, $t_0 = 1$

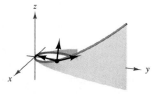

FIGURE FOR 34

35. *Projectile Motion*   Find the tangential and normal components of acceleration for a projectile fired at an angle θ with the horizontal at an initial speed of v_0. What are the components when the projectile is at its maximum height?

36. *Projectile Motion*   A plane flying at an altitude of 30,000 feet and a speed of 540 miles per hour (792 feet per second) releases a bomb. Find the tangential and normal components of acceleration acting on the bomb.

37. *Centripetal Acceleration*   An object is spinning at a constant speed on the end of a string, according to the position function given in Exercises 19–22.
   a. If the angular velocity ω is doubled, how is the centripetal component of acceleration changed?
   b. If the angular velocity is unchanged but the length of the string is halved, how is the centripetal component of acceleration changed?

38. *Centripetal Force*   An object of mass m moves at a constant speed v in a circular path of radius r. The force required to produce the centripetal component of acceleration is called the centripetal force and is given by $F = mv^2/r$. Newton's Law of Universal Gravitation is given by $F = GMm/d^2$, where d is the distance between the centers of the two bodies of masses M and m, and G is a gravitational constant. Use this law to show that the speed required for circular motion is $v = \sqrt{GM/r}$.

Orbital Speed   In Exercises 39–42, use the result of Exercise 38 to find the speed necessary for the given circular orbit around the earth. Let $GM = 9.56 \times 10^4$ cubic miles per second per second, and assume that the radius of the earth is 4000 miles.

39. The orbit of a space shuttle 100 miles above the surface of the earth

40. The orbit of a space shuttle 200 miles above the surface of the earth

41. The orbit of a heat capacity mapping satellite 385 miles above the surface of the earth (see figure)

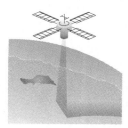

FIGURE FOR 41

42. The orbit of a SYNCOM satellite r miles above the surface of the earth that is in geosynchronous orbit. [The satellite completes one orbit per sidereal day (23 hours, 56 minutes), and thus appears to remain stationary above a point on the earth.]

43. Prove that the principal unit normal vector N points toward the concave side of a plane curve.

44. Prove that the vector $T'(t)$ is 0 for an object moving in a straight line.

45. Prove that $a_N = \dfrac{\|v \times a\|}{\|v\|}$.

46. Prove that $a_N = \sqrt{\|a\|^2 - a_T^2}$.

Arc Length

In Section 10.2, you saw that the arc length of a smooth *plane* curve C given by the parametric equations $x = x(t)$ and $y = y(t)$, $a \leq t \leq b$, is

$$s = \int_a^b \sqrt{[x'(t)]^2 + [y'(t)]^2}\, dt.$$

In vector form, where C is given by $\mathbf{r}(t) = x(t)\mathbf{i} + y(t)\mathbf{j}$, you can rewrite this equation for arc length as

$$s = \int_a^b \|\mathbf{r}'(t)\|\, dt.$$

EXAMPLE 1 Finding the Arc Length of a Plane Curve

Find the arc length of the curve given by $\mathbf{r}(t) = \cos t\, \mathbf{i} + \sin t\, \mathbf{j}$ from $t = 0$ to $t = 2\pi$.

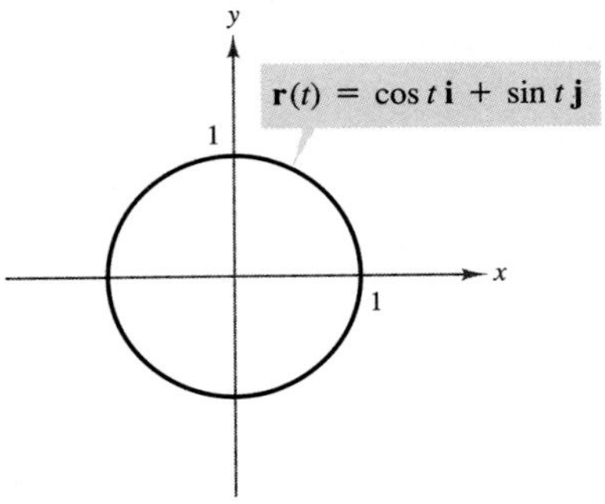

Solution Using $x(t) = \cos t$ and $y(t) = \sin t$, you obtain $x'(t) = -\sin t$ and $y'(t) = \cos t$. Thus, the arc length from $t = 0$ to $t = 2\pi$ is

$$
\begin{aligned}
s &= \int_0^{2\pi} \sqrt{[x'(t)]^2 + [y'(t)]^2}\, dt = \int_0^{2\pi} \sqrt{\sin^2 t + \cos^2 t}\, dt \\
&= \int_0^{2\pi} dt \\
&= t\Big]_0^{2\pi} = 2\pi.
\end{aligned}
$$

y

$\mathbf{r}(t) = \cos t\, \mathbf{i} + \sin t\, \mathbf{j}$

1

1

x

FIGURE 12.26
The arc length of the circle is 2π.

In Figure 12.26, notice that the curve is a circle of radius 1. Thus, the arc length formula confirms that the circumference of the circle is 2π.

The formula for the arc length of a plane curve has a natural extension to a smooth curve in *space*, as stated in the following theorem.

THEOREM 12.6 Arc Length of Space Curve

If C is a smooth curve given by $\mathbf{r}(t) = x(t)\mathbf{i} + y(t)\mathbf{j} + z(t)\mathbf{k}$, on an interval $[a, b]$, then the arc length of C on the interval is

$$s = \int_a^b \sqrt{[x'(t)]^2 + [y'(t)]^2 + [z'(t)]^2}\, dt = \int_a^b \|\mathbf{r}'(t)\|\, dt.$$

EXAMPLE 2 Finding the Arc Length of a Curve in Space

Find the arc length of the curve given by

$$\mathbf{r}(t) = t\mathbf{i} + \frac{4}{3}t^{3/2}\mathbf{j} + \frac{1}{2}t^2\mathbf{k}$$

from $t = 0$ to $t = 2$, as shown in Figure 12.27.

Solution Using $x(t) = t$, $y(t) = \frac{4}{3}t^{3/2}$, and $z(t) = \frac{1}{2}t^2$, you obtain $x'(t) = 1$, $y'(t) = 2t^{1/2}$, and $z'(t) = t$. Thus, the arc length from $t = 0$ to $t = 2$ is given by

$$s = \int_0^2 \sqrt{[x'(t)]^2 + [y'(t)]^2 + [z'(t)]^2}\, dt$$

$$= \int_0^2 \sqrt{1 + 4t + t^2}\, dt$$

$$= \int_0^2 \sqrt{(t + 2)^2 - 3}\, dt \qquad \text{Integration Formula 26}$$

$$= \left[\frac{t + 2}{2}\sqrt{(t + 2)^2 - 3} - \frac{3}{2}\ln\left|(t + 2) + \sqrt{(t + 2)^2 - 3}\right|\right]_0^2$$

$$= 2\sqrt{13} - \frac{3}{2}\ln\left(4 + \sqrt{13}\right) - 1 + \frac{3}{2}\ln 3$$

$$\approx 4.816.$$

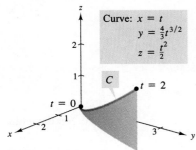

FIGURE 12.27
As t increases from 0 to 2, the vector $\mathbf{r}(t)$ traces out a curve whose length is approximately 4.816.

Curve: $x = t$
$y = \frac{4}{3}t^{3/2}$
$z = \frac{t^2}{2}$

REMARK The formula for arc length given in Theorem 12.6 is independent of the parameter used to represent C. To illustrate this independence, try using the vector-valued function

$$\mathbf{r}(t) = t^2\mathbf{i} + \frac{4}{3}t^3\mathbf{j} + \frac{1}{2}t^4\mathbf{k}$$

to represent the curve in Example 2. Then find the arc length from $t = 0$ to $t = \sqrt{2}$ and compare the result with that found in Example 2.

EXAMPLE 3 Finding the Arc Length of a Helix

Find the length of one turn of the helix given by

$$\mathbf{r}(t) = b\cos t\,\mathbf{i} + b\sin t\,\mathbf{j} + \sqrt{1 - b^2}\,t\,\mathbf{k}$$

as shown in Figure 12.28.

Solution Because $\mathbf{r}'(t) = -b\sin t\,\mathbf{i} + b\cos t\,\mathbf{j} + \sqrt{1 - b^2}\,\mathbf{k}$, the arc length of one turn is

$$s = \int_0^{2\pi} \|\mathbf{r}'(t)\|\, dt$$

$$= \int_0^{2\pi} \sqrt{b^2(\sin^2 t + \cos^2 t) + (1 - b^2)}\, dt$$

$$= \int_0^{2\pi} dt$$

$$= 2\pi.$$

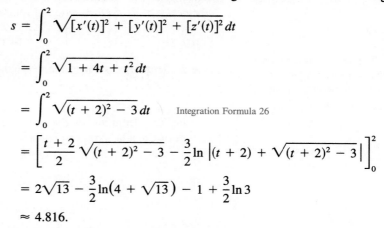

Curve:
$\mathbf{r}(t) = b\cos t\,\mathbf{i} + b\sin t\,\mathbf{j} + \sqrt{1 - b^2}\,t\,\mathbf{k}$

FIGURE 12.28
One turn of a helix.

$$s(t) = \int_a^t \sqrt{[x'(u)]^2 + [y'(u)]^2 + [z'(u)]^2}\,du$$

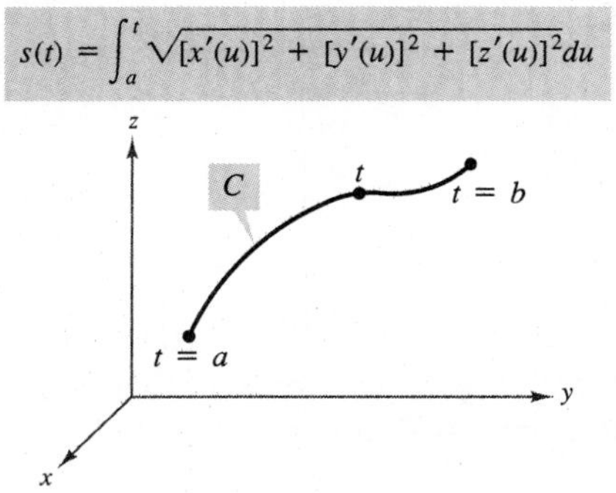

FIGURE 12.29

REMARK The arc length function s is *nonnegative*. It measures the distance along C from the initial point $(x(a), y(a), z(a))$ to the point $(x(t), y(t), z(t))$.

Arc Length Parameter

You have seen that curves can be represented by vector-valued functions in different ways, depending on the choice of parameter. For *motion* along a curve, the convenient parameter is time, t. However, for studying the *geometric properties* of a curve, the convenient parameter is often arc length, s.

Definition of Arc Length Function

Let C be a smooth curve given by $\mathbf{r}(t)$ defined on the closed interval $[a, b]$. For $a \le t \le b$, the **arc length function** is given by

$$s(t) = \int_a^t \| \mathbf{r}'(u) \| \, du = \int_a^t \sqrt{[x'(u)]^2 + [y'(u)]^2 + [z'(u)]^2}\,du.$$

The arc length, s, is called the **arc length parameter** (see Figure 12.29).

Using the definition of the arc length function and the Second Fundamental Theorem of Calculus, you can conclude that

$$\frac{ds}{dt} = \| \mathbf{r}'(t) \|.$$

THEOREM 12.7 The Derivative of the Arc Length Function

Let C be a smooth curve given by $\mathbf{r}(t)$ on the closed interval $[a, b]$. The derivative of the arc length function s for this curve is given by

$$\frac{ds}{dt} = \| \mathbf{r}'(t) \|.$$

In differential form, you can write $ds = \| \mathbf{r}'(t) \| \, dt$.

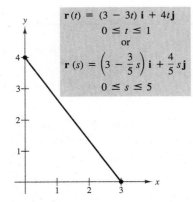

$$\mathbf{r}(t) = (3 - 3t)\,\mathbf{i} + 4t\,\mathbf{j}$$
$$0 \le t \le 1$$
or
$$\mathbf{r}(s) = \left(3 - \frac{3}{5}s\right)\mathbf{i} + \frac{4}{5}s\,\mathbf{j}$$
$$0 \le s \le 5$$

FIGURE 12.30
The line segment from $(3, 0)$ to $(0, 4)$ can be parametrized in many ways.

EXAMPLE 4 Finding the Arc Length Function for a Line

Find the arc length function $s(t)$ for the line segment given by

$$\mathbf{r}(t) = (3 - 3t)\mathbf{i} + 4t\,\mathbf{j}, \qquad 0 \le t \le 1$$

and express $\mathbf{r}$ as a function of the parameter s (see Figure 12.30).

Solution Because $\mathbf{r}'(t) = -3\mathbf{i} + 4\mathbf{j}$ and $\| \mathbf{r}'(t) \| = \sqrt{3^2 + 4^2} = 5$, you have

$$s(t) = \int_0^t \| \mathbf{r}'(u) \| \, du = \int_0^t 5 \, du = 5t.$$

Using $s = 5t$ (or $t = s/5$), you can rewrite $\mathbf{r}$ using the arc length parameter as follows.

$$\mathbf{r}(s) = \left(3 - \frac{3}{5}s\right)\mathbf{i} + \frac{4}{5}s\,\mathbf{j}, \qquad 0 \le s \le 5.$$

One of the advantages of writing a vector-valued function in terms of the arc length parameter is that $\| \mathbf{r}'(s) \| = 1$. For instance, in Example 4, you have

$$\| \mathbf{r}'(s) \| = \sqrt{\left(-\frac{3}{5}\right)^2 + \left(\frac{4}{5}\right)^2} = 1.$$

Thus, for a smooth curve C, represented by $\mathbf{r}(s)$, where s is the arc length parameter, the arc length between a and b is

$$\begin{aligned} \text{Length of arc} &= \int_a^b \| \mathbf{r}'(s) \| \, ds \\ &= \int_a^b ds = b - a \\ &= \text{length of interval.} \end{aligned}$$

Furthermore, if t is *any* parameter such that $\| \mathbf{r}'(t) \| = 1$, then t must be the arc length parameter. These results are summarized in the following theorem, which we state without proof.

THEOREM 12.8   Arc Length Parameter

If C is a smooth curve given by

$$\mathbf{r}(s) = x(s)\mathbf{i} + y(s)\mathbf{j} \quad \text{or} \quad \mathbf{r}(s) = x(s)\mathbf{i} + y(s)\mathbf{j} + z(s)\mathbf{k}$$

where s is the arc length parameter, then

$$\| \mathbf{r}'(s) \| = 1.$$

Moreover, if t is *any* parameter for the vector-valued function $\mathbf{r}$ such that $\| \mathbf{r}'(t) \| = 1$, then t must be the arc length parameter.

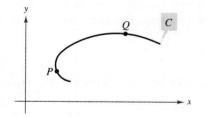

FIGURE 12.31
Curvature at P is greater than at Q.

Curvature

An important use of the arc length parameter is to find **curvature**—the measure of how sharply a curve bends. For instance, in Figure 12.31 the curve bends more sharply at P than at Q, and we say that the curvature is greater at P than at Q. You can calculate curvature by calculating the magnitude of the rate of change of the unit tangent vector $\mathbf{T}$ with respect to the arc length s, as indicated in Figure 12.32.

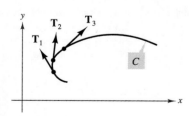

FIGURE 12.32
$\mathbf{T}$ changes as s changes.

Definition of Curvature

Let C be a smooth curve (in the plane *or* in space) given by $\mathbf{r}(s)$, where s is the arc length parameter. The **curvature** at s is given by

$$K = \left\| \frac{d\mathbf{T}}{ds} \right\| = \| \mathbf{T}'(s) \|.$$

Because a straight line doesn't "curve," its curvature should be 0, as demonstrated in Example 5.

EXAMPLE 5   Curvature of a Straight Line

Find the curvature of the line given by

$$\mathbf{r}(s) = \left(3 - \frac{3}{5}s\right)\mathbf{i} + \frac{4}{5}s\mathbf{j}.$$

Solution   To begin, note that $\mathbf{r}$ is written in terms of the arc length parameter (see Example 4). Because $\mathbf{r}'(s) = -\frac{3}{5}\mathbf{i} + \frac{4}{5}\mathbf{j}$, and $\|\mathbf{r}'(s)\| = 1$, you have

$$\mathbf{T}(s) = \frac{\mathbf{r}'(s)}{\|\mathbf{r}'(s)\|} = -\frac{3}{5}\mathbf{i} + \frac{4}{5}\mathbf{j}.$$

Therefore, the curvature is

$$K = \|\mathbf{T}'(s)\| = \|0\mathbf{i} + 0\mathbf{j}\| = 0$$

at every point on the line.

A circle has the same curvature at any point. Moreover, the curvature and the radius of the circle are inversely related. That is, a circle with a large radius has a small curvature, and a circle with a small radius has a large curvature. This inverse relationship is made explicit in the following example.

EXAMPLE 6   Finding the Curvature of a Circle

Show that the curvature of a circle of radius r is $K = 1/r$.

Solution   Without loss of generality, you can consider the circle to be centered at the origin. Let (x, y) be any point on the circle and let s be the length of the arc from $(r, 0)$ to (x, y), as shown in Figure 12.33. By letting θ be the central angle of the circle, you can represent the circle by

$$\mathbf{r}(\theta) = r\cos\theta\,\mathbf{i} + r\sin\theta\,\mathbf{j}. \qquad \textit{θ is the parameter}$$

Using the formula for the length of a circular arc $s = r\theta$, you can rewrite $\mathbf{r}(\theta)$ in terms of the arc length parameter as follows.

$$\mathbf{r}(s) = r\cos\frac{s}{r}\mathbf{i} + r\sin\frac{s}{r}\mathbf{j} \qquad \textit{Arc length s is the parameter}$$

Thus, $\mathbf{r}'(s) = -\sin\frac{s}{r}\mathbf{i} + \cos\frac{s}{r}\mathbf{j}$, and it follows that $\|\mathbf{r}'(s)\| = 1$, which implies that the unit tangent vector is

$$\mathbf{T}(s) = \frac{\mathbf{r}'(s)}{\|\mathbf{r}'(s)\|} = -\sin\frac{s}{r}\mathbf{i} + \cos\frac{s}{r}\mathbf{j}$$

and the curvature is given by

$$K = \|\mathbf{T}'(s)\| = \left\| -\frac{1}{r}\cos\frac{s}{r}\mathbf{i} - \frac{1}{r}\sin\frac{s}{r}\mathbf{j} \right\| = \frac{1}{r}$$

at every point on the circle.

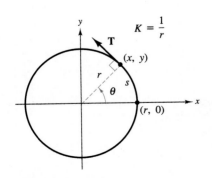

FIGURE 12.33
The curvature of a circle.

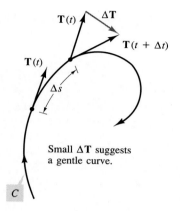

Small $\Delta \mathbf{T}$ suggests a gentle curve.

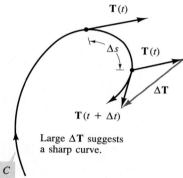

Large $\Delta \mathbf{T}$ suggests a sharp curve.

FIGURE 12.34

In Examples 5 and 6, the curvature was found by applying the definition directly. This requires that the curve be written in terms of the arc length parameter s. The following theorem gives two other formulas for finding the curvature of a curve written in terms of an arbitrary parameter t. We leave the proof of this theorem as an exercise (see Exercise 70, parts a and b).

THEOREM 12.9   Formulas for Curvature

If C is a smooth curve given by $\mathbf{r}(t)$, then the curvature of C at t is given by

$$K = \frac{\| \mathbf{T}'(t) \|}{\| \mathbf{r}'(t) \|} = \frac{\| \mathbf{r}'(t) \times \mathbf{r}''(t) \|}{\| \mathbf{r}'(t) \|^3}.$$

Because $\| \mathbf{r}'(t) \| = ds/dt$, the first formula implies that curvature is the ratio of the rate of change in the tangent vector $\mathbf{T}$ to the rate of change in arc length. To see the reasonableness of this, let Δt be a "small number." Then,

$$\frac{\mathbf{T}'(t)}{ds/dt} \approx \frac{[\mathbf{T}(t + \Delta t) - \mathbf{T}(t)]/\Delta t}{[s(t + \Delta t) - s(t)]/\Delta t} = \frac{\mathbf{T}(t + \Delta t) - \mathbf{T}(t)}{s(t + \Delta t) - s(t)} = \frac{\Delta \mathbf{T}}{\Delta s}.$$

In other words, for a given Δs, the greater the value of $\Delta \mathbf{T}$, the more the curve bends at t, as shown in Figure 12.34.

EXAMPLE 7   Finding the Curvature of a Space Curve

Find the curvature of the curve given by $\mathbf{r}(t) = 2t\,\mathbf{i} + t^2\,\mathbf{j} - \frac{1}{3}t^3\,\mathbf{k}$.

Solution   It is not apparent whether this parameter is arc length, so you should use the formula $K = \| \mathbf{T}'(t) \| / \| \mathbf{r}'(t) \|$.

$$\mathbf{r}'(t) = 2\mathbf{i} + 2t\,\mathbf{j} - t^2\,\mathbf{k}$$

$$\| \mathbf{r}'(t) \| = \sqrt{4 + 4t^2 + t^4} = t^2 + 2 \qquad \text{Length of } \mathbf{r}'(t)$$

$$\mathbf{T}(t) = \frac{\mathbf{r}'(t)}{\| \mathbf{r}'(t) \|} = \frac{2\mathbf{i} + 2t\,\mathbf{j} - t^2\,\mathbf{k}}{t^2 + 2}$$

$$\mathbf{T}'(t) = \frac{(t^2 + 2)(2\mathbf{j} - 2t\,\mathbf{k}) - (2t)(2\mathbf{i} + 2t\,\mathbf{j} - t^2\,\mathbf{k})}{(t^2 + 2)^2}$$

$$= \frac{-4t\,\mathbf{i} + (4 - 2t^2)\mathbf{j} - 4t\,\mathbf{k}}{(t^2 + 2)^2}$$

$$\| \mathbf{T}'(t) \| = \frac{\sqrt{16t^2 + 16 - 16t^2 + 4t^4 + 16t^2}}{(t^2 + 2)^2}$$

$$= \frac{2(t^2 + 2)}{(t^2 + 2)^2} = \frac{2}{t^2 + 2}. \qquad \text{Length of } \mathbf{T}'(t)$$

Therefore,

$$K = \frac{\| \mathbf{T}'(t) \|}{\| \mathbf{r}'(t) \|} = \frac{2}{(t^2 + 2)^2}. \qquad \text{Curvature}$$

The following theorem gives a formula for calculating the curvature of a plane curve given by $y = f(x)$.

THEOREM 12.10   Curvature in Rectangular Coordinates

If C is the graph of a twice-differentiable function given by $y = f(x)$, then the curvature at the point (x, y) is given by

$$K = \frac{|y''|}{[1 + (y')^2]^{3/2}}.$$

Proof   By representing the curve C by $\mathbf{r}(x) = x\mathbf{i} + f(x)\mathbf{j} + 0\mathbf{k}$ (where x is the parameter), you obtain $\mathbf{r}'(x) = \mathbf{i} + f'(x)\mathbf{j}$

$$\|\mathbf{r}'(x)\| = \sqrt{1 + [f'(x)]^2}$$

and $\mathbf{r}''(x) = f''(x)\mathbf{j}$. Because $\mathbf{r}'(x) \times \mathbf{r}''(x) = f''(x)\mathbf{k}$, it follows that the curvature is

$$K = \frac{\|\mathbf{r}'(x) \times \mathbf{r}''(x)\|}{\|\mathbf{r}'(x)\|^3} = \frac{|f''(x)|}{\{1 + [f'(x)]^2\}^{3/2}} = \frac{|y''|}{[1 + (y')^2]^{3/2}}.$$ ■

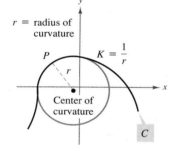

$r =$ radius of curvature

P $K = \dfrac{1}{r}$

r

Center of curvature

C

FIGURE 12.35
The circle of curvature.

Let C be a curve with curvature K at the point P. The circle passing through point P with radius $r = 1/K$ is called the **circle of curvature** if the circle lies on the concave side of the curve and shares a common tangent line with the curve at point P. The radius is called the **radius of curvature** at P, and the center of the circle is called the **center of curvature.**

The circle of curvature gives us a nice way to graphically estimate the curvature K at a point P on a curve. Using a compass, you can sketch a circle that approximates the concave side of the curve at point P, as shown in Figure 12.35. If the circle has a radius of r, then you can estimate the curvature to be $K = 1/r$.

EXAMPLE 8   Finding Curvature in Rectangular Coordinates

Find the curvature of the parabola given by $y = x - \frac{1}{4}x^2$ at $x = 2$. Sketch the circle of curvature at $(2, 1)$.

Solution   The curvature at $x = 2$ is as follows.

$$y' = 1 - \frac{x}{2} \qquad\qquad y' = 0$$

$$y'' = -\frac{1}{2} \qquad\qquad y'' = -\frac{1}{2}$$

$$K = \frac{|y''|}{[1 + (y')^2]^{3/2}} \qquad K = \frac{1}{2}$$

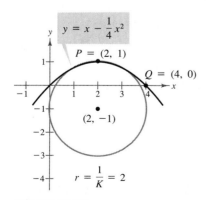

$y = x - \dfrac{1}{4}x^2$

$P = (2, 1)$

$Q = (4, 0)$

$(2, -1)$

$r = \dfrac{1}{K} = 2$

FIGURE 12.36
The circle of curvature.

Because the curvature at $(2, 1)$ is $\frac{1}{2}$, it follows that the radius of the circle of curvature at that point is 2. Thus, the center of curvature is $(2, -1)$, as shown in Figure 12.36. (In the figure, note that the curve has the greatest curvature at P. Try showing that the curvature at Q is $1/2^{5/2} \approx 0.177$.)

FIGURE 12.37
The amount of thrust felt by passengers in a car that is turning depends on two things—the speed of the car and the sharpness of the turn.

REMARK Note that Theorem 12.11 gives additional formulas for a_T and a_N.

Arc length and curvature are closely related to the tangential and normal components of acceleration. The tangential component of acceleration is the rate of change of the speed, which in turn is the rate of change of the arc length. This component is negative as a moving object slows down and positive as it speeds up—regardless of whether the object is turning or traveling in a straight line. Thus, the tangential component is solely a function of the arc length and is independent of the curvature. On the other hand, the normal component of acceleration is a function of **both** speed and curvature. This component measures the acceleration acting perpendicular to the direction of motion. To see why the normal component is affected by both speed and curvature, imagine that you are driving a car around a turn, as shown in Figure 12.37. If your speed is high and the turn is sharp, you feel yourself thrown against the car door. By lowering your speed *or* taking a more gentle turn, you are able to lessen this sideways thrust.

The next theorem explicitly states the relationship among speed, curvature, and the components of acceleration.

THEOREM 12.11   Acceleration, Speed, and Curvature

If $\mathbf{r}(t)$ is the position vector for a smooth curve C, then the acceleration vector is given by

$$\mathbf{a}(t) = \frac{d^2 s}{dt^2}\mathbf{T} + K\left(\frac{ds}{dt}\right)^2\mathbf{N}$$

where K is the curvature of C and ds/dt is the speed.

Proof For the position vector $\mathbf{r}(t)$, you have

$$\mathbf{a}(t) = a_T\mathbf{T} + a_N\mathbf{N} = D_t[\|\mathbf{v}\|]\mathbf{T} + \|\mathbf{v}\|\,\|\mathbf{T}'\|\,\mathbf{N}$$
$$= \frac{d^2 s}{dt^2}\mathbf{T} + \frac{ds}{dt}(\|\mathbf{v}\|K)\mathbf{N} = \frac{d^2 s}{dt^2}\mathbf{T} + K\left(\frac{ds}{dt}\right)^2\mathbf{N}.$$

EXAMPLE 9   Tangential and Normal Components of Acceleration

Find a_T and a_N for the curve given by $\mathbf{r}(t) = 2t\,\mathbf{i} + t^2\,\mathbf{j} - \frac{1}{3}t^3\,\mathbf{k}$.

Solution From Example 7, you know that

$$\frac{ds}{dt} = \|\mathbf{r}'(t)\| = t^2 + 2 \quad \text{and} \quad K = \frac{2}{(t^2 + 2)^2}.$$

Therefore,

$$a_T = \frac{d^2 s}{dt^2} = 2t \qquad \text{Tangential component}$$

and

$$a_N = K\left(\frac{ds}{dt}\right)^2 = \frac{2}{(t^2 + 2)^2}(t^2 + 2)^2 = 2. \qquad \text{Normal component}$$

Applications

There are many applications in physics and engineering dynamics that involve the relationship among speed, arc length, curvature, and acceleration. One such application concerns frictional force.

Suppose a moving object with mass m is in contact with a stationary object. The total force required to produce an acceleration **a** along a given path is

$$\mathbf{F} = m\mathbf{a}$$

$$= m\left(\frac{d^2s}{dt^2}\right)\mathbf{T} + mK\left(\frac{ds}{dt}\right)^2\mathbf{N}$$

$$= ma_\mathbf{T}\mathbf{T} + ma_\mathbf{N}\mathbf{N}.$$

The portion of this total force that is supplied by the stationary object is called the **force of friction.** For example, if a car is rounding a turn, the roadway exerts a frictional force that keeps the car from sliding off the road. If the car is not sliding, then the frictional force is perpendicular to the direction of motion and has magnitude equal to the normal component of acceleration, as shown in Figure 12.38. The potential frictional force of a road around a turn can be increased by banking the roadway.

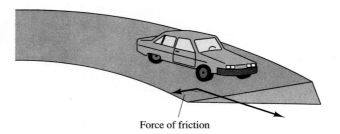

Force of friction

FIGURE 12.38
The force of friction is perpendicular to the direction of motion.

EXAMPLE 10   Frictional Force

A 360-kilogram go-cart is driven at a speed of 60 kilometers per hour around a circular racetrack of radius 12 meters. To keep the cart from skidding off course, what frictional force must the track surface exert on the tires?

Solution   The frictional force must equal the mass times the normal component of acceleration. For this circular path, we know that the curvature is $K = \frac{1}{12}$. Therefore, the frictional force is

$$ma_\mathbf{N} = mK\left(\frac{ds}{dt}\right)^2$$

$$= (360 \text{ kg})\left(\frac{1}{12 \text{ m}}\right)\left(\frac{60{,}000 \text{ m}}{3600 \text{ sec}}\right)^2$$

$$\approx 8333 \text{ (kg)(m)/sec}^2.$$

Several of the formulas dealing with vector-valued functions are summarized below.

Summary of Velocity, Acceleration, and Curvature

Let C be a curve given by the position function

$$\mathbf{r}(t) = x(t)\mathbf{i} + y(t)\mathbf{j} \qquad \text{Curve in the plane}$$

or

$$\mathbf{r}(t) = x(t)\mathbf{i} + y(t)\mathbf{j} + z(t)\mathbf{k}. \qquad \text{Curve in space}$$

Velocity vector, speed, and acceleration vector:

$$\mathbf{v}(t) = \mathbf{r}'(t)$$

$$\|\mathbf{v}(t)\| = \frac{ds}{dt} = \|\mathbf{r}'(t)\|$$

$$\mathbf{a}(t) = \mathbf{r}''(t) = a_{\mathbf{T}}\mathbf{T}(t) + a_{\mathbf{N}}\mathbf{N}(t)$$

Unit tangent vector and principal unit normal vector:

$$\mathbf{T}(t) = \frac{\mathbf{r}'(t)}{\|\mathbf{r}'(t)\|} \quad \text{and} \quad \mathbf{N}(t) = \frac{\mathbf{T}'(t)}{\|\mathbf{T}'(t)\|}$$

Components of acceleration:

$$a_{\mathbf{T}} = \mathbf{a} \cdot \mathbf{T} = \frac{\mathbf{v} \cdot \mathbf{a}}{\|\mathbf{v}\|} = \frac{d^2 s}{dt^2}$$

$$a_{\mathbf{N}} = \mathbf{a} \cdot \mathbf{N} = \sqrt{\|\mathbf{a}\|^2 - a_{\mathbf{T}}^2} = \frac{\|\mathbf{v} \times \mathbf{a}\|}{\|\mathbf{v}\|} = K\left(\frac{ds}{dt}\right)^2$$

Formulas for curvature in the plane:

$$K = \frac{|y''|}{[1 + (y')^2]^{3/2}} \qquad C \text{ given by } y = f(x)$$

$$K = \frac{|x'y'' - y'x''|}{[(x')^2 + (y')^2]^{3/2}} \qquad C \text{ given by } x = x(t), y = y(t)$$

Formulas for curvature in the plane or in space:

$$K = \|\mathbf{T}'(s)\| = \|\mathbf{r}''(s)\| \qquad s \text{ is arc length parameter}$$

$$K = \frac{\|\mathbf{T}'(t)\|}{\|\mathbf{r}'(t)\|} = \frac{\|\mathbf{r}'(t) \times \mathbf{r}''(t)\|}{\|\mathbf{r}'(t)\|^3} \qquad t \text{ is general parameter}$$

$$K = \frac{\mathbf{a}(t) \cdot \mathbf{N}(t)}{\|\mathbf{v}(t)\|^2}$$

Cross product formulas apply only to curves in space.

EXERCISES for Section 12.5

TECHNOLOGY
Laboratory Guide
Lab 12.5

In Exercises 1–4, sketch the plane curve and find its length over the indicated interval.

Function	Interval
1. $\mathbf{r}(t) = t\mathbf{i} + 3t\mathbf{j}$	$[0, 4]$
2. $\mathbf{r}(t) = t\mathbf{i} + t^2\mathbf{k}$	$[0, 4]$
3. $\mathbf{r}(t) = a\cos^3 t\,\mathbf{i} + a\sin^3 t\,\mathbf{j}$	$[0, 2\pi]$
4. $\mathbf{r}(t) = a\cos t\,\mathbf{i} + a\sin t\,\mathbf{j}$	$[0, 2\pi]$

In Exercises 5–8, sketch the space curve and find its length over the indicated interval.

Function	Interval
5. $\mathbf{r}(t) = 2t\mathbf{i} - 3t\mathbf{j} + t\mathbf{k}$	$[0, 2]$
6. $\mathbf{r}(t) = \langle 4t, 3\cos t, 3\sin t \rangle$	$\left[0, \dfrac{\pi}{2}\right]$
7. $\mathbf{r}(t) = a\cos t\,\mathbf{i} + a\sin t\,\mathbf{j} + bt\,\mathbf{k}$	$[0, 2\pi]$
8. $\mathbf{r}(t) = \langle \sin t - t\cos t, \cos t + t\sin t, t^2 \rangle$	$\left[0, \dfrac{\pi}{2}\right]$

C In Exercises 9 and 10, use a computer or calculator and Simpson's Rule with $n = 10$ to approximate the length of the space curve over the indicated interval.

Function	Interval
9. $\mathbf{r}(t) = t^2\mathbf{i} + t\mathbf{j} + \ln t\,\mathbf{k}$	$1 \le t \le 3$
10. $\mathbf{r}(t) = \sin \pi t\,\mathbf{i} + \cos \pi t\,\mathbf{j} + t^3\mathbf{k}$	$0 \le t \le 2$

11. Consider the helix represented by the vector-valued function

$$\mathbf{r}(t) = \langle 2\cos t, 2\sin t, t \rangle.$$

  a. Express the length of the arc s on the helix as a function of t by evaluating the integral

$$s = \int_0^t \sqrt{[x'(u)]^2 + [y'(u)]^2 + [z'(u)]^2}\,du.$$

  b. Solve for t in the relationship derived in part a, and substitute the result into the original set of parametric equations. This yields a parametrization of the curve in terms of the arc length parameter s.

  c. Find the coordinates of the point on the helix when the length of the arc is $s = \sqrt{5}$ and $s = 4$.

  d. Verify that $\| \mathbf{r}'(s) \| = 1$.

12. Repeat Exercise 11 for the curve represented by the vector-valued function

$$\mathbf{r}(t) = \langle 4(\sin t - t\cos t), 4(\cos t + t\sin t), \tfrac{3}{2}t^2 \rangle.$$

In Exercises 13–16, find the curvature K of the curve where s is the arc length parameter.

13. $\mathbf{r}(s) = [(2 - s)\mathbf{i} + (3 + 2s)] / \sqrt{5}$

14. $\mathbf{r}(s) = \dfrac{\sqrt{3}}{9}[(3 - 2s)^{3/2}\mathbf{i} + 2\sqrt{2}s^{3/2}\mathbf{j}]$

15. The arc length parametrization of the helix in Exercise 11

16. The arc length parametrization of the space curve in Exercise 12

In Exercises 17–20, find the curvature K of the plane curve at the specified value of the parameter.

17. $\mathbf{r}(t) = 4t\mathbf{i} - 2t\mathbf{j}$ **18.** $\mathbf{r}(t) = t^2\mathbf{j} + \mathbf{k}$
$t = 1$ $t = 0$

19. $\mathbf{r}(t) = t\mathbf{i} + \dfrac{1}{t}\mathbf{j}$ **20.** $\mathbf{r}(t) = t\mathbf{i} + t^2\mathbf{j}$
$t = 1$ $t = 1$

In Exercises 21–32, find the curvature K of the curve.

21. $\mathbf{r}(t) = 4\cos 2\pi t\,\mathbf{i} + 4\sin 2\pi t\,\mathbf{j}$

22. $\mathbf{r}(t) = 2\cos \pi t\,\mathbf{i} + \sin \pi t\,\mathbf{j}$

23. $\mathbf{r}(t) = a\cos \omega t\,\mathbf{i} + a\sin \omega t\,\mathbf{j}$

24. $\mathbf{r}(t) = a\cos \omega t\,\mathbf{i} + b\sin \omega t\,\mathbf{j}$

25. $\mathbf{r}(t) = e^t\cos t\,\mathbf{i} + e^t\sin t\,\mathbf{j}$

26. $\mathbf{r}(t) = \langle a(\omega t - \sin \omega t), a(1 - \cos \omega t) \rangle$

27. $\mathbf{r}(t) = \langle \cos \omega t + \omega t\sin \omega t, \sin \omega t - \omega t\cos \omega t \rangle$

28. $\mathbf{r}(t) = 4t\mathbf{i} - 4t\mathbf{j} + 2t\mathbf{k}$

29. $\mathbf{r}(t) = t\mathbf{i} + t^2\mathbf{j} + \dfrac{t^2}{2}\mathbf{k}$

30. $\mathbf{r}(t) = t\mathbf{i} + 3t^2\mathbf{j} + \dfrac{t^2}{2}\mathbf{k}$

31. $\mathbf{r}(t) = 4t\mathbf{i} + 3\cos t\,\mathbf{j} + 3\sin t\,\mathbf{k}$

32. $\mathbf{r}(t) = e^t\cos t\,\mathbf{i} + e^t\sin t\,\mathbf{j} + e^t\mathbf{k}$

In Exercises 33–38, find the curvature and radius of curvature of the plane curve at the specified value of x.

Function	Point
33. $y = 3x - 2$	$x = a$
34. $y = mx + b$	$x = a$
35. $y = 2x^2 + 3$	$x = -1$
36. $y = x + \dfrac{1}{x}$	$x = 1$
37. $y = \sqrt{a^2 - x^2}$	$x = 0$
38. $y = \tfrac{3}{4}\sqrt{16 - x^2}$	$x = 0$

Essay **In Exercises 39 and 40, two circles of curvature to the graph of the function are given. (a) Find the equation of the smaller circle, and (b) write a short paragraph explaining why the circles have different radii.**

39. $f(x) = \sin x$

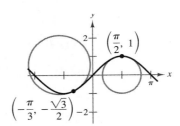

40. $f(x) = \dfrac{4x^2}{x^2 + 3}$

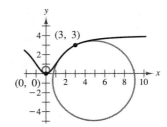

In Exercises 41–44, sketch the graph of the function and sketch the circle of curvature to the graph at the specified value of x.

Function	Point
41. $y = x + \dfrac{1}{x}$	$x = 1$
42. $y = \ln x$	$x = 1$
43. $y = e^x$	$x = 0$
44. $y = \tfrac{1}{3}x^3$	$x = 1$

In Exercises 45–48, (a) find the point on the curve at which curvature K is a maximum and (b) find the limit of K as $x \rightarrow \infty$.

45. $y = (x - 1)^2 + 3$ **46.** $y = x^3$

47. $y = x^{2/3}$ **48.** $y = \ln x$

49. Does the graph of $y = (x - 1)^3 + 3$ have points at which the curvature is 0? If so, find the points.

50. *Essay*   Use the result of Exercise 49 to write a paragraph describing the points on the graph of $y = f(x)$ at which the curvature is 0.

51. Show that the curvature is greatest at the endpoints of the major axis and least at the endpoints of the minor axis for the ellipse given by

$$x^2 + 4y^2 = 4.$$

52. Verify that the curvature at any point (x, y) on the graph of $y = \cosh x$ is y^2.

53. Find all a and b such that the two curves given by

$$y_1 = ax(b - x)$$

and

$$y_2 = \frac{x}{x + 2}$$

intersect at only one point and have a common tangent line and equal curvature at the point. Sketch a graph for each set of values for a and b.

54. Given a twice-differentiable function $y = f(x)$, determine its curvature at a relative extremum. Can the curvature ever be greater than it is at a relative extremum? Why or why not?

55. The smaller the curvature in a bend of a road, the faster a car can travel. Assume that the maximum speed around a turn is inversely proportional to the square root of the curvature. A car moving on the path $y = \frac{1}{3}x^3$ (x and y measured in miles) can safely go 30 miles per hour at $(1, \frac{1}{3})$. How fast can it go at $(\frac{3}{2}, \frac{9}{8})$?

56. The curve C is given by the polar equation $r = f(\theta)$. Show that the curvature K at the point (r, θ) is

$$K = \frac{|2(r')^2 - rr'' + r^2|}{[(r')^2 + r^2]^{3/2}}.$$

(*Hint:* Represent the curve by $\mathbf{r}(\theta) = r\cos\theta\,\mathbf{i} + r\sin\theta\,\mathbf{j}$.)

In Exercises 57–60, use the result of Exercise 56 to find the curvature of the polar curve.

57. $r = 1 + \sin\theta$ **58.** $r = \theta$

59. $r = a\sin\theta$ **60.** $r = e^\theta$

61. Given the polar curve $r = e^{a\theta}$, $a > 0$, find the curvature K and determine the limit of K as
a. $\theta \rightarrow \infty$.   **b.** $a \rightarrow \infty$.

62. Show that the formula for the curvature of a polar curve $r = f(\theta)$ given in Exercise 56 reduces to

$$K = \frac{2}{|r'|}$$

for the curvature *at the pole*.

In Exercises 63 and 64, use the result of Exercise 62 to find the curvature of the rose curve at the pole.

63. $r = 4\sin 2\theta$ **64.** $r = 6\cos 3\theta$

65. For a smooth curve given by the parametric equations $x = f(t)$ and $y = g(t)$, prove that the curvature is

$$K = \frac{|f'(t)g''(t) - g'(t)f''(t)|}{\{[f'(t)]^2 + [g'(t)]^2\}^{3/2}}.$$

66. Use the result of Exercise 65 to find the curvature of the curve represented by the parametric equations

$$x(t) = t^3 \quad \text{and} \quad y(t) = \frac{1}{2}t^2.$$

In Exercises 67 and 68, use Theorem 12.11 to find a_T and a_N for the curve given by the vector-valued function.

67. $\mathbf{r}(t) = 3t^2\mathbf{i} + (3t - t^3)\mathbf{j}$

68. $\mathbf{r}(t) = t^2\mathbf{i} + 2t\mathbf{j} + t^2\mathbf{k}$

69. *Frictional Force*   A 4000-pound vehicle is driven at a speed of 30 miles per hour on a circular interchange of radius 100 feet. To keep the vehicle from skidding off course, what frictional force must the road surface exert on the tires?

70. Use the definition of curvature in space, $K = \|\mathbf{T}'(s)\| = \|\mathbf{r}''(s)\|$, to verify the following three formulas.

a. $K = \dfrac{\|\mathbf{T}'(t)\|}{\|\mathbf{r}'(t)\|}$ **b.** $K = \dfrac{\|\mathbf{r}'(t) \times \mathbf{r}''(t)\|}{\|\mathbf{r}'(t)\|^3}$

c. $K = \dfrac{\mathbf{a}(t) \cdot \mathbf{N}(t)}{\|\mathbf{v}(t)\|^2}$

71. *Cornu Spiral*   The cornu spiral is given by

$$x = \int_0^s \cos\frac{\pi u^2}{2}\,du, \qquad y = \int_0^s \sin\frac{\pi u^2}{2}\,du.$$

The spiral shown in the figure was plotted over the interval $-\pi \le x \le \pi$.

a. Find the arc length of this curve from $s = 0$ to $s = a$.
b. Find the curvature of the graph when $s = a$.
c. The cornu spiral was discovered by James Bernoulli. He found that the spiral has an amazing relationship between curvature and arc length. What is this relationship?

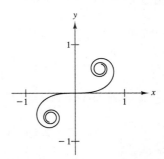

FIGURE FOR 71

72. A sphere of radius 4 is dropped into the paraboloid given by $z = x^2 + y^2$.
a. How close will the sphere come to the vertex of the paraboloid?
b. What is the radius of the largest sphere that will touch the vertex?

73. Find the curvature of the cycloid given by the parametric equations

$$x(\theta) = a(\theta - \sin\theta), \qquad y(\theta) = a(1 - \cos\theta).$$

What are the minimum and maximum values of K?

74. Let C be given by $y = f(x)$. Show that the center of curvature for (x, y) on C is $(x_0, y_0) = (x - y'z, y + z)$, where

$$z = \frac{1 + (y')^2}{y''}.$$

Find the center of curvature for $y = e^x$ at the point $(0, 1)$ on the curve.

In Exercises 75–82, you are asked to verify Kepler's Laws of Planetary Motion. For these exercises, assume that each planet moves in an orbit given by the vector-valued function r. Let $r = \|\mathbf{r}\|$, let G represent the universal gravitational constant, let M represent the mass of the sun, and let m represent the mass of the planet.

75. Prove that $\mathbf{r} \cdot \mathbf{r}' = r\dfrac{dr}{dt}$.

76. Using Newton's Second Law, $\mathbf{F} = m\,\mathbf{a}$, and Newton's Law of Gravitation,

$$\mathbf{F} = \frac{-GmM}{r^3}\mathbf{r},$$

show that $\mathbf{a}$ and $\mathbf{r}$ are parallel, and that

$$\mathbf{r}(t) \times \mathbf{r}'(t) = \mathbf{L}$$

is a constant vector. Hence, $\mathbf{r}(t)$ moves in a *fixed plane*, orthogonal to $\mathbf{L}$.

77. Prove that

$$\frac{d}{dt}\left[\frac{\mathbf{r}}{r}\right] = \frac{1}{r^3}\{[\mathbf{r} \times \mathbf{r}'(t)] \times \mathbf{r}\}.$$

78. Show that

$$\frac{\mathbf{r}'}{GM} \times \mathbf{L} - \frac{\mathbf{r}}{r} = \mathbf{e},$$

is a constant vector.

79. Prove Kepler's First Law: Each planet moves in an elliptical orbit with the sun as a focus.

80. Assume that the elliptical orbit

$$r = \frac{ed}{1 + e\cos\theta}$$

is in the xy-plane, with $\mathbf{L}$ along the z-axis. Prove that

$$\|\mathbf{L}\| = r^2\frac{d\theta}{dt}.$$

81. Prove Kepler's Second Law: Each ray from the sun to a planet sweeps out equal areas of the ellipse in equal times.

82. Prove Kepler's Third Law: The square of the period of a planet's orbit is proportional to the cube of the mean distance between the planet and the sun.

REVIEW EXERCISES for Chapter 12

In Exercises 1–4, (a) find the domain of r and (b) determine the values (if any) of t for which the function is discontinuous.

1. $\mathbf{r}(t) = t\mathbf{i} + \csc t\,\mathbf{k}$

2. $\mathbf{r}(t) = \sqrt{t}\mathbf{i} + \dfrac{1}{t - 4}\mathbf{j} + \mathbf{k}$

3. $\mathbf{r}(t) = \ln t\,\mathbf{i} + t\mathbf{j} + t\mathbf{k}$

4. $\mathbf{r}(t) = (2t + 1)\mathbf{i} + t^2\mathbf{j} + t\mathbf{k}$

In Exercises 5 and 6, sketch the plane curve represented by the vector-valued function.

5. $\mathbf{r}(t) = \cos t\,\mathbf{i} + 2\sin^2 t\,\mathbf{j}$

6. $\mathbf{r}(t) = t\mathbf{i} + \dfrac{t}{t - 1}\mathbf{j}$

In Exercises 7–10, sketch the space curve represented by the vector-valued function.

7. $\mathbf{r}(t) = \mathbf{i} + t\mathbf{j} + t^2\mathbf{k}$

8. $\mathbf{r}(t) = 2t\mathbf{i} + t\mathbf{j} + t^2\mathbf{k}$

9. $\mathbf{r}(t) = 2\cos t\,\mathbf{i} + t\mathbf{j} + 2\sin t\,\mathbf{k}$

10. $\mathbf{r}(t) = \mathbf{i} + \sin t\,\mathbf{j} + \mathbf{k}$

C **In Exercises 11 and 12, use a graphing utility to graph the space curve represented by the vector-valued function.**

11. $\mathbf{r}(t) = \frac{1}{2}t\mathbf{i} + \sqrt{t}\mathbf{j} + \frac{1}{4}t^3\mathbf{k}$

12. $\mathbf{r}(t) = t\mathbf{i} + \ln t\,\mathbf{j} + \frac{1}{2}t^2\mathbf{k}$

In Exercises 13 and 14, sketch the space curve represented by the intersection of the surfaces. Use the parameter $x = t$ to find a vector-valued function for the space curve.

13. $z = x^2 + y^2$
$\quad\; x + y = 0$

14. $x^2 + z^2 = 4$
$\quad\;\; x - y = 0$

In Exercises 15 and 16, find the indicated limit.

15. $\lim\limits_{t \to 2}\left(t^2\mathbf{i} + \sqrt{4 - t^2}\mathbf{j} + \mathbf{k}\right)$

16. $\lim\limits_{t \to 0}\left(\dfrac{\sin 2t}{t}\mathbf{i} + e^{-t}\mathbf{j} + e^t\mathbf{k}\right)$

In Exercises 17 and 18, find the following.
a. $\mathbf{r}'(t)$ **b.** $\mathbf{r}''(t)$
c. $D_t[\mathbf{r}(t) \cdot \mathbf{u}(t)]$ **d.** $D_t[\mathbf{u}(t) - 2\mathbf{r}(t)]$
e. $D_t[\|\mathbf{r}(t)\|], \quad t > 0$ **f.** $D_t[\mathbf{r}(t) \times \mathbf{u}(t)]$

17. $\mathbf{r}(t) = 3t\mathbf{i} + (t - 1)\mathbf{j}$
$\quad\;\; \mathbf{u}(t) = t\mathbf{i} + t^2\mathbf{j} + \frac{2}{3}t^3\mathbf{k}$

18. $\mathbf{r}(t) = \sin t\,\mathbf{i} + \cos t\,\mathbf{j} + t\mathbf{k}$
$\quad\;\; \mathbf{u}(t) = \sin t\,\mathbf{i} + \cos t\,\mathbf{j} + \dfrac{1}{t}\mathbf{k}$

In Exercises 19 and 20, find a set of parametric equations for the line tangent to the space curve at the indicated point.

19. $\mathbf{r}(t) = 2\cos t\,\mathbf{i} + 2\sin t\,\mathbf{j} + t\,\mathbf{k}$, $t = \dfrac{3\pi}{4}$

20. $\mathbf{r}(t) = t\,\mathbf{i} + t^2\,\mathbf{j} + \frac{2}{3}t^3\,\mathbf{k}$, $t = 2$

In Exercises 21–24, find the indefinite integral.

21. $\displaystyle\int (\cos t\,\mathbf{i} + t\cos t\,\mathbf{j})\,dt$

22. $\displaystyle\int (\ln t\,\mathbf{i} + t\ln t\,\mathbf{j} + \mathbf{k})\,dt$

23. $\displaystyle\int \|\cos t\,\mathbf{i} + \sin t\,\mathbf{j} + t\,\mathbf{k}\|\,dt$

24. $\displaystyle\int (t\,\mathbf{j} + t^2\,\mathbf{k}) \times (\mathbf{i} + t\,\mathbf{j} + t\,\mathbf{k})\,dt$

In Exercises 25 and 26, find r(t) for the given condition.

25. $\mathbf{r}'(t) = 2t\,\mathbf{i} + e^t\,\mathbf{j} + e^{-t}\,\mathbf{k}$
    $\mathbf{r}(0) = \mathbf{i} + 3\mathbf{j} - 5\mathbf{k}$

26. $\mathbf{r}'(t) = \sec t\,\mathbf{i} + \tan t\,\mathbf{j} + t^2\,\mathbf{k}$
    $\mathbf{r}(0) = 3\mathbf{k}$

In Exercises 27 and 28, evaluate the definite integral.

27. $\displaystyle\int_{-2}^{2} (3t\,\mathbf{i} + 2t^2\,\mathbf{j} - t^3\,\mathbf{k})\,dt$

28. $\displaystyle\int_{0}^{1} (\sqrt{t}\,\mathbf{j} + t\sin t\,\mathbf{k})\,dt$

Projectile Motion **In Exercises 29–32, use the model for projectile motion and assume there is no air resistance.**

29. *Projectile Motion* A projectile is fired from ground level at an angle of elevation of 30°. Find the range of the projectile if the initial velocity is 75 feet per second.

30. *Conveyor Belt* The center of a truckbed is 6 feet below and 4 feet horizontally from the end of a horizontal conveyor that is discharging gravel (see figure). Determine the speed ds/dt at which the conveyor belt should be moving so that the gravel falls onto the center of the truck bed.

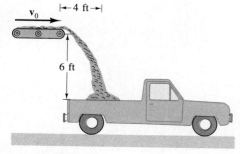

FIGURE FOR 30

31. *Projectile Motion* A projectile is fired from ground level at an angle of 20° with the horizontal. Find the minimum initial velocity necessary if the projectile is to have a range of 250 feet.

C 32. Use a graphing utility to graph the paths of a projectile if $v_0 = 50$ feet per second and
   a. $\theta = 30°$.   **b.** $\theta = 45°$.   **c.** $\theta = 60°$.
   Use the graphs to approximate the maximum height and range of the projectile for each case.

In Exercises 33–40, find the velocity, speed, and acceleration at time t. Then, find a·T, a·N, and the curvature at time t.

33. $\mathbf{r}(t) = (1 + 4t)\mathbf{i} + (2 - 3t)\mathbf{j}$

34. $\mathbf{r}(t) = 5t\,\mathbf{i}$

35. $\mathbf{r}(t) = 2(t + 1)\mathbf{i} + \dfrac{2}{t + 1}\mathbf{j}$

36. $\mathbf{r}(t) = t\,\mathbf{i} + \sqrt{t}\,\mathbf{j}$

37. $\mathbf{r}(t) = e^t\,\mathbf{i} + e^{-t}\,\mathbf{j}$

38. $\mathbf{r}(t) = t\cos t\,\mathbf{i} + t\sin t\,\mathbf{j}$

39. $\mathbf{r}(t) = t\,\mathbf{i} + t^2\,\mathbf{j} + \frac{1}{2}t^2\,\mathbf{k}$

40. $\mathbf{r}(t) = (t - 1)\mathbf{i} + t\,\mathbf{j} + \dfrac{1}{t}\mathbf{k}$

In Exercises 41 and 42, find the length of the space curve over the indicated interval.

41. $\mathbf{r}(t) = \frac{1}{2}t\,\mathbf{i} + \sin t\,\mathbf{j} + \cos t\,\mathbf{k}$, $0 \le t \le \pi$

42. $\mathbf{r}(t) = e^t\sin t\,\mathbf{i} + e^t\cos t\,\mathbf{k}$, $0 \le t \le \pi$

43. *Satellite Orbit* Find the speed necessary for a satellite to maintain a circular orbit 600 miles above the surface of the earth.

44. *Centripetal Force* An automobile is in a circular traffic exchange and its speed is twice that posted. By what factor is the centripetal force increased over that which would occur at the posted speed?

45. *Highway Construction* A civil engineer designs a highway as indicated in the figure. BC is an arc of a circle. AB and CD are straight lines tangent to the circular arc. Criticize the design.

46. *Exit Ramp* A highway has an exit ramp that begins at the origin of a coordinate system and follows the curve given by

$$y = \frac{1}{32}x^{5/2}$$

to the point (4, 1) (see figure). Then it follows a circular path whose curvature is that given by the curve at (4, 1). What is the radius of the circular arc?

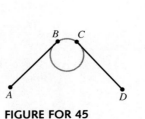

FIGURE FOR 45   **FIGURE FOR 46**

Chapter 13

Functions of Several Variables

SECTION
13.1
Introduction to Functions of Several Variables

Functions of Several Variables • The Graph of a Function of Two Variables • Level Curves • Level Surfaces • Computer Graphics

Functions of Several Variables

So far in the text, we have dealt only with functions of single (independent) variables. Many familiar quantities, however, are functions of two or more variables. For instance, the work done by a force ($W = FD$) and the volume of a right circular cylinder ($V = \pi r^2 h$) are both functions of two variables. The volume of a rectangular solid ($V = lwh$) is a function of three variables. The notation for a function of two or more variables is similar to that for a function of a single variable. Here are two examples.

$$z = \underbrace{f(x, y)}_{2 \text{ variables}} = x^2 + xy$$

and

$$w = \underbrace{f(x, y, z)}_{3 \text{ variables}} = x + 2y - 3z.$$

Definition of a Function of Two Variables

Let D be a set of ordered pairs of real numbers. If to each ordered pair (x, y) in D there corresponds a unique real number $f(x, y)$, then f is called a **function of x and y.** The set D is the **domain** of f, and the corresponding set of values for $f(x, y)$ is the **range** of f.

For the function given by $z = f(x, y)$, we call x and y the **independent variables** and z the **dependent variable.**

Similar definitions can be given to functions of three, four, or n variables, where the domains consist of ordered triples (x_1, x_2, x_3), quadruples (x_1, x_2, x_3, x_4), and n-tuples $(x_1, x_2, \ldots, x_n)$, respectively. In all cases, the range is a set of real numbers. In this chapter, we limit the discussion to functions of two or three variables.

As with functions of one variable, the most common way to describe a function of several variables is with an *equation,* and unless otherwise restricted, you can assume that the domain is the set of all points for which the equation is defined. For instance, the domain of the function given by

$$f(x, y) = x^2 + y^2$$

is assumed to be the entire xy-plane.

◄ *Computers can be used to sketch surfaces in space. In Section 13.1, Exercises 39–42, you are asked to use a computer graphing utility to sketch three-dimensional surfaces.*

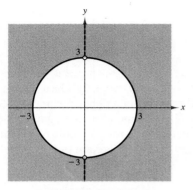

Domain of
$$f(x, y) = \frac{\sqrt{x^2 + y^2 - 9}}{x}$$

FIGURE 13.1

EXAMPLE 1   Finding the Domains of Functions of Several Variables

Find the domains of the following functions.

a. $f(x, y) = \dfrac{\sqrt{x^2 + y^2 - 9}}{x}$ **b.** $g(x, y, z) = \dfrac{x}{\sqrt{9 - x^2 - y^2 - z^2}}$

Solution

a. The function f is defined for all points (x, y) such that $x \ne 0$ and

$$x^2 + y^2 \ge 9.$$

Thus, the domain is the set of all points lying on or outside the circle $x^2 + y^2 = 9$, *except* those on the y-axis, as shown in Figure 13.1.

b. The function g is defined for all points (x, y, z) such that

$$x^2 + y^2 + z^2 < 9.$$

Consequently, the domain is the set of all points (x, y, z) lying inside a sphere of radius 3 that is centered at the origin.

Functions of several variables can be combined in the same ways as functions of single variables. For instance, you can form the sum, difference, product, and quotient of two functions of two variables as follows.

$$
\begin{aligned}
(f \pm g)(x, y) &= f(x, y) \pm g(x, y) && \text{Sum or difference} \\
(fg)(x, y) &= f(x, y)g(x, y) && \text{Product} \\
\frac{f}{g}(x, y) &= \frac{f(x, y)}{g(x, y)}, \quad g(x, y) \ne 0 && \text{Quotient}
\end{aligned}
$$

You cannot form the composite of two functions of several variables. However, if h is a function of several variables and g is a function of a single variable, then you can form the **composite** function $(g \circ h)(x, y)$ as follows.

$$(g \circ h)(x, y) = g(h(x, y)) \qquad \text{Composition}$$

The domain of this composite function consists of all (x, y) in the domain of h such that $h(x, y)$ is in the domain of g. For example, the function given by

$$f(x, y) = \sqrt{16 - 4x^2 - y^2}$$

can be viewed as the composite of the function of two variables given by $h(x, y) = 16 - 4x^2 - y^2$ and the function of a single variable given by $g(u) = \sqrt{u}$. The domain of this function is the set of all points lying on or inside the ellipse given by $4x^2 + y^2 = 16$.

A function that can be expressed as a sum of functions of the form $cx^m y^n$ (where c is a real number and m and n are nonnegative integers) is called a **polynomial function** of two variables. For instance, the functions given by

$$f(x, y) = x^2 + y^2 - 2xy + x + 2 \quad \text{and} \quad g(x, y) = 3xy^2 + x - 2$$

are polynomial functions of two variables. A **rational function** is the quotient of two polynomial functions. Similar terminology is used for functions of more than two variables.

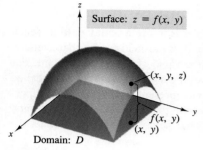

FIGURE 13.2

The Graph of a Function of Two Variables

As with functions of single variables, you can learn a lot about the behavior of a function of two variables by sketching its graph. The **graph** of a function f of two variables is the set of all points (x, y, z) for which $z = f(x, y)$ and (x, y) is in the domain of f. This graph can be interpreted geometrically as a *surface in space,* as discussed in Sections 11.5 and 11.6. In Figure 13.2, note that the graph of $z = f(x, y)$ is a surface whose projection onto the xy-plane is D, the domain of f. Consequently, to each point (x, y) in D there corresponds a point (x, y, z) on the surface, and, conversely, to each point (x, y, z) on the surface there corresponds a point (x, y) in D.

EXAMPLE 2   Describing the Graph of a Function of Two Variables

What is the range of $f(x, y) = \sqrt{16 - 4x^2 - y^2}$? Describe the graph of f.

Solution   The domain D implied by the equation for f is the set of all points (x, y) such that $16 - 4x^2 - y^2 \geq 0$. Thus, D is the set of all points lying on or inside the ellipse given by

$$\frac{x^2}{4} + \frac{y^2}{16} = 1.$$

The range of f is all values $z = f(x, y)$ such that $0 \leq z \leq \sqrt{16}$ or

$$0 \leq z \leq 4. \qquad \text{Range of } f$$

A point (x, y, z) is on the graph of f if and only if

$$z = \sqrt{16 - 4x^2 - y^2}$$
$$z^2 = 16 - 4x^2 - y^2$$
$$4x^2 + y^2 + z^2 = 16$$
$$\frac{x^2}{4} + \frac{y^2}{16} + \frac{z^2}{16} = 1, \qquad 0 \leq z \leq 4.$$

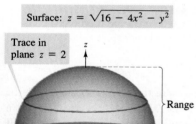

FIGURE 13.3
Graph of
$f(x, y) = \sqrt{16 - 4x^2 - y^2}$

From Section 11.6, you know that the graph of f is the upper half of an ellipsoid, as shown in Figure 13.3.

To sketch a surface in space *by hand,* it helps to use traces in planes parallel to the coordinate planes, as shown in Figure 13.3. For example, to find the trace of the surface in the plane $z = 2$, substitute $z = 2$ in the equation $z = \sqrt{16 - 4x^2 - y^2}$ and obtain

$$2 = \sqrt{16 - 4x^2 - y^2} \quad \longrightarrow \quad \frac{x^2}{3} + \frac{y^2}{12} = 1.$$

Thus, the trace is an ellipse centered at the point $(0, 0, 2)$ with major and minor axes of lengths $4\sqrt{3}$ and $2\sqrt{3}$, respectively.

Traces are also used with most three-dimensional graphing utilities. For instance, Figure 13.4 shows a computer-generated version of the surface given in Example 2. For this sketch, the computer took 20 traces parallel to the xy-plane and 10 traces in vertical planes.

If you have access to a three-dimensional graphing utility, try using it to sketch the graphs of several surfaces.

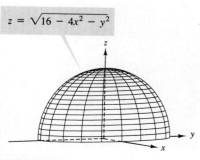

FIGURE 13.4
Computer-generated graph

Level Curves

A second way to visualize a function of two variables is to use a **scalar field** in which the scalar $z = f(x, y)$ is assigned to the point (x, y). A scalar field can be characterized by **level curves** (or **contour lines**) along which the value of $f(x, y)$ is constant. For instance, the weather map in Figure 13.5 shows level curves of equal pressure called **isobars.** In weather maps for which the level curves represent points of equal temperature, the level curves are called **isotherms,** as shown in Figure 13.6. Another common use of level curves is in representing electric potential fields. In this type of map, the level curves are called **equipotential lines.**

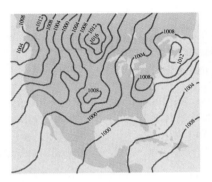

FIGURE 13.5
Level curves show the lines of
equal pressure (isobars)
measured in millibars.

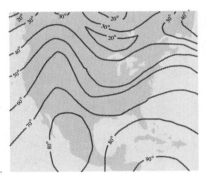

FIGURE 13.6
Level curves show the lines of
equal temperature (isotherms)
measured in degrees Fahrenheit.

Contour maps are commonly used to show regions of the earth's surface, with the level curves representing the height above sea level. This type of map is called a **topographic map.** For example, the topographic map in Figure 13.7 represents Half Dome and vicinity in Yosemite Valley, California, as shown in Figure 13.8.

A contour map depicts the variation of z with respect to x and y by the spacing between level curves. Much space between level curves indicates that z is changing slowly, whereas little space indicates a rapid change in z. Furthermore, to give a good three-dimensional illusion in a contour map, it is important to choose c-values that are *evenly spaced.*

FIGURE 13.7

FIGURE 13.8

EXAMPLE 3   Sketching a Contour Map

The hemisphere given by $f(x, y) = \sqrt{64 - x^2 - y^2}$ is shown in Figure 13.9. Sketch a contour map for this surface using level curves corresponding to $c = 0, 1, 2, \ldots, 8$.

Solution   For each value of c, the equation given by $f(x, y) = c$ is a circle (or point) in the xy-plane. For example, when $c_1 = 0$ the level curve is

$$x^2 + y^2 = 64 \qquad \text{Circle of radius 8}$$

which is a circle of radius 8. Figure 13.10 shows the nine level curves for the hemisphere.

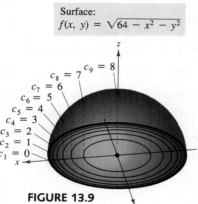

Surface:
$$f(x, y) = \sqrt{64 - x^2 - y^2}$$

$c_9 = 8$
$c_8 = 7$
$c_7 = 6$
$c_6 = 5$
$c_5 = 4$
$c_4 = 3$
$c_3 = 2$
$c_2 = 1$
$c_1 = 0$

FIGURE 13.9
Level curves

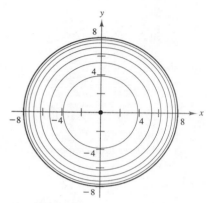

FIGURE 13.10
Contour map

EXAMPLE 4   Sketching a Contour Map

The hyperbolic paraboloid given by

$$z = y^2 - x^2$$

is shown in Figure 13.11. Sketch a contour map for this surface.

Solution   For each value of c, we let $f(x, y) = c$ and sketch the resulting level curve in the xy-plane. For this function, each of the level curves ($c \neq 0$) is a hyperbola whose asymptotes are the lines $y = \pm x$. If $c < 0$, the transverse axis is horizontal. For instance, the level curve for $c = -4$ is given by

$$\frac{x^2}{2^2} - \frac{y^2}{2^2} = 1. \qquad \text{Hyperbola with horizontal transverse axis}$$

If $c > 0$, the transverse axis is vertical. For instance, the level curve for $c = 4$ is given by

$$\frac{y^2}{2^2} - \frac{x^2}{2^2} = 1. \qquad \text{Hyperbola with vertical transverse axis}$$

If $c = 0$, the level curve is the degenerate conic representing the intersecting asymptotes, as shown in Figure 13.12.

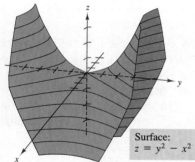

Surface:
$$z = y^2 - x^2$$

Hyperbolic Paraboloid

FIGURE 13.11

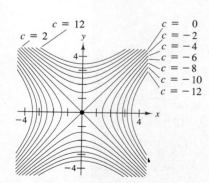

$c = 12$
$c = 2$
$c = 0$
$c = -2$
$c = -4$
$c = -6$
$c = -8$
$c = -10$
$c = -12$

FIGURE 13.12
Hyperbolic level curves (at increments of 2)

One example of a function of two variables used in economics is the **Cobb-Douglas production function.** This function is used as a model to represent the number of units produced by varying amounts of labor and capital. If x measures the units of labor and y measures the units of capital, then the number of units produced is given by

$$f(x, y) = Cx^a y^{1-a}$$

where C is constant and $0 < a < 1$.

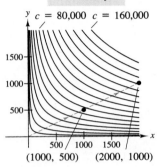

$$z = 100x^{0.6}y^{0.4}$$

EXAMPLE 5   The Cobb-Douglas Production Function

A manufacturer estimates a production function to be $f(x, y) = 100x^{0.6}y^{0.4}$, where x is the number of units of labor and y is the number of units of capital. Compare the production level when $x = 1000$ and $y = 500$ with the production level when $x = 2000$ and $y = 1000$.

Solution   When $x = 1000$ and $y = 500$, the production level is

$$f(1000, 500) = 100(1000^{0.6})(500^{0.4}) \approx 100(63.10)(12.01) \approx 75,786.$$

When $x = 2000$ and $y = 1000$, the production level is

$$f(2000, 1000) = 100(2000^{0.6})(1000^{0.4}) \approx 100(95.64)(15.85) \approx 151,572.$$

The level curves of the surface $z = f(x, y)$ are shown in Figure 13.13. Note that by doubling *both x and y*, you double the production level (see Exercise 66).

FIGURE 13.13
Level curves (at increments of 10,000)

Level Surfaces

The concept of a level curve can be extended by one dimension to define a **level surface.** If f is a function of three variables and c is a constant, then the graph of the equation $f(x, y, z) = c$ is a **level surface** of the function f, as shown in Figure 13.14.

With computers, engineers and scientists have developed other ways to view functions of three variables. For instance, Figure 13.15 shows a computer simulation that uses color to represent the pressure waves of a high-speed train traveling through a tunnel.

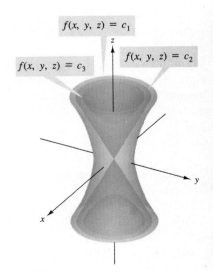

$$f(x, y, z) = c_1$$
$$f(x, y, z) = c_2$$
$$f(x, y, z) = c_3$$

FIGURE 13.14
Level surfaces of f

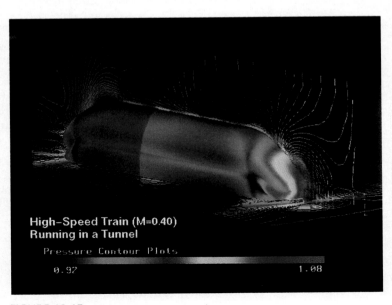

High-Speed Train (M=0.40)
Running in a Tunnel
Pressure Contour Plots
0.92   1.08

FIGURE 13.15

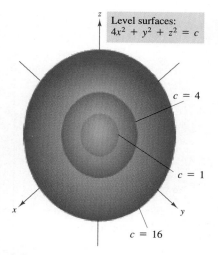

Level surfaces:
$4x^2 + y^2 + z^2 = c$

$c = 4$

$c = 1$

$c = 16$

FIGURE 13.16

MARY FAIRFAX SOMERVILLE

Somerville (1780–1872) was interested in the problem of creating geometric models for functions of several variables. Her most well-known book, *The Mechanics of the Heavens*, was published in 1831.

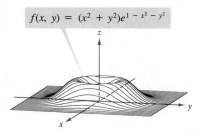

$f(x, y) = (x^2 + y^2)e^{1 - x^2 - y^2}$

FIGURE 13.17
Computer-generated graph

EXAMPLE 6   Level Surfaces

Describe the level surfaces of the function

$$f(x, y, z) = 4x^2 + y^2 + z^2.$$

Solution   Each level surface has an equation of the form

$$4x^2 + y^2 + z^2 = c. \qquad \text{Equation of level surface}$$

Therefore, the level surfaces are ellipsoids (whose cross sections parallel to the yz-plane are circles). As c increases, the radii of the circular cross sections increase according to the square root of c. For example, the level surfaces corresponding to the values $c = 1$, $c = 4$, and $c = 16$ are as follows.

$$\frac{x^2}{1/4} + \frac{y^2}{1} + \frac{z^2}{1} = 1 \qquad \text{Level surface for } c = 1 \text{ (Ellipse)}$$

$$\frac{x^2}{1} + \frac{y^2}{4} + \frac{z^2}{4} = 1 \qquad \text{Level surface for } c = 4 \text{ (Ellipse)}$$

$$\frac{x^2}{4} + \frac{y^2}{16} + \frac{z^2}{16} = 1 \qquad \text{Level surface for } c = 16 \text{ (Ellipse)}$$

These level surfaces are shown in Figure 13.16.

REMARK   If the function in Example 6 represents the *temperature* at the point (x, y, z), then the level surfaces shown in Figure 13.16 would be called **isothermal surfaces.**

Computer Graphics

The problem of sketching the graph of a surface in space can be simplified by using a computer. Although there are several types of three-dimensional graphing utilities, most use some form of trace analysis to give the illusion of three dimensions. To use such a graphing utility, you usually need to enter the equation of the surface, the region in the xy-plane over which the surface is to be plotted, and the number of traces to be taken. For instance, to sketch the surface given by

$$f(x, y) = (x^2 + y^2)e^{1-x^2-y^2}$$

you might choose the following bounds for x, y, and z.

$$-3 \leq x \leq 3 \qquad \text{Bounds for } x$$
$$-3 \leq y \leq 3 \qquad \text{Bounds for } y$$
$$0 \leq z \leq 3 \qquad \text{Bounds for } z$$

Figure 13.17 shows a computer-generated sketch of this surface using 26 traces taken parallel to the yz-plane. To heighten the three-dimensional effect, the program uses a "hidden line" routine. That is, it begins by plotting the traces in the foreground (those corresponding to the largest x-values), and then, as each new trace is plotted, the program determines whether all or only part of the next trace should be shown.

Table 13.1 shows a variety of surfaces that were plotted by computer.

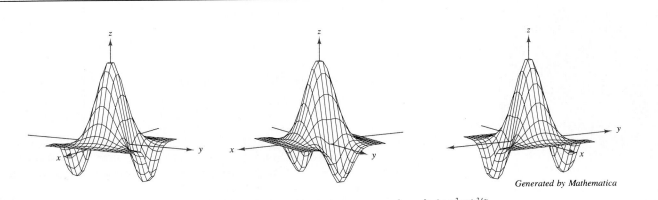

Three different views of the graph of $f(x, y) = (2 - y^2 + x^2)e^{1 - x^2 - (y^2/4)}$.

$$f(x, y) = \frac{-4x}{x^2 + y^2 + 1}$$

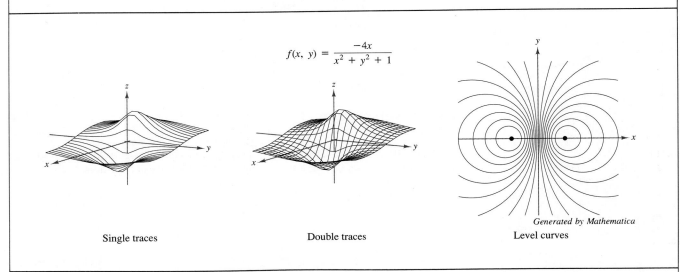

Single traces   Double traces   Level curves

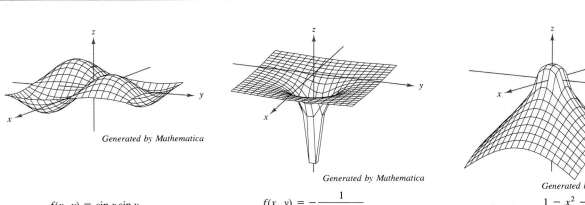

$f(x, y) = \sin x \sin y$ $f(x, y) = -\dfrac{1}{\sqrt{x^2 + y^2}}$ $f(x, y) = \dfrac{1 - x^2 - y^2}{\sqrt{|1 - x^2 - y^2|}}$

EXERCISES for Section 13.1

TECHNOLOGY
Laboratory Guide
Lab 13.1

In Exercises 1–12, find and simplify the function values.

1. $f(x, y) = \dfrac{x}{y}$

  a. $(3, 2)$ **b.** $(-1, 4)$ **c.** $(30, 5)$
  d. $(5, y)$ **e.** $(x, 2)$ **f.** $(5, t)$

2. $f(x, y) = 4 - x^2 - 4y^2$

  a. $(0, 0)$ **b.** $(0, 1)$ **c.** $(2, 3)$
  d. $(1, y)$ **e.** $(x, 0)$ **f.** $(t, 1)$

3. $f(x, y) = xe^y$

  a. $(5, 0)$ **b.** $(3, 2)$ **c.** $(2, -1)$
  d. $(5, y)$ **e.** $(x, 2)$ **f.** (t, t)

4. $g(x, y) = \ln |x + y|$

  a. $(2, 3)$ **b.** $(5, 6)$ **c.** $(e, 0)$
  d. $(0, 1)$ **e.** $(2, -3)$ **f.** (e, e)

5. $h(x, y, z) = \dfrac{xy}{z}$

  a. $(2, 3, 9)$ **b.** $(1, 0, 1)$

6. $f(x, y, z) = \sqrt{x + y + z}$

  a. $(0, 5, 4)$ **b.** $(6, 8, -3)$

7. $f(x, y) = x \sin y$

  a. $\left(2, \dfrac{\pi}{4}\right)$ **b.** $(3, 1)$

8. $V(r, h) = \pi r^2 h$

  a. $(3, 10)$ **b.** $(5, 2)$

9. $g(x, y) = \displaystyle\int_x^y (2t - 3)\, dt$

  a. $(0, 4)$ **b.** $(1, 4)$

10. $g(x, y) = \displaystyle\int_x^y \dfrac{1}{t}\, dt$

  a. $(4, 1)$ **b.** $(6, 3)$

11. $f(x, y) = x^2 - 2y$

  a. $\dfrac{f(x + \Delta x, y) - f(x, y)}{\Delta x}$ **b.** $\dfrac{f(x, y + \Delta y) - f(x, y)}{\Delta y}$

12. $f(x, y) = 3xy + y^2$

  a. $\dfrac{f(x + \Delta x, y) - f(x, y)}{\Delta x}$ **b.** $\dfrac{f(x, y + \Delta y) - f(x, y)}{\Delta y}$

In Exercises 13–24, describe the domain and range of the function.

13. $f(x, y) = \sqrt{4 - x^2 - y^2}$

14. $f(x, y) = \sqrt{4 - x^2 - 4y^2}$

15. $f(x, y) = \arcsin(x + y)$ **16.** $f(x, y) = \arccos(y/x)$

17. $f(x, y) = \ln(4 - x - y)$ **18.** $f(x, y) = \ln(4 - xy)$

19. $z = \dfrac{x + y}{xy}$ **20.** $z = \dfrac{xy}{x - y}$

21. $f(x, y) = e^{x/y}$ **22.** $f(x, y) = x^2 + y^2$

23. $g(x, y) = \dfrac{1}{xy}$ **24.** $g(x, y) = x\sqrt{y}$

25. The graphs labeled (a), (b), (c), and (d) are graphs of the function

$$f(x, y) = \frac{-4x}{x^2 + y^2 + 1}.$$

Match the four graphs with the points in space from which the surface is viewed. The four points are $(20, 15, 25)$, $(-15, 10, 20)$, $(20, 20, 0)$, and $(20, 0, 0)$.

(a)

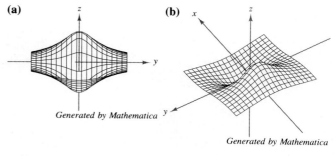

Generated by Mathematica

(b)

Generated by Mathematica

(c)

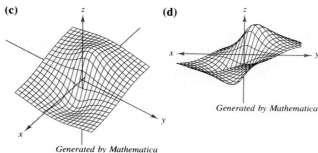

Generated by Mathematica

(d)

Generated by Mathematica

26. Use the function described in Exercise 25.

  a. Find the domain and range of the function.
  b. Identify the points in the xy-plane where the function value is 0.
  c. Does the surface pass through all the octants of the rectangular coordinate system? Give reasons for your answer.

In Exercises 27–30, match the graph of the given surface with one of the contour maps. [The contour maps are labeled (a), (b), (c), and (d).]

27. $f(x, y) = e^{1-x^2-y^2}$

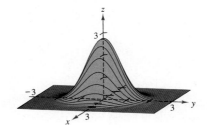

28. $f(x, y) = e^{1-x^2+y^2}$

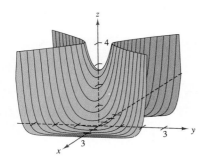

29. $f(x, y) = \ln|y - x^2|$

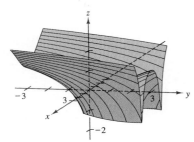

30. $f(x, y) = \cos\left(\dfrac{x^2 + 2y^2}{4}\right)$

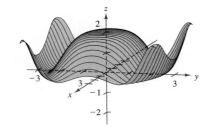

(a)

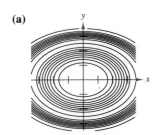

(b)

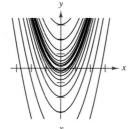

(c)

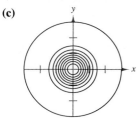

(d)

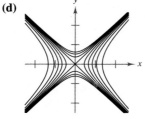

In Exercises 31–38, sketch the graph of the surface specified by the function.

31. $f(x, y) = 5$

32. $f(x, y) = 6 - 2x - 3y$

33. $f(x, y) = y^2$

34. $g(x, y) = \frac{1}{2}x$

35. $z = 4 - x^2 - y^2$

36. $z = \sqrt{x^2 + y^2}$

37. $f(x, y) = e^{-x}$

38. $f(x, y) = \begin{cases} xy, & x \geq 0, y \geq 0 \\ 0, & x < 0 \text{ or } y < 0 \end{cases}$

* **C** **In Exercises 39–42, use a graphing utility to graph the function.**

39. $z = y^2 - x^2 + 1$

40. $z = \frac{1}{12}\sqrt{144 - 16x^2 - 9y^2}$

41. $f(x, y) = x^2 e^{(-xy/2)}$

42. $f(x, y) = x \sin y$

43. a. Sketch the graph of the surface given by $f(x, y) = x^2 + y^2$.

   b. On the surface in part a, sketch the graphs of $z = f(1, y)$ and $z = f(x, 1)$.

44. a. Sketch the graph of the surface given by $f(x, y) = xy$ in the first octant.

   b. On the surface in part a, sketch the graph of $z = f(x, x)$.

In Exercises 45–52, describe the level curves of the function. Sketch the level curves for the given c-values.

45. $z = x + y$ $\qquad\qquad c = -1, 0, 2, 4$

46. $z = 6 - 2x - 3y$ $\qquad c = 0, 2, 4, 6, 8, 10$

47. $z = \sqrt{25 - x^2 - y^2}$ $\quad c = 0, 1, 2, 3, 4, 5$

48. $f(x, y) = x^2 + y^2$ $\qquad c = 0, 2, 4, 6, 8$

49. $f(x, y) = xy$ $\qquad\qquad c = \pm 1, \pm 2, \ldots, \pm 6$

50. $f(x, y) = e^{xy}$ $\qquad\quad c = 1, 2, 3, 4, \frac{1}{2}, \frac{1}{3}, \frac{1}{4}$

51. $f(x, y) = \dfrac{x}{x^2 + y}$ $\qquad c = \pm\frac{1}{2}, \pm 1, \pm\frac{3}{2}, \pm 2$

52. $f(x, y) = \ln(x - y)$ $\quad c = 0, \pm\frac{1}{2}, \pm 1, \frac{3}{2}, \pm 2$

53. All of the level curves of the surface given by $z = f(x, y)$ are circles. Does this imply that the graph of f is a hemisphere? Illustrate your answer with an example.

54. Construct a function whose level curves are lines passing through the origin.

In Exercises 55–60, sketch the level surface $f(x, y, z) = c$ at the specified value of c.

55. $f(x, y, z) = x - 2y + 3z$ $\qquad c = 6$

56. $f(x, y, z) = 4x + y + 2z$ $\qquad c = 4$

57. $f(x, y, z) = x^2 + y^2 + z^2$ $\qquad c = 9$

58. $f(x, y, z) = x^2 + y^2 - z$ $\qquad c = 1$

59. $f(x, y, z) = 4x^2 + 4y^2 - z^2$ $\quad c = 0$

60. $f(x, y, z) = \sin x - z$ $\qquad\quad c = 0$

*A **C** indicates an exercise in which you are instructed to use graphing technology or a symbolic computer algebra system. The solutions of other exercises may also be facilitated by appropriate technology.

61. *Investment*   In 1994, an investment of $1000 was made in a bond earning 10 percent compounded annually. Assume that the buyer pays tax at rate R and the annual rate of inflation is I. In the year 2004, the value V of the investment in constant 1994 dollars is

$$V(I, R) = 1000\left[\frac{1 + 0.10(1 - R)}{1 + I}\right]^{10}.$$

Use this function of two variables to complete the table.

	Inflation rate		
Tax rate	0	0.03	0.05
0			
0.28			
0.35			

62. *Investment*   A principal of $1000 is deposited in a savings account that earns an interest rate of r (expressed as a decimal), compounded continuously. The amount $A(r, t)$ after t years is given by

$$A(r, t) = 1000e^{rt}.$$

Use this function of two variables to complete the table.

	Number of years			
Rate	5	10	15	20
0.08				
0.10				
0.12				
0.14				

63. *Forestry*   The **Doyle Log Rule** is one of several methods used to determine the lumber yield of a log (in board-feet) in terms of its diameter d (in inches) and its length L (in feet). The number of board-feet is given by

$$N(d, L) = \left(\frac{d - 4}{4}\right)^2 L.$$

a. Find the number of board-feet of lumber in a log 22 inches in diameter and 12 feet in length.
b. Find $N(30, 12)$.

64. *Queuing Model*   The average length of time that a customer waits in line for service is given by

$$W(x, y) = \frac{1}{x - y}, \qquad y < x$$

where y is the average arrival rate, expressed as the number of customers per unit of time, and x is the average service rate, expressed in the same units. Evaluate W at the following points.
a. $(15, 10)$ **b.** $(12, 9)$ **c.** $(12, 6)$ **d.** $(4, 2)$

65. *Temperature Distribution*   The temperature T (in degrees Celsius) at any point (x, y) in a circular steel plate of radius 10 feet is

$$T = 600 - 0.75x^2 - 0.75y^2$$

where x and y are measured in feet. Sketch some of the isothermal curves.

66. *Cobb-Douglas Production Function*   Use the Cobb-Douglas production function (see Example 5) to show that if the number of units of labor and the number of units of capital are doubled, then the production level is also doubled.

67. *Construction Cost*   A rectangular box with an open top has a length of x feet, a width of y feet, and a height of z feet. Express the cost C of constructing the box as a function of x, y, and z if it costs $0.75 per square foot to build the base and $0.40 per square foot to build the sides.

68. *Volume*   A propane tank is constructed by welding hemispheres to the ends of a right circular cylinder. Write the volume V of the tank as a function of r and l, where r is the radius of the cylinder and hemispheres and l is the length of the cylinder.

69. *Ideal Gas Law*   According to the Ideal Gas Law, $PV = kT$, where P is pressure, V is volume, T is temperature (in Kelvins), and k is a constant of proportionality. A tank contains 2600 cubic inches of nitrogen at a pressure of 20 pounds per square inch and a temperature of $300°K$.
a. Determine k.
b. Express P as a function of V and T and describe the level curves.

70. *Equity*   The table gives the total revenue x (in billions of dollars), the total assets in properties, plants, and equipment y (in billions of dollars), and the common stockholder's equity per share z for Phillips Petroleum Company for the years 1986 through 1991. (*Source:* 1992 Annual Report)

Year	1986	1987	1988
Revenue (x)	10.018	10.917	11.490
Assets (y)	9.186	8.772	8.417
Equity (z)	7.55	7.08	8.69

Year	1989	1990	1991
Revenue (x)	12.492	13.975	13.259
Assets (y)	7.832	8.301	8.298
Equity (z)	8.74	10.51	10.61

A model for these data is

$$z = f(x, y) = 1.085x + 0.779y - 10.778.$$

a. Use the model to approximate the equity per share if $x = 15$ and $y = 10$.
b. Which of the two variables in this model has the greater influence on the equity per share of common stock?

71. *Meteorology* Meteorologists measure the atmospheric pressure in units called millibars. From these observations they create weather maps on which the curves of equal atmospheric pressure (isobars) are drawn (see figure). If the closer the isobars the higher the wind speed, match points *A*, *B*, and *C* with

a. the highest pressure.
b. the lowest pressure.
c. the highest wind velocity.

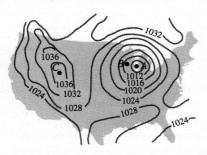

FIGURE FOR 71

72. *Acid Rain* The acidity of rainwater is measured in units called pH. A pH of 7 is neutral, smaller values are increasingly acidic, and larger values are increasingly alkaline. The map shows the curves of equal pH and gives evidence that downwind of heavily industrialized areas the acidity has been increasing. Using the level curves on the map, determine the direction of the prevailing winds in the northeastern United States.

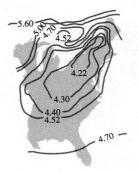

FIGURE FOR 72

13.2

Neighborhoods in the Plane • Limit of a Function of Two Variables • Continuity of a Function of Two Variables • Continuity of a Function of Three Variables

SONYA KOVALEVSKY

Much of the terminology used to define limits and continuity of a function of two or three variables was introduced by the German mathematician Karl Weierstrass (1815–1897). Weierstrass was a gifted teacher. One of his best known students was the Russian mathematician Sonya Kovalevsky (1850–1891), who applied many of Weierstrass's techniques to problems in mathematical physics and became one of the first women to gain acceptance as a research mathematician. (For more information on Sonya Kovalevsky, see the article "S. Kovalevsky: A Mathematical Lesson" by Karen D. Rappaport in the October, 1981 issue of the *American Mathematical Monthly.*)

Neighborhoods in the Plane

In this section, you will study limits and continuity involving functions of two or three variables. The section begins with functions of two variables. Then, at the end of the section, the concepts are extended to functions of three variables.

We begin our discussion of the limit of a function of two variables by defining a two-dimensional analog to an interval on the real line. Using the formula for the distance between two points (x, y) and (x_0, y_0) in the plane, you can define the **δ-neighborhood** about (x_0, y_0) to be the **disc** centered at (x_0, y_0) with radius $\delta > 0$

$$\{(x, y): \sqrt{(x - x_0)^2 + (y - y_0)^2} < \delta\} \qquad \text{Open disc}$$

as shown in Figure 13.18. When this formula contains the *less than* inequality, $<$, the disc is called **open,** and when it contains the *less than or equal to* inequality, $\leq$, the disc is called **closed.** This corresponds to the use of $<$ and $\leq$ to define open and closed intervals.

A point (x_0, y_0) in a plane region R is an **interior point** of R if there exists a δ-neighborhood about (x_0, y_0) that lies entirely in R, as shown in Figure 13.19. If every point in R is an interior point, then R is an **open region.** A point (x_0, y_0) is a **boundary point** of R if every open disc centered at (x_0, y_0) contains points inside R *and* points outside R. By definition, a region must contain its interior points, but it need not contain its boundary points. If a region contains all its boundary points, then the region is **closed.** A region that contains some but not all of its boundary points is neither open nor closed.

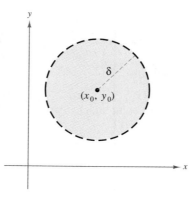

FIGURE 13.18
An open disc

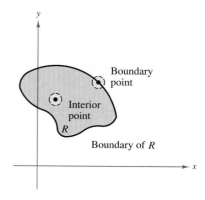

FIGURE 13.19
The boundary and interior points of a region R.

Limit of a Function of Two Variables

Definition of the Limit of a Function of Two Variables

Let f be a function of two variables defined on an open disc centered at (x_0, y_0), except possibly at (x_0, y_0), and let L be a real number. Then

$$\lim_{(x, y) \to (x_0, y_0)} f(x, y) = L$$

if for each $\varepsilon > 0$, there corresponds a $\delta > 0$ such that

$$|f(x, y) - L| < \varepsilon \quad \text{whenever} \quad 0 < \sqrt{(x - x_0)^2 + (y - y_0)^2} < \delta.$$

REMARK Graphically, this definition of a limit implies that for any point $(x, y) \ne (x_0, y_0)$ in the disc of radius δ, the value $f(x, y)$ lies between $L + \varepsilon$ and $L - \varepsilon$, as shown in Figure 13.20.

The definition of the limit of a function of two variables is similar to the definition of the limit of a function of a single variable, yet there is a critical difference. To determine whether a function of a single variable possesses a limit, you need only test the approach from two directions— from the left and from the right. If the function approaches the same limit from the right and from the left, you can conclude that the limit exists. However, for a function of two variables, the statement

$$(x, y) \longrightarrow (x_0, y_0)$$

means that the point (x, y) is allowed to approach (x_0, y_0) from any "direction." If the value of

$$\lim_{(x, y) \to (x_0, y_0)} f(x, y)$$

is not the same for all possible approaches, or **paths,** to (x_0, y_0), then the limit does not exist.

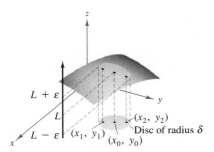

FIGURE 13.20
For any (x, y) in the circle of radius δ, the value $f(x, y)$ lies between $L + \varepsilon$ and $L - \varepsilon$.

EXAMPLE 1   Verifying a Limit by the Definition

Show that $\displaystyle \lim_{(x, y) \to (a, b)} x = a$.

Solution   Let $f(x, y) = x$ and $L = a$. You need to show that for each $\varepsilon > 0$, there exists a δ-neighborhood about (a, b) such that

$$|f(x, y) - L| = |x - a| < \varepsilon$$

whenever $(x, y) \ne (a, b)$ lies in the neighborhood. You can first observe that from

$$0 < \sqrt{(x - a)^2 + (y - b)^2} < \delta$$

it follows that

$$|f(x, y) - a| = |x - a| = \sqrt{(x - a)^2} \le \sqrt{(x - a)^2 + (y - b)^2} < \delta.$$

Thus, you can choose $\delta = \varepsilon$, and the limit is verified.

Limits of functions of several variables have the same properties regarding sums, differences, products, and quotients as do limits of functions of single variables. (See Theorem 1.2 in Chapter 1.) Some of these properties are used in the next example.

EXAMPLE 2   Verifying a Limit

Evaluate the following limits.

a. $\displaystyle\lim_{(x, y)\to(1, 2)} \frac{5x^2y}{x^2 + y^2}$ **b.** $\displaystyle\lim_{(x, y)\to(0, 0)} \frac{5x^2y}{x^2 + y^2}$

Solution

a. By using the properties of limits of products and sums, you obtain

$$\lim_{(x, y)\to(1, 2)} 5x^2y = 5(1^2)(2) = 10$$

and

$$\lim_{(x, y)\to(1, 2)} (x^2 + y^2) = (1^2 + 2^2) = 5.$$

Because the limit of a quotient is equal to the quotient of the limits (and the denominator is not 0), you have

$$\lim_{(x, y)\to(1, 2)} \frac{5x^2y}{x^2 + y^2} = \frac{10}{5} = 2.$$

b. In this case, the limits of the numerator and of the denominator are both 0, and so you cannot determine the existence (or nonexistence) of a limit by taking the limits of the numerator and denominator separately and then dividing. However, from the graph of f in Figure 13.21, it seems reasonable that the limit might be 0. Thus, you try applying the definition to $L = 0$. First, note that

$$|y| \le \sqrt{x^2 + y^2} \quad\text{and}\quad \frac{x^2}{x^2 + y^2} \le 1.$$

Then, in a δ-neighborhood about $(0, 0)$, you have $0 < \sqrt{x^2 + y^2} < \delta$, and it follows that for $(x, y) \ne (0, 0)$

$$\begin{aligned}
|f(x, y) - 0| &= \left| \frac{5x^2y}{x^2 + y^2} \right| \\
&= 5|y|\left(\frac{x^2}{x^2 + y^2} \right) \\
&\le 5|y| \\
&\le 5\sqrt{x^2 + y^2} \\
&< 5\delta.
\end{aligned}$$

Thus, you can choose $\delta = \varepsilon/5$ and conclude that

$$\lim_{(x, y)\to(0, 0)} \frac{5x^2y}{x^2 + y^2} = 0.$$

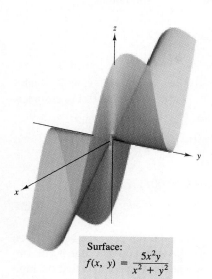

Surface:
$$f(x, y) = \frac{5x^2y}{x^2 + y^2}$$

FIGURE 13.21

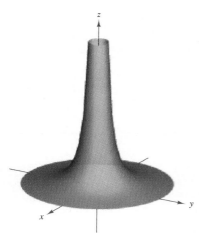

FIGURE 13.22

$\lim\limits_{(x,y)\to(0,0)} \dfrac{1}{x^2 + y^2}$ does not exist.

For some functions, it is easy to recognize that a limit does not exist. For instance, it is clear that the limit

$$\lim_{(x,y)\to(0,0)} \frac{1}{x^2 + y^2}$$

does not exist because the values of $f(x, y)$ increase without bound as (x, y) approaches 0 along *any* path (see Figure 13.22).

For other functions, it is not so easy to recognize that a limit does not exist. For instance, the next example describes a limit that does not exist because the function approaches different values along different paths.

EXAMPLE 3   A Limit that Does Not Exist

Show that the following limit does not exist.

$$\lim_{(x,y)\to(0,0)} \left(\frac{x^2 - y^2}{x^2 + y^2}\right)^2$$

Solution   The domain of the function given by

$$f(x, y) = \left(\frac{x^2 - y^2}{x^2 + y^2}\right)^2$$

consists of all points in the xy-plane except for the point $(0, 0)$. To show that the limit as (x, y) approaches $(0, 0)$ does not exist, consider approaching $(0, 0)$ along two different "paths," as shown in Figure 13.23. Along the x-axis, every point is of the form $(x, 0)$, and the limit along this approach is

$$\lim_{(x,0)\to(0,0)} \left(\frac{x^2 - 0^2}{x^2 + 0^2}\right)^2 = \lim_{(x,0)\to(0,0)} (1)^2$$

$$= 1. \qquad \text{\footnotesize Limit along line } y = x$$

However, if (x, y) approaches $(0, 0)$ along the line $y = x$, you obtain

$$\lim_{(x,x)\to(0,0)} \left(\frac{x^2 - x^2}{x^2 + x^2}\right)^2 = \lim_{(x,x)\to(0,0)} \left(\frac{0}{2x^2}\right)^2$$

$$= 0. \qquad \text{\footnotesize Limit along } x\text{-axis}$$

This means that in any open disc centered at $(0, 0)$ there are points (x, y) at which f takes on the value 1, and other points at which f takes on the value 0. For instance, $f(x, y) = 1$ at the points

$$(1, 0), \quad (0.1, 0), \quad (0.01, 0), \quad \text{and} \quad (0.001, 0)$$

and $f(x, y) = 0$ at the points

$$(1, 1), \quad (0.1, 0.1), \quad (0.01, 0.01), \quad \text{and} \quad (0.001, 0.001).$$

Hence, f does not have a limit as $(x, y) \to (0, 0)$.

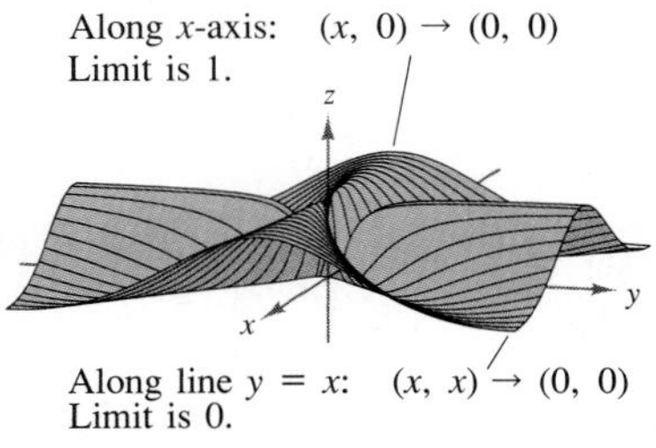

Along x-axis: $(x, 0) \to (0, 0)$
Limit is 1.

Along line $y = x$: $(x, x) \to (0, 0)$
Limit is 0.

FIGURE 13.23

$\lim\limits_{(x,y)\to(0,0)} \left(\dfrac{x^2 - y^2}{x^2 + y^2}\right)^2$ does not exist.

In Example 3, you were able to conclude that the limit did not exist because you found two approaches that yielded different limits. Be sure you see that if the two approaches had yielded the same limit, you still could not have concluded that the limit exists. To form such a conclusion, you must show that the limit is the same along *all* possible approaches.

Continuity of a Function of Two Variables

Notice in Example 2a that the limit of

$$f(x, y) = \frac{5x^2y}{(x^2 + y^2)}$$

as $(x, y) \to (1, 2)$ can be evaluated by direct substitution. That is, the limit is $f(1, 2) = 2$. In such cases the function f is said to be **continuous** at the point $(1, 2)$.

Definition of Continuity of a Function of Two Variables

A function f of two variables is **continuous at a point** (x_0, y_0) in an open region R if $f(x_0, y_0)$ is equal to the limit of $f(x, y)$ as (x, y) approaches (x_0, y_0). That is,

$$\lim_{(x, y) \to (x_0, y_0)} f(x, y) = f(x_0, y_0).$$

The function f is **continuous in the open region R** if it is continuous at every point in R.

REMARK   This definition of continuity can be extended to *boundary points* of the open region R by considering a special type of limit in which (x, y) is allowed to approach (x_0, y_0) along paths lying in the region R. This notion is similar to that of one-sided limits, as discussed in Chapter 1.

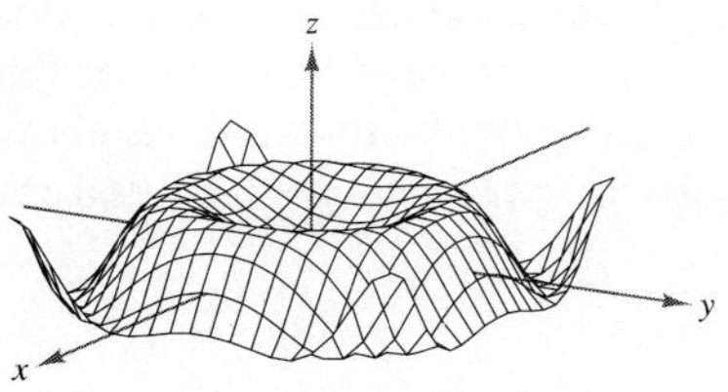

In Example 2b, it is shown that the function $f(x, y) = 5x^2y/(x^2 + y^2)$ is not continuous at $(0, 0)$. However, because the limit at this point exists, you can remove the discontinuity by defining f at $(0, 0)$ as being equal to its limit there. Such a discontinuity is called **removable**. As shown in Example 3, the function $f(x, y) = [(x^2 - y^2)/(x^2 + y^2)]^2$ is also not continuous at $(0, 0)$, but this discontinuity is **nonremovable.**

Surface: $f(x, y) = \frac{1}{2}\sin(x^2 + y^2)$

Generated by Mathematica

FIGURE 13.24
The function f is continuous at every point in the plane.

Surface:
$f(x, y) = \cos(y^2)e^{-\sqrt{x^2 + y^2}}$

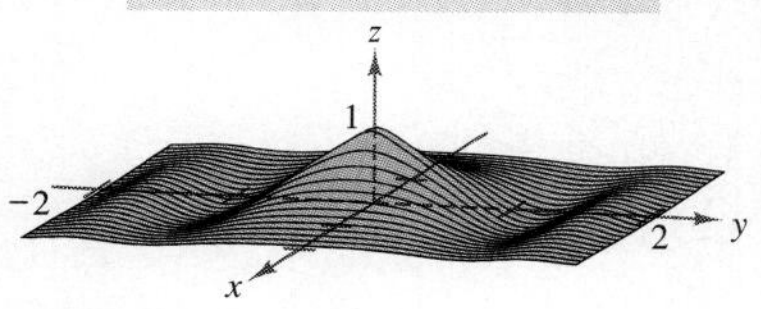

FIGURE 13.25
The function f is continuous at every point in the plane.

THEOREM 13.1   Properties of Continuous Functions of Two Variables

If k is a real number and f and g are continuous at (x_0, y_0), then the following functions are continuous at (x_0, y_0).

1. Scalar multiple kf
2. Sum and difference $f \pm g$
3. Product fg
4. Quotient f/g,   if $g(x_0, y_0) \neq 0$

Theorem 13.1 establishes the continuity of *polynomial* and *rational* functions at every point in their domains. Furthermore, the continuity of other types of functions can be extended naturally from one to two variables. For instance, the functions whose graphs are shown in Figures 13.24 and 13.25 are continuous at every point in the plane.

The next theorem states conditions under which a composite function is continuous.

THEOREM 13.2   Continuity of a Composite Function

If h is continuous at (x_0, y_0) and g is continuous at $h(x_0, y_0)$, then the composite function given by $(g \circ h)(x, y) = g(h(x, y))$ is continuous at (x_0, y_0). That is,

$$\lim_{(x, y) \to (x_0, y_0)} g(h(x, y)) = g(h(x_0, y_0)).$$

REMARK   Note in Theorem 13.2 that h is a function of two variables and g is a function of one variable.

EXAMPLE 4   Testing for Continuity

Discuss the continuity of the following functions.

a. $f(x, y) = \dfrac{x - 2y}{x^2 + y^2}$ **b.** $g(x, y) = \dfrac{2}{y - x^2}$

Solution

a. Because a rational function is continuous at every point in its domain, you can conclude that f is continuous at each point in the xy-plane except at $(0, 0)$, as shown in Figure 13.26.

b. The function given by $g(x, y) = 2/(y - x^2)$ is continuous except at the points at which the denominator is 0, $y - x^2 = 0$. Thus, you can conclude that the function is continuous at all points except those lying on the parabola $y = x^2$. Inside this parabola, you have $y > x^2$, and the surface represented by the function lies above the xy-plane, as shown in Figure 13.27. Outside the parabola, $y < x^2$, and the surface lies below the xy-plane.

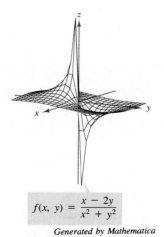

$$f(x, y) = \frac{x - 2y}{x^2 + y^2}$$

Generated by Mathematica

FIGURE 13.26
The function f is not continuous at $(0, 0)$.

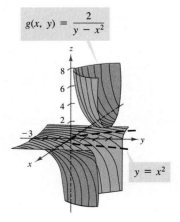

$$g(x, y) = \frac{2}{y - x^2}$$

$$y = x^2$$

FIGURE 13.27
The function g is not continuous. on the parabola $y = x^2$.

Continuity of a Function of Three Variables

The preceding definitions of limits and continuity can be extended to functions of three variables by considering points (x, y, z) within the *open sphere*

$$(x - x_0)^2 + (y - y_0)^2 + (z - z_0)^2 < \delta^2.$$ Open sphere

The radius of this sphere is δ, and the sphere is centered at (x_0, y_0, z_0), as shown in Figure 13.28. A point (x_0, y_0, z_0) in a region R in space is an **interior point** of R if there exists a δ-sphere about (x_0, y_0, z_0), that lies entirely in R. If every point in R is an interior point, then R is called **open.**

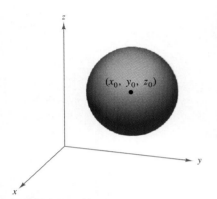

FIGURE 13.28
Open sphere in space

Definition of Continuity of a Function of Three Variables

A function f of three variables is **continuous at a point** (x_0, y_0, z_0) in an open region R if $f(x_0, y_0, z_0)$ is defined and equal to the limit of $f(x, y, z)$ as (x, y, z) approaches (x_0, y_0, z_0). That is,

$$\lim_{(x, y, z) \to (x_0, y_0, z_0)} f(x, y, z) = f(x_0, y_0, z_0)$$

The function f is **continuous in the open region R** if it is continuous at every point in R.

EXAMPLE 5   Testing Continuity of a Function of Three Variables

The function

$$f(x, y, z) = \frac{1}{x^2 + y^2 - z}$$

is continuous at each point in space except at the points on the paraboloid given by $z = x^2 + y^2$.

EXERCISES for Section 13.2

TECHNOLOGY
Laboratory Guide
Lab 13.2

In Exercises 1–4, find the indicated limit by using the limits

$$\lim_{(x, y) \to (a, b)} f(x, y) = 5 \quad \text{and} \quad \lim_{(x, y) \to (a, b)} g(x, y) = 3.$$

1. $\displaystyle \lim_{(x, y) \to (a, b)} [f(x, y) - g(x, y)]$

2. $\displaystyle \lim_{(x, y) \to (a, b)} \left[\frac{4f(x, y)}{g(x, y)} \right]$

3. $\displaystyle \lim_{(x, y) \to (a, b)} [f(x, y) g(x, y)]$

4. $\displaystyle \lim_{(x, y) \to (a, b)} \left[\frac{f(x, y) - g(x, y)}{f(x, y)} \right]$

In Exercises 5–14, find the limit and discuss the continuity of the function.

5. $\displaystyle \lim_{(x, y) \to (2, 1)} (x + 3y^2)$

6. $\displaystyle \lim_{(x, y) \to (0, 0)} (5x + 3xy + y + 1)$

7. $\displaystyle \lim_{(x, y) \to (2, 4)} \frac{x + y}{x - y}$

8. $\displaystyle \lim_{(x, y) \to (1, 1)} \frac{x}{\sqrt{x + y}}$

9. $\displaystyle \lim_{(x, y) \to (0, 1)} \frac{\arcsin(x/y)}{1 + xy}$

10. $\displaystyle \lim_{(x, y) \to (\pi/4, 2)} y \sin xy$

11. $\lim\limits_{(x,y)\to(0,0)} e^{xy}$

12. $\lim\limits_{(x,y)\to(1,1)} \dfrac{xy}{x^2 + y^2}$

13. $\lim\limits_{(x,y,z)\to(1,2,5)} \sqrt{x + y + z}$

14. $\lim\limits_{(x,y,z)\to(2,0,1)} xe^{yz}$

In Exercises 15–18, discuss the continuity of the function and evaluate the limit of $f(x, y)$ (if it exists) as $(x, y) \to (0, 0)$.

15. $f(x, y) = e^{xy}$

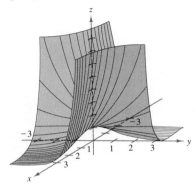

16. $f(x, y) = \dfrac{x^2}{(x^2 + 1)(y^2 + 1)}$

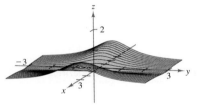

17. $f(x, y) = \ln(x^2 + y^2)$

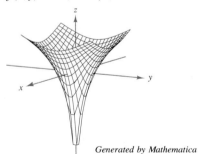

Generated by Mathematica

18. $f(x, y) = 1 - \dfrac{\cos(x^2 + y^2)}{x^2 + y^2}$

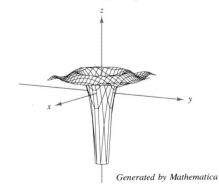

Generated by Mathematica

In Exercises 19–22, discuss the continuity of the function and evaluate the limit along the suggested paths. Does the limit exist? Why or why not?

19. $\lim\limits_{(x,y)\to(0,0)} \dfrac{xy}{x^2 + y^2}$

Paths: $y = 0$ and $y = x$

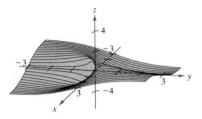

20. $\lim\limits_{(x,y)\to(0,0)} \dfrac{y}{x^2 + y^2}$

Paths: $y = 0$ and $y = x$

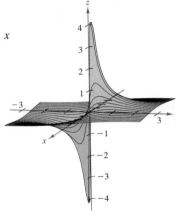

21. $\lim\limits_{(x,y)\to(0,0)} -\dfrac{xy^2}{x^2 + y^4}$

Paths: $x = y^2$ and $x = -y^2$

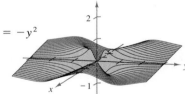

22. $\lim\limits_{(x,y)\to(0,0)} \dfrac{2x - y^2}{2x^2 + y}$

Paths: $y = 0$ and $y = x$

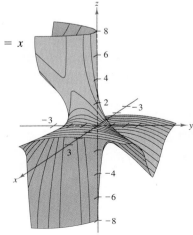

C In Exercises 23–26, use a graphing utility to graph the function and find (if it exists)

$$\lim_{(x,y)\to(0,0)} f(x,y).$$

23. $f(x,y) = \sin x + \cos y$

24. $f(x,y) = \sin\dfrac{1}{x} + \cos\dfrac{1}{x}$

25. $f(x,y) = \dfrac{x^2 y}{x^4 + 4y^2}$

26. $f(x,y) = \dfrac{x^2 + y^2}{x^2 y}$

In Exercises 27–30, use polar coordinates to find the limit. (*Hint*: Let $x = r\cos\theta$ and $y = r\sin\theta$, and note that $(x,y) \to (0,0)$ is equivalent to $r \to 0$.)

27. $\displaystyle\lim_{(x,y)\to(0,0)} \dfrac{\sin(x^2 + y^2)}{x^2 + y^2}$

28. $\displaystyle\lim_{(x,y)\to(0,0)} \dfrac{xy^2}{x^2 + y^2}$

29. $\displaystyle\lim_{(x,y)\to(0,0)} \dfrac{x^3 + y^3}{x^2 + y^2}$

30. $\displaystyle\lim_{(x,y)\to(0,0)} \dfrac{x^2 y^2}{x^2 + y^2}$

In Exercises 31–34, discuss the continuity of the function.

31. $f(x,y,z) = \dfrac{1}{\sqrt{x^2 + y^2 + z^2}}$

32. $f(x,y,z) = \dfrac{z}{x^2 + y^2 - 4}$

33. $f(x,y,z) = \dfrac{\sin z}{e^x + e^y}$

34. $f(x,y,z) = xy\sin z$

In Exercises 35–38, discuss the continuity of the composite function $f \circ g$.

35. $f(t) = t^2$
    $g(x,y) = 3x - 2y$

36. $f(t) = \dfrac{1}{t}$
    $g(x,y) = x^2 + y^2$

37. $f(t) = \dfrac{1}{t}$
    $g(x,y) = 3x - 2y$

38. $f(t) = \dfrac{1}{4 - t}$
    $g(x,y) = x^2 + y^2$

In Exercises 39–42, find the following limits.

a. $\displaystyle\lim_{\Delta x\to 0} \dfrac{f(x + \Delta x, y) - f(x,y)}{\Delta x}$

b. $\displaystyle\lim_{\Delta y\to 0} \dfrac{f(x, y + \Delta y) - f(x,y)}{\Delta y}$

39. $f(x,y) = x^2 - 4y$

40. $f(x,y) = x^2 + y^2$

41. $f(x,y) = 2x + xy - 3y$

42. $f(x,y) = \sqrt{y}(y + 1)$

43. Prove that

$$\lim_{(x,y)\to(a,b)} [f(x,y) + g(x,y)] = L_1 + L_2$$

where $f(x,y)$ approaches L_1 and $g(x,y)$ approaches L_2 as $(x,y) \to (a,b)$.

44. Prove that if f is continuous and $f(a,b) < 0$, then there exists a δ-neighborhood about (a,b) such that $f(x,y) < 0$ for every point (x,y) in the neighborhood.

True or False In Exercises 45–48, determine whether the statement is true or false. If it is false, explain why or give an example that shows it is false.

45. If $\displaystyle\lim_{(x,y)\to(0,0)} f(x,y) = 0$, then $\displaystyle\lim_{x\to 0} f(x,0) = 0$.

46. If $\displaystyle\lim_{(x,y)\to(0,0)} f(0,y) = 0$, then $\displaystyle\lim_{(x,y)\to(0,0)} f(x,y) = 0$.

47. If f is continuous for all nonzero x and y and $f(0,0) = 0$, then $\displaystyle\lim_{(x,y)\to(0,0)} f(x,y) = 0$.

48. If g and h are continuous functions of x and y, respectively, and $f(x,y) = g(x) + h(y)$, then f is continuous.

49. Prove that

$$\lim_{(x,y)\to(0,0)} \dfrac{xy^3}{x^2 + 2y^6}$$

does not exist.

13.3

Partial Derivatives of a Function of Two Variables • Partial Derivatives of a Function of Three or More Variables • Higher-Order Partial Derivatives

JEAN LE ROND D'ALEMBERT

The introduction of partial derivatives followed Newton's and Leibniz's work in calculus by several years. Between 1730 and 1760, Leonhard Euler and Jean Le Rond d'Alembert (1717–1783) separately published several papers on dynamics, in which they established much of the theory of partial derivatives. These papers used functions of two or more variables to study problems involving equilibrium, fluid motion, and vibrating strings.

Partial Derivatives of a Function of Two Variables

In applications of functions of several variables, the question often arises, "How will a function be affected by a change in one of its independent variables?" You can answer this by considering the independent variables one at a time. For example, to determine the effect of a catalyst in an experiment, a chemist could conduct the experiment several times using varying amounts of the catalyst, while keeping constant other variables such as temperature and pressure. You can use a similar procedure to determine the rate of change of a function f with respect to one of its several independent variables. The process is called **partial differentiation,** and the result is referred to as the **partial derivative** of f with respect to the chosen independent variable.

Definition of Partial Derivatives of a Function of Two Variables

If $z = f(x, y)$, then the **first partial derivatives** of f with respect to x and y are the functions f_x and f_y defined by

$$f_x(x, y) = \lim_{\Delta x \to 0} \frac{f(x + \Delta x, y) - f(x, y)}{\Delta x}$$

$$f_y(x, y) = \lim_{\Delta y \to 0} \frac{f(x, y + \Delta y) - f(x, y)}{\Delta y}$$

provided the limits exist.

This definition indicates that if $z = f(x, y)$, then to find f_x you *consider y constant* and differentiate with respect to x. Similarly, to find f_y, you *consider x constant* and differentiate with respect to y.

EXAMPLE 1   Finding Partial Derivatives

Find f_x and f_y for $f(x, y) = 3x - x^2y^2 + 2x^3y$.

Solution   Considering y to be constant and differentiating with respect to x produces

$$f_x(x, y) = 3 - 2xy^2 + 6x^2y.$$

Considering x to be constant and differentiating with respect to y produces

$$f_y(x, y) = -2x^2y + 2x^3.$$

Notation for First Partial Derivatives

For $z = f(x, y)$, the partial derivatives f_x and f_y are denoted by

$$\frac{\partial}{\partial x} f(x, y) = f_x(x, y) = z_x = \frac{\partial z}{\partial x}$$

and

$$\frac{\partial}{\partial x} f(x, y) = f_x(x, y) = z_x = \frac{\partial z}{\partial x}$$

The first partials evaluated at the point (a, b) are denoted by

$$\frac{\partial z}{\partial x}\bigg|_{(a, b)} = f_x(a, b) \quad \text{and} \quad \frac{\partial z}{\partial y}\bigg|_{(a, b)} = f_y(a, b).$$

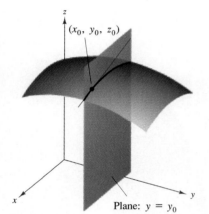

FIGURE 13.29

$\dfrac{\partial f}{\partial x} =$ (slope in x-direction)

EXAMPLE 2   Finding and Evaluating Partial Derivatives

For $f(x, y) = xe^{x^2 y}$, find f_x and f_y, and evaluate each at the point $(1, \ln 2)$.

Solution   Because

$$f_x(x, y) = xe^{x^2 y}(2xy) + e^{x^2 y}$$

the partial derivative of f with respect to x at $(1, \ln 2)$ is

$$f_x(1, \ln 2) = e^{\ln 2}(2 \ln 2) + e^{\ln 2} = 4 \ln 2 + 2.$$

Because

$$f_y(x, y) = xe^{x^2 y}(x^2) = x^3 e^{x^2 y}$$

the partial derivative of f with respect to y at $(1, \ln 2)$ is

$$f_y(1, \ln 2) = e^{\ln 2} = 2.$$

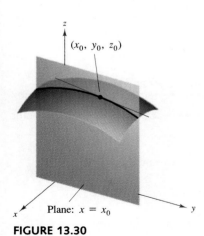

FIGURE 13.30

$\dfrac{\partial f}{\partial y} =$ (slope in y-direction)

The partial derivatives of a function of two variables, $z = f(x, y)$, have a useful geometric interpretation. If $y = y_0$, then $z = f(x, y_0)$ represents the curve formed by intersecting the surface $z = f(x, y)$ with the plane $y = y_0$, as shown in Figure 13.29. Therefore,

$$f_x(x_0, y_0) = \lim_{\Delta x \to 0} \frac{f(x_0 + \Delta x, y_0) - f(x_0, y_0)}{\Delta x}$$

represents the slope of this curve at the point $(x_0, y_0, f(x_0, y_0))$. Note that both the curve and the tangent line lie in the plane $y = y_0$. Similarly,

$$f_y(x_0, y_0) = \lim_{\Delta y \to 0} \frac{f(x_0, y_0 + \Delta y) - f(x_0, y_0)}{\Delta y}$$

represents the slope of the curve given by the intersection of $z = f(x, y)$ and the plane $x = x_0$ at $(x_0, y_0, f(x_0, y_0))$, as shown in Figure 13.30.

Informally, we say that the values of $\partial f / \partial x$ and $\partial f / \partial y$ at the point (x_0, y_0, z_0) denote the **slope of the surface in the x- and y-directions,** respectively.

EXAMPLE 3   **Finding the Slope of a Surface in the *x*- and *y*-Directions**

Find the slopes of the surface given by

$$f(x, y) = -\frac{x^2}{2} - y^2 + \frac{25}{8}$$

at the point $\left(\frac{1}{2}, 1, 2\right)$ in the *x*-direction and the *y*-direction.

Solution   The partial derivatives of *f* with respect to *x* and *y* are

$$f_x(x, y) = -x \quad \text{and} \quad f_y(x, y) = -2y.$$

Thus, in the *x*-direction, the slope is

$$f_x\left(\frac{1}{2}, 1\right) = -\frac{1}{2} \qquad \text{Figure 13.31(a)}$$

and in the *y*-direction, the slope is

$$f_y\left(\frac{1}{2}, 1\right) = -2. \qquad \text{Figure 13.31(b)}$$

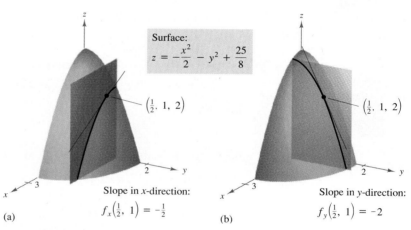

Surface:
$$z = -\frac{x^2}{2} - y^2 + \frac{25}{8}$$

$\left(\frac{1}{2}, 1, 2\right)$

(a) Slope in *x*-direction:
$$f_x\left(\frac{1}{2}, 1\right) = -\frac{1}{2}$$

(b) Slope in *y*-direction:
$$f_y\left(\frac{1}{2}, 1\right) = -2$$

FIGURE 13.31

EXAMPLE 4   **Finding the Slope of a Surface in the *x*- and *y*-Directions**

Find the slope of the surface given by $f(x, y) = 1 - (x - 1)^2 - (y - 2)^2$ at the point $(1, 2, 1)$ in the *x*-direction and in the *y*-direction.

Solution   The partial derivatives of *f* with respect to *x* and *y* are

$$f_x(x, y) = -2(x - 1) \quad \text{and} \quad f_y(x, y) = -2(y - 2).$$

Thus, at the point $(1, 2, 1)$, the slopes in the *x*- and *y*-directions are

$$f_x(1, 2) = -2(1 - 1) = 0 \quad \text{and} \quad f_y(1, 2) = -2(2 - 2) = 0$$

as indicated in Figure 13.32.

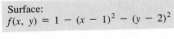

Surface:
$$f(x, y) = 1 - (x - 1)^2 - (y - 2)^2$$

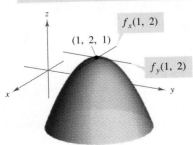

$(1, 2, 1)$

$f_x(1, 2)$

$f_y(1, 2)$

FIGURE 13.32

No matter how many variables are involved, partial derivatives of several variables can be interpreted as *rates of change*.

EXAMPLE 5 Using Partial Derivatives to Find Rates of Change

The area of a parallelogram with adjacent sides a and b and included angle θ is given by $A = ab \sin\theta$, as shown in Figure 13.33.

a. Find the rate of change of A with respect to a when $a = 10$, $b = 20$, and $\theta = \pi/6$.
b. Find the rate of change of A with respect to θ when $a = 10$, $b = 20$, and $\theta = \pi/6$.

Solution

a. To find the rate of change of the area with respect to a, hold b and θ constant and differentiate with respect to a to obtain

$$\frac{\partial A}{\partial a} = b \sin\theta.$$

When $a = 10$, $b = 20$, and $\theta = \pi/6$, you have

$$\partial A/\partial a = 20 \sin(\pi/6) = 10.$$

b. To find the rate of change of the area with respect to θ, hold a and b constant and differentiate with respect to θ to obtain

$$\frac{\partial A}{\partial \theta} = ab \cos\theta.$$

When $a = 10$, $b = 20$, and $\theta = \pi/6$, you have

$$\partial A/\partial\theta = 200 \cos(\pi/6) = 100\sqrt{3}.$$

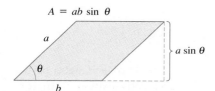

FIGURE 13.33
The area of the parallelogram is $ab \sin\theta$.

Partial Derivatives of a Function of Three or More Variables

The concept of a partial derivative can be extended naturally to functions of three or more variables. For instance, if $w = f(x, y, z)$, then there are three partial derivatives, each of which is formed by holding two of the variables constant. That is, to define the partial derivative of w with respect to x, consider y and z to be constant and differentiate with respect to x. A similar process is used to find the derivatives of w with respect to y and with respect to z.

$$\frac{\partial w}{\partial x} = f_x(x, y, z) = \lim_{\Delta x \to 0} \frac{f(x + \Delta x, y, z) - f(x, y, z)}{\Delta x}$$

$$\frac{\partial w}{\partial y} = f_y(x, y, z) = \lim_{\Delta y \to 0} \frac{f(x, y + \Delta y, z) - f(x, y, z)}{\Delta y}$$

$$\frac{\partial w}{\partial z} = f_z(x, y, z) = \lim_{\Delta z \to 0} \frac{f(x, y, z + \Delta z) - f(x, y, z)}{\Delta z}$$

In general, if $w = f(x_1, x_2, \ldots, x_n)$, then there are n partial derivatives denoted by

$$\frac{\partial w}{\partial x_k} = f_{x_k}(x_1, x_2, \ldots, x_n), \qquad k = 1, 2, \ldots, n.$$

To find the partial derivative with respect to one of the variables, hold the other variables constant and differentiate with respect to the given variable.

EXAMPLE 6   Finding Partial Derivatives

a. To find the partial derivative of $f(x, y, z) = xy + yz^2 + xz$ with respect to z, consider x and y to be constant and obtain

$$\frac{\partial}{\partial z}[xy + yz^2 + xz] = 2yz + x.$$

b. To find the partial derivative of $f(x, y, z) = z \sin(xy^2 + 2z)$ with respect to z, consider x and y to be constant. Then, using the Product Rule, you obtain

$$\frac{\partial}{\partial z}[z \sin(xy^2 + 2z)] = (z)\frac{\partial}{\partial z}[\sin(xy^2 + 2z)] + \sin(xy^2 + 2z)\frac{\partial}{\partial z}[z]$$

$$= (z)[\cos(xy^2 + 2z)](2) + \sin(xy^2 + 2z)$$

$$= 2z \cos(xy^2 + 2z) + \sin(xy^2 + 2z).$$

c. To find the partial derivative of $f(x, y, z, w) = (x + y + z)/w$ with respect to w, consider x, y, and z to be constant and obtain

$$\frac{\partial}{\partial w}\left[\frac{x + y + z}{w}\right] = -\frac{x + y + z}{w^2}.$$

Higher-Order Partial Derivatives

As is true for ordinary derivatives, it is possible to take second, third, and higher partial derivatives of a function of several variables, provided such derivatives exist. Higher-order derivatives are denoted by the order in which the differentiation occurs. For instance, the function $z = f(x, y)$ has the following second partial derivatives.

1. Differentiate twice with respect to x:

$$\frac{\partial}{\partial x}\left(\frac{\partial f}{\partial x}\right) = \frac{\partial^2 f}{\partial x^2} = f_{xx}.$$

2. Differentiate twice with respect to y:

$$\frac{\partial}{\partial y}\left(\frac{\partial f}{\partial y}\right) = \frac{\partial^2 f}{\partial y^2} = f_{yy}.$$

3. Differentiate first with respect to x and then with respect to y:

$$\frac{\partial}{\partial y}\left(\frac{\partial f}{\partial x}\right) = \frac{\partial^2 f}{\partial y \partial x} = f_{xy}.$$

4. Differentiate first with respect to y and then with respect to x:

$$\frac{\partial}{\partial x}\left(\frac{\partial f}{\partial y}\right) = \frac{\partial^2 f}{\partial x \partial y} = f_{yx}.$$

REMARK Note that the two types of notation for mixed partials have different conventions for indicating the order of differentiation.

$$\frac{\partial}{\partial y}\left(\frac{\partial f}{\partial x}\right) = \frac{\partial^2 f}{\partial y \partial x} \qquad \text{Right-to-left order}$$

$$(f_x)_y = f_{xy} \qquad \text{Left-to-right order}$$

You can remember the order by observing that in both notations, you differentiate first with respect to the variable "nearest" f.

The third and fourth cases are called **mixed partial derivatives.**

EXAMPLE 7   Finding Second Partial Derivatives

Find the second partial derivatives of $f(x, y) = 3xy^2 - 2y + 5x^2y^2$, and determine the value of $f_{xy}(-1, 2)$.

Solution   Begin by finding the first partial derivatives with respect to x and y.

$$f_x(x, y) = 3y^2 + 10xy^2 \quad \text{and} \quad f_y(x, y) = 6xy - 2 + 10x^2y$$

Then, differentiate each of these with respect to x and y.

$$f_{xx}(x, y) = 10y^2 \quad \text{and} \quad f_{yy}(x, y) = 6x + 10x^2$$
$$f_{xy}(x, y) = 6y + 20xy \quad \text{and} \quad f_{yx}(x, y) = 6y + 20xy$$

At $(-1, 2)$, the value of f_{xy} is $f_{xy}(-1, 2) = 12 - 40 = -28$.

Notice in Example 7 that the two mixed partials are equal. Sufficient conditions for this occurrence are given in the next theorem.

THEOREM 13.3   Equality of Mixed Partial Derivatives

If f is a function of x and y such that f_{xy} and f_{yx} are continuous on an open disc R, then for every (x, y) in R,

$$f_{xy}(x, y) = f_{yx}(x, y).$$

Theorem 13.3 also applies to a function f of *three or more variables* so long as all second partial derivatives are continuous. For example, if $w = f(x, y, z)$ and all the second partial derivatives are continuous in an open region R, then at each point in R the order of differentiation in the mixed second partial derivatives is irrelevant. If the third partial derivatives of f are also continuous, then the order of differentiation of the mixed third partial derivatives is irrelevant.

EXAMPLE 8   Finding Higher-Order Partial Derivatives

Show that $f_{xz} = f_{zx}$ and $f_{xzz} = f_{zxz} = f_{zzx}$ for the function given by

$$f(x, y, z) = ye^x + x \ln z.$$

Solution
First partials:

$$f_x(x, y, z) = ye^x + \ln z, \qquad f_z(x, y, z) = \frac{x}{z}$$

Second partials: (Note that the first two are equal.)

$$f_{xz}(x, y, z) = \frac{1}{z}, \qquad f_{zx}(x, y, z) = \frac{1}{z}, \qquad f_{zz}(x, y, z) = -\frac{x}{z^2}$$

Third partials: (Note that all three are equal.)

$$f_{xzz}(x, y, z) = -\frac{1}{z^2}, \qquad f_{zxz}(x, y, z) = -\frac{1}{z^2}, \qquad f_{zzx}(x, y, z) = -\frac{1}{z^2}$$

EXERCISES for Section 13.3

In Exercises 1–20, find the first partial derivatives with respect to x and with respect to y.

1. $f(x, y) = 2x - 3y + 5$ **2.** $f(x, y) = x^2 - 3y^2 + 7$

3. $z = x\sqrt{y}$ **4.** $z = x^2 - 3xy + y^2$

5. $z = x^2 e^{2y}$ **6.** $z = xe^{x/y}$

7. $z = \ln(x^2 + y^2)$ **8.** $z = \ln\sqrt{xy}$

9. $z = \ln\dfrac{x + y}{x - y}$ **10.** $z = \dfrac{x^2}{2y} + \dfrac{4y^2}{x}$

11. $h(x, y) = e^{-(x^2 + y^2)}$ **12.** $g(x, y) = \ln\sqrt{x^2 + y^2}$

13. $f(x, y) = \sqrt{x^2 + y^2}$ **14.** $f(x, y) = \dfrac{xy}{x^2 + y^2}$

15. $z = \tan(2x - y)$ **16.** $z = \sin 3x \cos 3y$

17. $z = e^y \sin xy$ **18.** $z = \cos(x^2 + y^2)$

19. $f(x, y) = \displaystyle\int_x^y (t^2 - 1)\, dt$

20. $f(x, y) = \displaystyle\int_x^y (2t + 1)\, dt + \int_y^x (2t - 1)\, dt$

In Exercises 21–24, use the limit definition of partial derivatives to find $f_x(x, y)$ and $f_y(x, y)$.

21. $f(x, y) = 2x + 3y$ **22.** $f(x, y) = \dfrac{1}{x + y}$

23. $f(x, y) = \sqrt{x + y}$ **24.** $f(x, y) = x^2 - 2xy + y^2$

In Exercises 25–28, find the slopes of the surface at the specified point in the x- and y-directions.

25. $g(x, y) = 4 - x^2 - y^2$
$(1, 1, 2)$

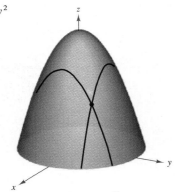

26. $h(x, y) = x^2 - y^2$
$(-2, 1, 3)$

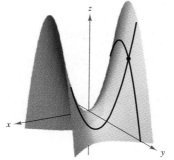

27. $z = e^{-x} \cos y$
$(0, 0, 1)$

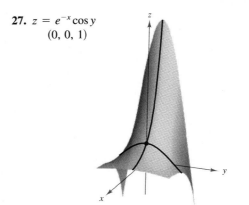

28. $z = \frac{1}{2}\sin(2x - y)$
$\left(\dfrac{\pi}{2}, \dfrac{\pi}{3}, \dfrac{\sqrt{3}}{4}\right)$

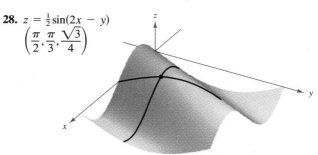

In Exercises 29–32, evaluate f_x and f_y at the specified point.

Function	Point
29. $f(x, y) = \arctan\dfrac{y}{x}$	$\left(2, -2, -\dfrac{\pi}{4}\right)$
30. $f(x, y) = \arcsin xy$	$\left(1, 0, \dfrac{\pi}{2}\right)$
31. $f(x, y) = \dfrac{xy}{x - y}$	$(2, -2, -1)$
32. $f(x) = \dfrac{4xy}{\sqrt{x^2 + y^2}}$	$(1, 0, 0)$

In Exercises 33–36, sketch the curve formed by the intersection of the given surface and plane. Find the slope of the curve at the given point.

Surface	Plane	Point
33. $z = \sqrt{49 - x^2 - y^2}$	$x = 2$	$(2, 3, 6)$
34. $z = x^2 + 4y^2$	$y = 1$	$(2, 1, 8)$
35. $z = 9x^2 - y^2$	$y = 3$	$(1, 3, 0)$
36. $z = 9x^2 - y^2$	$x = 1$	$(1, 3, 0)$

In Exercises 37–44, find the second partial derivatives
$$\dfrac{\partial^2 z}{\partial x^2}, \quad \dfrac{\partial^2 z}{\partial y^2}, \quad \dfrac{\partial^2 z}{\partial y\, \partial x}, \quad \text{and} \quad \dfrac{\partial^2 z}{\partial x\, \partial y}.$$

Observe that the second mixed partials are equal.

37. $z = x^2 - 2xy + 3y^2$ **38.** $z = x^4 - 3x^2 y^2 + y^4$

39. $z = \sqrt{x^2 + y^2}$

40. $z = \ln(x - y)$

41. $z = e^x \tan y$

42. $z = xe^y + ye^x$

43. $z = \arctan\dfrac{y}{x}$

44. $z = \sin(x - 2y)$

C In Exercises 45–48, use a symbolic differentiation utility to find the first and second partial derivatives of the function.

45. $z = x \sec y$

46. $z = \sqrt{9 - x^2 - y^2}$

47. $z = \ln\dfrac{x}{x^2 + y^2}$

48. $z = \dfrac{xy}{x - y}$

In Exercises 49–54, find the first partial derivatives with respect to x, y, and z.

49. $w = \sqrt{x^2 + y^2 + z^2}$

50. $w = \dfrac{xy}{x + y + z}$

51. $F(x, y, z) = \ln\sqrt{x^2 + y^2 + z^2}$

52. $G(x, y, z) = \dfrac{1}{\sqrt{1 - x^2 - y^2 - z^2}}$

53. $H(x, y, z) = \sin(x + 2y + 3z)$

54. $f(x, y, z) = 3x^2y - 5xyz + 10yz^2$

In Exercises 55–58, show that the mixed partials $f_{xyy}, f_{yxy},$ and f_{yyx} are equal.

55. $w = xyz$

56. $w = x^2 - 3xy + 4yz + z^3$

57. $f(x, y, z) = e^{-x} \sin yz$

58. $f(x, y, z) = \dfrac{x}{y + z}$

Laplace's Equation In Exercises 59–62, show that each function satisfies Laplace's equation

$$\dfrac{\partial^2 z}{\partial x^2} + \dfrac{\partial^2 z}{\partial y^2} = 0.$$

59. $z = 5xy$

60. $z = \frac{1}{2}(e^y - e^{-y})\sin x$

61. $z = e^x \sin y$

62. $z = \arctan\dfrac{y}{x}$

Wave Equation In Exercises 63 and 64, show that the function satisfies the wave equation

$$\dfrac{\partial^2 z}{\partial t^2} = c^2 \dfrac{\partial^2 z}{\partial x^2}.$$

63. $z = \sin(x - ct)$

64. $z = \sin \omega ct \sin \omega x$

Heat Equation In Exercises 65 and 66, show that the function satisfies the heat equation

$$\dfrac{\partial z}{\partial t} = c^2 \dfrac{\partial^2 z}{\partial x^2}.$$

65. $z = e^{-t} \cos\dfrac{x}{c}$

66. $z = e^{-t} \sin\dfrac{x}{c}$

67. *Marginal Costs* A company manufactures two types of wood-burning stoves: a freestanding model and a fireplace-insert model. The cost function for producing x freestanding and y fireplace-insert stoves is

$$C = 32\sqrt{xy} + 175x + 205y + 1050.$$

Find the marginal costs ($\partial C/\partial x$ and $\partial C/\partial y$) when $x = 80$ and $y = 20$.

68. *Marginal Productivity* Consider the Cobb-Douglas production function

$$f(x, y) = 100x^{0.6}y^{0.4}.$$

When $x = 1000$ and $y = 500$, find
a. the marginal productivity of labor, $\partial f/\partial x$.
b. the marginal productivity of capital, $\partial f/\partial y$.

69. *University Admissions* Let N be the number of applicants to a university, p the charge for food and housing at the university, and t the tuition. Suppose that N is a function of p and t such that $\partial N/\partial p < 0$ and $\partial N/\partial t < 0$. What information is gained by noticing that both partials are negative?

70. *Investment* The value of an investment of $1000 earning 10 percent compounded annually is given by

$$V(I, R) = 1000\left[\dfrac{1 + 0.10(1 - R)}{1 + I}\right]^{10}$$

where I is the annual rate of inflation and R is the tax rate for the person making the investment. Calculate $V_I(0.03, 0.28)$ and $V_R(0.03, 0.28)$. Determine whether the tax rate or the rate of inflation has the greater "negative" influence on the growth of the investment.

71. *Temperature Distribution* The temperature at any point (x, y) in a steel plate is

$$T = 500 - 0.6x^2 - 1.5y^2$$

where x and y are measured in feet. At the point $(2, 3)$, find the rate of change of the temperature with respect to the distance moved along the plate in the directions of the x- and y-axes, respectively.

72. *Ideal Gas Law* According to the Ideal Gas Law, $PV = kT$, where P is pressure, V is volume, T is temperature, and k is a constant of proportionality. Find
a. $\partial P/\partial T$.   **b.** $\partial V/\partial P$.

73. *Projectile Motion* The range of a projectile fired at an angle θ above the horizontal with veolcity v_0 is

$$R = \dfrac{v_0^2 \sin 2\theta}{32}.$$

Evaluate $\partial R/\partial v_0$ and $\partial R/\partial\theta$ when $v_0 = 2000$ feet per second and $\theta = 5°$.

74. Consider the function defined by

$$f(x, y) = \begin{cases} \dfrac{xy(x^2 - y^2)}{x^2 + y^2}, & (x, y) \neq (0, 0) \\ 0, & (x, y) = (0, 0). \end{cases}$$

a. Find $f_x(x, y)$ and $f_y(x, y)$ for $(x, y) \neq (0, 0)$.
b. Use the definition of partial derivatives to find $f_x(0, 0)$ and $f_y(0, 0)$.

$\left(\textit{Hint: } f_x(0, 0) = \lim_{\Delta x \to 0} \dfrac{f(\Delta x, 0) - f(0, 0)}{\Delta x}.\right)$

  c. Use the definition of partial derivatives to find $f_{xy}(0, 0)$ and $f_{yx}(0, 0)$.

  d. Using Theorem 13.3 and the result of part c, what can be said about f_{xy} or f_{yx}?

True or False **In Exercises 75–78, determine whether the statement is true or false. If it is false, explain why or give an example that shows it is false.**

75. If $z = f(x, y)$ and $\partial z/\partial x = \partial z/\partial y$, then $z = c(x + y)$.

76. If $z = f(x)g(y)$, then $(\partial z/\partial x) + (\partial z/\partial y) = f'(x)g(y) + f(x)g'(y)$.

77. If $z = e^{xy}$, then $\dfrac{\partial^2 z}{\partial y \partial x} = (xy + 1)e^{xy}$.

78. If a cylindrical surface, $z = f(x, y)$, has rulings parallel to the y-axis, then $\partial z/\partial y = 0$.

79. The ideal gas law is $PV = mRT$, where P is the pressure, V is the volume, m is the mass, R is a fixed constant ("the gas constant"), and T is the absolute temperature. Show that

$$\frac{\partial T}{\partial P}\frac{\partial P}{\partial V}\frac{\partial V}{\partial T} = -1.$$

80. Let $f(x, y) = \displaystyle\int_x^y \sqrt{1 + t^3}\, dt$. Find $\dfrac{\partial f}{\partial x}$ and $\dfrac{\partial f}{\partial y}$.

81. ***Moiré Patterns***   Read the article "Moiré Fringes and the Conic Sections" by Mike Cullen in the November, 1990 issue of the *College Mathematics Journal*. The article describes how two families of level curves given by

$$f(x, y) = a \quad \text{and} \quad g(x, y) = b$$

can form Moiré patterns. After reading the article, write a paper explaining how the expression

$$\frac{\partial f}{\partial x} \cdot \frac{\partial g}{\partial x} + \frac{\partial f}{\partial y} \cdot \frac{\partial g}{\partial y}$$

is related to the Moiré patterns formed by intersecting the two families of level curves. Use one of the following patterns as an example in your paper.

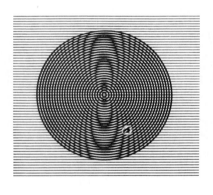

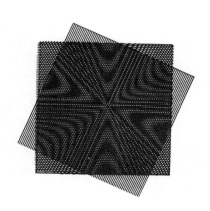

Differentials

Increments and Differentials • Differentiability • Approximation by Differentials

Increments and Differentials

In this section, we generalize the concepts of increments and differentials to functions of two or more variables. Recall from Section 3.9 that for $y = f(x)$, the differential of y was defined as $dy = f'(x)\,dx$. Similar terminology is used for a function of two variables, $z = f(x, y)$. That is, Δx and Δy are the **increments of x and y,** and the **increment of z** is given by

$$\Delta z = f(x + \Delta x, y + \Delta y) - f(x, y).$$ Increment of z

---

Definition of Total Differential

If $z = f(x, y)$ and Δx and Δy are increments of x and y, then the **differentials** of the independent variables x and y are

$dx = \Delta x$ and $dy = \Delta y$

and the **total differential** of the dependent variable z is

$$dz = \frac{\partial z}{\partial x}dx + \frac{\partial z}{\partial y}dy = f_x(x, y)\,dx + f_y(x, y)\,dy.$$

This definition can be extended to a function of three or more variables. For instance, if $w = f(x, y, z, u)$, then $dx = \Delta x$, $dy = \Delta y$, $dz = \Delta z$, $du = \Delta u$, and the total differential of w is

$$dw = \frac{\partial w}{\partial x}dx + \frac{\partial w}{\partial y}dy + \frac{\partial w}{\partial z}dz + \frac{\partial w}{\partial u}du.$$

EXAMPLE 1   Finding the Total Differential

a. The total differential dz for $z = 2x\sin y - 3x^2y^2$ is

$$dz = \frac{\partial z}{\partial x}dx + \frac{\partial z}{\partial y}dy$$

$$= (2\sin y - 6xy^2)\,dx + (2x\cos y - 6x^2y)\,dy.$$

b. The total differential dw for $w = x^2 + y^2 + z^2$ is

$$dw = \frac{\partial w}{\partial x}dx + \frac{\partial w}{\partial y}dy + \frac{\partial w}{\partial z}dz$$

$$= 2x\,dx + 2y\,dy + 2z\,dz.$$

Differentiability

In Section 3.9, you learned that for a *differentiable* function given by $y = f(x)$, you can use the differential $dy = f'(x)\,dx$ as an approximation (for small Δx) to the value $\Delta y = f(x + \Delta x) - f(x)$. When a similar approximation is possible for a function of two variables, the function is said to be **differentiable.** This is stated explicitly in the following definition.

Definition of Differentiability

A function f given by $z = f(x, y)$ is **differentiable** at (x_0, y_0) if Δz can be expressed in the form

$$\Delta z = f_x(x_0, y_0)\,\Delta x + f_y(x_0, y_0)\,\Delta y + \varepsilon_1\,\Delta x + \varepsilon_2\,\Delta y$$

where both ε_1 and $\varepsilon_2 \to 0$ as $(\Delta x, \Delta y) \to (0, 0)$. The function f is **differentiable in a region R** if it is differentiable at each point of R.

EXAMPLE 2   Showing that a Function is Differentiable

Show that the function given by $f(x, y) = x^2 + 3y$ is differentiable at every point in the plane.

Solution   Letting $z = f(x, y)$, the increment of z at an arbitrary point (x, y) in the plane is

$$\begin{aligned}
\Delta z &= f(x + \Delta x, y + \Delta y) - f(x, y) \\
&= (x^2 + 2x\,\Delta x + \Delta x^2) + 3(y + \Delta y) - (x^2 + 3y) \\
&= 2x\,\Delta x + \Delta x^2 + 3\,\Delta y \\
&= 2x(\Delta x) + 3(\Delta y) + \Delta x(\Delta x) + 0(\Delta y) \\
&= f_x(x, y)\,\Delta x + f_y(x, y)\,\Delta y + \varepsilon_1\,\Delta x + \varepsilon_2\,\Delta y
\end{aligned}$$

where $\varepsilon_1 = \Delta x$ and $\varepsilon_2 = 0$. Because $\varepsilon_1 \to 0$ and $\varepsilon_2 \to 0$ as $(\Delta x, \Delta y) \to (0, 0)$, it follows that f is differentiable at every point in the plane.

Be sure you see that the term "differentiable" is used differently for functions of two variables than for one variable. A function of one variable is differentiable at a point if its derivative exists at the point. However, for a function of two variables, the existence of the partial derivatives f_x and f_y does not guarantee that the function is differentiable (see Example 5). The following theorem gives a *sufficient* condition for differentiability of a function of two variables.

THEOREM 13.4   Sufficient Condition for Differentiability

If f is a function of x and y, where f_x and f_y are continuous in an open region R, then f is differentiable on R.

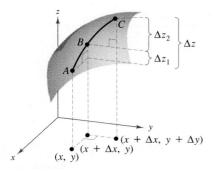

FIGURE 13.34
$\Delta z = f(x + \Delta x, y + \Delta y) - f(x, y)$

Proof   Let S be the surface defined by $z = f(x, y)$, where f, f_x, and f_y are continuous at (x, y). Let A, B, and C be points on surface S, as shown in Figure 13.34. From this figure, you can see that the change in f from point A to point C is given by

$$\begin{aligned}
\Delta z &= f(x + \Delta x, y + \Delta y) - f(x, y) \\
&= [f(x + \Delta x, y) - f(x, y)] + [f(x + \Delta x, y + \Delta y) - f(x + \Delta x, y)] \\
&= \Delta z_1 + \Delta z_2.
\end{aligned}$$

Between A and B, y is fixed and x changes. Hence, by the Mean Value Theorem, there is a value x_1 between x and $x + \Delta x$ such that

$$\Delta z_1 = f(x + \Delta x, y) - f(x, y) = f_x(x_1, y)\Delta x.$$

Similarly, between B and C, x is fixed and y changes, and there is a value y_1 between y and $y + \Delta y$ such that

$$\Delta z_2 = f(x + \Delta x, y + \Delta y) - f(x + \Delta x, y) = f_y(x + \Delta x, y_1)\,\Delta y.$$

By combining these two results, you can write

$$\Delta z = \Delta z_1 + \Delta z_2 = f_x(x_1, y)\,\Delta x + f_y(x + \Delta x, y_1)\,\Delta y.$$

If you define ε_1 and ε_2 by

$$\varepsilon_1 = f_x(x_1, y) - f_x(x, y) \quad \text{and} \quad \varepsilon_2 = f_y(x + \Delta x, y_1) - f_y(x, y)$$

it follows that

$$\begin{aligned}
\Delta z = \Delta z_1 + \Delta z_2 &= [\varepsilon_1 + f_x(x, y)]\,\Delta x + [\varepsilon_2 + f_y(x, y)]\,\Delta y \\
&= [f_x(x, y)\,\Delta x + f_y(x, y)\,\Delta y] + \varepsilon_1\,\Delta x + \varepsilon_2\,\Delta y.
\end{aligned}$$

By the continuity of f_x and f_y and the fact that $x \le x_1 \le x + \Delta x$ and $y \le y_1 \le y + \Delta y$, it follows that $\varepsilon_1 \to 0$ and $\varepsilon_2 \to 0$ as $\Delta x \to 0$ and $\Delta y \to 0$. Therefore, by definition, f is differentiable.

Approximation by Differentials

Theorem 13.4 tells you that you can choose $(x + \Delta x, y + \Delta y)$ close enough to (x, y) to make $\varepsilon_1\,\Delta x$ and $\varepsilon_2\,\Delta y$ insignificant. In other words, for small Δx and Δy, you can use the approximation

$$\Delta z \approx dz.$$

This approximation is illustrated graphically in Figure 13.35. Recall that the partial derivatives $\partial z / \partial x$ and $\partial z / \partial y$ can be interpreted as the slopes of the surface in the x and y directions, respectively. This means that

$$dz = \frac{\partial z}{\partial x}\Delta x + \frac{\partial z}{\partial y}\Delta y$$

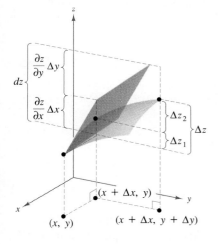

$\Delta z = f(x + \Delta x, y + \Delta y) - f(x, y)$

FIGURE 13.35
The exact change in z is Δz. This change can be approximated by the differential dz.

represents the change in height of a plane that is tangent to the surface at the point $(x, y, f(x, y))$. Because a plane in space is represented by a linear equation in the variables x, y, and z, the approximation of Δz by dz is called a **linear approximation.** You will learn more about this geometric interpretation in Section 13.7.

EXAMPLE 3 Using a Differential as an Approximation

Use the differential dz to approximate the change in

$$z = \sqrt{4 - x^2 - y^2}$$

as (x, y) moves from the point $(1, 1)$ to $(1.01, 0.97)$. Compare this approximation with the exact change in z.

Solution Letting $(x, y) = (1, 1)$ and $(x + \Delta x, y + \Delta y) = (1.01, 0.97)$ produces

$$dx = \Delta x = 0.01 \quad \text{and} \quad dy = \Delta y = -0.03.$$

Thus, the change in z can be approximated by

$$\begin{aligned}
\Delta z &\approx dz \\
&= \frac{\partial z}{\partial x} dx + \frac{\partial z}{\partial y} dy \\
&= \frac{-x}{\sqrt{4 - x^2 - y^2}} \Delta x + \frac{-y}{\sqrt{4 - x^2 - y^2}} \Delta y.
\end{aligned}$$

When $x = 1$ and $y = 1$, you have

$$\begin{aligned}
\Delta z &\approx -\frac{1}{\sqrt{2}}(0.01) - \frac{1}{\sqrt{2}}(-0.03) \\
&= \frac{0.02}{\sqrt{2}} \\
&= \sqrt{2}(0.01) \\
&\approx 0.0141. \qquad \text{\small Approximation of } \Delta x \text{ by } dx
\end{aligned}$$

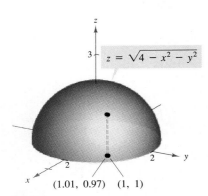

$z = \sqrt{4 - x^2 - y^2}$

$(1.01, 0.97) \quad (1, 1)$

FIGURE 13.36
As (x, y) moves from $(1, 1)$ to the point $(1.01, 0.97)$, the value of $f(x, y)$ changes by about 0.0137.

In Figure 13.36 you can see that the exact change corresponds to the difference in the heights of two points on the surface of a hemisphere. This difference is given by

$$\begin{aligned}
\Delta z &= f(1.01, 0.97) - f(1, 1) \\
&= \sqrt{4 - (1.01)^2 - (0.97)^2} - \sqrt{4 - 1^2 - 1^2} \\
&\approx 0.0137. \qquad \text{\small Actual value of } \Delta x
\end{aligned}$$

A function of three variables, $w = f(x, y, z)$, is called **differentiable** at (x, y, z) provided that

$$\Delta w = f(x + \Delta x, y + \Delta y, z + \Delta z) - f(x, y, z)$$

can be expressed in the form

$$\Delta w = f_x \Delta x + f_y \Delta y + f_z \Delta z + \varepsilon_1 \Delta x + \varepsilon_2 \Delta y + \varepsilon_3 \Delta z$$

where ε_1, ε_2, and $\varepsilon_3 \to 0$ as $(\Delta x, \Delta y, \Delta z) \to (0, 0, 0)$. With this definition of differentiability, Theorem 13.4 has the following extension for functions of three variables. If f is a function of x, y, and z, where f, f_x, f_y, and f_z are continuous in an open region R, then f is differentiable on R.

In Section 3.9, you used differentials to approximate the propagated error introduced by an error in measurement. This application of differentials is further illustrated in Example 4.

EXAMPLE 4   Error Analysis

The possible error involved in measuring each dimension of a rectangular box is ± 0.1 millimeter. The dimensions of the box are $x = 50$ centimeters, $y = 20$ centimeters, and $z = 15$ centimeters, as shown in Figure 13.37. Use dV to estimate the propagated error and the relative error in the calculated volume of the box.

Solution   The volume of the box is given by $V = xyz$, and thus

$$dV = \frac{\partial V}{\partial x}dx + \frac{\partial V}{\partial y}dy + \frac{\partial V}{\partial z}dz = yz\,dx + xz\,dy + xy\,dz.$$

Using 0.1 millimeter = 0.01 centimeter, you have $dx = dy = dz = \pm 0.01$, and the propagated error is approximately

$$\begin{aligned}
dV &= (20)(15)(\pm 0.01) + (50)(15)(\pm 0.01) + (50)(20)(\pm 0.01) \\
&= 300(\pm 0.01) + 750(\pm 0.01) + 1000(\pm 0.01) \\
&= 2050(\pm 0.01) = \pm 20.5 \text{ cm}^3.
\end{aligned}$$

Because the measured volume is

$$V = (50)(20)(15) = 15{,}000 \text{ cm}^3$$

the relative error, $\Delta V/V$, is approximately

$$\frac{\Delta V}{V} \approx \frac{dV}{V} = \frac{20.5}{15{,}000} \approx 0.14\%.$$

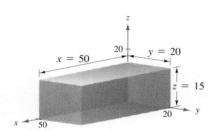

FIGURE 13.37
Volume = xyz

As is true for a function of a single variable, if a function of two or more variables is differentiable at a point, then it is also continuous there.

THEOREM 13.5   Differentiability Implies Continuity

If a function of x and y is differentiable at (x_0, y_0), then it is continuous at (x_0, y_0).

Proof   Let f be differentiable at (x_0, y_0), where $z = f(x, y)$. Then

$$\Delta z = [f_x(x_0, y_0) + \varepsilon_1]\Delta x + [f_y(x_0, y_0) + \varepsilon_2]\Delta y$$

where both ε_1 and $\varepsilon_x \to 0$ as $(\Delta x, \Delta y) \to (0, 0)$. However, by definition, you know that Δz is given by

$$\Delta z = f(x_0 + \Delta x, y_0 + \Delta y) - f(x_0, y_0).$$

Letting $x = x_0 + \Delta x$ and $y = y_0 + \Delta y$ produces

$$\begin{aligned}
f(x, y) - f(x_0, y_0) &= [f_x(x_0, y_0) + \varepsilon_1]\Delta x + [f_y(x_0, y_0) + \varepsilon_2]\Delta y \\
&= [f_x(x_0, y_0) + \varepsilon_1](x - x_0) + [f_y(x_0, y_0) + \varepsilon_2](y - y_0).
\end{aligned}$$

Taking the limit as $(x, y) \to (x_0, y_0)$, you have

$$\lim_{(x, y) \to (x_0, y_0)} f(x, y) = f(x_0, y_0)$$

which means that f is continuous at (x_0, y_0).

Remember that the existence of f_x and f_y is not sufficient to guarantee differentiability, as illustrated in the next example.

EXAMPLE 5   A Function That is Not Differentiable

Show that $f_x(0, 0)$ and $f_y(0, 0)$ both exist, but that f is not differentiable at $(0, 0)$ where f is defined as

$$f(x, y) = \begin{cases} \dfrac{-3xy}{x^2 + y^2}, & \text{if} (x, y) \neq (0, 0) \\ 0, & \text{if } (x, y) = (0, 0). \end{cases}$$

Solution   You can show that f is not differentiable at $(0, 0)$ by showing that it is not continuous at this point. To see that f is not continuous at $(0, 0)$, look at the values of $f(x, y)$ along two different approaches to $(0, 0)$, as shown in Figure 13.38. Along the line $y = x$, the limit is

$$\lim_{(x, x) \to (0, 0)} f(x, y) = \lim_{(x, x) \to (0, 0)} \frac{-3x^2}{2x^2} = -\frac{3}{2}$$

whereas along $y = -x$ you have

$$\lim_{(x, -x) \to (0, 0)} f(x, y) = \lim_{(x, -x) \to (0, 0)} \frac{3x^2}{2x^2} = \frac{3}{2}.$$

Thus, the limit of $f(x, y)$ as $(x, y) \to (0, 0)$ does not exist, and you can conclude that f is not continuous at $(0, 0)$. Therefore, by Theorem 13.5, you know that f is not differentiable at $(0, 0)$. On the other hand, by the definition of the partial derivatives f_x and f_y, you have

$$f_x(0, 0) = \lim_{\Delta x \to 0} \frac{f(\Delta x, 0) - f(0, 0)}{\Delta x} = \lim_{\Delta x \to 0} \frac{0 - 0}{\Delta x} = 0$$

and

$$f_y(0, 0) = \lim_{\Delta y \to 0} \frac{f(0, \Delta y) - f(0, 0)}{\Delta y} = \lim_{\Delta y \to 0} \frac{0 - 0}{\Delta y} = 0.$$

Thus, the partial derivatives at $(0, 0)$ exist.

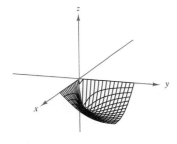

(a)

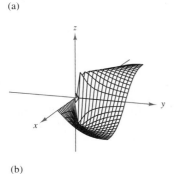

(b)

Generated by Mathematica

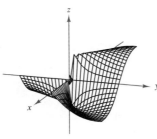

(c)

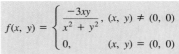

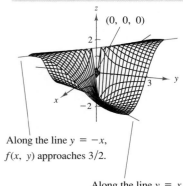

$$f(x, y) = \begin{cases} \dfrac{-3xy}{x^2 + y^2}, & (x, y) \neq (0, 0) \\ 0, & (x, y) = (0, 0) \end{cases}$$

Along the line $y = -x$,
$f(x, y)$ approaches $3/2$.

Along the line $y = x$,
$f(x, y)$ approaches $-3/2$.

(d)

FIGURE 13.38

EXERCISES for Section 13.4

In Exercises 1–10, find the total differential.

1. $z = 3x^2y^3$

2. $z = \dfrac{x^2}{y}$

3. $z = \dfrac{-1}{x^2 + y^2}$

4. $z = e^x \sin y$

5. $z = x \cos y - y \cos x$

6. $z = \frac{1}{2}(e^{x^2+y^2} - e^{-x^2-y^2})$

7. $w = 2z^3 y \sin x$

8. $w = e^x \cos y + z$

9. $w = \dfrac{x + y}{z - 2y}$

10. $w = x^2yz^2 + \sin yz$

In Exercises 11–16, (a) evaluate $f(1, 2)$ and $f(1.05, 2.1)$ and calculate Δz and (b) use the total differential dz to approximate Δz.

11. $f(x, y) = 9 - x^2 - y^2$

12. $f(x, y) = \sqrt{x^2 + y^2}$

13. $f(x, y) = x \sin y$

14. $f(x, y) = xy$

15. $f(x, y) = 3x - 4y$

16. $f(x, y) = \dfrac{x}{y}$

In Exercises 17–20, use a total differential to approximate the quantity.

17. $\sqrt{(5.05)^2 + (3.1)^2} - \sqrt{5^2 + 3^2}$

18. $(2.03)^2(1 + 8.9)^3 - 2^2(1 + 9)^3$

19. $\dfrac{1 - (3.05)^2}{(5.95)^2} - \dfrac{1 - 3^2}{6^2}$

20. $\sin[(1.05)^2 + (0.95)^2] - \sin(1^2 + 1^2)$

21. *Area* The area of the rectangle in the figure is $A = lh$. Find dA and identify the regions in the figure whose areas are given by its terms. What region represents the difference between ΔA and dA?

22. *Volume* The volume of the right circular cylinder in the figure is $V = \pi r^2 h$. Find dV and identify the regions in the figure whose volumes are given by its terms. What region represents the difference between ΔV and dV?

23. *Volume* The radius r and height h of a right circular cylinder are measured with possible errors of 4 percent and 2 percent, respectively. Approximate the maximum possible percentage error in measuring the volume.

24. *Volume* A right circular cone of height $h = 6$ and radius $r = 3$ is constructed, and in the process errors Δr and Δh are made in the radius and height, respectively. Complete the table to show the relationship between ΔV and dV for the given errors.

Δr	Δh	dV	ΔV	$\Delta v - dV$
0.1	0.1			
0.1	−0.1			
0.001	0.002			
−0.0001	0.0002			

25. *Volume* A trough is 16 feet long (see figure). Its cross sections are isosceles triangles—each of the two equal sides are 18 inches long. The angle between the two equal sides is θ.
 a. Express the volume of the trough as a function of θ and determine the value of θ such that the volume is maximum.
 b. Approximate the change from the maximum volume if the maximum error in the linear measurements is one-half inch and the maximum error in the angle measurement is 2°.

26. *Baseball* A baseball player in center field is playing approximately 330 feet from the television camera that is behind home plate. A batter hits a fly ball that goes to the wall that is 420 feet from the camera (see figure).
 a. Approximate the number of feet that the center fielder has to run to make the catch if the camera turns 9° in following the play.
 b. Approximate the maximum possible error in the result of part a if the position of the center fielder could be in error by as much as 6 feet and the maximum error in measuring the rotation of the camera is 1°.

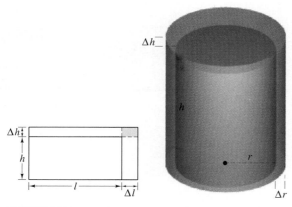

FIGURE FOR 21   **FIGURE FOR 22**

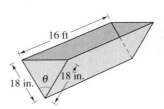
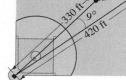

FIGURE FOR 25   **FIGURE FOR 26**

27. *Area* A triangle is measured and two adjacent sides are found to be 3 and 4 inches long, with an included angle of $\pi/4$. The possible errors in measurement are $\frac{1}{16}$ inch in the sides and 0.02 radian in the angle. Approximate the maximum possible error in the computation of the area.

28. *Acceleration* The centripetal acceleration of a particle moving in a circle is $a = v^2/r$, where v is the velocity and r is the radius of the circle. Approximate the maximum percentage error in measuring the acceleration due to errors of 2 percent in v and 1 percent in r.

29. *Power* Electrical power P is given by $P = E^2/R$, where E is voltage and R is resistance. Approximate the maximum percentage error in calculating power if 200 volts is applied to a 4000-ohm resistor and the possible percentage errors in measuring E and R are 2 percent and 3 percent, respectively.

30. *Resistance* The total resistance R of two resistors connected in parallel is given by

$$\frac{1}{R} = \frac{1}{R_1} + \frac{1}{R_2}.$$

Approximate the change in R as R_1 is increased from 10 ohms to 10.5 ohms and R_2 is decreased from 15 ohms to 13 ohms.

31. *Inductance* The inductance L (in microhenrys) of a straight nonmagnetic wire in free space is given by

$$L = 0.00021\left(\ln\frac{2h}{r} - 0.75\right)$$

where h is the length of the wire in millimeters and r is the radius of a circular cross section. Approximate L when $r = 2 \pm \frac{1}{16}$ millimeters and $h = 100 \pm \frac{1}{100}$ millimeters.

32. *Pendulum* The period T of a pendulum of length L is given by $T = 2\pi\sqrt{L/g}$, where g is the acceleration due to gravity. A pendulum is moved from the Canal Zone, where $g = 32.09$ feet per second per second, to Greenland, where $g = 32.24$ feet per second per second. Because of the change in temperature, the length of the pendulum changes from 2.5 feet to 2.48 feet. Approximate the change in the period of the pendulum.

In Exercises 33–36, show that the given function is differentiable by finding values for ε_1 and ε_2 as designated in the definition of differentiability, and verify that both ε_1 and $\varepsilon_2 \to 0$ as $(\Delta x, \Delta y) \to (0, 0)$.

33. $f(x, y) = x^2 - 2x + y$ **34.** $f(x, y) = x^2 + y^2$

35. $f(x, y) = x^2 y$ **36.** $f(x, y) = 5x - 10y + y^3$

In Exercises 37 and 38, use the given function to prove that (a) $f_x(0, 0)$ and $f_y(0, 0)$ exist, and (b) f is not differentiable at $(0, 0)$.

37. $f(x, y) = \begin{cases} \dfrac{3x^2 y}{x^4 + y^2}, & (x, y) \neq (0, 0) \\ 0, & (x, y) = (0, 0) \end{cases}$

38. $f(x, y) = \begin{cases} \dfrac{2x^2 y^2}{x^4 + y^4}, & (x, y) \neq (0, 0) \\ 0, & (x, y) = (0, 0) \end{cases}$

CAREER INTERVIEW

S. S. Chen

Chemical Engineer

Director of Research and Development

Badger Company

Weymouth, MA 02189

At the chemical process laboratory, I lead a team of chemists and engineers in developing processes that produce chemicals used in products as diverse as soda bottles, automobile tires, and fertilizers. Working with raw materials derived from petroleum, we convert them into polymers, which you may know better as plastics. We create new processes by finding ways to employ less raw materials and energy for manufacturing products of higher purity, with smaller environmental impact.

Because calculus is the natural language for describing motion, it is utilized in our daily work to express the speed of chemical reactions. For example, you may have encountered in chemistry the first order rate equation that describes the rate of conversion of a substance into another substance; that is, if substance A is being converted irreversibly to substance B, then the rate at which A decreases and B increases is proportional to the concentration of A at any given moment:

$$A \rightarrow B$$

$$-\frac{dA}{dt} = \frac{dB}{dt} = kA$$

SECTION 13.5 Chain Rules for Functions of Several Variables

Chain Rules for Functions of Several Variables • Implicit Partial Differentiation

Chain Rules for Functions of Several Variables

Your work with differentials in the previous section provides the basis for the extension of the Chain Rule to functions of two variables. There are two cases—the first case involves w as a function of x and y, where x and y are functions of a single independent variable t. (A proof of this theorem is given in Appendix A.)

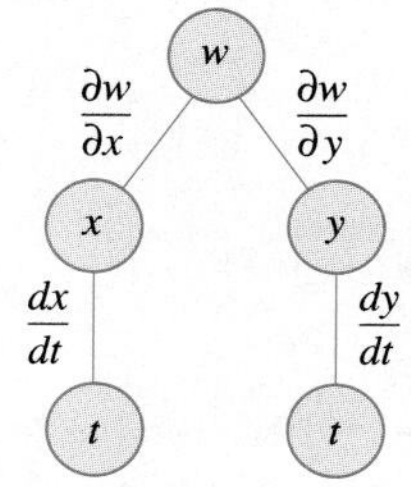

FIGURE 13.39
Chain Rule: one independent variable. w is a function of x and y, which are each functions of t. This diagram represents the derivative of w with respect to t.

THEOREM 13.6 Chain Rule: One Independent Variable

Let $w = f(x, y)$, where f is a differentiable function of x and y. If $x = g(t)$ and $y = h(t)$, where g and h are differentiable functions of t, then w is a differentiable function of t, and

$$\frac{dw}{dt} = \frac{\partial w}{\partial x}\frac{dx}{dt} + \frac{\partial w}{\partial y}\frac{dy}{dt}.$$

REMARK The Chain Rule presented in this theorem can be represented schematically as shown in Figure 13.39.

EXAMPLE 1 Using the Chain Rule with One Independent Variable

Let $w = x^2y - y^2$, where $x = \sin t$ and $y = e^t$. Find dw/dt when $t = 0$.

Solution By the Chain Rule for one independent variable, you have

$$\begin{aligned}\frac{dw}{dt} &= \frac{\partial w}{\partial x}\frac{dx}{dt} + \frac{\partial w}{\partial y}\frac{dy}{dt}\\ &= 2xy(\cos t) + (x^2 - 2y)e^t.\end{aligned}$$

When $t = 0$, $x = 0$, and $y = 1$, it follows that

$$\frac{dw}{dt} = 0 - 2 = -2.$$

The Chain Rules presented in this section provide alternative techniques for solving many problems in single-variable calculus. For instance, in Example 1, you could have used single-variable techniques to find dw/dt by first writing w as a function of t,

$$w = x^2y - y^2 = (\sin t)^2(e^t) - (e^t)^2 = e^t\sin^2 t - e^{2t}$$

and then differentiating as usual. (Try doing this.)

The Chain Rule in Theorem 13.6 can be extended to any number of variables. For example, if each x_i is a differentiable function of a single variable t, then for

$$w = f(x_1, x_2, \ldots, x_n)$$

you have

$$\frac{dw}{dt} = \frac{\partial w}{\partial x_1} \frac{dx_1}{dt} + \frac{\partial w}{\partial x_2} \frac{dx_2}{dt} + \cdots + \frac{\partial w}{\partial x_n} \frac{dx_n}{dt}.$$

EXAMPLE 2   An Application of a Chain Rule to Related Rates

Two objects are traveling in elliptical paths given by the following parametric equations.

$$x_1 = 4\cos t \quad \text{and} \quad y_1 = 2\sin t \qquad \text{First object}$$
$$x_2 = 2\sin 2t \quad \text{and} \quad y_2 = 3\cos 2t \qquad \text{Second object}$$

At what rate is the distance between the two objects changing when $t = \pi$?

Solution   From Figure 13.40, you can see that the distance s between the two objects is given by

$$s = \sqrt{(x_2 - x_1)^2 + (y_2 - y_1)^2}$$

and when $t = \pi$, you have $x_1 = -4$, $y_1 = 0$, $x_2 = 0$, $y_2 = 3$, and

$$s = \sqrt{(0 + 4)^2 + (3 - 0)^2} = 5.$$

When $t = \pi$, the partial derivatives of s are as follows.

$$\frac{\partial s}{\partial x_1} = \frac{-(x_2 - x_1)}{\sqrt{(x_2 - x_1)^2 + (y_2 - y_1)^2}} = -\frac{1}{5}(0 + 4) = -\frac{4}{5}$$

$$\frac{\partial s}{\partial y_1} = \frac{-(y_2 - y_1)}{\sqrt{(x_2 - x_1)^2 + (y_2 - y_1)^2}} = -\frac{1}{5}(3 - 0) = -\frac{3}{5}$$

$$\frac{\partial s}{\partial x_2} = \frac{(x_2 - x_1)}{\sqrt{(x_2 - x_1)^2 + (y_2 - y_1)^2}} = \frac{1}{5}(0 + 4) = \frac{4}{5}$$

$$\frac{\partial s}{\partial y_2} = \frac{(y_2 - y_1)}{\sqrt{(x_2 - x_1)^2 + (y_2 - y_1)^2}} = \frac{1}{5}(3 - 0) = \frac{3}{5}$$

When $t = \pi$, the derivatives of x_1, y_1, x_2, and y_2 are

$$\frac{dx_1}{dt} = -4\sin t = 0 \qquad \frac{dy_1}{dt} = 2\cos t = -2$$

$$\frac{dx_2}{dt} = 4\cos 2t = 4 \qquad \frac{dy_2}{dt} = -6\sin 2t = 0.$$

Therefore, using the appropriate Chain Rule, you know that the distance is changing at the rate of

$$\frac{ds}{dt} = \frac{\partial s}{\partial x_1} \frac{dx_1}{dt} + \frac{\partial s}{\partial y_1} \frac{dy_1}{dt} + \frac{\partial s}{\partial x_2} \frac{dx_2}{dt} + \frac{\partial s}{\partial y_2} \frac{dy_2}{dt}$$

$$= \left(-\frac{4}{5}\right)(0) + \left(-\frac{3}{5}\right)(-2) + \left(\frac{4}{5}\right)(4) + \left(\frac{3}{5}\right)(0)$$

$$= \frac{22}{5}.$$

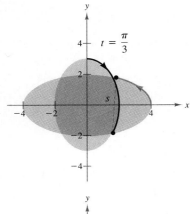
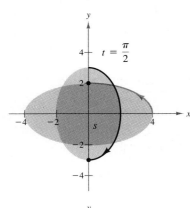
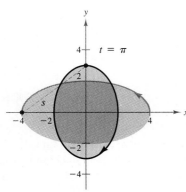

FIGURE 13.40
Paths of two objects traveling in elliptical orbits.

In Example 2, note that s is the function of four *intermediate* variables, x_1, y_1, x_2, and y_2, which in turn are each functions of a single variable t. Another type of composite function is one in which the intermediate variables are themselves functions of more than one variable. For instance, if $w = f(x, y)$, where $x = g(s, t)$ and $y = h(s, t)$, then it follows that w is a function of s and t, and you can consider the partial derivatives of w with respect to s and t. One way to find these partial derivatives is to write w as a function of s and t explicitly by substituting the equations $x = g(s, t)$ and $y = h(s, t)$ into the equation $w = f(x, y)$. Then you can find the partial derivatives in the usual way, as demonstrated in the next example.

EXAMPLE 3   Finding Partial Derivatives by Substitution

Find $\partial w/\partial s$ and $\partial w/\partial t$ for $w = 2xy$, where $x = s^2 + t^2$ and $y = s/t$.

Solution   Begin by substituting $x = s^2 + t^2$ and $y = s/t$ into the equation $w = 2xy$ to obtain

$$w = 2xy = 2(s^2 + t^2)\left(\frac{s}{t}\right) = 2\left(\frac{s^3}{t} + st\right).$$

Then, to find $\partial w/\partial s$, hold t constant and differentiate with respect to s.

$$\frac{\partial w}{\partial s} = 2\left(\frac{3s^2}{t} + t\right) = \frac{6s^2 + 2t^2}{t}$$

Similarly, to find $\partial w/\partial t$, hold s constant and differentiate with respect to t to obtain

$$\frac{\partial w}{\partial t} = 2\left(-\frac{s^3}{t^2} + s\right) = 2\left(\frac{-s^3 + st^2}{t^2}\right) = \frac{2st^2 - 2s^3}{t^2}.$$

Theorem 13.7 gives an alternative method for finding the partial derivatives in Example 3—without explicitly writing w as a function of s and t.

THEOREM 13.7   Chain Rule: Two Independent Variables

Let $w = f(x, y)$, where f is a differentiable function of x and y. If $x = g(s, t)$ and $y = h(s, t)$ such that the first partials $\partial x/\partial s$, $\partial x/\partial t$, $\partial y/\partial s$, and $\partial y/\partial t$ all exist, then $\partial w/\partial s$ and $\partial w/\partial t$ exist and are given by

$$\frac{\partial w}{\partial s} = \frac{\partial w}{\partial x}\frac{\partial x}{\partial s} + \frac{\partial w}{\partial y}\frac{\partial y}{\partial s} \quad \text{and} \quad \frac{\partial w}{\partial t} = \frac{\partial w}{\partial x}\frac{\partial x}{\partial t} + \frac{\partial w}{\partial y}\frac{\partial y}{\partial t}.$$

Proof   To obtain $\partial w/\partial s$, hold t constant and apply Theorem 13.6 to obtain the desired result. Similarly, for $\partial w/\partial t$ hold s constant and apply Theorem 13.6.

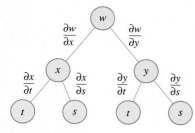

FIGURE 13.41
Chain Rule: two independent variables

REMARK   The Chain Rule in this theorem is shown schematically in Figure 13.41.

EXAMPLE 4   The Chain Rule with Two Independent Variables

Use the Chain Rule to find $\partial w/\partial s$ and $\partial w/\partial t$ for

$$w = 2xy$$

where $x = s^2 + t^2$ and $y = s/t$.

Solution   (These same partials were found in Example 3.) Using Theorem 13.7, you can hold t constant and differentiate with respect to s to obtain

$$\frac{\partial w}{\partial s} = \frac{\partial w}{\partial x}\frac{\partial x}{\partial s} + \frac{\partial w}{\partial y}\frac{\partial y}{\partial s}$$

$$= 2y(2s) + 2x\left(\frac{1}{t}\right)$$

$$= 4\left(\frac{s^2}{t}\right) + \frac{2s^2 + 2t^2}{t} \qquad \text{Substitute } s/t \text{ for } y \text{ and } s^2 + t^2 \text{ for } x$$

$$= \frac{6s^2 + 2t^2}{t}.$$

Similarly, holding s fixed gives

$$\frac{\partial w}{\partial t} = \frac{\partial w}{\partial x}\frac{\partial x}{\partial t} + \frac{\partial w}{\partial y}\frac{\partial y}{\partial t}$$

$$= 2y(2t) + 2x\left(\frac{-s}{t^2}\right)$$

$$= 2\left(\frac{s}{t}\right)(2t) + 2(s^2 + t^2)\left(\frac{-s}{t^2}\right) \qquad \text{Substitute } s/t \text{ for } y \text{ and } s^2 + t^2 \text{ for } x$$

$$= 4s - \frac{2s^3 + 2st^2}{t^2}$$

$$= \frac{4st^2 - 2s^3 - 2st^2}{t^2}$$

$$= \frac{2st^2 - 2s^3}{t^2}.$$

The Chain Rule in Theorem 13.7 can also be extended to any number of variables. For example, if w is a differentiable function of the n variables $x_1, x_2, \ldots, x_n$ where each x_i is a differentiable function of the m variables $t_1, t_2, \ldots, t_m$, then for

$$w = f(x_1, x_2, \ldots, x_n)$$

you obtain the following.

$$\frac{\partial w}{\partial t_1} = \frac{\partial w}{\partial x_1}\frac{\partial x_1}{\partial t_1} + \frac{\partial w}{\partial x_2}\frac{\partial x_2}{\partial t_1} + \cdots + \frac{\partial w}{\partial x_n}\frac{\partial x_n}{\partial t_1}$$

$$\frac{\partial w}{\partial t_2} = \frac{\partial w}{\partial x_1}\frac{\partial x_1}{\partial t_2} + \frac{\partial w}{\partial x_2}\frac{\partial x_2}{\partial t_2} + \cdots + \frac{\partial w}{\partial x_n}\frac{\partial x_n}{\partial t_2}$$

$$\vdots$$

$$\frac{\partial w}{\partial t_m} = \frac{\partial w}{\partial x_1}\frac{\partial x_1}{\partial t_m} + \frac{\partial w}{\partial x_2}\frac{\partial x_2}{\partial t_m} + \cdots + \frac{\partial w}{\partial x_n}\frac{\partial x_n}{\partial t_m}$$

EXAMPLE 5   The Chain Rule for a Function of Three Variables

Find $\partial w/\partial s$ and $\partial w/\partial t$ when $s = 1$ and $t = 2\pi$ for the function given by

$$w = xy + yz + xz$$

where $x = s \cos t$, $y = s \sin t$, and $z = t$.

Solution   By extending the result of Theorem 13.7, you have

$$\frac{\partial w}{\partial s} = \frac{\partial w}{\partial x}\frac{\partial x}{\partial s} + \frac{\partial w}{\partial y}\frac{\partial y}{\partial s} + \frac{\partial w}{\partial z}\frac{\partial z}{\partial s}$$

$$= (y + z)(\cos t) + (x + z)(\sin t) + (y + x)(0)$$

$$= (y + z)(\cos t) + (x + z)(\sin t).$$

When $s = 1$ and $t = 2\pi$, you have $x = 1$, $y = 0$, and $z = 2\pi$. Therefore, $\partial w/\partial s = 2\pi(1) + (1 + 2\pi)(0) + 0 = 2\pi$. Furthermore,

$$\frac{\partial w}{\partial t} = \frac{\partial w}{\partial x}\frac{\partial x}{\partial t} + \frac{\partial w}{\partial y}\frac{\partial y}{\partial t} + \frac{\partial w}{\partial z}\frac{\partial z}{\partial t}$$

$$= (y + z)(-s \sin t) + (x + z)(s \cos t) + (y + x)(1)$$

and for $s = 1$ and $t = 2\pi$ it follows that

$$\frac{\partial w}{\partial t} = (0 + 2\pi)(0) + (1 + 2\pi)(1) + (0 + 1)(1)$$

$$= 2 + 2\pi.$$

Implicit Partial Differentiation

We conclude this section with an application of the Chain Rule to determine the derivative of a function defined *implicitly*. Suppose that x and y are related by the equation $F(x, y) = 0$, where it is assumed that $y = f(x)$ is a differentiable function of x. To find dy/dx, you could use the techniques discussed in Section 2.5. However, you will see that the Chain Rule provides a convenient alternative. If you consider the function given by

$$w = F(x, y) = F(x, f(x))$$

you can apply Theorem 13.6 to obtain

$$\frac{dw}{dx} = F_x(x, y)\frac{dx}{dx} + F_y(x, y)\frac{dy}{dx}.$$

Because $w = F(x, y) = 0$ for all x in the domain of f, you know that $dw/dx = 0$ and you have

$$F_x(x, y)\frac{dx}{dx} + F_y(x, y)\frac{dy}{dx} = 0.$$

Now, if $F_y(x, y) \neq 0$, you can use the fact that $dx/dx = 1$ to conclude that

$$\frac{dy}{dx} = -\frac{F_x(x, y)}{F_y(x, y)}.$$

A similar procedure can be used to find the partial derivatives of functions of several variables that are defined implicitly.

THEOREM 13.8   Chain Rule: Implicit Differentiation

If the equation $F(x, y) = 0$ defines y implicity as a differentiable function of x, then

$$\frac{dy}{dx} = -\frac{F_x(x, y)}{F_y(x, y)}, \qquad F_y(x, y) \neq 0.$$

If the equation $F(x, y, z) = 0$ defines z implicitly as a differentiable function of x and y, then

$$\frac{\partial z}{\partial x} = -\frac{F_x(x, y, z)}{F_z(x, y, z)} \quad \text{and} \quad \frac{\partial z}{\partial y} = -\frac{F_y(x, y, z)}{F_z(x, y, z)}, \qquad F_z(x, y, z) \neq 0.$$

This theorem can be extended to differentiable functions defined implicitly with any number of variables.

EXAMPLE 6   Finding a Derivative Implicitly

REMARK   Compare the solution of Example 6 with the solution of Example 2 in Section 2.5.

Find dy/dx, given $y^3 + y^2 - 5y - x^2 + 4 = 0$.

Solution   Begin by defining a function F as

$$F(x, y) = y^3 + y^2 - 5y - x^2 + 4.$$

Then, using Theorem 13.8, you have

$$F_x(x, y) = -2x \quad \text{and} \quad F_y(x, y) = 3y^2 + 2y - 5$$

and it follows that

$$\frac{dy}{dx} = -\frac{F_x(x, y)}{F_y(x, y)} = \frac{-(-2x)}{3y^2 + 2y - 5} = \frac{2x}{3y^2 + 2y - 5}.$$

EXAMPLE 7   Finding Partial Derivatives Implicitly

Find $\partial z/\partial x$ and $\partial z/\partial y$, given $3x^2 z - x^2 y^2 + 2z^3 + 3yz - 5 = 0$.

Solution   To apply Theorem 13.8, let

$$F(x, y, z) = 3x^2 z - x^2 y^2 + 2z^3 + 3yz - 5.$$

Then

$$F_x(x, y, z) = 6xz - 2xy^2$$
$$F_y(x, y, z) = -2x^2 y + 3z$$
$$F_z(x, y, z) = 3x^2 + 6z^2 + 3y$$

and you obtain

$$\frac{\partial z}{\partial x} = -\frac{F_x}{F_z} = \frac{2xy^2 - 6xz}{3x^2 + 6z^2 + 3y}$$

$$\frac{\partial z}{\partial y} = -\frac{F_y}{F_z} = \frac{2x^2 y - 3z}{3x^2 + 6z^2 + 3y}.$$

EXERCISES for Section 13.5

In Exercises 1–4, find dw/dt using the appropriate Chain Rule.

1. $w = x^2 + y^2$
$x = e^t, y = e^{-t}$

2. $w = \sqrt{x^2 + y^2}$
$x = \sin t, y = e^t$

3. $w = x \sec y$
$x = e^t, y = \pi - t$

4. $w = \ln\dfrac{y}{x}$
$x = \cos t, y = \sin t$

In Exercises 5–8, find $\partial w/\partial s$ and $\partial w/\partial t$ using the appropriate Chain Rule, and evaluate each partial derivative at the indicated values of s and t.

Function	Point
5. $w = x^2 + y^2$ $x = s + t, y = s - t$	$s = 2, t = -1$
6. $w = y^3 - 3x^2y$ $x = e^s, y = e^t$	$s = 0, t = 1$
7. $w = x^2 - y^2$ $x = s\cos t, y = s\sin t$	$s = 3, t = \dfrac{\pi}{4}$
8. $w = \sin(2x + 3y)$ $x = s + t, y = s - t$	$s = 0, t = \dfrac{\pi}{2}$

In Exercises 9–14, find dw/dt (a) by the appropriate Chain Rule and (b) by converting w to a function of t before differentiating.

9. $w = xy$
$x = 2\sin t, y = \cos t$

10. $w = \cos(x - y)$
$x = t^2, y = 1$

11. $w = x^2 + y^2 + z^2$
$x = e^t\cos t, y = e^t\sin t, z = e^t$

12. $w = xy\cos z$
$x = t, y = t^2, z = \arccos t$

13. $w = xy + xz + yz$
$x = t - 1, y = t^2 - 1, z = t$

14. $w = xyz$
$x = t^2, y = 2t, z = e^{-t}$

In Exercises 15–18, find $\partial w/\partial r$ and $\partial w/\partial \theta$ (a) by the appropriate Chain Rule and (b) by converting w to a function of r and θ before differentiating.

15. $w = x^2 - 2xy + y^2$
$x = r + \theta, y = r - \theta$

16. $w = \sqrt{4 - 2x^2 - 2y^2}$
$x = r\cos\theta, y = r\sin\theta$

17. $w = \arctan\dfrac{y}{x}$
$x = r\cos\theta, y = r\sin\theta$

18. $w = \dfrac{xy}{z}$
$x = r + \theta, y = r - \theta, z = \theta^2$

In Exercises 19–22, differentiate implicitly to find the first partial derivatives of z.

19. $x^2 + y^2 + z^2 = 25$

20. $xz + yz + xy = 0$

21. $\tan(x + y) + \tan(y + z) = 1$

22. $z = e^x\sin(y + z)$

In Exercises 23 and 24, differentiate implicitly to find all first and second partial derivatives of z.

23. $x^2 + 2yz + z^2 = 1$

24. $x + \sin(y + z) = 0$

In Exercises 25 and 26, differentiate implicitly to find the first partial derivatives of w.

25. $xyz + xzw - yzw + w^2 = 5$

26. $x^2 + y^2 + z^2 + 6xw - 8w^2 = 5$

27. *Volume and Surface Area* Let θ be the angle between the equal sides of an isosceles triangle, and x the length of these sides. If x is increasing at $\frac{1}{2}$ m/hr and θ is increasing at $\pi/90$ rad/hr, find the rate of increase of the area when $x = 6$ and $\theta = \pi/4$.

28. *Volume and Surface Area* The radius of a right circular cylinder is increasing at the rate of 6 inches per minute, and the height is decreasing at the rate of 4 inches per minute. What is the rate of change of the volume and surface area when the radius is 12 inches and the height is 36 inches?

29. *Volume and Surface Area* Repeat Exercise 28 for a right circular cone.

30. *Volume and Surface Area* The two radii of the frustum of a right circular cone are increasing at the rate of 4 centimeters per minute, and the height is increasing at the rate of 12 centimeters per minute (see figure). Find the rate at which the volume and surface area are changing when the two radii are 15 and 25 centimeters and the height is 10 centimeters.

31. *Moment of Inertia* An annular cylinder has an inside radius of r_1 and an outside radius of r_2 (see figure). The moment of inertia is given by

$$I = \frac{1}{2}m(r_1^2 + r_2^2)$$

where m is the mass. Find the rate at which I is changing at the instant the radii are 6 and 8 centimeters, respectively, if the two radii are increasing at the rate of 2 centimeters per second.

FIGURE FOR 30

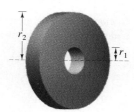

FIGURE FOR 31

32. Ideal Gas Law The Ideal Gas Law is $pV = RT$, where R is a constant. If p and V are functions of time, find dT/dt, the rate at which the temperature changes with respect to time.

C **33. Projectile Motion** A projectile is launched at an angle of $45°$ with the horizontal and with an initial velocity of 64 feet per second. A television camera is located in the plane of the path of the projectile and 50 feet behind the launch site (see figure).

a. Find parametric equations for the path of the projectile in terms of the parameter t representing time.

b. Express the angle α that the camera makes with the horizontal in terms of x and y and in terms of the parameter t.

c. Use the results of part b to find $d\alpha/dt$.

d. Use a graphing utility to obtain a graph of α in terms of t. Is this graph symmetric with the axis of the parabolic arch of the projectile? Why or why not? At what time is the rate of change of α greatest?

e. At what time is the angle α maximum? Does this occur when the projectile is at its greatest height?

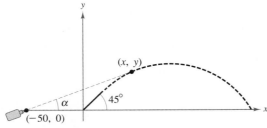

FIGURE FOR 33

34. Projectile Motion Consider the distance between the launch site and the projectile in Exercise 33 (see figure below).

a. Express the distance d in terms of x and y and in terms of the parameter t.

b. Use the results of part a to find the rate of change of d.

c. Find the rate of change of the distance when $t = 2$.

d. When is the rate of change of d minimum during the flight of the projectile? Does it occur at the time the projectile reaches its maximum height?

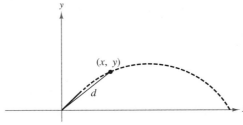

FIGURE FOR 34

Homogeneous Functions **In Exercises 35–38, a function f in x and y is homogeneous of degree n, if**

$$f(tx, ty) = t^n f(x, y).$$

Determine the degree of the function, and show that

$$xf_x(x, y) + yf_y(x, y) = nf(x, y).$$

35. $f(x, y) = x^3 - 3xy^2 + y^3$

36. $f(x, y) = \dfrac{xy}{\sqrt{x^2 + y^2}}$

37. $f(x, y) = e^{x/y}$ **38.** $f(x, y) = \dfrac{x^2}{\sqrt{x^2 + y^2}}$

39. Show that if $f(x, y)$ is homogeneous of degree n, then

$$xf_x(x, y) + yf_y(x, y) = nf(x, y).$$

(*Hint:* Let $g(t) = f(tx, ty) = t^n f(x, y)$. Find $g'(t)$ and then let $t = 1$.)

40. Show that

$$\frac{\partial w}{\partial u} + \frac{\partial w}{\partial v} = 0$$

for $w = f(x, y)$, $x = u - v$, and $y = v - u$.

41. Demonstrate the result of Exercise 40 for the function given by

$$w = (x - y)\sin(y - x).$$

42. Consider the function $w = f(x, y)$ where $x = r\cos\theta$ and $y = r\sin\theta$. Prove the following.

a. $\dfrac{\partial w}{\partial x} = \dfrac{\partial w}{\partial r}\cos\theta - \dfrac{\partial w}{\partial \theta}\dfrac{\sin\theta}{r}$

$\dfrac{\partial w}{\partial y} = \dfrac{\partial w}{\partial r}\sin\theta + \dfrac{\partial w}{\partial \theta}\dfrac{\cos\theta}{r}$

b. $\left(\dfrac{\partial w}{\partial x}\right)^2 + \left(\dfrac{\partial w}{\partial y}\right)^2 = \left(\dfrac{\partial w}{\partial r}\right)^2 + \left(\dfrac{1}{r^2}\right)\left(\dfrac{\partial w}{\partial \theta}\right)^2$

43. Demonstrate the result of Exercise 42b for the function given by

$$w = \arctan\frac{y}{x}.$$

44. Cauchy-Riemann Equations Given the functions $u(x, y)$ and $v(x, y)$, show that the **Cauchy-Riemann differential equations**

$$\frac{\partial u}{\partial x} = \frac{\partial v}{\partial y} \quad \text{and} \quad \frac{\partial u}{\partial y} = -\frac{\partial v}{\partial x}$$

can be written in polar coordinate form as

$$\frac{\partial u}{\partial r} = \frac{1}{r}\frac{\partial v}{\partial \theta} \quad \text{and} \quad \frac{\partial v}{\partial r} = -\frac{1}{r}\frac{\partial u}{\partial \theta}.$$

45. Demonstrate the result of Exercise 44 for the functions

$$u = \ln\sqrt{x^2 + y^2} \quad \text{and} \quad v = \arctan\frac{y}{x}.$$

46. Wave Equation Show that

$$u(x, t) = \frac{1}{2}[f(x - ct) + f(x + ct)]$$

is a solution to the one-dimensional wave equation

$$\frac{\partial^2 u}{\partial t^2} = c^2\frac{\partial^2 u}{\partial x^2}.$$

(This equation describes the small transverse vibration of elastic strings such as those on certain musical instruments.)

Directional Derivatives and Gradients

Directional Derivative • The Gradient of a Function of Two Variables • Applications of the Gradient • Functions of Three Variables

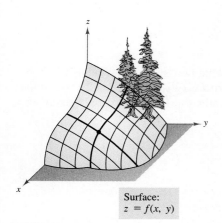

FIGURE 13.42

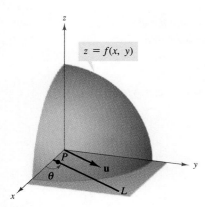

FIGURE 13.43

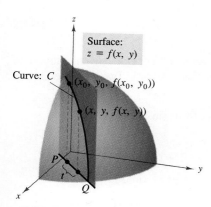

FIGURE 13.44

Directional Derivative

Suppose you are standing on the hillside pictured in Figure 13.42 and want to determine the hill's incline toward the z-axis. If the hill were represented by $z = f(x, y)$, then you would already know how to determine the slopes in two different directions—the slope in the y-direction would be given by the partial derivative $f_y(x, y)$, and the slope in the x-direction would be given by the partial derivative $f_x(x, y)$. In this section, you will see that these two partial derivatives can be used to find the slope in *any* direction.

To determine the slope at a point on a surface, we define a new type of derivative called a **directional derivative.** We begin by letting $z = f(x, y)$ be a *surface* and $P = (x_0, y_0)$ a *point* in the domain of f, as shown in Figure 13.43. The "direction" of the directional derivative is given by a unit vector

$$\mathbf{u} = \cos\theta\,\mathbf{i} + \sin\theta\,\mathbf{j}$$

where θ is the angle the vector makes with the positive x-axis. To find the desired slope, reduce the problem to two dimensions by intersecting the surface with a vertical plane passing through the point P and parallel to $\mathbf{u}$, as shown in Figure 13.44. This vertical plane intersects the surface to form a curve C. The slope of the surface at $(x_0, y_0, f(x_0, y_0))$ in the direction of $\mathbf{u}$ is defined as the slope of the curve C at that point.

Informally, you can write the slope of the curve C as a limit that looks much like those used in single-variable calculus. The vertical plane used to form C intersects the xy-plane in a line L, represented by the parametric equations

$$x = x_0 + t\cos\theta \quad \text{and} \quad y = y_0 + t\sin\theta$$

so that for any value of t, the point $Q = (x, y)$ lies on the line L. For each of the points P and Q, there is a corresponding point on the surface.

$(x_0, y_0, f(x_0, y_0))$ Point above P

$(x, y, f(x, y))$ Point above Q

Moreover, because the distance between P and Q is

$$\sqrt{(x - x_0)^2 + (y - y_0)^2} = \sqrt{(t\cos\theta)^2 + (t\sin\theta)^2} = |t|$$

you can write the slope of the secant line through $(x_0, y_0, f(x_0, y_0))$ and $(x, y, f(x, y))$ as

$$\frac{f(x, y) - f(x_0, y_0)}{t} = \frac{f(x_0 + t\cos\theta, y_0 + t\sin\theta) - f(x_0, y_0)}{t}.$$

Finally, by letting t approach 0, you arrive at the following definition.

Definition of Directional Derivative

Let f be a function of two variables x and y and let $\mathbf{u} = \cos\theta\,\mathbf{i} + \sin\theta\,\mathbf{j}$ be a unit vector. Then the **directional derivative of f in the direction of u**, denoted by $D_{\mathbf{u}}f$, is

$$D_{\mathbf{u}}f(x, y) = \lim_{t \to 0} \frac{f(x + t\cos\theta, y + t\sin\theta) - f(x, y)}{t}$$

provided this limit exists.

Calculating directional derivatives by this definition is similar to finding the derivative of a function of one variable by the limit process (given in Section 2.1). A simpler "working" formula for finding directional derivatives involves the partial derivatives f_x and f_y.

THEOREM 13.9 Directional Derivative

If f is a differentiable function of x and y, then the directional derivative of f in the direction of the unit vector $\mathbf{u} = \cos\theta\,\mathbf{i} + \sin\theta\,\mathbf{j}$ is

$$D_{\mathbf{u}}f(x, y) = f_x(x, y)\cos\theta + f_y(x, y)\sin\theta.$$

Proof   For a fixed point (x_0, y_0), let $x = x_0 + t\cos\theta$ and $y = y_0 + t\sin\theta$. Then, let $g(t) = f(x, y)$. Because f is differentiable, you can apply the Chain Rule given in Theorem 13.7 to obtain

$$g'(t) = f_x(x, y)\frac{\partial x}{\partial t} + f_y(x, y)\frac{\partial y}{\partial t} = f_x(x, y)\cos\theta + f_y(x, y)\sin\theta.$$

If $t = 0$, then $x = x_0$ and $y = y_0$, so

$$g'(0) = f_x(x_0, y_0)\cos\theta + f_y(x_0, y_0)\sin\theta.$$

By the definition of $g'(t)$, it is also true that

$$g'(0) = \lim_{t \to 0}\frac{g(t) - g(0)}{t} = \lim_{t \to 0}\frac{f(x_0 + t\cos\theta, y_0 + t\sin\theta) - f(x_0, y_0)}{t}.$$

Consequently, $D_{\mathbf{u}}f(x_0, y_0) = f_x(x_0, y_0)\cos\theta + f_y(x_0, y_0)\sin\theta.$ ▬

There are infinitely many directional derivatives to a surface at a given point—one for each direction specified by $\mathbf{u}$, as indicated in Figure 13.45. Two of these are the partial derivatives f_x and f_y.

1. Direction of positive x-axis ($\theta = 0$): $\mathbf{u} = \cos 0\,\mathbf{i} + \sin 0\,\mathbf{j} = \mathbf{i}$

$$D_{\mathbf{i}}f(x, y) = f_x(x, y)\cos 0 + f_y(x, y)\sin 0 = f_x(x, y)$$

2. Direction of positive y-axis ($\theta = \pi/2$): $\mathbf{u} = \cos\dfrac{\pi}{2}\mathbf{i} + \sin\dfrac{\pi}{2}\mathbf{j} = \mathbf{j}$

$$D_{\mathbf{j}}f(x, y) = f_x(x, y)\cos\frac{\pi}{2} + f_y(x, y)\sin\frac{\pi}{2} = f_y(x, y)$$

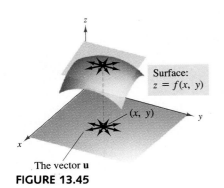

Surface:
$z = f(x, y)$

(x, y)

The vector **u**

FIGURE 13.45

EXAMPLE 1   Finding a Directional Derivative

Find the directional derivative of

$$f(x, y) = 4 - x^2 - \frac{1}{4}y^2 \qquad \text{Surface}$$

at $(1, 2)$ in the direction of

$$\mathbf{u} = \left(\cos\frac{\pi}{3}\right)\mathbf{i} + \left(\sin\frac{\pi}{3}\right)\mathbf{j}. \qquad \text{Direction}$$

Solution   Because f_x and f_y are continuous, f is differentiable, and you can apply Theorem 13.9.

$$\begin{aligned}
D_{\mathbf{u}}f(x, y) &= f_x(x, y)\cos\theta + f_y(x, y)\sin\theta \\
&= (-2x)\cos\theta + \left(-\frac{y}{2}\right)\sin\theta
\end{aligned}$$

Evaluating at $\theta = \pi/3$, $x = 1$, and $y = 2$ produces

$$\begin{aligned}
D_{\mathbf{u}}f(1, 2) &= (-2)\left(\frac{1}{2}\right) + (-1)\left(\frac{\sqrt{3}}{2}\right) \\
&= -1 - \frac{\sqrt{3}}{2} \\
&\approx -1.866.
\end{aligned}$$

We have been specifying direction by a unit vector $\mathbf{u}$. If the direction is given by a vector whose length is not 1, then we must normalize the vector before applying the formula in Theorem 13.9.

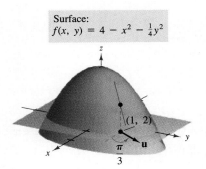

Surface:
$f(x, y) = 4 - x^2 - \frac{1}{4}y^2$

FIGURE 13.46

REMARK   Note in Figure 13.46 that you can interpret the directional derivative as giving the slope of the surface at the point $(1, 2, 2)$ in the direction of the unit vector $\mathbf{u}$.

EXAMPLE 2   Finding a Directional Derivative

Find the directional derivative of

$$f(x, y) = x^2 \sin 2y \qquad \text{Surface}$$

at $(1, \pi/2)$ in the direction of

$$\mathbf{v} = 3\mathbf{i} - 4\mathbf{j}. \qquad \text{Direction}$$

Solution   Because f_x and f_y are continuous, f is differentiable, and you can apply Theorem 13.9. Begin by finding a unit vector in the direction of $\mathbf{v}$.

$$\mathbf{u} = \frac{\mathbf{v}}{\|\mathbf{v}\|} = \frac{3}{5}\mathbf{i} - \frac{4}{5}\mathbf{j} = \cos\theta\,\mathbf{i} + \sin\theta\,\mathbf{j}$$

Using this unit vector, you have

$$\begin{aligned}
D_{\mathbf{u}}f(x, y) &= (2x\sin 2y)(\cos\theta) + (2x^2\cos 2y)(\sin\theta) \\
D_{\mathbf{u}}f\left(1, \frac{\pi}{2}\right) &= (2\sin\pi)\left(\frac{3}{5}\right) + (2\cos\pi)\left(-\frac{4}{5}\right) \\
&= (0)\left(\frac{3}{5}\right) + (-2)\left(-\frac{4}{5}\right) \\
&= \frac{8}{5}.
\end{aligned}$$

(See Figure 13.47.)

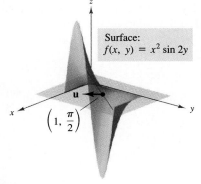

Surface:
$f(x, y) = x^2 \sin 2y$

FIGURE 13.47

The Gradient of a Function of Two Variables

The **gradient** of a function of two variables is a vector-valued function of two variables. This function has many important uses, some of which are described later in this section.

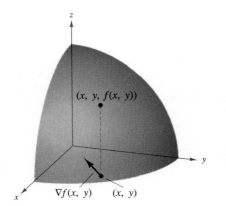

FIGURE 13.48
The gradient of f is a vector in the xy-plane.

> ### Definition of Gradient of a Function of Two Variables
>
> Let $z = f(x, y)$ be a function of x and y such that f_x and f_y exist. Then the **gradient of f,** denoted by $\nabla f(x, y)$, is the vector
>
> $$\nabla f(x, y) = f_x(x, y)\mathbf{i} + f_y(x, y)\mathbf{j}.$$
>
> We read ∇f as "del f." Another notation for the gradient is **grad** $f(x, y)$. In Figure 13.48, note that for each (x, y), the gradient $\nabla f(x, y)$ is a vector in the plane (not a vector in space).

REMARK   No value is assigned to the symbol ∇ by itself. It is an operator in the same sense that d/dx is an operator. When ∇ operates on $f(x, y)$, it produces the vector $\nabla f(x, y)$.

EXAMPLE 3   Finding the Gradient of a Function

Find the gradient of $f(x, y) = y \ln x + xy^2$ at the point $(1, 2)$.

Solution   Using $f_x(x, y) = \dfrac{y}{x} + y^2$ and $f_y(x, y) = \ln x + 2xy$, you have

$$\nabla f(x, y) = \left(\frac{y}{x} + y^2\right)\mathbf{i} + (\ln x + 2xy)\mathbf{j}.$$

At the point $(1, 2)$, the gradient is

$$\nabla f(1, 2) = \left(\frac{2}{1} + 2^2\right)\mathbf{i} + [\ln 1 + 2(1)(2)]\mathbf{j}$$
$$= 6\mathbf{i} + 4\mathbf{j}.$$

Because the gradient of f is a vector, you can write the directional derivative of f in the direction of $\mathbf{u}$ as

$$D_\mathbf{u} f(x, y) = [f_x(x, y)\mathbf{i} + f_y(x, y)\mathbf{j}] \cdot [\cos\theta\,\mathbf{i} + \sin\theta\,\mathbf{j}].$$

In other words, the directional derivative is the dot product of the gradient and the direction vector. This useful result is summarized in the following theorem.

> ### THEOREM 13.10   Alternative Form of the Directional Derivative
>
> If f is a differentiable function of x and y, then the directional derivative of f in the direction of the unit vector $\mathbf{u}$ is
>
> $$D_\mathbf{u}f(x, y) = \nabla f(x, y) \cdot \mathbf{u}.$$

EXAMPLE 4   Using $\nabla f(x, y)$ to Find a Directional Derivative

Find the directional derivative of

$$f(x, y) = 3x^2 - 2y^2$$

at $\left(-\frac{3}{4}, 0\right)$ in the direction from $P = \left(-\frac{3}{4}, 0\right)$ to $Q = (0, 1)$.

Solution   Because the partials of f are continuous, f is differentiable and you can apply Theorem 13.10. A vector in the specified direction is

$$\overrightarrow{PQ} = \mathbf{v} = \left(0 + \frac{3}{4}\right)\mathbf{i} + (1 - 0)\mathbf{j}$$

$$= \frac{3}{4}\mathbf{i} + \mathbf{j}$$

and a unit vector in this direction is

$$\mathbf{u} = \frac{\mathbf{v}}{\|\mathbf{v}\|} = \frac{3}{5}\mathbf{i} + \frac{4}{5}\mathbf{j}. \qquad \text{Unit vector in direction of } \overrightarrow{PQ}$$

Because $\nabla f(x, y) = f_x(x, y)\mathbf{i} + f_y(x, y)\mathbf{j} = 6x\,\mathbf{i} - 4y\,\mathbf{j}$, the gradient at $\left(-\frac{3}{4}, 0\right)$ is

$$\nabla f\left(-\frac{3}{4}, 0\right) = -\frac{9}{2}\mathbf{i} + 0\mathbf{j}. \qquad \text{Gradient at } \left(-\frac{3}{4}, 0\right)$$

Consequently, at $\left(-\frac{3}{4}, 0\right)$ the directional derivative is

$$D_{\mathbf{u}}f\left(-\frac{3}{4}, 0\right) = \nabla f\left(-\frac{3}{4}, 0\right) \cdot \mathbf{u}$$

$$= \left(-\frac{9}{2}\mathbf{i} + 0\mathbf{j}\right) \cdot \left(\frac{3}{5}\mathbf{i} + \frac{4}{5}\mathbf{j}\right)$$

$$= -\frac{27}{10}. \qquad \text{Directional derivative at } \left(-\frac{3}{4}, 0\right)$$

(See Figure 13.49.)

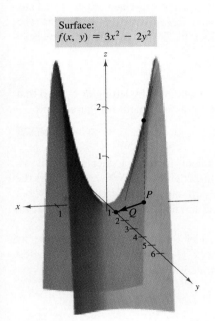

Surface:
$f(x, y) = 3x^2 - 2y^2$

FIGURE 13.49

Applications of the Gradient

You have already seen that there are many directional derivatives at the point (x, y) on a surface. In many applications we would like to know in which direction to move so that $f(x, y)$ increases most rapidly. This direction is called the direction of *steepest ascent*, and it is given by the gradient, as stated in the following theorem.

THEOREM 13.11   Properties of the Gradient

Let f be differentiable at the point (x, y).

1. If $\nabla f(x, y) = \mathbf{0}$, then $D_{\mathbf{u}}f(x, y) = 0$ for all $\mathbf{u}$.
2. The direction of *maximum* increase of f is given by $\nabla f(x, y)$. The maximum value of $D_{\mathbf{u}}f(x, y)$ is $\|\nabla f(x, y)\|$.
3. The direction of *minimum* increase of f is given by $-\nabla f(x, y)$. The minimum value of $D_{\mathbf{u}}f(x, y)$ is $-\|\nabla f(x, y)\|$.

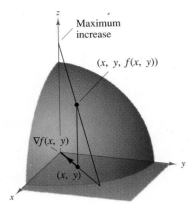

FIGURE 13.50
The gradient of f is a vector in the xy-plane that points in the direction of maximum increase on the surface given by $z = f(x, y)$.

Proof   If $\nabla f(x, y) = \mathbf{0}$, then for any direction (any $\mathbf{u}$), you have

$$D_{\mathbf{u}}f(x, y) = \nabla f(x, y) \cdot \mathbf{u} = (0\mathbf{i} + 0\mathbf{j}) \cdot (\cos\theta\,\mathbf{i} + \sin\theta\,\mathbf{j}) = 0.$$

If $\nabla f(x, y) \neq \mathbf{0}$, then let ϕ be the angle between $\nabla f(x, y)$ and a unit vector $\mathbf{u}$. Using the dot product, you can apply Theorem 11.6 to conclude that

$$\begin{aligned}
D_{\mathbf{u}}f(x, y) &= \nabla f(x, y) \cdot \mathbf{u} \\
&= \| \nabla f(x, y) \| \, \| \mathbf{u} \| \cos\phi \\
&= \| \nabla f(x, y) \| \cos\phi
\end{aligned}$$

and it follows that the maximum value of $D_{\mathbf{u}}f(x, y)$ will occur when $\cos\phi = 1$. Thus $\phi = 0$, and the maximum value for the directional derivative occurs when $\mathbf{u}$ has the same direction as $\nabla f(x, y)$. Moreover, this largest value for $D_{\mathbf{u}}f(x, y)$ is precisely

$$\| \nabla f(x, y) \| \cos\phi = \| \nabla f(x, y) \|.$$

Similarly, the minimum value of $D_{\mathbf{u}}f(x, y)$ can be obtained by letting $\phi = \pi$ so that $\mathbf{u}$ points in the direction opposite that of $\nabla f(x, y)$, as indicated in Figure 13.50.

To visualize one of the properties of the gradient, imagine a skier coming down a mountainside. If $f(x, y)$ denotes the altitude of the skier, then $-\nabla f(x, y)$ indicates the *compass direction* the skier should take to ski the path of steepest descent. (Remember that the gradient indicates direction in the xy-plane and does not itself point up or down the mountainside.)

As another illustration of the gradient, consider the temperature $T(x, y)$ at any point (x, y) on a flat metal plate. In this case, $\nabla T(x, y)$ gives the direction of greatest temperature increase at the point (x, y), as illustrated in the next example.

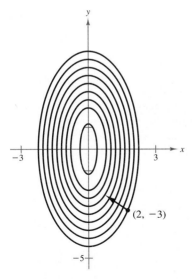

FIGURE 13.51
Direction of most rapid increase in temperature at $(2, -3)$.

EXAMPLE 5   Finding the Direction of Maximum Increase

The temperature in degrees Celsius on the surface of a metal plate is

$$T(x, y) = 20 - 4x^2 - y^2$$

where x and y are measured in inches. In what direction from $(2, -3)$ does the temperature increase most rapidly? What is this rate of increase?

Solution   The gradient is

$$\begin{aligned}
\nabla T(x, y) &= T_x(x, y)\mathbf{i} + T_y(x, y)\mathbf{j} \\
&= -8x\,\mathbf{i} - 2y\,\mathbf{j}.
\end{aligned}$$

It follows that the direction of maximum increase is given by

$$\nabla T(2, -3) = -16\mathbf{i} + 6\mathbf{j}$$

as shown in Figure 13.51, and the rate of increase is

$$\| \nabla T(2, -3) \| = \sqrt{256 + 36} = \sqrt{292} \approx 17.09° \text{ per inch.}$$

The solution presented in Example 5 can be misleading. Although the gradient points in the direction of maximum temperature increase, it does not necessarily point toward the hottest spot on the plate. In other words, the gradient provides a local solution to finding an increase relative to the temperature at the point $(2, -3)$. *Once you leave that position, the direction of maximum increase may change.*

EXAMPLE 6   Finding the Path of a Heat-Seeking Particle

A heat-seeking particle is located at the point $(2, -3)$ on a metal plate whose temperature at (x, y) is

$$T(x, y) = 20 - 4x^2 - y^2.$$

Find the path of the particle as it continuously moves in the direction of maximum temperature increase.

Solution   Let the path be represented by the position function

$$\mathbf{r}(t) = x(t)\mathbf{i} + y(t)\mathbf{j}.$$

A tangent vector at each point $(x(t), y(t))$ is given by

$$\mathbf{r}'(t) = \frac{dx}{dt}\mathbf{i} + \frac{dy}{dt}\mathbf{j}.$$

Because the particle seeks maximum temperature increase, the directions of $\mathbf{r}'(t)$ and $\nabla T(x, y) = -8x\,\mathbf{i} - 2y\,\mathbf{j}$ are the same at each point of the path. Thus,

$$-8x = k\frac{dx}{dt} \quad \text{and} \quad -2y = k\frac{dy}{dt}$$

where k depends on t. By solving each equation for dt/k and equating the results, you obtain

$$\frac{dx}{-8x} = \frac{dy}{-2y}.$$

The solution of this differential equation is $x = Cy^4$. Because the particle starts at the point $(2, -3)$, you can determine that $C = \frac{2}{81}$. Thus, the path of the heat-seeking particle is

$$x = \frac{2}{81}y^4.$$

The path is shown in Figure 13.52.   ▬▬

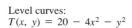

Level curves:
$T(x, y) = 20 - 4x^2 - y^2$

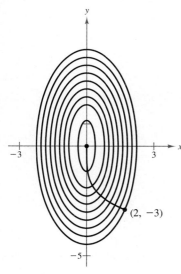

(2, −3)

FIGURE 13.52
Path followed by a heat-seeking particle.

In Figure 13.52, the path of the particle (determined by the gradient at each point) appears to be orthogonal to each of the level curves. This becomes clear when you consider that the temperature $T(x, y)$ is constant along a given level curve. Hence, at any point (x, y) on the curve, the rate of change of T in the direction of a unit tangent vector $\mathbf{u}$ is 0, and you can write

$$\nabla f(x, y) \cdot \mathbf{u} = D_\mathbf{u}T(x, y) = 0. \qquad \text{\small u is a unit tangent vector}$$

Because the dot product of $\nabla f(x, y)$ and $\mathbf{u}$ is 0, you can conclude that they must be orthogonal. This result is stated in the following theorem.

> **THEOREM 13.12**   **Gradient is Normal to Level Curves**
>
> If f is differentiable at (x_0, y_0) and $\nabla f(x_0, y_0) \neq \mathbf{0}$, then $\nabla f(x_0, y_0)$ is normal to the level curve through (x_0, y_0).

EXAMPLE 7   Finding a Normal Vector to a Level Curve

Sketch the level curve corresponding to $c = 0$ for the function given by

$$f(x, y) = y - \sin x$$

and find a normal vector at several points on the curve.

Solution   The level curve for $c = 0$ is given by

$$0 = y - \sin x$$
$$y = \sin x$$

as shown in Figure 13.53. Because the gradient vector of f at (x, y) is

$$\nabla f(x, y) = f_x(x, y)\mathbf{i} + f_y(x, y)\mathbf{j}$$
$$= -\cos x\,\mathbf{i} + \mathbf{j}$$

you can use Theorem 13.12 to conclude that $\nabla f(x, y)$ is normal to the level curve at the point (x, y). Some gradient vectors are

$$\nabla f(-\pi, 0) = \mathbf{i} + \mathbf{j}$$
$$\nabla f\left(-\frac{2\pi}{3}, -\frac{\sqrt{3}}{2}\right) = \frac{1}{2}\mathbf{i} + \mathbf{j}$$
$$\nabla f\left(-\frac{\pi}{2}, -1\right) = \mathbf{j}.$$

Several others are shown in Figure 13.53.

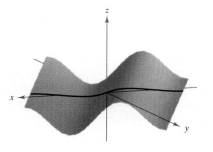

(a) The surface is given by $f(x, y) = y - \sin x$.

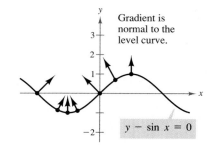

(b) The level curve is given by $f(x, y) = 0$.

FIGURE 13.53

Functions of Three Variables

The definitions of the directional derivative and the gradient can be extended naturally to functions of three or more variables. As often happens, some of the geometric interpretation is lost in the generalization from functions of two variables to those of three variables. For example, you cannot interpret the directional derivative of a function of three variables to represent slope.

The definitions and properties of the directional derivative and the gradient of a function of three variables are given in the following summary.

Directional Derivative and Gradient for a Function of Three Variables

Let f be a function of x, y, and z, with continuous first partial derivatives. The **directional derivative of f** in the direction of a unit vector

$$\mathbf{u} = a\mathbf{i} + b\mathbf{j} + c\mathbf{k}$$

is given by

$$D_{\mathbf{u}}f(x, y, z) = af_x(x, y, z) + bf_y(x, y, z) + cf_z(x, y, z).$$

The **gradient of f** is defined to be

$$\nabla f(x, y, z) = f_x(x, y, z)\mathbf{i} + f_y(x, y, z)\mathbf{j} + f_z(x, y, z)\mathbf{k}.$$

Properties of the gradient are as follows.

1. $D_{\mathbf{u}}f(x, y, z) = \nabla f(x, y, z) \cdot \mathbf{u}$
2. If $\nabla f(x, y, z) = \mathbf{0}$, then $D_{\mathbf{u}}f(x, y, z) = 0$ for all $\mathbf{u}$.
3. The direction of *maximum* increase of f is given by $\nabla f(x, y, z)$. The maximum value of $D_{\mathbf{u}}f(x, y, z)$ is $\| \nabla f(x, y, z) \|$.
4. The direction of *minimum* increase of f is given by $-\nabla f(x, y, z)$. The minimum value of $D_{\mathbf{u}}f(x, y, z)$ is $-\| \nabla f(x, y, z) \|$.

EXAMPLE 8   Finding the Gradient for a Function of Three Variables

Find $\nabla f(x, y, z)$ for the function given by

$$f(x, y, z) = x^2 + y^2 - 4z$$

and find the direction of maximum increase of f at the point $(2, -1, 1)$.

Solution   The gradient vector is given by

$$\begin{aligned} \nabla f(x, y, z) &= f_x(x, y, z)\mathbf{i} + f_y(x, y, z)\mathbf{j} + f_z(x, y, z)\mathbf{k} \\ &= 2x\mathbf{i} + 2y\mathbf{j} - 4\mathbf{k}. \end{aligned}$$

Hence, it follows that the direction of maximum increase at $(2, -1, 1)$ is

$$\nabla f(2, -1, 1) = 4\mathbf{i} - 2\mathbf{j} - 4\mathbf{k}.$$

EXERCISES for Section 13.6

In Exercises 1–12, find the directional derivative of the function at P in the direction of v.

1. $f(x, y) = 3x - 4xy + 5y$,
$P = (1, 2)$, $\mathbf{v} = \frac{1}{2}(\mathbf{i} + \sqrt{3}\mathbf{j})$

2. $f(x, y) = x^2 - y^2$,
$P = (4, 3)$, $\mathbf{v} = \dfrac{\sqrt{2}}{2}(\mathbf{i} + \mathbf{j})$

3. $f(x, y) = xy$,
$P = (2, 3)$, $\mathbf{v} = \mathbf{i} + \mathbf{j}$

4. $f(x, y) = \dfrac{x}{y}$,
$P = (1, 1)$, $\mathbf{v} = -\mathbf{j}$

5. $g(x, y) = \sqrt{x^2 + y^2}$,
$P = (3, 4)$, $\mathbf{v} = 3\mathbf{i} - 4\mathbf{j}$

6. $g(x, y) = \arcsin xy$,
$P = (1, 0)$, $\mathbf{v} = \mathbf{i} + 5\mathbf{j}$

7. $h(x, y) = e^x \sin y$,
$P = \left(1, \dfrac{\pi}{2}\right)$, $\mathbf{v} = -\mathbf{i}$

8. $h(x, y) = e^{-(x^2+y^2)}$,
$P = (0, 0)$, $\mathbf{v} = \mathbf{i} + \mathbf{j}$

9. $f(x, y, z) = xy + yz + xz$,
$P = (1, 1, 1)$, $\mathbf{v} = 2\mathbf{i} + \mathbf{j} - \mathbf{k}$

10. $f(x, y, z) = x^2 + y^2 + z^2$,
$P = (1, 2, -1)$, $\mathbf{v} = \mathbf{i} - 2\mathbf{j} + 3\mathbf{k}$

11. $h(x, y, z) = x \arctan yz$,
$P = (4, 1, 1)$, $\mathbf{v} = \langle 1, 2, -1 \rangle$

12. $h(x, y, z) = xyz$,
$P = (2, 1, 1)$, $\mathbf{v} = \langle 2, 1, 2 \rangle$

In Exercises 13–16, find the directional derivative of the function in the direction $\mathbf{u} = \cos\theta\,\mathbf{i} + \sin\theta\,\mathbf{j}$.

13. $f(x, y) = x^2 + y^2$
$\theta = \dfrac{\pi}{4}$

14. $f(x, y) = \dfrac{y}{x + y}$
$\theta = -\dfrac{\pi}{6}$

15. $f(x, y) = \sin(2x - y)$
$\theta = -\dfrac{\pi}{3}$

16. $g(x, y) = xe^y$
$\theta = \dfrac{2\pi}{3}$

In Exercises 17–20, find the directional derivative of the function at the point P in the direction of Q.

17. $f(x, y) = x^2 + 4y^2$
$P = (3, 1)$, $Q = (1, -1)$

18. $f(x, y) = \cos(x + y)$
$P = (0, \pi)$, $Q = \left(\dfrac{\pi}{2}, 0\right)$

19. $h(x, y, z) = \ln(x + y + z)$
$P = (1, 0, 0)$, $Q = (4, 3, 1)$

20. $g(x, y, z) = xye^z$
$P = (2, 4, 0)$, $Q = (0, 0, 0)$

In Exercises 21 and 22, use the graph to estimate the components of the vector in the direction of the maximum increase in the function at the specified point. Then find the gradient at the point and compare it with your estimate.

21. $f(x, y) = \frac{1}{10}(x^2 - 3xy + y^2)$
$(1, 2)$

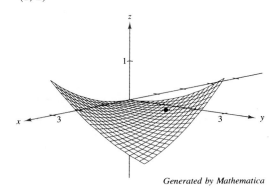

Generated by Mathematica

22. $f(x, y) = \frac{1}{2}y\sqrt{x}$
$(1, 2)$

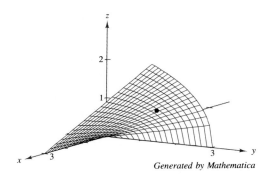

Generated by Mathematica

In Exercises 23–30, find the gradient of the function and the maximum value of the directional derivative at the indicated point.

Function	Point
23. $h(x, y) = x \tan y$	$\left(2, \dfrac{\pi}{4}\right)$
24. $h(x, y) = y \cos(x - y)$	$\left(0, \dfrac{\pi}{3}\right)$
25. $g(x, y) = \ln \sqrt[3]{x^2 + y^2}$	$(1, 2)$
26. $g(x, y) = ye^{-x^2}$	$(0, 5)$
27. $f(x, y, z) = \sqrt{x^2 + y^2 + z^2}$	$(1, 4, 2)$
28. $f(x, y, z) = xe^{yz}$	$(2, 0, -4)$
29. $w = \dfrac{1}{\sqrt{1 - x^2 - y^2 - z^2}}$	$(0, 0, 0)$
30. $w = xy^2z^2$	$(2, 1, 1)$

In Exercises 31–38, use the function given by

$$f(x,y) = 3 - \frac{x}{3} - \frac{y}{2}.$$

31. Sketch the graph of f in the first octant and plot the point $(3, 2, 1)$.

32. Find $D_{\mathbf{u}}f(3, 2)$ where $\mathbf{u} = \cos\theta\,\mathbf{i} + \sin\theta\,\mathbf{j}$.

    a. $\theta = \dfrac{\pi}{4}$ **b.** $\theta = \dfrac{2\pi}{3}$

33. Find $D_{\mathbf{u}}f(3, 2)$ where $\mathbf{u} = \cos\theta\,\mathbf{i} + \sin\theta\,\mathbf{j}$.

    a. $\theta = \dfrac{4\pi}{3}$ **b.** $\theta = -\dfrac{\pi}{6}$

34. Find $D_{\mathbf{u}}f(3, 2)$ where $\mathbf{u} = \mathbf{v}/\|\mathbf{v}\|$.
    a. $\mathbf{v} = \mathbf{i} + \mathbf{j}$ **b.** $\mathbf{v} = -3\mathbf{i} - 4\mathbf{j}$

35. Find $D_{\mathbf{u}}f(3, 2)$ where $\mathbf{u} = \mathbf{v}/\|\mathbf{v}\|$.
    a. $\mathbf{v}$ is the vector from $(1, 2)$ to $(-2, 6)$.
    b. $\mathbf{v}$ is the vector from $(3, 2)$ to $(4, 5)$.

36. Find $\nabla f(x, y)$.

37. Find the maximum value of the directional derivative at $(3, 2)$.

38. Find a unit vector $\mathbf{u}$ orthogonal to $\nabla f(3, 2)$ and calculate $D_{\mathbf{u}}f(3, 2)$. Discuss the geometric meaning of the result.

In Exercises 39–42, use the function given by

$$f(x, y) = 9 - x^2 - y^2.$$

39. Sketch the graph of f in the first octant and plot the point $(1, 2, 4)$ on the surface.

40. Find $D_{\mathbf{u}}f(1, 2)$ where $\mathbf{u} = \cos\theta\,\mathbf{i} + \sin\theta\,\mathbf{j}$.

    a. $\theta = -\dfrac{\pi}{4}$ **b.** $\theta = \dfrac{\pi}{3}$

41. Find $\nabla f(1, 2)$ and $\|\nabla f(1, 2)\|$.

42. Find a unit vector $\mathbf{u}$ orthogonal to $\nabla f(1, 2)$ and calculate $D_{\mathbf{u}}f(1, 2)$. Discuss the geometric meaning of the result.

In Exercises 43–46, find a normal vector to the level curve $f(x, y) = c$ at P.

43. $f(x, y) = x^2 + y^2$ **44.** $f(x, y) = 6 - 2x - 3y$
    $c = 25,\ P = (3, 4)$ $c = 6,\ P = (0, 0)$

45. $f(x, y) = \dfrac{x}{x^2 + y^2}$ **46.** $f(x, y) = xy$
    $c = \frac{1}{2},\ P = (1, 1)$ $c = -3,\ P = (-1, 3)$

In Exercises 47–50, use the gradient to find a unit normal vector to the graph of the equation at the indicated point. Sketch your results.

Equation	Point
47. $4x^2 - y = 6$	$(2, 10)$
48. $3x^2 - 2y^2 = 1$	$(1, 1)$
49. $9x^2 + 4y^2 = 40$	$(2, -1)$
50. $xe^y - y = 5$	$(5, 0)$

51. *Temperature Distribution* The temperature at the point (x, y) on a metal plate is given by

$$T = \frac{x}{x^2 + y^2}.$$

Find the direction of greatest increase in heat from the point $(3, 4)$.

52. *Topography* The surface of a mountain is described by the equation

$$h(x, y) = 4000 - 0.001x^2 - 0.004y^2.$$

Suppose a mountain climber is at the point $(500, 300, 3390)$. In what direction should the climber move in order to ascend at the greatest rate?

Heat-Seeking Path In Exercises 53 and 54, find the path followed by a heat-seeking particle placed at point P on a metal plate with a temperature field given by $T(x, y)$.

Temperature field	Point
53. $T(x, y) = 400 - 2x^2 - y^2$	$P = (10, 10)$
54. $T(x, y) = 50 - x^2 - 2y^2$	$P = (4, 3)$

55. *Meteorology* Meteorologists measure the atmospheric pressure in units called millibars. From these observations they create weather maps on which the curves of equal atmospheric pressure (isobars) are drawn (see figure). These are level curves of the function $P(x, y)$ yielding the pressure at any point. Sketch the gradients to the isobars at the points A, B, and C. Although the magnitudes of the gradients are unknown, their lengths relative to each other can be estimated. At which of the three points is the wind speed greatest if the speed increases as the pressure gradient increases?

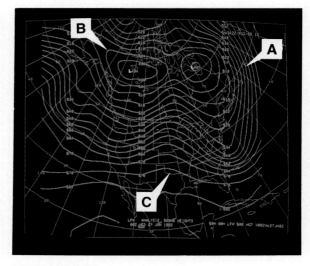

FIGURE FOR 55

56. Let P be a point on the ellipse given by

$$\frac{x^2}{a^2} + \frac{y^2}{b^2} = 1$$

where $\mathbf{T}$ is a tangent vector to the ellipse at P and $f(x, y) = d_1 + d_2$ is the sum of the distances from the foci to P (see figure). Show that $\mathbf{T} \cdot \nabla f(x, y)$ is 0, and give a geometric interpretation of this result.

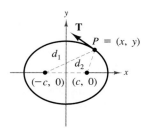

FIGURE FOR 56

True or False   In Exercises 57–60, determine whether the statement is true or false. If it is false, explain why or give an example that shows it is false.

57. If $f(x, y) = \sqrt{1 - x^2 - y^2}$, then $D_{\mathbf{u}}f(0, 0) = 0$ for any unit vector $\mathbf{u}$.

58. If $f(x, y) = x + y$, then $-1 \le D_{\mathbf{u}}f(x, y) \le 1$.

59. If $D_{\mathbf{u}}f(x, y)$ exists, then $D_{\mathbf{u}}f(x, y) = -D_{-\mathbf{u}}f(x, y)$.

60. If $D_{\mathbf{u}}f(x_0, y_0) = c$ for any unit vector $\mathbf{u}$, then $c = 0$.

61. The computer-generated figure shows the graph of

$$f(x, y) = \frac{-4y}{1 + x^2 + y^2}$$

over the square domain in which $-4 \le x \le 4$ and $-4 \le y \le 4$. Use the graph to estimate the value of the gradient at the indicated point. Then, confirm your estimate analytically.

a. $(0, 1, -2)$ **b.** $(0, -1, 2)$
c. $(2, 0, 0)$ **d.** $(-2, 0, 0)$
e. $(0, 0, 0)$ **f.** $(1, 1, -\frac{4}{3})$

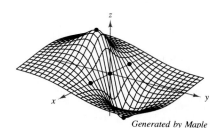

Generated by Maple

62. Let $f(x, y) = \begin{cases} \dfrac{4xy}{x^2 + y^2}, & \text{if } (x, y) \ne (0, 0) \\ 0, & \text{if } (x, y) = (0, 0) \end{cases}$

Let $\mathbf{u} = 1/\sqrt{2}\,(\mathbf{i} + \mathbf{j})$. Does the directional derivative of f at $P = (0, 0)$ in the direction of $\mathbf{u}$ exist? If $f(0, 0)$ were defined as 2 instead of 0, would $\mathbf{u}$ exist?

63. Find a function f such that

$$\nabla f = e^x \cos y\, \mathbf{i} - e^x \sin y\, \mathbf{j} + z\, \mathbf{k}.$$

Tangent Planes and Normal Lines

13.7

Tangent Plane and Normal Line to a Surface • The Angle of Inclination of a Plane • A Comparison of the Gradients $\nabla f(x, y)$ and $\nabla F(x, y, z)$

Tangent Plane and Normal Line to a Surface

So far we have represented surfaces in space primarily by equations of the form

$$z = f(x, y). \qquad \text{Equation of a surface } S$$

In the development to follow, however, it is convenient to use the more general representation $F(x, y, z) = 0$. For a surface S given by $z = f(x, y)$, you can convert to the general form by defining F as

$$F(x, y, z) = f(x, y) - z.$$

Then, because $f(x, y) - z = 0$, you can consider S to be the level surface of F given by

$$F(x, y, z) = 0. \qquad \text{Alternative equation of surface } S$$

EXAMPLE 1   Writing an Equation of a Surface

For the function given by $F(x, y, z) = x^2 + y^2 + z^2 - 4$, describe the level surface given by $F(x, y, z) = 0$.

Solution   The level surface given by $F(x, y, z) = 0$ can be written as

$$x^2 + y^2 + z^2 = 4$$

which is a sphere of radius 2 whose center is at the origin.

You have seen many examples of the usefulness of normal lines in applications involving curves. Normal lines are equally important in analyzing surfaces and solids. For example, consider the collision of two billiard balls. When a stationary ball is struck at a point P on its surface, it moves along the **line of impact** determined by P and the center of the ball. The impact can occur in *two* ways. If the cue ball is moving along the line of impact, it stops dead and imparts all of its momentum to the stationary ball, as shown in Figure 13.54. This kind of shot requires precision, because the line of impact must coincide exactly with the direction of the cue ball. More often, the cue ball is deflected to one side or the other and retains part of its momentum. That part of the momentum that is transferred to the stationary ball occurs along the line of impact, *regardless* of the direction of the cue ball, as shown in Figure 13.55. This line of impact is called the **normal line** to the surface of the ball at the point P.

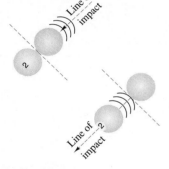

FIGURE 13.54

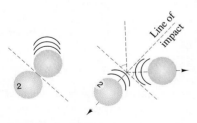

FIGURE 13.55

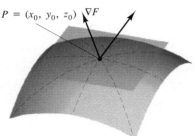

FIGURE 13.56
Tangent plane to surface S at P

In the process of finding a normal line to a surface, you are also able to solve the problem of finding a **tangent plane** to the surface. Let S be a surface given by $F(x, y, z) = 0$, and let $P = (x_0, y_0, z_0)$ be a point on S. Let C be a curve on S through P that is defined by the vector-valued function $\mathbf{r}(t) = x(t)\mathbf{i} + y(t)\mathbf{j} + z(t)\mathbf{k}$. Then, for all t

$$F(x(t), y(t), z(t)) = 0.$$

If F is differentiable and $x'(t)$, $y'(t)$, and $z'(t)$ all exist, it follows from the Chain Rule that

$$0 = F'(t) = F_x(x, y, z)x'(t) + F_y(x, y, z)y'(t) + F_z(x, y, z)z'(t).$$

At (x_0, y_0, z_0), the equivalent vector form is

$$0 = \underbrace{\nabla F(x_0, y_0, z_0)}_{\text{Gradient}} \cdot \underbrace{\mathbf{r}'(t_0)}_{\substack{\text{Tangent} \\ \text{vector}}}.$$

This result means that the gradient at P is orthogonal to the tangent vector of every curve on S through P. Thus, all tangent lines at P lie in a plane that is normal to $\nabla F(x_0, y_0, z_0)$ and contains P, as shown in Figure 13.56.

Definition of Tangent Plane and Normal Line

Let F be differentiable at the point $P = (x_0, y_0, z_0)$ on the surface S given by $F(x, y, z) = 0$ such that $\nabla F(x_0, y_0, z_0) \neq \mathbf{0}$.

1. The plane through P that is normal to $\nabla F(x_0, y_0, z_0)$ is called the **tangent plane to S at P**.
2. The line through P having the direction of $\nabla F(x_0, y_0, z_0)$ is called the **normal line to S at P**.

REMARK   In the remainder of this section, we assume $\nabla F(x_0, y_0, z_0)$ to be nonzero unless stated otherwise.

To find an equation for the tangent plane to S at (x_0, y_0, z_0), let (x, y, z) be an arbitrary point in the tangent plane. Then the vector

$$\mathbf{v} = (x - x_0)\mathbf{i} + (y - y_0)\mathbf{j} + (z - z_0)\mathbf{k}$$

lies in the tangent plane. Because $\nabla F(x_0, y_0, z_0)$ is normal to the tangent plane at (x_0, y_0, z_0), it must be orthogonal to every vector in the tangent plane, and you have $\nabla F(x_0, y_0, z_0) \cdot \mathbf{v} = 0$, which leads to the result in the following theorem.

THEOREM 13.13   Equation of Tangent Plane

If F is differentiable at (x_0, y_0, z_0), then an equation of the tangent plane to the surface given by $F(x, y, z) = 0$ at (x_0, y_0, z_0) is

$$F_x(x_0, y_0, z_0)(x - x_0) + F_y(x_0, y_0, z_0)(y - y_0) + F_z(x_0, y_0, z_0)(z - z_0) = 0.$$

EXAMPLE 2   Finding an Equation of a Tangent Plane

Find an equation of the tangent plane to the hyperboloid given by

$$z^2 - 2x^2 - 2y^2 = 12$$

at the point $(1, -1, 4)$.

Solution   Begin by writing the equation of the surface as

$$z^2 - 2x^2 - 2y^2 - 12 = 0.$$

Then, considering

$$F(x, y, z) = z^2 - 2x^2 - 2y^2 - 12$$

you have

$$F_x(x, y, z) = -4x, \qquad F_y(x, y, z) = -4y, \qquad F_z(x, y, z) = 2z.$$

At the point $(1, -1, 4)$, the partial derivatives are

$$F_x(1, -1, 4) = -4, \qquad F_y(1, -1, 4) = 4, \qquad F_z(1, -1, 4) = 8.$$

Therefore, an equation of the tangent plane at $(1, -1, 4)$ is

$$-4(x - 1) + 4(y + 1) + 8(z - 4) = 0$$
$$-4x + 4 + 4y + 4 + 8z - 32 = 0$$
$$-4x + 4y + 8z - 24 = 0$$
$$x - y - 2z + 6 = 0.$$

Figure 13.57 shows a portion of the hyperboloid and tangent plane.

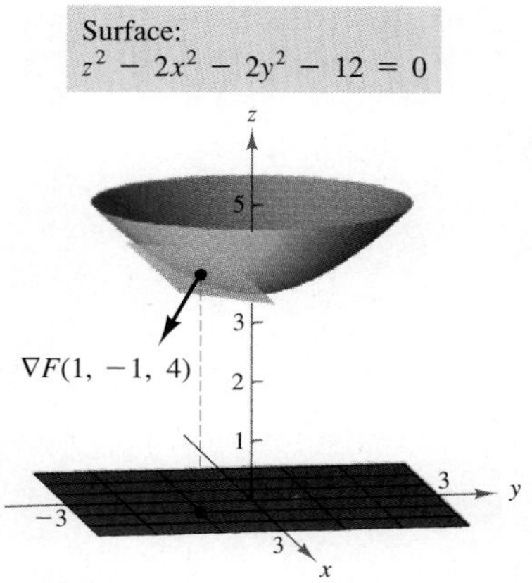

Surface:
$$z^2 - 2x^2 - 2y^2 - 12 = 0$$

$\nabla F(1, -1, 4)$

FIGURE 13.57
Tangent plane to surface.

TECHNOLOGY   Some three-dimensional graphing utilities are capable of sketching tangent planes to surfaces. Two examples are shown in Figure 13.58. The first of these computer drawings depicts a tangent plane to the sphere $x^2 + y^2 + z^2 = 1$, and the second depicts a tangent plane to the paraboloid $z = 2 - x^2 - y^2$.

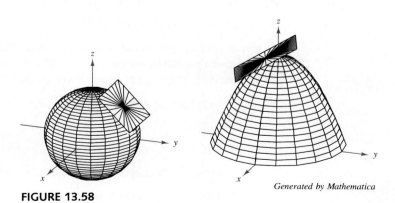

Generated by Mathematica

FIGURE 13.58

To find the equation of the tangent plane at a point on a surface given by $z = f(x, y)$, you can define the function F by

$$F(x, y, z) = f(x, y) - z.$$

Then S is given by the level surface $F(x, y, z) = 0$, and by Theorem 13.13 an equation of the tangent plane to S at the point (x_0, y_0, z_0) is

$$f_x(x_0, y_0)(x - x_0) + f_y(x_0, y_0)(y - y_0) - (z - z_0) = 0.$$

EXAMPLE 3   Finding an Equation of the Tangent Plane

Find the equation of the tangent plane to the paraboloid

$$z = 1 - \frac{1}{10}(x^2 + 4y^2)$$

at the point $(1, 1, \frac{1}{2})$.

Solution   From $z = f(x, y) = 1 - \frac{1}{10}(x^2 + 4y^2)$, you obtain

$$f_x(x, y) = -\frac{x}{5} \quad \longrightarrow \quad f_x(1, 1) = -\frac{1}{5}$$

and

$$f_y(x, y) = -\frac{4y}{5} \quad \longrightarrow \quad f_y(1, 1) = -\frac{4}{5}.$$

Therefore, an equation of the tangent plane at $(1, 1, \frac{1}{2})$ is

$$f_x(1, 1)(x - 1) + f_y(1, 1)(y - 1) - \left(z - \frac{1}{2}\right) = 0$$

$$-\frac{1}{5}(x - 1) - \frac{4}{5}(y - 1) - \left(z - \frac{1}{2}\right) = 0$$

$$-\frac{1}{5}x - \frac{4}{5}y - z + \frac{3}{2} = 0.$$

This tangent plane is shown in Figure 13.59.

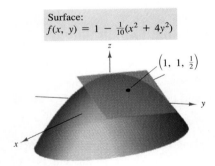

FIGURE 13.59
Tangent plane to surface

In Section 13.4, you saw that the total differential

$$dz = f_x(x, y)dx + f_y(x, y)dy$$

can be used to approximate the increment Δz. (See Figure 13.35 in Section 13.4.) We now give a geometric interpretation of this approximation in terms of the tangent plane to a surface. The tangent plane to the surface $z = f(x, y)$ at (x_0, y_0, z_0) is given by

$$f_x(x_0, y_0)(x - x_0) + f_y(x_0, y_0)(y - y_0) - (z - z_0) = 0$$

or, equivalently,

$$z = z_0 + f_x(x_0, y_0)(x - x_0) + f_y(x_0, y_0)(y - y_0).$$

Thus, at (x_0, y_0), the *tangent plane* has height z_0 and at $(x_0 + dx, y_0 + dy)$ it has height

$$z = z_0 + f_x(x_0, y_0)(x_0 + dx - x_0) + f_y(x_0, y_0)(y_0 + dy - y_0)$$
$$= z_0 + f_x(x_0, y_0)\, dx + f_y(x_0, y_0)\, dy.$$

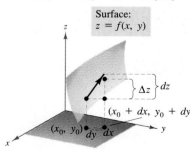

$$\Delta z = f(x_0 + dx, y_0 + dy) - f(x_0, y_0)$$

FIGURE 13.60
When dx and dy are small, $dz \approx \Delta z$.

That is, $z = z_0 + dz$. You can see from Figure 13.60 that for points near (x_0, y_0, z_0) the increments $dx = \Delta x$ and $dy = \Delta y$ are small and $dz \approx \Delta z$.

The gradient $\nabla F(x, y, z)$ gives a convenient way to find equations of normal lines, as shown in Example 4.

EXAMPLE 4   Finding an Equation of a Normal Line to a Surface

Find a set of symmetric equations for the normal line to the surface given by $xyz = 6$ at the point $(2, 3, 1)$.

Solution   Begin by letting $F(x, y, z) = xyz - 6$. Then, the gradient is given by

$$\nabla F(x, y, z) = F_x(x, y, z)\mathbf{i} + F_y(x, y, z)\mathbf{j} + F_z(x, y, z)\mathbf{k}$$
$$= yz\,\mathbf{i} + xz\,\mathbf{j} + xy\,\mathbf{k}$$

and at the point $(2, 3, 1)$ you have

$$\nabla F(2, 3, 1) = (3)(1)\mathbf{i} + (2)(1)\mathbf{j} + (2)(3)\mathbf{k}$$
$$= 3\mathbf{i} + 2\mathbf{j} + 6\mathbf{k}.$$

The normal line at $(2, 3, 1)$ has direction numbers 3, 2, and 6, and the corresponding set of symmetric equations is

$$\frac{x - 2}{3} = \frac{y - 3}{2} = \frac{z - 1}{6}.$$

(See Figure 13.61.)

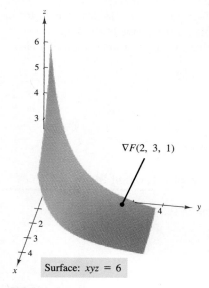

FIGURE 13.61

Surface: $xyz = 6$

$\nabla F(2, 3, 1)$

Knowing that the gradient $\nabla F(x, y, z)$ is normal to the surface given by $F(x, y, z) = 0$ allows you to solve a variety of problems dealing with surfaces and curves in space.

EXAMPLE 5   Finding the Equation of a Tangent Line to a Curve

Describe the tangent line to the curve of intersection of the surfaces

$$x^2 + 2y^2 + 2z^2 = 20 \qquad \text{Ellipsoid}$$

and

$$x^2 + y^2 + z = 4 \qquad \text{Paraboloid}$$

at the point $(0, 1, 3)$, as shown in Figure 13.62.

Solution   Begin by finding the gradients to both surfaces at the point $(0, 1, 3)$.

Ellipsoid	Paraboloid
$F(x, y, z) = x^2 + 2y^2 + 2z^2 - 20$	$G(x, y, z) = x^2 + y^2 + z - 4$
$\nabla F(x, y, z) = 2x\mathbf{i} + 4y\mathbf{j} + 4z\,\mathbf{k}$	$\nabla G(x, y, z) = 2x\mathbf{i} + 2y\mathbf{j} + \mathbf{k}$
$\nabla F(0, 1, 3) = 4\mathbf{j} + 12\mathbf{k}$	$\nabla G(0, 1, 3) = 2\mathbf{j} + \mathbf{k}$

The cross product of these two gradients is a vector that is tangent to both surfaces at the point $(0, 1, 3)$.

$$\nabla F(0, 1, 3) \times \nabla G(0, 1, 3) = \begin{vmatrix} \mathbf{i} & \mathbf{j} & \mathbf{k} \\ 0 & 4 & 12 \\ 0 & 2 & 1 \end{vmatrix} = -20\mathbf{i}.$$

Thus, the tangent line to the curve of intersection of the two surfaces at the point $(0, 1, 3)$ is a line that is parallel to the x-axis and passes through the point $(0, 1, 3)$.

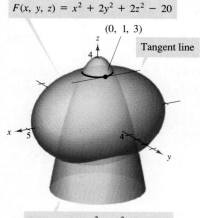

$F(x, y, z) = x^2 + 2y^2 + 2z^2 - 20$

$(0, 1, 3)$

Tangent line

$G(x, y, z) = x^2 + y^2 + z - 4$

FIGURE 13.62

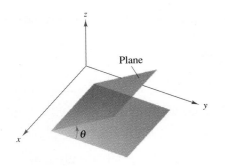

FIGURE 13.63
The angle of inclination.

The Angle of Inclination of a Plane

Another use of the gradient $\nabla F(x, y, z)$ is to determine the angle of inclination of the tangent plane to a surface. The **angle of inclination** of a plane is defined as the angle θ, $0 \le \theta \le \pi/2$, between the given plane and the xy-plane, as shown in Figure 13.63. (The angle of inclination of a horizontal plane is defined as 0.) Because the vector $\mathbf{k}$ is normal to the xy-plane, you can use the formula for the cosine of the angle between two planes (given in Section 11.5) to conclude that the angle of inclination of a plane with normal vector $\mathbf{n}$ is given by

$$\cos\theta = \frac{|\mathbf{n} \cdot \mathbf{k}|}{\|\mathbf{n}\| \|\mathbf{k}\|} = \frac{|\mathbf{n} \cdot \mathbf{k}|}{\|\mathbf{n}\|}. \qquad \text{Angle of inclination of a plane}$$

EXAMPLE 6   Finding the Angle of Inclination of a Tangent Plane

Find the angle of inclination of the tangent plane to the ellipsoid given by

$$\frac{x^2}{12} + \frac{y^2}{12} + \frac{z^2}{3} = 1$$

at the point $(2, 2, 1)$.

Solution   If you let

$$F(x, y, z) = \frac{x^2}{12} + \frac{y^2}{12} + \frac{z^2}{3} - 1$$

then the gradient of F at the point $(2, 2, 1)$ is given by

$$\nabla F(x, y, z) = \frac{x}{6}\mathbf{i} + \frac{y}{6}\mathbf{j} + \frac{2z}{3}\mathbf{k}$$

$$\nabla F(2, 2, 1) = \frac{1}{3}\mathbf{i} + \frac{1}{3}\mathbf{j} + \frac{2}{3}\mathbf{k}.$$

Because $\nabla F(2, 2, 1)$ is normal to the tangent plane and $\mathbf{k}$ is normal to the xy-plane, it follows that the angle of inclination of the tangent plane is given by

$$\cos\theta = \frac{|\nabla F(2, 2, 1) \cdot \mathbf{k}|}{\|\nabla F(2, 2, 1)\|}$$

$$= \frac{2/3}{\sqrt{(1/3)^2 + (1/3)^2 + (2/3)^2}} = \sqrt{\frac{2}{3}}$$

which implies that $\theta = \arccos\sqrt{2/3} \approx 35.3°$, as shown in Figure 13.64. ▬

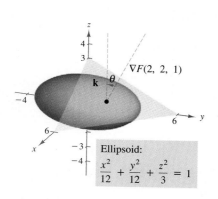

Ellipsoid:
$$\frac{x^2}{12} + \frac{y^2}{12} + \frac{z^2}{3} = 1$$

FIGURE 13.64

A special case of the procedure shown in Example 6 is worth noting. The angle of inclination θ of the tangent plane to the surface $z = f(x, y)$ at (x_0, y_0, z_0) is given by

$$\cos\theta = \frac{1}{\sqrt{[f_x(x_0, y_0)]^2 + [f_y(x_0, y_0)]^2 + 1}}. \qquad \begin{array}{l}\text{Alternative formula for}\\ \text{angle of inclination}\end{array}$$

(See Exercise 50.)

A Comparison of the Gradients $\nabla f(x, y)$ and $\nabla F(x, y, z)$

We conclude this section with a comparison of the gradients $\nabla f(x, y)$ and $\nabla F(x, y, z)$. In the previous section, you saw that the gradient of a function f of two variables is normal to the *level curves* of f. Specifically, Theorem 13.12 stated that if f is differentiable at (x_0, y_0) and $\nabla f(x_0, y_0) \neq \mathbf{0}$, then $\nabla f(x_0, y_0)$ is normal to the level curve through (x_0, y_0). Having developed normal lines to surfaces, you can now extend this result to a function of three variables.

THEOREM 13.14   Gradient is Normal to Level Surfaces

If F is differentiable at (x_0, y_0, z_0) and $\nabla F(x_0, y_0, z_0) \neq \mathbf{0}$, then $\nabla F(x_0, y_0, z_0)$ is normal to the level surface through (x_0, y_0, z_0).

When working with the gradients $\nabla f(x, y)$ and $\nabla F(x, y, z)$, be sure you remember that $\nabla f(x, y)$ is a vector in the xy-plane and $\nabla F(x, y, z)$ is a vector in space.

EXERCISES for Section 13.7

TECHNOLOGY
Laboratory Guide
Lab 13.7

In Exercises 1–10, find a unit normal vector to the surface at the indicated point. (*Hint:* Normalize the gradient vector $\nabla F(x,y,z)$.)

Surface	Point
1. $x + y + z = 4$	$(2, 0, 2)$
2. $x^2 + y^2 + z^2 = 11$	$(3, 1, 1)$
3. $z = \sqrt{x^2 + y^2}$	$(3, 4, 5)$
4. $z = x^3$	$(2, 1, 8)$
5. $x^2 y^4 - z = 0$	$(1, 2, 16)$
6. $x^2 + 3y + z^3 = 9$	$(2, -1, 2)$
7. $z - x\sin y = 4$	$\left(6, \dfrac{\pi}{6}, 7\right)$
8. $ze^{x^2 - y^2} - 3 = 0$	$(2, 2, 3)$
9. $\ln\left(\dfrac{x}{y - z}\right) = 0$	$(1, 4, 3)$
10. $\sin(x - y) - z = 2$	$\left(\dfrac{\pi}{3}, \dfrac{\pi}{6}, -\dfrac{3}{2}\right)$

In Exercises 11–14, find an equation of the tangent plane to the surface at the indicated point.

11. $z = 25 - x^2 - y^2$
$(3, 1, 15)$

12. $z = \sqrt{x^2 + y^2}$
$(3, 4, 5)$

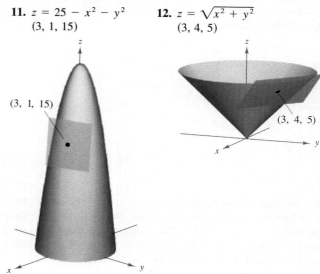

13. $f(x, y) = \dfrac{y}{x}$

(1, 2, 2)

14. $g(x, y) = \arctan \dfrac{y}{x}$

(1, 0, 0)

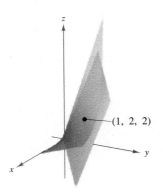

(1, 2, 2)

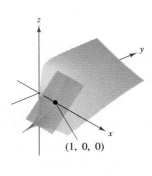

(1, 0, 0)

In Exercises 15–24, find an equation of the tangent plane to the surface at the indicated point.

Surface	Point
15. $g(x, y) = x^2 - y^2$	(5, 4, 9)
16. $f(x, y) = 2 - \frac{2}{3}x - y$	(3, −1, 1)
17. $z = e^x(\sin y + 1)$	$\left(0, \dfrac{\pi}{2}, 2\right)$
18. $z = x^3 - 3xy + y^3$	(1, 2, 3)
19. $h(x, y) = \ln\sqrt{x^2 + y^2}$	(3, 4, ln 5)
20. $h(x, y) = \cos y$	$\left(5, \dfrac{\pi}{4}, \dfrac{\sqrt{2}}{2}\right)$
21. $x^2 + 4y^2 + z^2 = 36$	(2, −2, 4)
22. $x^2 + 2z^2 = y^2$	(1, 3, −2)
23. $xy^2 + 3x - z^2 = 4$	(2, 1, −2)
24. $y = x(2z - 1)$	(4, 4, 1)

In Exercises 25–30, find an equation for the tangent plane and find symmetric equations for the normal line to the surface at the indicated point.

Surface	Point
25. $x^2 + y^2 + z = 9$	(1, 2, 4)
26. $x^2 + y^2 + z^2 = 9$	(1, 2, 2)
27. $xy - z = 0$	(−2, −3, 6)
28. $x^2 + y^2 - z^2 = 0$	(5, 12, 13)
29. $z = \arctan \dfrac{y}{x}$	$\left(1, 1, \dfrac{\pi}{4}\right)$
30. $xyz = 10$	(1, 2, 5)

In Exercises 31–36, (a) find symmetric equations of the tangent line to the curve of intersection of the surfaces at the indicated point and (b) find the cosine of the angle between the gradient vectors at this point. State whether the surfaces are orthogonal at the point of intersection.

Surfaces	Point
31. $x^2 + y^2 = 5$ $z = x$	(2, 1, 2)

Surfaces	Point
32. $z = x^2 + y^2$ $z = 4 - y$	(2, −1, 5)
33. $x^2 + z^2 = 25$ $y^2 + z^2 = 25$	(3, 3, 4)
34. $z = \sqrt{x^2 + y^2}$ $2x + y + 2z = 20$	(3, 4, 5)
35. $x^2 + y^2 + z^2 = 6$ $x - y - z = 0$	(2, 1, 1)
36. $z = x^2 + y^2$ $x + y + 6z = 33$	(1, 2, 5)

In Exercises 37–40, find the angle of inclination θ of the tangent plane to the surface at the indicated point.

Surface	Point
37. $3x^2 + 2y^2 - z = 15$	(2, 2, 5)
38. $xy - z^2 = 0$	(2, 2, 2)
39. $x^2 - y^2 + z = 0$	(1, 2, 3)
40. $x^2 + y^2 = 5$	(2, 1, 3)

In Exercises 41 and 42, find the point on the surface where the tangent plane is horizontal.

41. $z = 3 - x^2 - y^2 + 6y$

42. $z = 3x^2 + 2y^2 - 3x + 4y - 5$

In Exercises 43 and 44, find the path of a heat-seeking particle in the temperature field T, starting at the specified point.

43. $T(x, y, z) = 400 - 2x^2 - y^2 - 4z^2$, (4, 3, 10)

44. $T(x, y, z) = 100 - 3x - y - z^2$, (2, 2, 5)

In Exercises 45 and 46, show that the tangent plane to the quadric surface at the point (x_0, y_0, z_0) can be written in the given form.

45. **Ellipsoid** $\dfrac{x^2}{a^2} + \dfrac{y^2}{b^2} + \dfrac{z^2}{c^2} = 1$

Plane $\dfrac{x_0 x}{a^2} + \dfrac{y_0 y}{b^2} + \dfrac{z_0 z}{c^2} = 1$

46. **Hyperboloid** $\dfrac{x^2}{a^2} + \dfrac{y^2}{b^2} - \dfrac{z^2}{c^2} = 1$

Plane $\dfrac{x_0 x}{a^2} + \dfrac{y_0 y}{b^2} - \dfrac{z_0 z}{c^2} = 1$

47. Show that any tangent plane to the cone $z^2 = a^2x^2 + b^2y^2$ passes through the origin.

48. Show that any line normal to a sphere passes through the center of the sphere.

49. Prove Theorem 13.14.

50. Prove that the angle of inclination θ of the tangent plane to the surface $z = f(x, y)$ at the point (x_0, y_0, z_0) is given by

$$\cos \theta = \dfrac{1}{\sqrt{[f_x(x_0, y_0)]^2 + [f_y(x_0, y_0)]^2 + 1}}.$$

C **51.** *Approximation* Consider the following approximations centered at (0, 0) for a function $f(x, y)$.

Linear Approximation

$$P_1(x, y) \approx f(0, 0) + f_x(0, 0)x + f_y(0, 0)y$$

Quadratic Approximation

$$P_2(x, y) \approx f(0, 0) + f_x(0, 0)x + f_y(0, 0)y$$
$$+ \frac{1}{2}f_{xx}(0, 0)x^2 + f_{xy}(0, 0)xy + \frac{1}{2}f_{yy}(0, 0)y^2$$

[Note that the linear approximation is the tangent plane to the surface at $(0, 0, f(0, 0))$.]

a. Find the linear approximation of $f(x, y) = e^{(x-y)}$ centered at $(0, 0)$.

b. Find the quadratic approximation of $f(x, y) = e^{(x-y)}$ centered at $(0, 0)$.

c. If $x = 0$ in the quadratic approximation, then you obtain the second-degree Taylor polynomial for what function? Answer the same question for $y = 0$.

d. Complete the table.

x	y	$f(x,y)$	$P_1(x,y)$	$P_2(x,y)$
0	0			
0	0.1			
0.2	0.1			
0.2	0.5			
1	0.5			

e. Use a graphing utility to graph the surfaces given by $z = f(x, y)$, $z = P_1(x, y)$, and $z = P_2(x, y)$.

52. *Approximation* Repeat Exercise 51 for the function $f(x, y) = \cos(x + y)$.

53. Let f be a differentiable function, and consider the surface $z = xf(y/x)$. Show that the tangent plane at any point $P = (x_0, y_0, z_0)$ on the surface passes through the origin.

FOR FURTHER INFORMATION
Biologists use the concept of diversity to measure the proportions of different types of organisms within an environment. For more information on this, see the article "Information Theory and Biological Diversity" by Steven Kolmes and Kevin Mitchell in the 1990 *UMAP Modules.*

54. *Wildflower Diversity* The diversity of wildflowers in a meadow can be measured by counting the number of daisies, buttercups, shooting stars, and so on. If there are n types of wildflowers, each with a proportion of p_i of the total population, then it follows that $p_1 + p_2 + \cdots + p_n = 1$. The measure of diversity of the population is defined as

$$H = -\sum_{i=1}^{n} p_i \log_2 p_i.$$

In this definition, it is understood that $p_i \log_2 p_i = 0$ when $p_i = 0$. The tables show the proportions of wildflowers in a meadow in May, June, August, and September.

a. Determine the wildflower diversity for each month. How would you interpret September's diversity? Which month had the greatest diversity?

b. If the meadow contains 10 types of wildflowers in roughly equal proportions, is the diversity of the population greater or less than the diversity of a similar distribution of four types of wildflowers? What type of distribution (of 10 types of wildflowers) would produce a maximum diversity?

c. Let H_n represent the maximum diversity of n types of wildflowers. Does H_n approach a limit as n approaches infinity?

May

Flower type	1	2	3	4
Proportion	$\frac{5}{16}$	$\frac{5}{16}$	$\frac{5}{16}$	$\frac{1}{16}$

June

Flower type	1	2	3	4
Proportion	$\frac{1}{4}$	$\frac{1}{4}$	$\frac{1}{4}$	$\frac{1}{4}$

August

Flower type	1	2	3	4
Proportion	$\frac{1}{4}$	0	$\frac{1}{4}$	$\frac{1}{2}$

September

Flower type	1	2	3	4
Proportion	0	0	0	1

Extrema of Functions of Two Variables

Absolute Extrema and Relative Extrema • The Second Partials Test

KARL WEIERSTRASS

Although the Extreme Value Theorem had been used by earlier mathematicians, the first to provide a rigorous proof was the German mathematician Karl Weierstrass (1815–1897). Weierstrass also provided rigorous justifications for many other mathematical results already in common use. We are indebted to him for much of the logical foundation upon which modern calculus is built.

Absolute Extrema and Relative Extrema

In Chapter 3, you studied techniques for finding the extreme values of a function of a single variable. In this section, we extend these techniques to functions of two variables. For example, in Theorem 13.15 the Extreme Value Theorem for a function of a single variable is extended to a function of two variables.

The values $f(a, b)$ and $f(c, d)$ such that

$$f(a, b) \leq f(x, y) \leq f(c, d)$$

for all (x, y) in R are called the **minimum** and **maximum** of f in the region R, as shown in Figure 13.65.

Recall from Section 13.2 that a region in the plane is *closed* if it contains all of its boundary points. The Extreme Value Theorem deals with a region in the plane that is both closed and *bounded*. A region in the plane is called **bounded** if it is a subregion of a closed disc in the plane.

THEOREM 13.15   Extreme Value Theorem

Let f be a continuous function of two variables x and y defined on a closed bounded region R in the xy-plane.

1. There is at least one point in R where f takes on a minimum value.
2. There is at least one point in R where f takes on a maximum value.

A minimum is also called an **absolute minimum** and a maximum is also called an **absolute maximum.** As in single-variable calculus, we distinguish between absolute extrema and **relative extrema.**

Definition of Relative Extrema

Let f be a function defined on a region R containing (x_0, y_0).

1. The function f has a **relative minimum** at (x_0, y_0) if

$$f(x, y) \geq f(x_0, y_0)$$

for all (x, y) in an *open* disc containing (x_0, y_0).
2. The function f has a **relative maximum** at (x_0, y_0) if

$$f(x, y) \leq f(x_0, y_0)$$

for all (x, y) in an *open* disc containing (x_0, y_0).

Surface:
$z = f(x, y)$

Maximum

Minimum

Closed bounded region R

FIGURE 13.65
R contains point(s) at which $f(x, y)$ is minimum and point(s) at which $f(x, y)$ is maximum.

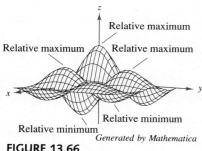

FIGURE 13.66
Relative extrema

To say that f has a relative maximum at (x_0, y_0) means that the point (x_0, y_0, z_0) is at least as high as all nearby points on the graph of $z = f(x, y)$. Similarly, f has a relative minimum at (x_0, y_0) if (x_0, y_0, z_0) is at least as low as all nearby points on the graph (see Figure 13.66).

To locate relative extreme of f, you can investigate the points at which the gradient of f is $\mathbf{0}$ or undefined. Such points are called **critical points** of f.

Definition of Critical Point

Let f be defined on an open region R containing (x_0, y_0). The point (x_0, y_0) is a **critical point** of f if one of the following is true.
1. $f_x(x_0, y_0) = 0$ and $f_y(x_0, y_0) = 0$.
2. $f_x(x_0, y_0)$ or $f_y(x_0, y_0)$ does not exist.

Recall from Theorem 13.11 that if f is differentiable and

$$\nabla f(x_0, y_0) = f_x(x_0, y_0)\mathbf{i} + f_y(x_0, y_0)\mathbf{j}$$
$$= 0\mathbf{i} + 0\mathbf{j}$$

then every directional derivative at (x_0, y_0) must be 0. In Exercise 46 you are asked to show that this implies that the function has a horizontal tangent plane at the point (x_0, y_0), as shown in Figure 13.67. It appears that such a point is a likely location of a relative extremum. This is confirmed by Theorem 13.16. (A proof of this theorem is given in Appendix A.)

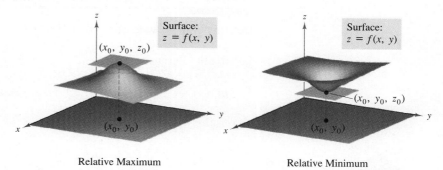

FIGURE 13.67

THEOREM 13.16

If f has a relative extremum at (x_0, y_0) on an open region R, then (x_0, y_0) is a critical point of f.

EXAMPLE 1 Finding a Relative Extremum

Determine the relative extrema of

$$f(x, y) = 2x^2 + y^2 + 8x - 6y + 20.$$

Solution Begin by finding the critical points of f. Because

$$f_x(x, y) = 4x + 8 \qquad \text{Partial with respect to } x$$

and

$$f_y(x, y) = 2y - 6 \qquad \text{Partial with respect to } y$$

are defined for all x and y, the only critical points are those for which both first partial derivatives are 0. To locate these points, let $f_x(x, y)$ and $f_y(x, y)$ be 0, and solve the system of equations

$$4x + 8 = 0 \quad \text{and} \quad 2y - 6 = 0$$

to obtain the critical point $(-2, 3)$. By completing the square, you can conclude that for all $(x, y) \ne (-2, 3)$,

$$f(x, y) = 2(x + 2)^2 + (y - 3)^2 + 3 > 3.$$

Therefore, a relative *minimum* of f occurs at $(-2, 3)$. The value of the relative minimum is $f(-2, 3) = 3$, as shown in Figure 13.68. ▬

Example 1 shows a relative minimum occurring at one type of critical point—the type for which both $f_x(x, y)$ and $f_y(x, y)$ are 0. The next example concerns a relative maximum that occurs at the other type of critical point—the type for which either $f_x(x, y)$ or $f_y(x, y)$ is undefined.

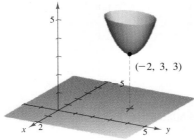

Surface:
$f(x, y) = 2x^2 + y^2 + 8x - 6y + 20$

FIGURE 13.68
The function $z = f(x, y)$ has a relative minimum at $(-2, 3)$.

EXAMPLE 2 Finding a Relative Extremum

Determine the relative extrema of $f(x, y) = 1 - (x^2 + y^2)^{1/3}$.

Solution Because

$$f_x(x, y) = -\frac{2x}{3(x^2 + y^2)^{2/3}} \qquad \text{Partial with respect to } x$$

and

$$f_y(x, y) = -\frac{2y}{3(x^2 + y^2)^{2/3}} \qquad \text{Partial with respect to } y$$

it follows that both partial derivatives are defined for all points in the xy-plane except for $(0, 0)$. Moreover, because the partial derivatives cannot both be 0 unless both x and y are 0, you can conclude that $(0, 0)$ is the only critical point. In Figure 13.69, note that $f(0, 0)$ is 1. For all other (x, y) it is clear that

$$f(x, y) = 1 - (x^2 + y^2)^{1/3} < 1.$$

Therefore, f has a relative *maximum* at $(0, 0)$. ▬

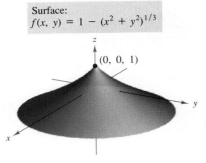

Surface:
$f(x, y) = 1 - (x^2 + y^2)^{1/3}$

FIGURE 13.69
$f_x(x, y)$ and $f_y(x, y)$ are undefined at $(0, 0)$.

REMARK In Example 2, $f_x(x, y) = 0$ for every point on the y-axis other than $(0, 0)$. However, because $f_y(x, y)$ is nonzero, these are not critical points. Remember that *one* of the partials must be undefined or *both* must be 0 in order to yield a critical point.

The Second Partials Test

Theorem 13.16 tells you that to find relative extrema you need only examine values of $f(x, y)$ at critical points. However, as is true for a function of one variable, the critical points of a function of two variables do not always yield relative maxima or minima. Some critical points yield **saddle points,** which are neither relative maxima nor relative minima.

As an example of a critical point that does not yield a relative extremum, consider the surface given by

$$f(x, y) = y^2 - x^2 \qquad \text{Hyperbolic paraboloid}$$

as shown in Figure 13.70. At the point $(0, 0)$, both partial derivatives are 0. The function f does not, however, have a relative extremum at this point because in any open disc centered at $(0, 0)$ the function takes on both negative values (along the x-axis) *and* positive values (along the y-axis). Thus, the point $(0, 0, 0)$ is a saddle point of the surface. (The name "saddle point" comes from the fact that the surface shown in Figure 13.70 resembles a saddle.)

For the functions in Examples 1 and 2, it is relatively easy to determine the relative extrema, because each function was either given, or able to be written, in completed square form. For more complicated functions, algebraic arguments are less convenient and it is better to rely on the analytic means presented in the following Second Partials Test. This is the two-variable counterpart of the Second Derivative Test for functions of one variable. The proof of this theorem is best left to a course in advanced calculus.

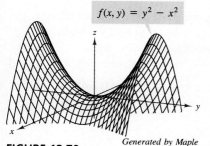

$f(x, y) = y^2 - x^2$

Generated by Maple

FIGURE 13.70
Saddle point at
$(0, 0, 0)$: $f_x(0, 0) = f_y(0, 0) = 0$

THEOREM 13.17   Second Partials Test

Let f have continuous second partial derivatives on an open region containing a point (a, b) for which

$$f_x(a, b) = 0 \quad \text{and} \quad f_y(a, b) = 0.$$

To test for relative extrema of f, we define the quantity

$$d = f_{xx}(a, b)f_{yy}(a, b) - [f_{xy}(a, b)]^2.$$

1. If $d > 0$ and $f_{xx}(a, b) > 0$, then f has a **relative minimum** at (a, b).
2. If $d > 0$ and $f_{xx}(a, b) < 0$, then f has a **relative maximum** at (a, b).
3. If $d < 0$, then $(a, b, f(a, b))$ is a **saddle point.**
4. The test is inconclusive if $d = 0$.

REMARK   If $d > 0$, then $f_{xx}(a, b)$ and $f_{yy}(a, b)$ must have the same sign. This means that $f_{xx}(a, b)$ can be replaced by $f_{yy}(a, b)$ in the first two parts of the test.

A convenient device for remembering the formula for d in the Second Partials Test is given by the 2×2 determinant

$$d = \begin{vmatrix} f_{xx}(a, b) & f_{xy}(a, b) \\ f_{yx}(a, b) & f_{yy}(a, b) \end{vmatrix}$$

where $f_{xy}(a, b) = f_{yx}(a, b)$ by Theorem 13.3.

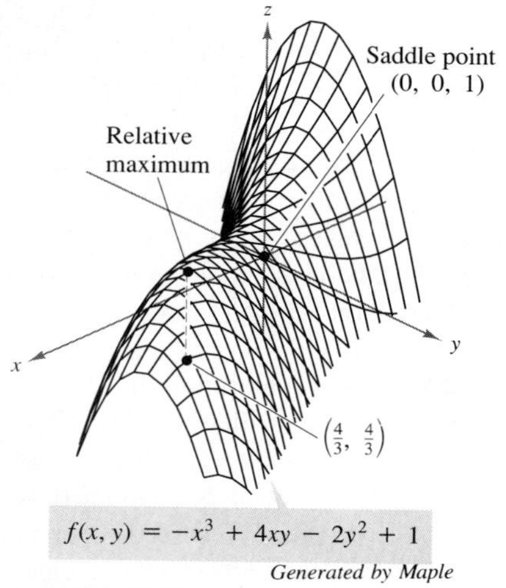

EXAMPLE 3 Using the Second Partials Test

Find the relative extrema of $f(x, y) = -x^3 + 4xy - 2y^2 + 1$.

Solution Begin by finding the critical points of f. Because

$$f_x(x, y) = -3x^2 + 4y \quad \text{and} \quad f_y(x, y) = 4x - 4y$$

are defined for all x and y, the only critical points are those for which both first partial derivatives are 0. To locate these points, let $f_x(x, y)$ and $f_y(x, y)$ be 0 to obtain $-3x^2 + 4y = 0$ and $4x - 4y = 0$. From the second equation you know that $x = y$, and, by substitution into the first equation, you obtain two solutions: $y = x = 0$ and $y = x = \frac{4}{3}$. Because

$$f_{xx}(x, y) = -6x, \quad f_{yy}(x, y) = -4, \quad \text{and} \quad f_{xy}(x, y) = 4$$

it follows that, for the critical point $(0, 0)$,

$$d = f_{xx}(0, 0) f_{yy}(0, 0) - [f_{xy}(0, 0)]^2 = 0 - 16 < 0$$

and, by the Second Partials Test, you can conclude that $(0, 0, 1)$ is a saddle point of f. Furthermore, for the critical point $\left(\frac{4}{3}, \frac{4}{3}\right)$,

$$d = f_{xx}\left(\tfrac{4}{3}, \tfrac{4}{3}\right) f_{yy}\left(\tfrac{4}{3}, \tfrac{4}{3}\right) - \left[f_{xy}\left(\tfrac{4}{3}, \tfrac{4}{3}\right)\right]^2$$
$$= -8(-4) - 16 = 16 > 0$$

and because $f_{xx}\left(\frac{4}{3}, \frac{4}{3}\right) = -8 < 0$ you can conclude that f has a relative maximum at $\left(\frac{4}{3}, \frac{4}{3}\right)$, as shown in Figure 13.71.

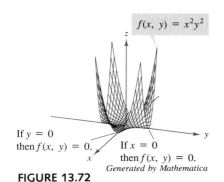

Saddle point
(0, 0, 1)

Relative maximum

$\left(\frac{4}{3}, \frac{4}{3}\right)$

$f(x, y) = -x^3 + 4xy - 2y^2 + 1$

Generated by Maple

FIGURE 13.71

The Second Partials Test can fail to find relative extrema in two ways. If either of the first partial derivatives is undefined, then you cannot use the test. Also, if

$$d = f_{xx}(a, b) f_{yy}(a, b) - [f_{xy}(a, b)]^2 = 0$$

the test fails. In such cases, you can try a sketch or some other approach, as demonstrated in the next example.

EXAMPLE 4 Failure of the Second Partials Test

Find the relative extrema of $f(x, y) = x^2 y^2$.

Solution Because $f_x(x, y) = 2xy^2$ and $f_y(x, y) = 2x^2 y$, you know that both partial derivatives are 0 if $x = 0$ or $y = 0$. That is, every point along the x- or y-axis is a critical point. Moreover, because

$$f_{xx}(x, y) = 2y^2, \quad f_{yy}(x, y) = 2x^2, \quad \text{and} \quad f_{xy}(x, y) = 4xy$$

you know that if either $x = 0$ or $y = 0$, then

$$d = f_{xx}(x, y) f_{yy}(x, y) - [f_{xy}(x, y)]^2$$
$$= 4x^2 y^2 - 16x^2 y^2 = -12x^2 y^2 = 0.$$

Thus, the Second Partials Test fails. However, because $f(x, y) = 0$ for every point along the x- or y-axis and $f(x, y) = x^2 y^2 > 0$ for all other points, you can conclude that each of these critical points yields an absolute minimum, as shown in Figure 13.72.

$f(x, y) = x^2 y^2$

If $y = 0$
then $f(x, y) = 0$.

If $x = 0$
then $f(x, y) = 0$.

Generated by Mathematica

FIGURE 13.72

Absolute extrema of a function can occur in two ways. First, some relative extrema also happen to be absolute extrema. For instance, in Example 1, $f(-2, 3)$ is an absolute minimum of the function. (On the other hand, the relative maximum found in Example 3 is not an absolute maximum of the function.) Second, absolute extrema can occur at a boundary point of the domain. This is illustrated in Example 5.

EXAMPLE 5   Finding Absolute Extrema

Find the absolute extrema of the function

$$f(x, y) = \sin xy$$

on the closed region given by $0 \le x \le \pi$ and $0 \le y \le 1$.

Solution   From the partial derivatives

$$f_x(x, y) = y \cos xy \quad \text{and} \quad f_y(x, y) = x \cos xy$$

you can see that each point lying on the hyperbola given by $xy = \pi/2$ is a critical point. These points each yield the value

$$f(x, y) = \sin\left(\frac{\pi}{2}\right) = 1$$

which you know is the absolute maximum, as shown in Figure 13.73. The only other critical point of f *lying in the given region* is $(0, 0)$. It yields an absolute minimum of 0, because

$$0 \le xy \le \pi$$

implies that

$$0 \le \sin xy \le 1.$$

To hunt for other absolute extrema, you should consider the four boundaries of the region formed by taking traces with the vertical planes $x = 0$, $x = \pi$, $y = 0$, and $y = 1$. In doing this, you will find that $\sin xy = 0$ at all points on the x-axis, the y-axis, and at the point $(\pi, 1)$. Each of these points yields an absolute minimum for the surface, as shown in Figure 13.73.

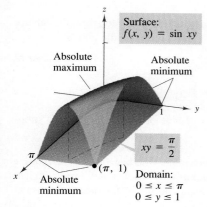

Surface:
$f(x, y) = \sin xy$

Absolute maximum

Absolute minimum

$xy = \dfrac{\pi}{2}$

$(\pi, 1)$

Absolute minimum

Domain:
$0 \le x \le \pi$
$0 \le y \le 1$

FIGURE 13.73

The concepts of relative extrema and critical points can be extended to functions of three or more variables. If all first partial derivatives of

$$w = f(x_1, x_2, x_3, \ldots, x_n)$$

exist, then it can be shown that a relative maximum or minimum can occur at $(x_1, x_2, x_3, \ldots, x_n)$ only if every first partial derivative is 0 at that point. This means that the critical points are obtained by solving the following system of equations.

$$f_{x_1}(x_1, x_2, x_3, \ldots, x_n) = 0$$
$$f_{x_2}(x_1, x_2, x_3, \ldots, x_n) = 0$$
$$\vdots$$
$$f_{x_n}(x_1, x_2, x_3, \ldots, x_n) = 0$$

The extension of Theorem 13.17 to three or more variables is also possible, although we will not consider such an extension in this text.

EXERCISES for Section 13.8

TECHNOLOGY
Laboratory Guide
Labs 13.8–13.9

In Exercises 1–4, identify any extrema of the function by recognizing its given form or its form after completing the square. Verify your results by using the partial derivatives to locate any critical points and test for relative extrema.

1. $f(x, y) = x^2 + y^2 + 2x - 6y + 6$

2. $f(x, y) = -x^2 - y^2 + 4x + 8y - 11$

3. $f(x, y) = \sqrt{25 - (x - 2)^2 - y^2}$

4. $f(x, y) = \sqrt{x^2 + y^2 + 1}$

In Exercises 5–20, examine each function for relative extrema and saddle points.

5. $g(x, y) = (x - 1)^2 + (y - 3)^2$

6. $g(x, y) = 9 - (x - 3)^2 - (y + 2)^2$

7. $f(x, y) = 2x^2 + 2xy + y^2 + 2x - 3$

8. $f(x, y) = -x^2 - 5y^2 + 8x - 10y - 13$

9. $f(x, y) = -5x^2 + 4xy - y^2 + 16x + 10$

10. $f(x, y) = x^2 + 6xy + 10y^2 - 4y + 4$

11. $z = 2x^2 + 3y^2 - 4x - 12y + 13$

12. $z = -3x^2 - 2y^2 + 3x - 4y + 5$

13. $h(x, y) = x^2 - y^2 - 2x - 4y - 4$

14. $h(x, y) = x^2 - 3xy - y^2$

15. $g(x, y) = xy$

16. $g(x, y) = 120x + 120y - xy - x^2 - y^2$

17. $f(x, y) = x^3 - 3xy + y^3$

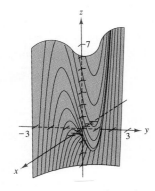

18. $f(x, y) = 4xy - x^4 - y^4$

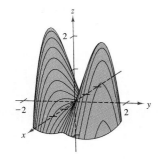

19. $z = e^{-x} \sin y$

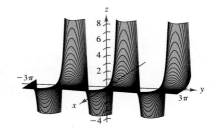

20. $z = (\frac{1}{2} - x^2 + y^2)e^{1 - x^2 - y^2}$

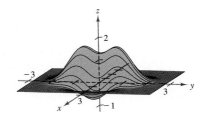

C In Exercises 21–24, use a graphing utility to graph the surface and locate any relative extrema and saddle points.

21. $z = \dfrac{-4x}{x^2 + y^2 + 1}$

22. $f(x, y) = y^3 - 3yx^2 - 3y^2 - 3x^2 + 1$

23. $z = (x^2 + 4y^2)e^{1 - x^2 - y^2}$

24. $z = e^{xy}$

In Exercises 25–28, determine whether there is a relative maximum, a relative minimum, a saddle point, or insufficient information to determine the nature of the function $f(x, y)$ at the critical point (x_0, y_0).

25. $f_{xx}(x_0, y_0) = 9$
$f_{yy}(x_0, y_0) = 4$
$f_{xy}(x_0, y_0) = 6$

26. $f_{xx}(x_0, y_0) = -3$
$f_{yy}(x_0, y_0) = -8$
$f_{xy}(x_0, y_0) = 2$

27. $f_{xx}(x_0, y_0) = -9$
$f_{yy}(x_0, y_0) = 6$
$f_{xy}(x_0, y_0) = 10$

28. $f_{xx}(x_0, y_0) = 25$
$f_{yy}(x_0, y_0) = 8$
$f_{xy}(x_0, y_0) = 10$

In Exercises 29–36, find the absolute extrema of the function over the region R. (In each case, R contains the boundaries.)

29. $f(x, y) = 12 - 3x - 2y$
R: The triangular region in the xy-plane with vertices $(2, 0)$, $(0, 1)$, and $(1, 2)$.

30. $f(x, y) = (2x - y)^2$
R: The triangular region in the xy-plane with vertices $(2, 0)$, $(0, 1)$, and $(1, 2)$.

31. $f(x, y) = 3x^2 + 2y^2 - 4y$
R: The region in the xy-plane bounded by the graphs of $y = x^2$ and $y = 4$.

32. $f(x, y) = 2x - 2xy + y^2$

R: The region in *xy*-plane bounded by the graphs of $y = x^2$ and $y = 1$.

33. $f(x, y) = x^2 + xy,$

$R = \{(x, y): |x| \leq 2, |y| \leq 1\}$

34. $f(x, y) = x^2 + 2xy + y^2,$

$R = \{(x, y): |x| \leq 2, |y| \leq 1\}$

35. $f(x, y) = x^2 + 2xy + y^2,$

$R = \{(x, y): x^2 + y^2 \leq 8\}$

36. $r(x, y) = x^2 - 4xy,$

$R = \{(x, y): 0 \leq x \leq 4, 0 \leq y \leq \sqrt{x}\}$

In Exercises 37–42, find the critical points and test for relative extrema. List the critical points for which the Second Partials Test fails.

37. $f(x, y) = x^3 + y^3$

38. $f(x, y) = x^3 + y^3 - 3x^2 + 6y^2 + 3x + 12y + 7$

39. $f(x, y) = (x - 1)^2(y + 4)^2$

40. $f(x, y) = \sqrt{(x - 1)^2 + (y + 2)^2}$

41. $f(x, y) = x^{2/3} + y^{2/3}$

42. $f(x, y) = (x^2 + y^2)^{2/3}$

In Exercises 43 and 44, find the critical points of the function and from the form of the function determine whether each point is a relative maximum or a relative minimum.

43. $f(x, y, z) = x^2 + (y - 3)^2 + (x + 1)^2$

44. $f(x, y, z) = 4 - [x(y - 1)(z + 2)]^2$

45. The figure shows the level curves for an unknown function $f(x, y)$. What, if any, information can be given about the points *A*, *B*, *C*, and *D*?

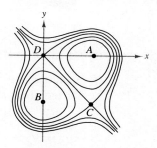

FIGURE FOR 45

46. Prove that if f is a differentiable function such that $\nabla f(x_0, y_0) = \mathbf{0}$, then the tangent plane at (x_0, y_0) is horizontal.

True or False **In Exercises 47–50, determine whether the statement is true or false. If it is false, explain why or give an example that shows it is false.**

47. If f has a relative maximum at (x_0, y_0, z_0), then $f_x(x_0, y_0) = f_y(x_0, y_0) = 0$.

48. The function given by $f(x, y) = \sqrt[3]{x^2 + y^2}$ has a relative minimum at the origin.

49. If f is continuous for all x and y and has two relative minima, then f must have at least one relative maximum.

50. If $f_x(x_0, y_0) = 0$ and $f_y(x_0, y_0) = 0$, then at the point (x_0, y_0, z_0), the tangent plane to the surface given by $z = f(x, y)$ is horizontal.

Applied Optimization Problems

In this section, we survey a few of the many applications of extrema of functions of two (or more) variables.

EXAMPLE 1   Finding Maximum Volume

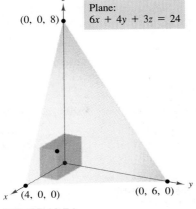

Plane:
$6x + 4y + 3z = 24$

(0, 0, 8)

(4, 0, 0)   (0, 6, 0)

FIGURE 13.74
The maximum volume of the box is $\frac{64}{9}$ cubic units.

REMARK   In many applied problems, the domain of the function to be optimized is a closed bounded region. To find minimum or maximum points, you must not only test critical points, but also consider the values of the function at points on the boundary.

A rectangular box is resting on the xy-plane with one vertex at the origin. The opposite vertex lies in the plane $6x + 4y + 3z = 24$, as shown in Figure 13.74. Find the maximum volume of such a box.

Solution   Let x, y, and z represent the length, width, and height of the box. Because one vertex of the box lies in the plane $6x + 4y + 3z = 24$, you know that $z = \frac{1}{3}(24 - 6x - 4y)$, and you can write the volume xyz of the box as a function of two variables.

$$V(x, y) = (x)(y)\left[\frac{1}{3}(24 - 6x - 4y)\right] = \frac{1}{3}(24xy - 6x^2y - 4xy^2)$$

By setting the first partial derivatives equal to 0

$$V_x(x, y) = \frac{1}{3}(24y - 12xy - 4y^2) = \frac{y}{3}(24 - 12x - 4y) = 0$$

$$V_y(x, y) = \frac{1}{3}(24x - 6x^2 - 8xy) = \frac{x}{3}(24 - 6x - 8y) = 0$$

you obtain the critical points $(0, 0)$ and $\left(\frac{4}{3}, 2\right)$. At $(0, 0)$ the volume is 0, so that point does not yield a maximum volume. At the point $\left(\frac{4}{3}, 2\right)$, you can apply the Second Partials Test.

$$V_{xx}(x, y) = -4y, \qquad V_{yy}(x, y) = \frac{-8x}{3}, \qquad V_{xy}(x, y) = \frac{1}{3}(24 - 12x - 8y)$$

Because

$$V_{xx}\left(\frac{4}{3}, 2\right)V_{yy}\left(\frac{4}{3}, 2\right) - \left[V_{xy}\left(\frac{4}{3}, 2\right)\right]^2 = (-8)\left(-\frac{32}{9}\right) - \left(-\frac{8}{3}\right)^2 = \frac{64}{3} > 0$$

and

$$V_{xx}\left(\frac{4}{3}, 2\right) = -8 < 0$$

you can conclude from the Second Partials Test that the maximum volume is

$$V\left(\frac{4}{3}, 2\right) = \frac{1}{3}\left[24\left(\frac{4}{3}\right)(2) - 6\left(\frac{4}{3}\right)^2(2) - 4\left(\frac{4}{3}\right)(2^2)\right]$$

$$= \frac{64}{9} \text{ cubic units.}$$

(Note that the volume is 0 at the boundary points of the triangular domain of V.)

In Section 3.10, you studied several applications of extrema in economics and business. In practice, such applications often involve more than one independent variable. For instance, a company may produce several models of one type of product. The price per unit and profit per unit are usually different for each model. Moreover, the demand for each model is often a function of the prices of the other models (as well as its own price). The next example illustrates an application involving two products.

EXAMPLE 2   Finding the Maximum Profit

The profit obtained by producing x units of product A and y units of product B is approximated by the model

$$P(x, y) = 8x + 10y - (0.001)(x^2 + xy + y^2) - 10,000.$$

Find the production level that produces a maximum profit.

Solution   The partial derivatives of the profit function are

$$P_x(x, y) = 8 - (0.001)(2x + y)$$

and

$$P_y(x, y) = 10 - (0.001)(x + 2y).$$

By setting these partial derivatives equal to 0, you obtain the following system of equations.

$$8 - (0.001)(2x + y) = 0$$
$$10 - (0.001)(x + 2y) = 0$$

After simplifying, this system of linear equations can be written as

$$2x + y = 8000$$
$$x + 2y = 10,000.$$

FOR FURTHER INFORMATION
For more information on the use of mathematics in economics, see the article "Mathematical Methods of Economics" by Joel Franklin in the April, 1983 issue of the *American Mathematical Monthly*.

Solving this system produces $x = 2000$ and $y = 4000$. The second partial derivatives of P are

$$P_{xx}(2000, 4000) = -0.002$$
$$P_{yy}(2000, 4000) = -0.002$$
$$P_{xy}(2000, 4000) = -0.001.$$

Moreover, because $P_{xx} < 0$ and

$$P_{xx}(2000, 4000)P_{yy}(2000, 4000) - [P_{xy}(2000, 4000)]^2$$
$$= (-0.002)^2 - (-0.001)^2 > 0$$

you can conclude that the production level of $x = 2000$ units and $y = 4000$ units yields a *maximum* profit.

REMARK   In Example 2, we assumed that the manufacturing plant is able to produce the required number of units to yield a maximum profit. In actual practice, the production would be bounded by physical constraints. You will study such constrained optimization problems in the next section.

The Method of Least Squares

Many of the examples in this text have involved **mathematical models.** For instance, Example 2 involves a quadratic model for profit. There are several ways to develop such models—one is called the **method of least squares.**

In constructing a model to represent a particular phenomenon, the goals are simplicity and accuracy. Of course, these goals often conflict. For instance, a simple linear model for the points in Figure 13.75 is

$$y = 1.8566x - 5.0246.$$

However, Figure 13.76 shows that by choosing the slightly more complicated quadratic model*

$$y = 0.1996x^2 - 0.7281x + 1.3749$$

you can achieve greater accuracy.

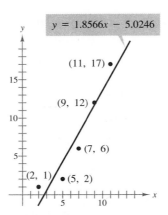

FIGURE 13.75

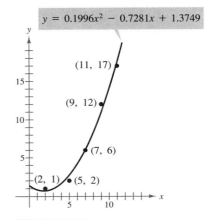

FIGURE 13.76

As a measure of how well the model $y = f(x)$ fits the collection of points

$$\{(x_1, y_1), (x_2, y_2), (x_3, y_3), \ldots, (x_n, y_n)\}$$

you can add the squares of the differences between the actual y-values and the values given by the model to obtain the **sum of the squared errors**

$$S = \sum_{i=1}^{n} [f(x_i) - y_i]^2.$$

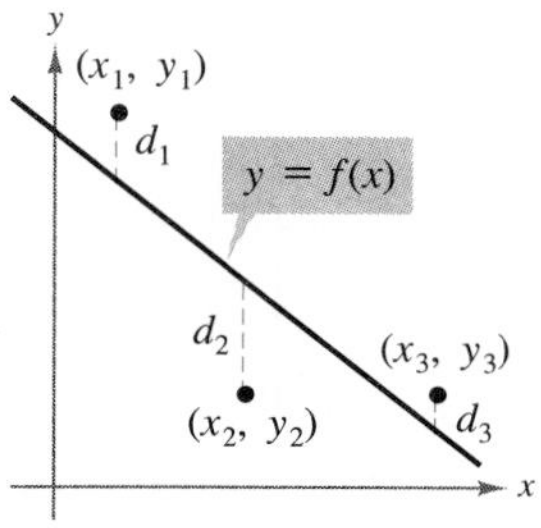

Graphically, S can be interpreted as the sum of the squares of the vertical distances between the graph of f and the given points in the plane, as shown in Figure 13.77. If the model is perfect, then $S = 0$. However, when perfection is not feasible, we settle for a model that minimizes S. Statisticians call the *linear model* that minimizes S the **least squares regression line.** The proof that this line actually minimizes S involves the minimizing of a function of two variables.

FIGURE 13.77
Sum of the squared errors:
$S = d_1^2 + d_2^2 + d_3^2$

*A method for finding the least squares quadratic model for a collection of data is described in Exercise 35.

THEOREM 13.18   Least Squares Regression Line

The **least squares regression line** for $\{(x_1, y_1), (x_2, y_2), \ldots, (x_n, y_n)\}$ is given by $f(x) = ax + b$, where

$$a = \frac{n \sum\limits_{i=1}^{n} x_i y_i - \sum\limits_{i=1}^{n} x_i \sum\limits_{i=1}^{n} y_i}{n \sum\limits_{i=1}^{n} x_i^2 - \left(\sum\limits_{i=1}^{n} x_i\right)^2} \quad \text{and} \quad b = \frac{1}{n}\left(\sum\limits_{i=1}^{n} y_i - a \sum\limits_{i=1}^{n} x_i\right).$$

ADRIEN-MARIE LEGENDRE

The method of least squares was introduced by the French mathematician Adrien-Marie Legendre (1752–1833). Legendre is best known for his work in geometry. In fact, his text *Elements of Geometry* was so popular in the United States that it continued to be used for 33 editions, spanning a period of more than 100 years.

Proof   Let $S(a, b)$ represent the sum of the squared errors for the model $f(x) = ax + b$ and the given set of points. That is,

$$S(a, b) = \sum_{i=1}^{n} [f(x_i) - y_i]^2$$

$$= \sum_{i=1}^{n} (ax_i + b - y_i)^2$$

where the points (x_i, y_i) represent constants. Because S is a function of a and b, you can use the methods discussed in the previous section to find the minimum value of S. Specifically, the first partial derivatives of S are

$$S_a(a, b) = \sum_{i=1}^{n} 2x_i(ax_i + b - y_i)$$

$$= 2a \sum_{i=1}^{n} x_i^2 + 2b \sum_{i=1}^{n} x_i - 2 \sum_{i=1}^{n} x_i y_i$$

$$S_b(a, b) = \sum_{i=1}^{n} 2(ax_i + b - y_i)$$

$$= 2a \sum_{i=1}^{n} x_i + 2nb - 2 \sum_{i=1}^{n} y_i.$$

By setting these two partial derivatives equal to 0, you obtain the values for a and b that are listed in the theorem. We leave it to you to apply the Second Partials Test (see Exercise 36) to verify that these values of a and b yield a minimum. ▬

If the x-values are symmetrically spaced about the y-axis, then $\sum x_i = 0$, and the formulas for a and b simplify to

$$a = \frac{\sum\limits_{i=1}^{n} x_i y_i}{\sum\limits_{i=1}^{n} x_i^2} \quad \text{and} \quad b = \frac{1}{n} \sum_{i=1}^{n} y_i.$$

This simplification is often possible with a translation of the x-values. For instance, if the x-values in a data collection consist of the years 1980, 1981, 1982, 1983, and 1984, you could let 1982 be represented by 0.

EXAMPLE 3   Finding the Least Squares Regression Line

Find the least squares regression line for the following points.

$$(-3, 0), \qquad (-1, 1), \qquad (0, 2), \qquad (2, 3)$$

Solution   Table 13.2 shows the calculations involved in finding the least squares regression line using $n = 4$.

TABLE 13.2

x	y	xy	x^2
-3	0	0	9
-1	1	-1	1
0	2	0	0
2	3	6	4
$\displaystyle\sum_{i=1}^{n} x_i = -2$	$\displaystyle\sum_{i=1}^{n} y_i = 6$	$\displaystyle\sum_{i=1}^{n} x_i y_i = 5$	$\displaystyle\sum_{i=1}^{n} x_i^2 = 14$

Applying Theorem 13.18 produces

$$a = \frac{n \displaystyle\sum_{i=1}^{n} x_i y_i - \displaystyle\sum_{i=1}^{n} x_i \displaystyle\sum_{i=1}^{n} y_i}{n \displaystyle\sum_{i=1}^{n} x_i^2 - \left(\displaystyle\sum_{i=1}^{n} x_i \right)^2}$$

$$= \frac{4(5) - (-2)(6)}{4(14) - (-2)^2}$$

$$= \frac{8}{13}$$

and

$$b = \frac{1}{n} \left(\sum_{i=1}^{n} y_i - a \sum_{i=1}^{n} x_i \right)$$

$$= \frac{1}{4} \left[6 - \frac{8}{13}(-2) \right]$$

$$= \frac{47}{26}.$$

Thus, the least squares regression line is

$$y = \frac{8}{13}x + \frac{47}{26}$$

as shown in Figure 13.78.

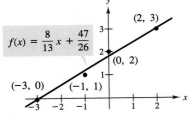

FIGURE 13.78
Least squares regression line

TECHNOLOGY   Many calculators have "built-in" least squares regression programs. If your calculator has such a program, try using it to duplicate the results of Example 3.

TECHNOLOGY
Laboratory Guide
Labs 13.8–13.9

EXERCISES for Section 13.9

In Exercises 1 and 2, find the minimum distance from the point to the plane given by $2x + 3y + z = 12$. (*Hint:* To simplify the computations, minimize the square of the distance.)

1. $(0, 0, 0)$ **2.** $(1, 2, 3)$

In Exercises 3 and 4, find the minimum distance from the point to the paraboloid given by $z = x^2 + y^2$.

3. $(5, 5, 0)$ **4.** $(5, 0, 0)$

In Exercises 5–8, find three positive numbers x, y, and z that satisfy the given conditions.

5. The sum is 30 and the product is maximum.

6. The sum is 32 and $P = xy^2z$ is maximum.

7. The sum is 30 and the sum of the squares is minimum.

8. The sum is 1 and the sum of the squares is minimum.

9. *Volume* The sum of the length and the girth (perimeter of a cross section) of packages carried by parcel post cannot exceed 108 inches. Find the dimensions of the rectangular package of largest volume that may be sent by parcel post.

10. *Volume* Repeat Exercise 9 under the condition that the sum of the two perimeters of the two cross sections shown in the figure cannot exceed 108 inches.

11. *Minimum Cost* A water line is to be built from point P to point S and must pass through regions where construction costs differ (see figure). Find x and y so that the total cost C will be minimum if the cost per mile in dollars is $3k$ from P to Q, $2k$ from Q to R, and k from R to S.

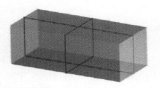

FIGURE FOR 10

FIGURE FOR 11

12. *Volume* The material for constructing the base of an open box costs 1.5 times as much per unit area as the material for constructing the sides. For a fixed amount of money C, find the dimensions of the box of largest volume that can be made.

13. *Volume* The volume of an ellipsoid

$$\frac{x^2}{a^2} + \frac{y^2}{b^2} + \frac{z^2}{c^2} = 1$$

is $4\pi abc/3$. For fixed $a + b + c$, show that the ellipsoid of maximum volume is a sphere.

14. *Volume* Show that the rectangular box of maximum volume inscribed in a sphere of radius r is a cube.

15. *Volume and Surface Area* Show that the rectangular box of given volume and minimum surface area is a cube.

16. *Area* A trough with trapezoidal cross sections is formed by turning up the edges of a 10-inch-wide sheet of aluminum. Find the cross section of maximum area.

17. *Area* Repeat Exercise 16 for a sheet of aluminum that is w inches wide.

18. *Revenue* A company manufactures two products. The total revenue from x_1 units of product 1 and x_2 units of product 2 is

$$R = -5x_1^2 - 8x_2^2 - 2x_1x_2 + 42x_1 + 102x_2.$$

Find x_1 and x_2 so as to maximize the revenue.

19. *Revenue* A retail outlet sells two competitive products, the prices of which are p_1 and p_2. Find p_1 and p_2 so as to maximize total revenue, where

$$R = 500p_1 + 800p_2 + 1.5p_1p_2 - 1.5p_1^2 - p_2^2.$$

20. *Profit* A corporation manufactures a product at two locations. The cost of producing x_1 units at location 1 is

$$C_1 = 0.02x_1^2 + 4x_1 + 500$$

and the cost of producing x_2 units at location 2 is

$$C_2 = 0.05x_2^2 + 4x_2 + 275.$$

If the product sells for $15 per unit, find the quantity that should be produced at each location to maximize the profit, $P = 15(x_1 + x_2) - C_1 - C_2$.

21. *Distance* A company has retail outlets located at the points $(0, 0)$, $(2, 2)$, and $(-2, 2)$ (see figure). Management plans to build a distribution center so that the sum of the distances S from the center to the outlets is minimum. From the symmetry of the problem it is clear that the distribution center will be located on the y-axis, and therefore, S is a function of the single variable y. Using techniques of Chapter 3, find the required value of y.

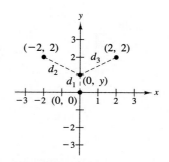

FIGURE FOR 21

C **22.** The retail outlets described in Exercise 21 are located at (0, 0), (4, 2), and (−2, 2) (see figure). The location of the distribution center is (x, y), and therefore the sum of the distances S is a function of x and y.

  a. Write the expression giving the sum of the distances S. Use a computer algebra system to obtain a graph of the surface. Does the surface have a minimum?

  b. Use a computer algebra system to obtain S_x and S_y. Observe that solving the system $S_x = 0$ and $S_y = 0$ is very difficult. Therefore, we will approximate the location of the distribution center.

  c. An initial estimate of the critical point is $(x_1, y_1) = (1, 1)$. Calculate $-\nabla S(1, 1)$ with components $-S_x(1, 1)$ and $-S_y(1, 1)$. What direction is given by the vector $-\nabla S(1, 1)$?

  d. The second estimate of the critical point is

$$(x_2, y_2) = (x_1 - S_x(x_1, y_1)t, \; y_1 - S_y(x_1, y_1)t).$$

  If these coordinates are substituted into $S(x, y)$, then S becomes a function of the single variable t. Find the value of t that minimizes S. Use this value of t to find the estimate (x_2, y_2).

  e. Complete two more iterations of the process in part d to obtain (x_4, y_4).

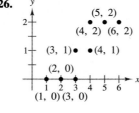

FIGURE FOR 22

In Exercises 23–26, (a) find the least squares regression line and (b) calculate S, the sum of the squared errors.

23.
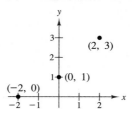

24.
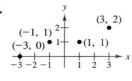

25.
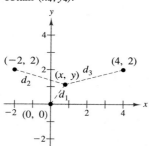

26.
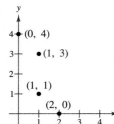

In Exercises 27–30, find the least squares regression line for the given points.

27. (0, 0), (1, 1), (3, 4), (4, 2), (5, 5)

28. (1, 0), (3, 3), (5, 6)

29. (0, 6), (4, 3), (5, 0), (8, −4), (10, −5)

30. (5, 2), (0, 0), (2, 1), (7, 4), (10, 6), (12, 6)

31. *Demand Equation* A store manager wants to know the demand for a certain product as a function of price. The daily sales for three different prices of the product are given in the following table.

Price (x)	$1.00	$1.25	$1.50
Demand (y)	450	375	330

  a. Find the least squares regression line for these data.

  b. Estimate the demand when the price is $1.40.

32. *Carcinogens* After contamination with a carcinogen, people in different geographic regions were assigned an exposure index, which represented the degree of contamination. Using the following data, find a least squares regression line to estimate the mortality per 100,000 people for a given exposure.

Exposure (x)	2.67	1.35	3.93	5.14	7.43
Mortality (y)	135.2	118.5	167.3	197.6	204.7

33. *Agriculture* An agronomist used four test plots to determine the relationship between the wheat yield (in bushels per acre) and the amount of fertilizer (in hundreds of pounds per acre). The results are given in the following table.

Fertilizer (x)	1.0	1.5	2.0	2.5
Yield (y)	32	41	48	53

Find the least squares regression line for these data, and estimate the yield for a fertilizer application of 160 pounds per acre.

34. *Women in the Work Force* The following table gives the percentage and number (in millions) of women in the work force for selected years. (*Source:* U.S. Department of Labor)

Year	1940	1950	1960	1970
Percentage (x)	24.3	29.0	32.5	37.2
Number (y)	12.8	18.4	23.3	31.6

Year	1980	1988	1989	1990
Percentage (x)	42.0	44.5	44.8	45.3
Number (y)	45.6	54.9	56.2	56.6

  a. Find the least squares regression line for these data.

  b. According to this model, approximately how many women enter the labor force for each one point increase in the percentage of women in the labor force?

35. Find a system of equations whose solution yields the coefficients a, b, and c for the least squares regression quadratic $y = ax^2 + bx + c$ for the points

$(x_1, y_1), (x_2, y_2), \ldots, (x_n, y_n)$

by minimizing the sum

$$S(a, b, c) = \sum_{i=1}^{n} (y_i - ax_i^2 - bx_i - c)^2.$$

36. Use the Second Partials Test to verify that the formulas for a and b given in Theorem 13.18 yield a minimum.

$$\left(\textit{Hint: } \text{Use the fact that } n \sum_{i=1}^{n} x_i^2 \geq \left(\sum_{i=1}^{n} x_i \right)^2. \right)$$

In Exercises 37–40, use the result of Exercise 35 to find the least squares regression quadratic for the given points. Then plot the points and sketch the graph of the least squares quadratic.

37. $(-2, 0), (-1, 0), (0, 1), (1, 2), (2, 5)$

38. $(-4, 5), (-2, 6), (2, 6), (4, 2)$

39. $(0, 0), (2, 2), (3, 6), (4, 12)$

40. $(0, 10), (1, 9), (2, 6), (3, 0)$

41. *Engine Performance*   After developing a new turbocharger for an automobile engine, the following experimental data were obtained for speed in miles per hour at 2-second intervals. Fit a least squares quadratic to the data.

Time (x)	0	2	4	6	8	10
Speed (y)	0	15	30	50	65	70

42. The following table gives the world population in billions for five different years. (*Source:* World Population Data Sheet)

Year	1970	1975	1980	1985	1990
Population (y)	3.7	4.1	4.5	4.8	5.3

Let $x = 0$ represent the year 1980.

a. Find the least squares regression quadratic for these data.

b. Use this quadratic to estimate the world population for the year 2010.

43. How would the procedure of Exercise 22 change if you are searching for a maximum value of a function $S = f(x, y)$?

13.10   Lagrange Multipliers • Constrained Optimization Problems • The Method of Lagrange Multipliers with Two Constraints

Lagrange Multipliers

The Method of Lagrange Multipliers is named after the French mathematician Joseph Louis Lagrange (1736–1813). Lagrange first introduced the method in his famous paper on mechanics, written when he was just 19 years old!

Many optimization problems have restrictions or **constraints** on the values that can be used to produce the optimal solution. Such constraints tend to complicate optimization problems because the optimal solution can occur at a boundary point of the domain. In this section, you will study an ingenious technique for solving such problems. It is called the **Method of Lagrange Multipliers.**

To see how this technique works, suppose you want to find the rectangle of maximum area that can be inscribed in the ellipse given by

$$\frac{x^2}{3^2} + \frac{y^2}{4^2} = 1.$$

Let (x, y) be the vertex of the rectangle in the first quadrant, as shown in Figure 13.79. Because the rectangle has sides of length $2x$ and $2y$, its area is given by

$$f(x, y) = 4xy. \qquad \text{Objective function}$$

You want to find x and y such that $f(x, y)$ is a maximum. Your choice of (x, y) is restricted to first-quadrant points that lie on the ellipse.

$$\frac{x^2}{3^2} + \frac{y^2}{4^2} = 1 \qquad \text{Constraint}$$

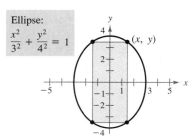

Ellipse:
$\frac{x^2}{3^2} + \frac{y^2}{4^2} = 1$

FIGURE 13.79

Objective function: $f(x, y) = 4xy$

Now, consider the constraint equation to be a fixed level curve of

$$g(x, y) = \frac{x^2}{3^2} + \frac{y^2}{4^2}.$$

The level curves of f represent a family of hyperbolas

$$f(x, y) = 4xy = k.$$

In this family, the level curves that meet the given constraint correspond to the hyperbolas that intersect the ellipse. Moreover, to maximize $f(x, y)$, you want to find the hyperbola that just barely satisfies the constraint. The level curve that does this is the one that is *tangent* to the ellipse, as shown in Figure 13.80.

To find the appropriate hyperbola, use the fact that two curves are tangent at a point if and only if their gradient vectors are parallel. This means that $\nabla f(x, y)$ must be a scalar multiple of $\nabla g(x, y)$ at the point of tangency. In the context of constrained optimization problems, this scalar is denoted by λ.

$$\nabla f(x, y) = \lambda \nabla g(x, y)$$

The scalar λ is called a **Lagrange multiplier.** Theorem 13.19 gives the necessary conditions for the existence of such multipliers.

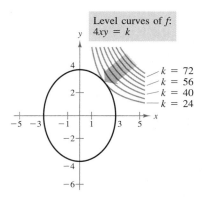

Level curves of f:
$4xy = k$

$k = 72$
$k = 56$
$k = 40$
$k = 24$

FIGURE 13.80

Constraint: $g(x, y) = 1$

THEOREM 13.19 Lagrange's Theorem

Let f and g have continuous first partial derivatives such that f has an extremum at a point (x_0, y_0) on the smooth constraint curve $g(x, y) = c$. If $\nabla g(x_0, y_0) \neq \mathbf{0}$, then there is a real number λ such that

$$\nabla f(x_0, y_0) = \lambda \nabla g(x_0, y_0).$$

Proof. To begin, represent the smooth curve given by $g(x, y) = c$ by the vector-valued function

$$\mathbf{r}(t) = x(t)\mathbf{i} + y(t)\mathbf{j}, \qquad \mathbf{r}'(t) \neq 0$$

where x' and y' are continuous on an open interval I. Define the function h by $h(t) = f(x(t), y(t))$. Then, because $f(x_0, x_0)$ is an extreme value of f, you know that

$$h(t_0) = f(x(t_0), y(t_0)) = f(x_0, y_0)$$

is an extreme value of h. This implies that $h'(t_0) = 0$, and, by the Chain Rule,

$$h'(t_0) = f_x(x_0, y_0)x'(t_0) + f_y(x_0, y_0)y'(t_0) = \nabla f(x_0, y_0) \cdot \mathbf{r}'(t_0) = 0.$$

REMARK Lagrange's Theorem can be shown to be true for functions of three variables, using a similar argument with level surfaces and Theorem 13.14.

Therefore, $\nabla f(x_0, y_0)$ is orthogonal to $\mathbf{r}'(t_0)$. Moreover, by Theorem 13.12, $\nabla g(x_0, y_0)$ is also orthogonal to $\mathbf{r}'(t_0)$. Consequently, the gradients $\nabla f(x_0, y_0)$ and $\nabla g(x_0, y_0)$ are parallel, and there must exist a scalar λ such that

$$\nabla f(x_0, y_0) = \lambda \nabla g(x_0, y_0).$$

The Method of Lagrange Multipliers uses Theorem 13.19 to find the extreme values of a function f subject to a constraint.

Method of Lagrange Multipliers

Let f and g satisfy the hypothesis of Lagrange's Theorem, and let f have a minimum or maximum subject to the constraint $g(x, y) = c$. To find the minimum or maximum of f, use the following steps.

1. Simultaneously solve the equations

   $$\nabla f(x, y) = \lambda \nabla g(x, y) \quad \text{and} \quad g(x, y) = c$$

   by solving the following system of equations.

   $$f_x(x, y) = \lambda g_x(x, y)$$

   $$f_y(x, y) = \lambda g_y(x, y)$$

   $$g(x, y) = c$$

2. Evaluate f at each solution point obtained in the first step. The largest value yields the maximum of f subject to the constraint $g(x, y) = c$, and the smallest value yields the minimum of f subject to the constraint $g(x, y) = c$.

Constrained Optimization Problems

At the beginning of this section, we described a problem in which we wanted to maximize the area of a rectangle that is inscribed in an ellipse. Example 1 shows how to use Lagrange multipliers to solve this problem.

EXAMPLE 1   Using a Lagrange Multiplier with One Constraint

Find the maximum value of

$$f(x, y) = 4xy, \qquad x > 0, \, y > 0$$

subject to the constraint $(x^2/3^2) + (y^2/4^2) = 1$.

Solution   To begin, let

$$g(x, y) = \frac{x^2}{3^2} + \frac{y^2}{4^2} = 1.$$

By equating $\nabla f(x, y) = 4y\mathbf{i} + 4x\mathbf{j}$ and $\lambda \nabla g(x, y) = (2\lambda x/9)\mathbf{i} + (\lambda y/8)\mathbf{j}$, you can obtain the following system of equations.

$$4y = \frac{2}{9}\lambda x \qquad f_x(x, y) = \lambda g_x(x, y)$$

$$4x = \frac{1}{8}\lambda y \qquad f_y(x, y) = \lambda g_y(x, y)$$

$$\frac{x^2}{3^2} + \frac{y^2}{4^2} = 1 \qquad \text{Constraint}$$

REMARK   Writing the constraint as

$$g(x, y) = \frac{x^2}{3^2} + \frac{y^2}{4^2} = 1$$

or as

$$g(x, y) = \frac{x^2}{3^2} + \frac{y^2}{4^2} - 1 = 0$$

does not affect the solution—the constant is eliminated when you form ∇g.

From the first equation you obtain $\lambda = 18y/x$, and substitution into the second equation produces

$$4x = \frac{1}{8}\left(\frac{18y}{x}\right)y \quad \rightarrow \quad x^2 = \frac{9}{16}y^2.$$

Substituting this value for x^2 into the third equation produces

$$\frac{1}{9}\left(\frac{9}{16}y^2\right) + \frac{1}{16}y^2 = 1 \quad \rightarrow \quad y^2 = 8.$$

Thus, $y = \pm 2\sqrt{2}$. Because it is required that $y > 0$, choose the positive value and find that

$$x^2 = \frac{9}{16}y^2 = \frac{9}{16}(8) = \frac{9}{2} \quad \rightarrow \quad x^2 = \frac{9}{2} \quad \rightarrow \quad x = \frac{3}{\sqrt{2}}.$$

Thus, the maximum of f is

$$f\left(\frac{3}{\sqrt{2}}, 2\sqrt{2}\right) = 4\left(\frac{3}{\sqrt{2}}\right)(2\sqrt{2}) = 24. \qquad \blacksquare$$

Example 1 can also be solved using techniques you learned in Chapter 3. To see how, try to find the maximum value of $A = 4xy$ given that $(x^2/3^2) + (y^2/4^2) = 1$. To begin, solve the second equation for y to obtain $y = \frac{4}{3}\sqrt{9 - x^2}$. Then substitute into the first equation to obtain

$$A = 4x\left(\frac{4}{3}\sqrt{9 - x^2}\right).$$

Finally, use the techniques of Chapter 3 to maximize A.

EXAMPLE 2   A Business Application

The Cobb-Douglas production function (see Example 5, Section 13.1) for a particular manufacturer is given by

$$f(x, y) = 100x^{3/4}y^{1/4} \qquad \text{Objective function}$$

where x represents the units of labor (at \$150 per unit) and y represents the units of capital (at \$250 per unit). The total cost of labor and capital is limited to \$50,000. Find the maximum production level for this manufacturer.

Solution   From the given function, you have

$$\nabla f(x, y) = 75x^{-1/4}y^{1/4}\mathbf{i} + 25x^{3/4}y^{-3/4}\mathbf{j}.$$

FOR FURTHER INFORMATION
For more information on the use of Lagrange multipliers in economics, see the article "Lagrange Multiplier Problems in Economics" by John V. Baxley and John C. Moorhouse in the August-September, 1984 issue of the *American Mathematical Monthly*.

The limit on the cost of labor and capital produces the constraint

$$g(x, y) = 150x + 250y = 50,000. \qquad \text{Constraint}$$

Thus, $\lambda\nabla g(x, y) = 150\lambda\,\mathbf{i} + 250\lambda\,\mathbf{j}$. This gives rise to the following system of equations.

$$75x^{-1/4}y^{1/4} = 150\lambda \qquad f_x(x, y) = \lambda g_x(x, y)$$
$$25x^{3/4}y^{-3/4} = 250\lambda \qquad f_y(x, y) = \lambda g_y(x, y)$$
$$150x + 250y = 50,000 \qquad \text{Constraint}$$

By solving for λ in the first equation

$$\lambda = \frac{75x^{-1/4}y^{1/4}}{150} = \frac{x^{-1/4}y^{1/4}}{2}$$

and substituting into the second equation, you obtain

$$25x^{3/4}y^{-3/4} = 250\left(\frac{x^{-1/4}y^{1/4}}{2}\right) \qquad \text{Multiply by } x^{1/4}y^{3/4}$$
$$25x = 125y.$$

Thus, $x = 5y$. By substituting into the third equation, you have

$$150(5y) + 250y = 50,000$$
$$1000y = 50,000$$
$$y = 50 \text{ units of capital}$$
$$x = 250 \text{ units of labor.}$$

Thus, the maximum production is

$$f(250, 50) = 100(250)^{3/4}(50)^{1/4} \approx 16,719 \text{ product units.} \qquad \blacksquare$$

Economists call the Lagrange multiplier obtained in a production function the **marginal productivity of money.** For instance, in Example 2 the marginal productivity of money at $x = 250$ and $y = 50$ is

$$\lambda = \frac{x^{-1/4}y^{1/4}}{2} = \frac{(250)^{-1/4}(50)^{1/4}}{2} \approx 0.334$$

which means that for each additional dollar spent on production, 0.334 additional units of the product can be produced.

EXAMPLE 3   Lagrange Multipliers and Three Variables

Find the minimum value of

$$f(x, y, z) = 2x^2 + y^2 + 3z^2 \qquad \text{Objective function}$$

subject to the constraint $2x - 3y + 4z = 49$.

Solution   Let $g(x, y, z) = 2x - 3y + 4z = 49$. Then, because $\nabla f(x, y, z) = 4x\mathbf{i} + 2y\mathbf{j} + 6z\mathbf{k}$ and $\lambda \nabla g(x, y, z) = 2\lambda \mathbf{i} - 3\lambda \mathbf{j} + 4\lambda \mathbf{k}$, you obtain the following system of equations.

$$4x = 2\lambda \qquad \qquad f_x(x, y, z) = \lambda g_x(x, y, z)$$
$$2y = -3\lambda \qquad \qquad f_y(x, y, z) = \lambda g_y(x, y, z)$$
$$6z = 4\lambda \qquad \qquad f_z(x, y, z) = \lambda g_z(x, y, z)$$
$$2x - 3y + 4z = 49 \qquad \qquad \text{Constraint}$$

The solution of this system is $x = 3$, $y = -9$, and $z = 4$. Therefore, the optimum value of f is

$$f(3, -9, 4) = 2(3)^2 + (-9)^2 + 3(4)^2 = 147.$$

From the original function and constraint, it is clear that $f(x, y, z)$ has no maximum. Thus, the above optimum value of f is a minimum.

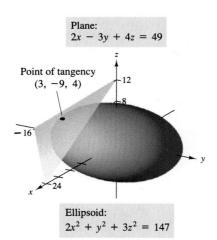

Plane:
$2x - 3y + 4z = 49$

Point of tangency
$(3, -9, 4)$

Ellipsoid:
$2x^2 + y^2 + 3z^2 = 147$

FIGURE 13.81

At the beginning of this section, we gave a graphical interpretation of constrained optimization problems in two variables. In three variables, the interpretation is similar, except that we use level surfaces instead of level curves. For instance, in Example 3, the level surfaces of f are ellipsoids centered at the origin, and the constraint $2x - 3y + 4z = 49$ is a plane. The minimum value of f is represented by the ellipsoid that is tangent to the constraint plane, as shown in Figure 13.81.

EXAMPLE 4   Optimization Inside a Region

Find the extreme values of

$$f(x, y) = x^2 + 2y^2 - 2x + 3 \qquad \text{Objective function}$$

subject to the constraint $x^2 + y^2 \le 10$.

Solution   To solve this problem, you can break the constraint into two cases.

a. For points *on the circle*, $x^2 + y^2 = 10$, you can use Lagrange multipliers to find that the maximum value of $f(x, y)$ is 24—this value occurs at $(-1, 3)$ and at $(-1, -3)$. In a similar way, you can determine that the minimum value of $f(x, y)$ is 6.675—this value occurs at $(\sqrt{10}, 0)$.

b. For points *inside the circle*, you can use the techniques discussed in Section 13.8 to conclude that the function has a relative minimum of 2 at the point $(1, 0)$.

By combining these two results, you can conclude that f has a maximum of 24 at $(-1, \pm 3)$ and a minimum of 2 at $(1, 0)$.

The Method of Lagrange Multipliers with Two Constraints

For optimization problems involving *two* constraint functions g and h, we introduce a second Lagrange multiplier, μ (the lowercase Greek letter mu), and solve the equation

$$\nabla f = \lambda \nabla g + \mu \nabla h$$

as illustrated in Example 5.

EXAMPLE 5   Optimization with Two Constraints

Let $T(x, y, z) = 20 + 2x + 2y + z^2$ represent the temperature at each point on the sphere $x^2 + y^2 + z^2 = 11$. Find the extreme temperatures on the curve formed by the intersection of the plane $x + y + z = 3$ and the sphere.

Solution   The two constraints are $g(x, y, z) = x^2 + y^2 + z^2 = 11$ and $h(x, y, z) = x + y + z = 3$. Using

$$\nabla T(x, y, z) = 2\mathbf{i} + 2\mathbf{j} + 2z\,\mathbf{k}, \quad \lambda \nabla g(x, y, z) = 2\lambda x\,\mathbf{i} + 2\lambda y\,\mathbf{j} + 2\lambda z\,\mathbf{k}$$

and $\mu \nabla h(x, y, z) = \mu\,\mathbf{i} + \mu\,\mathbf{j} + \mu\,\mathbf{k}$, you can write the following system of equations.

$$
\begin{aligned}
2 &= 2\lambda x + \mu & T_x(x, y, z) &= \lambda g_x(x, y, z) + \mu h_x(x, y, z) \\
2 &= 2\lambda y + \mu & T_y(x, y, z) &= \lambda g_y(x, y, z) + \mu h_y(x, y, z) \\
2z &= 2\lambda z + \mu & T_z(x, y, z) &= \lambda g_z(x, y, z) + \mu h_z(x, y, z) \\
x^2 + y^2 + z^2 &= 11 & \text{Constraint 1} \\
x + y + z &= 3 & \text{Constraint 2}
\end{aligned}
$$

By subtracting the second equation from the first, you can obtain the following system.

$$
\begin{aligned}
\lambda(x - y) &= 0 \\
2z(1 - \lambda) - \mu &= 0 \\
x^2 + y^2 + z^2 &= 11 \\
x + y + z &= 3
\end{aligned}
$$

From the first equation, you can conclude that $\lambda = 0$ or $x = y$. If $\lambda = 0$, you can show that the critical points are $(3, -1, 1)$ and $(-1, 3, 1)$. (Try doing this—it takes a little work!) If $\lambda \neq 0$, then $x = y$ and you can show that the critical points occur when $x = y = (3 \pm 2\sqrt{3})/3$ and $z = (3 \mp 4\sqrt{3})/3$. Finally, to find the optimal solutions, compare the temperatures at the four critical points.

$$T(3, -1, 1) = T(-1, 3, 1) = 25$$

$$T\left(\frac{3 - 2\sqrt{3}}{3}, \frac{3 - 2\sqrt{3}}{3}, \frac{3 + 4\sqrt{3}}{3}\right) = \frac{91}{3} \approx 30.33$$

$$T\left(\frac{3 + 2\sqrt{3}}{3}, \frac{3 + 2\sqrt{3}}{3}, \frac{3 - 4\sqrt{3}}{3}\right) = \frac{91}{3} \approx 30.33$$

REMARK   The system of equations that arises in the method of Lagrange multipliers is not, in general, a linear system, and the solution often requires ingenuity.

Thus, $T = 25$ is the minimum temperature and $T = \frac{91}{3}$ is the maximum temperature on the curve.

EXERCISES for Section 13.10

In Exercises 1–12, use Lagrange multipliers to find the indicated extrema. In each case, assume that x and y are positive.

1. Maximize $f(x, y) = xy$
   Constraint: $x + y = 10$

2. Maximize $f(x, y) = xy$
   Constraint: $2x + y = 4$

3. Minimize $f(x, y) = x^2 + y^2$
   Constraint: $x + y - 4 = 0$

4. Minimize $f(x, y) = x^2 + y^2$
   Constraint: $-2x - 4y + 5 = 0$

5. Minimize $f(x, y) = x^2 - y^2$
   Constraint: $x - 2y + 6 = 0$

6. Maximize $f(x, y) = x^2 - y^2$
   Constraint: $y - x^2 = 0$

7. Maximize $f(x, y) = 2x + 2xy + y$
   Constraint: $2x + y = 100$

8. Minimize $f(x, y) = 3x + y + 10$
   Constraint: $x^2 y = 6$

9. Maximize $f(x, y) = \sqrt{6 - x^2 - y^2}$
   Constraint: $x + y - 2 = 0$

10. Minimize $f(x, y) = \sqrt{x^2 + y^2}$
    Constraint: $2x + 4y - 15 = 0$

11. Maximize $f(x, y) = e^{xy}$
    Constraint: $x^2 + y^2 - 8 = 0$

12. Minimize $f(x, y) = 2x + y$
    Constraint: $xy = 32$

In Exercises 13–16, use Lagrange multipliers to find the indicated extrema. In each case, assume that x, y, and z are positive.

13. Minimize $f(x, y, z) = x^2 + y^2 + z^2$
    Constraint: $x + y + z - 6 = 0$

14. Maximize $f(x, y, z) = xyz$
    Constraint: $x + y + z - 6 = 0$

15. Minimize $f(x, y, z) = x^2 + y^2 + z^2$
    Constraint: $x + y + z = 1$

16. Minimize $f(x, y, z) = 2x + y + 2z$
    Constraint: $x^2 + y^2 + z^2 = 4$

In Exercises 17–20, use Lagrange multipliers to find the indicated extrema of f subject to two constraints. In each case, assume x, y, and z are nonnegative.

17. Maximize $f(x, y, z) = xyz$
    Constraints: $x + y + z = 32$
    $\qquad\qquad\ x - y + z = 0$

18. Minimize $f(x, y, z) = x^2 + y^2 + z^2$
    Constraints: $x + 2z = 4$
    $\qquad\qquad\ x + y = 8$

19. Maximize $f(x, y, z) = xy + yz$
    Constraints: $x + 2y = 6$
    $\qquad\qquad\ x - 3z = 0$

20. Maximize $f(x, y, z) = xyz$
    Constraints: $x^2 + z^2 = 5$
    $\qquad\qquad\ x - 2y = 0$

In Exercises 21 and 22, use Lagrange multipliers to find any extrema of the function subject to the constraint $x^2 + y^2 \leq 1$.

21. $f(x, y) = x^2 + 3xy + y^2$

22. $f(x, y) = e^{-xy}$

In Exercises 23–26, use Lagrange multipliers to find the minimum distance from the curve or surface to the specified point. (*Hint:* In Exercise 23, minimize $f(x, y) = x^2 + y^2$ subject to the constraint $2x + 3y = -1$.)

Curve	Point
23. Line: $2x + 3y = -1$	$(0, 0)$
24. Circle: $(x - 4)^2 + y^2 = 4$	$(0, 10)$

Surface	Point
25. Plane: $x + y + z = 1$	$(2, 1, 1)$
26. Cone: $z = \sqrt{x^2 + y^2}$	$(4, 0, 0)$

In Exercises 27 and 28, find the highest point on the curve of intersection of the given surfaces.

27. Sphere: $x^2 + y^2 + z^2 = 36$
    Plane: $2x + y - z = 2$

28. Cone: $x^2 + y^2 - z^2 = 0$
    Plane: $x + 2z = 4$

29. *Volume* Find the dimensions of the rectangular package of largest volume subject to the constraint that the sum of the length and the girth cannot exceed 108 inches. (Maximize $V = xyz$ subject to the constraint $x + 2y + 2z = 108$.)

30. *Volume* The material for the base of an open box costs 1.5 times as much as the material for the sides. Find the dimensions of the box of largest volume that can be made for a fixed cost C. (Maximize $V = xyz$ subject to $1.5xy + 2xz + 2yz = C$.)

31. *Cost* A cargo container (in the shape of a rectangular solid) must have a volume of 480 cubic feet. Use Lagrange multipliers to find the dimensions of the container of this size that has minimum cost if the bottom will cost $5 per square foot to construct and the sides and top will cost $3 per square foot to construct.

32. *Surface Area* Use Lagrange multipliers to find the dimensions of the right circular cylinder with volume V_0 cubic units and minimum surface area.

33. *Volume* Use Lagrange multipliers to find the dimensions of the rectangular box of maximum volume that can be inscribed (with edges parallel to the coordinate axes) in the ellipsoid

$$\frac{x^2}{a^2} + \frac{y^2}{b^2} + \frac{z^2}{c^2} = 1.$$

34. *Geometric and Arithmetic Means*
  a. Use Lagrange multipliers to prove that the product of three positive numbers, x, y, and z, whose sum has the constant value S, is maximum when the three numbers are equal. Use this result to prove that

$$\sqrt[3]{xyz} \le \frac{x + y + z}{3}.$$

  b. Generalize the result of part a to prove that the product $x_1 x_2 x_3 \cdots x_n$ is maximum when $x_1 = x_2 = x_3 = \cdots = x_n$, $\sum_{i=1}^{n} x_i = S$, and all $x_i \ge 0$. Use this result to prove that

$$\sqrt[n]{x_1 x_2 x_3 \cdots x_n} \le \frac{x_1 + x_2 + x_3 + \cdots + x_n}{n}.$$

  This shows that the geometric mean is never greater than the arithmetic mean.

35. *Refraction of Light* When light waves traveling in a transparent medium strike the surface of a second transparent medium, they tend to "bend" in order to follow the path of minimum time. This tendency is called refraction and is described by **Snell's Law of Refraction,**

$$\frac{\sin \theta_1}{v_1} = \frac{\sin \theta_2}{v_2}$$

where θ_1 and θ_2 are the magnitudes of the angles shown in the figure, and v_1 and v_2 are the velocities of light in the two media. Use Lagrange multipliers to derive this law using the constraint $x + y = a$.

36. *Area and Perimeter* A semicircle is situated on top of a rectangle (see figure). If the area is fixed and the perimeter is minimum, or if the perimeter is fixed and the area is maximum, use Lagrange multipliers to verify that the length of the rectangle is twice its height.

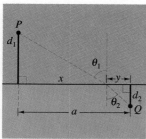

FIGURE FOR 35   **FIGURE FOR 36**

C **37.** Consider the function $g(\alpha, \beta, \gamma) = \cos \alpha \cos \beta \cos \gamma$ subject to the constraint that α, β and γ are the angles of a triangle.
  a. Use Lagrange multipliers to maximize g.
  b. Use the constraint to reduce the function g to a function of two independent variables. Use a computer algebra system to obtain a graph of the surface represented by g. Identify the maximum values on the graphs.

38. *Temperature Distribution* Let

$$T(x, y, z) = 100 + x^2 + y^2$$

represent the temperature at each point on the sphere $x^2 + y^2 + z^2 = 50$. Find the maximum temperature on the curve formed by the intersection of the sphere and the plane $x - z = 0$.

Production Level **In Exercises 39 and 40, find the maximum production level P if the total cost of labor (at \$48 per unit) and capital (at \$36 per unit) is limited to \$100,000.**

39. $P(x, y) = 100x^{0.25}y^{0.75}$
40. $P(x, y) = 100x^{0.6}y^{0.4}$

Cost **In Exercises 41 and 42, find the minimum cost of producing 20,000 units of a product, where x is the number of units of labor (at \$48 per unit) and y is the number of units of capital (at \$36 per unit).**

41. $P(x, y) = 100x^{0.25}y^{0.75}$
42. $P(x, y) = 100x^{0.6}y^{0.4}$

43. **a.** Maximize

$$\sum_{i=1}^{n} x_i y_i$$

  subject to

$$\sum_{i=1}^{n} x_i^2 = 1 \quad \text{and} \quad \sum_{i=1}^{n} y_i^2 = 1.$$

  b. Prove that

$$\sum_{i=1}^{n} a_i b_i \le \left(\sum_{i=1}^{n} a_i^2 \right)^{1/2} \left(\sum_{i=1}^{n} b_i^2 \right)^{1/2}$$

  for any numbers $a_1, \ldots, a_n$, and $b_1, \ldots, b_n$.

REVIEW EXERCISES for Chapter 13

In Exercises 1–4, sketch several level curves for the given function.

1. $f(x, y) = e^{x^2 + y^2}$ **2.** $f(x, y) = \ln xy$

3. $f(x, y) = x^2 - y^2$ **4.** $f(x, y) = \dfrac{x}{x + y}$

C In Exercises 5 and 6, use a graphing utility to graph the function.

5. $f(x, y) = e^{-(x^2 + y^2)}$ **6.** $g(x, y) = |y|^{1 + |x|}$

In Exercises 7–10, discuss the continuity of the function and evaluate the limit, if it exists.

7. $\displaystyle\lim_{(x, y) \to (1,1)} \frac{xy}{x^2 + y^2}$ **8.** $\displaystyle\lim_{(x, y) \to (1,1)} \frac{xy}{x^2 - y^2}$

9. $\displaystyle\lim_{(x, y) \to (0,0)} \frac{-4x^2 y}{x^4 + y^2}$ **10.** $\displaystyle\lim_{(x, y) \to (0,0)} \frac{y + xe^{-y^2}}{1 + x^2}$

In Exercises 11–20, find all first partial derivatives.

11. $f(x, y) = e^x \cos y$ **12.** $f(x, y) = \dfrac{xy}{x + y}$

13. $z = xe^y + ye^x$ **14.** $z = \ln(x^2 + y^2 + 1)$

15. $g(x, y) = \dfrac{xy}{x^2 + y^2}$ **16.** $w = \sqrt{x^2 + y^2 + z^2}$

17. $f(x, y, z) = z \arctan \dfrac{y}{x}$

18. $f(x, y, z) = \dfrac{1}{\sqrt{1 - x^2 - y^2 - z^2}}$

19. $u(x, t) = ce^{-n^2 t} \sin nx$ **20.** $u(x, t) = c \sin(akx) \cos kt$

In Exercises 21 and 22, find $\partial z / \partial x$ and $\partial z / \partial y$.

21. $x^2 y - 2yz - xz - z^2 = 0$

22. $xz^2 - y \sin z = 0$

In Exercises 23–26, find all second partial derivatives and verify that the second mixed partials are equal.

23. $f(x, y) = 3x^2 - xy + 2y^3$

24. $h(x, y) = \dfrac{x}{x + y}$

25. $h(x, y) = x \sin y + y \cos x$

26. $g(x, y) = \cos(x - 2y)$

Laplace Equation In Exercises 27–30, show that the function satisfies the Laplace equation

$$\frac{\partial^2 z}{\partial x^2} + \frac{\partial^2 z}{\partial y^2} = 0.$$

27. $z = x^2 - y^2$ **28.** $z = x^3 - 3xy^2$

29. $z = \dfrac{y}{x^2 + y^2}$ **30.** $z = e^x \sin y$

In Exercises 31 and 32, find dz.

31. $z = x \sin \dfrac{y}{x}$ **32.** $z = \dfrac{xy}{\sqrt{x^2 + y^2}}$

33. *Error Analysis* The legs of a right triangle are measured at 5 inches and 12 inches, with a possible error of $\frac{1}{16}$ inch. Approximate the maximum possible error in computing the length of the hypotenuse. Approximate the maximum percentage error.

34. *Error Analysis* To determine the height of a tower, the angle of elevation to the top of the tower was measured from a point $100 \pm \frac{1}{2}$ foot from the base. The angle is measured at 33°, with a possible error of 1°. Assuming the ground to be horizontal, approximate the maximum error in determining the height of the tower.

35. *Error Analysis* The volume of a right circular cone is $V = \frac{1}{3}\pi r^2 h$. Find the approximate error in the volume due to possible errors of $\frac{1}{8}$ inch in the measured values of r and h, if these are found to be 2 and 5 inches, respectively.

36. *Error Analysis* Approximate the error in the lateral surface area of the cone of Exercise 35. (The lateral surface area is given by $A = \pi r \sqrt{r^2 + h^2}$.)

In Exercises 37 and 38, find the required derivatives (a) by the Chain Rule and (b) by substitution before differentiation.

37. $u = x^2 + y^2 + z^2$, $\dfrac{\partial u}{\partial r}, \dfrac{\partial u}{\partial t}$ **38.** $u = y^2 - x$, $\dfrac{du}{dt}$

$x = r \cos t, \ y = r \sin t, \ z = t$ $x = \cos t, \ y = \sin t$

In Exercises 39–42, find the directional derivative in the direction of v at the specified point.

Function	Direction	Point
39. $f(x, y) = x^2 y$	$v = i - j$	$(2, 1)$
40. $f(x, y) = \frac{1}{4}y^2 - x^2$	$v = 2i + j$	$(1, 4)$
41. $w = y^2 + xz$	$v = 2i - j + 2k$	$(1, 2, 2)$
42. $w = 6x^2 + 3xy - 4y^2 z$	$v = i + j - k$	$(1, 0, 1)$

In Exercises 43–46, find the gradient and the maximum value of the directional derivative of the function at the specified point.

Function	Point
43. $z = \dfrac{y}{x^2 + y^2}$	$(1, 1)$
44. $z = \dfrac{x^2}{x - y}$	$(2, 1)$
45. $z = e^{-x} \cos y$	$\left(0, \dfrac{\pi}{4}\right)$
46. $z = x^2 y$	$(2, 1)$

In Exercises 47–50, find an equation of the tangent plane and equations for the normal line to the given surface at the specified point.

Surface	Point
47. $f(x, y) = x^2 y$	$(2, 1, 4)$
48. $f(x, y) = \sqrt{25 - y^2}$	$(2, 3, 4)$
49. $z = -9 + 4x - 6y - x^2 - y^2$	$(2, -3, 4)$
50. $z = \sqrt{9 - x^2 - y^2}$	$(1, 2, 2)$

In Exercises 51 and 52, find symmetric equations of the tangent line to the curve of intersection of the given surfaces at the indicated point.

Surfaces	Point
51. $z = x^2 - y^2, z = 3$	$(2, 1, 3)$
52. $z = 25 - y^2, y = x$	$(4, 4, 9)$

In Exercises 53–56, locate and classify any extrema of the function.

53. $f(x, y) = x^3 - 3xy + y^2$

54. $f(x, y) = 2x^2 + 6xy + 9y^2 + 8x + 14$

55. $f(x, y) = xy + \dfrac{1}{x} + \dfrac{1}{y}$

56. $z = 50(x + y) - (0.1x^3 + 20x + 150)$
$$- (0.05y^3 + 20.6y + 125)$$

Essay   **In Exercises 57 and 58, write a short paragraph about the surface whose level curves are given. Comment on possible extrema, saddle points, the magnitude of the gradient, etc.**

57.   **58.**

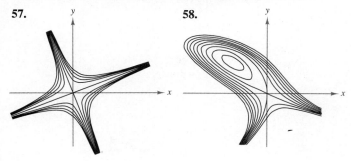

In Exercises 59 and 60, locate and classify any extrema of the function by using Lagrange multipliers.

59. $z = x^2 y$
Constraint: $x + 2y = 2$

60. $w = xy + yz + xz$
Constraint: $x + y + z = 1$

61. *Profit*   A corporation manufactures a product at two locations. The cost functions for producing x_1 units at location 1 and x_2 units at location 2 are given by

$$C_1 = 0.05x_1^2 + 15x_1 + 5400$$
$$C_2 = 0.03x_2^2 + 15x^2 + 6100$$

and the total revenue function is

$$R = [225 - 0.4(x_1 + x_2)](x_1 + x_2).$$

Find the production levels at the two locations that will maximize the profit $P(x_1, x_2) = R - C_1 - C_2$.

62. *Cost*   A manufacturer has an order for 1000 units that can be produced at two locations. Let x_1 and x_2 be the numbers of units produced at the two locations. Find the number that should be produced at each location to meet the order and minimize cost, if the cost function is

$$C = 0.25x_1^2 + 10x_1 + 0.15x_2^2 + 12x_2.$$

63. *Production Level*   The production function for a manufacturer is

$$f(x, y) = 4x + xy + 2y.$$

Assume that the total amount available for labor and capital is $2000, and that units of labor and capital cost $20 and $4, respectively. Find the maximum production level for this manufacturer.

64. *Motor Vehicle Sales*   The following table gives passenger car retail sales (y in millions) and truck and bus retail sales (x in millions) in the United States for selected years. (*Source:* U.S. Department of Commerce)

Year	1975	1980	1983	1984
Trucks/Buses (x)	2.4	2.2	2.7	3.5
Cars (y)	8.6	9.0	9.2	10.4

Year	1985	1986	1987	1988
Trucks/Buses (x)	4.0	4.0	4.2	4.6
Cars (y)	11.0	11.5	10.3	10.6

a. Find the least squares regression line for these data.
b. What information does the slope of the regression line give about the relationship between the sales of passenger cars and trucks?

65. *Aerodynamics*   The following table gives the drag force y in kilograms for a certain motor vehicle at specified speeds x in kilometers per hour.

Speed (x)	25	50	75	100	125
Drag (y)	28	38	54	75	102

a. Find the least squares regression quadratic for these data.
b. Use the quadratic to estimate the total drag when the vehicle is moving at 80 kilometers per hour.

True or False   **In Exercises 66–68, determine whether the statement is true or false. If it is false, explain why or give an example that shows it is false.**

66. Of all parallelepipeds having a fixed surface area, the cube has the largest volume.

67. The gradient $\nabla f(x_0, y_0)$ is normal to the surface given by $z = f(x, y)$ at the point (x_0, y_0, z_0).

68. The plane $x_0 x + y_0 y + z_0 z = c^2$ is tangent to the sphere $x^2 + y^2 + z^2 = c^2$ at the point (x_0, y_0, z_0).

14.1 Iterated Integrals • Area of a Plane Region

In Chapters 14 and 15, you will survey several applications of integration involving functions of several variables. Chapter 14 is much like Chapter 6 in that it surveys the use of integration to find plane areas, volumes, surface areas, moments, and centers of mass.

Iterated Integrals

In Chapter 13, you saw that it is meaningful to differentiate functions of several variables with respect to one variable while holding the other variables constant. You can *integrate* functions of several variables by a similar procedure. For example, if you are given the partial derivative $f_x(x, y) = 2xy$, then, by considering y constant, you can integrate with respect to x to obtain

$$f(x, y) = \int f_x(x, y)\, dx \qquad \text{Integrate with respect to } x$$

$$= \int 2xy\, dx \qquad y \text{ is held constant}$$

$$= y \int 2x\, dx \qquad \text{Factor out constant } y$$

$$= y(x^2) + C(y) \qquad \text{Antiderivative of } 2x \text{ is } x^2$$

$$= x^2y + C(y). \qquad C(y) \text{ is function of } y$$

Note that the "constant" of integration, $C(y)$, is a function of y. In other words, by integrating with respect to x, you are able to recover $f(x, y)$ only partially. The total recovery of a function of x and y from its partial derivatives is a topic you will study in Chapter 15. For now, we are more concerned with extending definite integrals to functions of several variables. For instance, by considering y constant, you can apply the Fundamental Theorem of Calculus to evaluate

$$\int_1^{2y} 2xy\, dx = x^2y \Big]_1^{2y} = (2y)^2y - (1)^2y = 4y^3 - y.$$

x is the variable of integration and y is fixed.

Replace x by the limits of integration.

The result is a function of y.

Similarly, you can integrate with respect to y by holding x fixed. Both procedures are summarized as follows.

$$\int_{h_1(y)}^{h_2(y)} f_x(x, y)\, dx = f(x, y) \Big]_{h_1(y)}^{h_2(y)} = f(h_2(y), y) - f(h_1(y), y)$$

$$\int_{g_1(x)}^{g_2(x)} f_y(x, y)\, dy = f(x, y) \Big]_{g_1(x)}^{g_2(x)} = f(x, g_2(x)) - f(x, g_1(x))$$

Note that the variable of integration cannot appear in either limit of integration. For instance, it makes no sense to write $\int_0^x y\, dx$.

◄ This photo shows the 1992 winner of the America's Cup. In Section 14.2, Exercise 62, you are asked to find the center of pressure of a sailboat's sail.

EXAMPLE 1   Integrating with Respect to y

Evaluate $\displaystyle\int_{1}^{x} (2x^2 y^{-2} + 2y)\, dy$.

Solution   Considering x to be constant and integrating with respect to y produces

$$\int_{1}^{x} (2x^2 y^{-2} + 2y)\, dy = \left[\frac{-2x^2}{y} + y^2 \right]_{1}^{x}$$

$$= \left(\frac{-2x^2}{x} + x^2 \right) - \left(\frac{-2x^2}{1} + 1 \right)$$

$$= 3x^2 - 2x - 1.$$

Notice in Example 1 that the integral defines a function of x and can *itself* be integrated, as shown in the next example.

EXAMPLE 2   The Integral of an Integral

Evaluate $\displaystyle\int_{1}^{2} \left[\int_{1}^{x} (2x^2 y^{-2} + 2y)\, dy \right] dx$.

Solution   Using the result of Example 1, you have

$$\int_{1}^{2} \left[\int_{1}^{x} (2x^2 y^{-2} + 2y)\, dy \right] dx = \int_{1}^{2} (3x^2 - 2x - 1)\, dx$$

$$= \left[x^3 - x^2 - x \right]_{1}^{2}$$

$$= 2 - (-1)$$

$$= 3.$$

The integral in Example 2 is an **iterated integral.** The brackets used in Example 2 are normally not written. Instead, iterated integrals are usually written simply as

$$\int_{a}^{b} \int_{g_1(x)}^{g_2(x)} f(x, y)\, dy\, dx \quad \text{and} \quad \int_{c}^{d} \int_{h_1(y)}^{h_2(y)} f(x, y)\, dx\, dy.$$

The **inside limits of integration** can be variable with respect to the outer variable of integration. However, the **outside limits of integration** must be constant with respect to both variables of integration. After performing the inside integration, you obtain a definite integral, and the second integration produces a real number. The limits of integration for an iterated integral identify two sets of boundary intervals for the variables. For instance, in Example 2, the outside limits indicate that x lies in the interval $1 \le x \le 2$ and the inside limits indicate that y lies in the interval $1 \le y \le x$. Together, these two intervals determine the **region of integration** R of the iterated integral, as shown in Figure 14.1.

Because an iterated integral is just a special type of definite integral—one in which the integrand is also an integral—you can use the properties of definite integrals to evaluate iterated integrals.

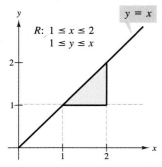

FIGURE 14.1

The region of integration for $\displaystyle\int_{1}^{2} \int_{1}^{x} f(x, y)\, dy\, dx$.

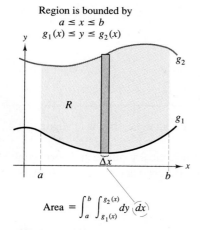

Region is bounded by
$a \leq x \leq b$
$g_1(x) \leq y \leq g_2(x)$

$\text{Area} = \int_a^b \int_{g_1(x)}^{g_2(x)} dy\, dx$

FIGURE 14.2
Vertically simple region

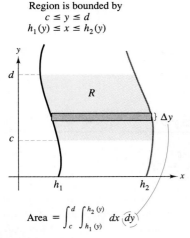

Region is bounded by
$c \leq y \leq d$
$h_1(y) \leq x \leq h_2(y)$

$\text{Area} = \int_c^d \int_{h_1(y)}^{h_2(y)} dx\, dy$

FIGURE 14.3
Horizontally simple region

Area of a Plane Region

In the remainder of this section, you will take a new look at an old problem—that of finding the area of a plane region. Consider the plane region R bounded by $a \leq x \leq b$ and $g_1(x) \leq y \leq g_2(x)$, as shown in Figure 14.2. The area of R is given by the definite integral

$$\int_a^b [g_2(x) - g_1(x)]\, dx. \qquad \text{Area of } R$$

Using the Fundamental Theorem of Calculus, you can rewrite the integrand $g_2(x) - g_1(x)$ as a definite integral. Specifically, if you consider x to be fixed and let y vary from $g_1(x)$ to $g_2(x)$, you can write

$$\int_{g_1(x)}^{g_2(x)} dy = y \bigg]_{g_1(x)}^{g_2(x)} = g_2(x) - g_1(x).$$

Combining these two integrals, you can write the area of the region R as an iterated integral

$$\int_a^b \int_{g_1(x)}^{g_2(x)} dy\, dx = \int_a^b y \bigg]_{g_1(x)}^{g_2(x)} dx \qquad \text{Area of } R$$

$$= \int_a^b [g_2(x) - g_1(x)]\, dx.$$

Placing a representative rectangle in the region R helps determine both the order and the limits of integration. A vertical rectangle implies the order $dy\, dx$, with the inside limits corresponding to the upper and lower bounds of the rectangle, as shown in Figure 14.2. This type of region is called **vertically simple,** because the outside limits of integration represent the vertical lines $x = a$ and $x = b$.

Similarly, a horizontal rectangle implies the order $dx\, dy$, with the inside limits determined by the left and right bounds of the rectangle, as shown in Figure 14.3. This type of region is called **horizontally simple,** because the outside limits represent the horizontal lines $y = c$ and $y = d$. The iterated integrals used for these two types of simple regions are summarized as follows.

Area of a Region in the Plane

1. If R is defined by $a \leq x \leq b$ and $g_1(x) \leq y \leq g_2(x)$, where g_1 and g_2 are continuous on $[a, b]$, then the area of R is given by

$$A = \int_a^b \int_{g_1(x)}^{g_2(x)} dy\, dx. \qquad \text{Figure 14.2 (vertically simple)}$$

2. If R is defined by $c \leq y \leq d$ and $h_1(y) \leq x \leq h_2(y)$, where h_1 and h_2 are continuous on $[c, d]$, then the area of R is given by

$$A = \int_c^d \int_{h_1(y)}^{h_2(y)} dx\, dy. \qquad \text{Figure 14.3 (horizontally simple)}$$

REMARK Be sure you see that the order of integration of these two integrals is different—the order $dy\, dx$ corresponds to a vertically simple region, and the order $dx\, dy$ corresponds to a horizontally simple region.

If all four limits of integration happen to be constants, then the region of integration is rectangular, as shown in Example 3.

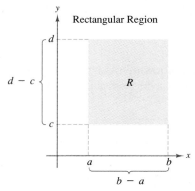

FIGURE 14.4

Area $= \displaystyle\int_a^b \int_c^d dy\, dx =$
$(d - c)(b - a)$.

EXAMPLE 3   The Area of a Rectangular Region

Use an iterated integral to represent the area of the rectangle shown in Figure 14.4.

Solution   The region shown in Figure 14.4 is both vertically simple and horizontally simple, so you can use either order of integration. By choosing the order $dy\, dx$, you obtain the following.

$$\int_a^b \int_c^d dy\, dx = \int_a^b \Big] y \Big]_c^d dx$$

$$= \int_a^b (d - c)\, dx$$

$$= (d - c)x \Big]_a^b$$

$$= (d - c)(b - a)$$

EXAMPLE 4   Finding Area by an Iterated Integral

Use an iterated integral to find the area of the region bounded by the graphs of $f(x) = \sin x$ and $g(x) = \cos x$ between $x = \pi/4$ and $x = 5\pi/4$.

Solution   Because f and g are given as functions of x, a vertical representative rectangle is convenient, and you can choose $dy\, dx$ as the order of integration, as shown in Figure 14.5. The outside limits of integration are $\pi/4 \le x \le 5\pi/4$. Moreover, because the rectangle is bounded above by $f(x) = \sin x$ and below by $g(x) = \cos x$, you have

$$\text{Area of } R = \int_{\pi/4}^{5\pi/4} \int_{\cos x}^{\sin x} dy\, dx$$

$$= \int_{\pi/4}^{5\pi/4} \Big] y \Big]_{\cos x}^{\sin x} dx$$

$$= \int_{\pi/4}^{5\pi/4} (\sin x - \cos x)\, dx$$

$$= \Big[-\cos x - \sin x \Big]_{\pi/4}^{5\pi/4}$$

$$= 2\sqrt{2}.$$

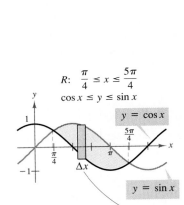

FIGURE 14.5

REMARK   The region of integration of an iterated integral need not have any straight lines as boundaries. For instance, the region of integration shown in Figure 14.5 is *vertically simple* even though it has no vertical lines as left and right boundaries. The quality that makes the region vertically simple is that it is bounded above and below by the graphs of *functions of x*.

One order of integration will often produce a simpler integration problem than the other order. For instance, try reworking Example 4 with the order $dx\,dy$—you may be surprised to see that the task is formidable! However, if you succeed, you will see that the answer is the same. In other words, the order of integration affects the ease of integration, but not the value of the integral.

EXAMPLE 5   Comparing Different Orders of Integration

Sketch the region whose area is represented by the integral

$$\int_0^2 \int_{y^2}^4 dx\,dy.$$

Then find another iterated integral using the order $dy\,dx$ to represent the same area, and show that both integrals yield the same value.

Solution   From the given limits of integration, you know that

$$y^2 \leq x \leq 4 \qquad \text{\small Inner limits of integration}$$

which means that the region R is bounded on the left by the parabola $x = y^2$ and on the right by the line $x = 4$. Furthermore, because

$$0 \leq y \leq 2 \qquad \text{\small Outer limits of integration}$$

you know that R is bounded below by the x-axis, as shown in Figure 14.6(a). The value of this integral is

$$\int_0^2 \int_{y^2}^4 dx\,dy = \int_0^2 x\Big]_{y^2}^4 dy$$

$$= \int_0^2 (4 - y^2)\,dy$$

$$= \left[4y - \frac{y^3}{3}\right]_0^2 = \frac{16}{3}.$$

To change the order of integration to $dy\,dx$, place a vertical rectangle in the region, as shown in Figure 14.6(b). From this you can see that the constant bounds $0 \leq x \leq 4$ serve as the outer limits of integration. By solving for y in the equation $x = y^2$, you can conclude that the inner bounds are $0 \leq y \leq \sqrt{x}$. Therefore, the area of the region can also be represented by

$$\int_0^4 \int_0^{\sqrt{x}} dy\,dx.$$

By evaluating this integral, you can see that it has the same value as the original integral.

$$\int_0^4 \int_0^{\sqrt{x}} dy\,dx = \int_0^4 y\Big]_0^{\sqrt{x}} dx$$

$$= \int_0^4 \sqrt{x}\,dx$$

$$= \frac{2}{3}x^{3/2}\Big]_0^4 = \frac{16}{3}$$

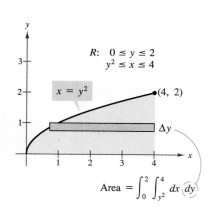

(a)

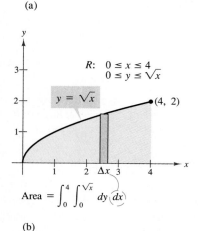

(b)

FIGURE 14.6

Sometimes it is not possible to calculate the area of a region with a single iterated integral. In such cases you can divide the region into subregions such that the area of each subregion can be calculated by an iterated integral. The total area is then the sum of the iterated integrals.

EXAMPLE 6   An Area Represented by Two Iterated Integrals

Find the area of the region R that lies below the parabola

$$y = 4x - x^2 \qquad \text{\small Parabola forms upper boundary}$$

above the x-axis, and above the line

$$y = -3x + 6 \qquad \text{\small x-axis and line form lower boundary}$$

as shown in Figure 14.7.

Solution   Begin by dividing R into the two subregions R_1 and R_2 shown in Figure 14.7. In both regions, it is convenient to use vertical rectangles, and you have

$$
\begin{aligned}
\text{Area} &= \int_1^2 \int_{-3x+6}^{4x-x^2} dy\,dx + \int_2^4 \int_0^{4x-x^2} dy\,dx \\[2mm]
&= \int_1^2 (4x - x^2 + 3x - 6)\,dx + \int_2^4 (4x - x^2)\,dx \\[2mm]
&= \left[\frac{7x^2}{2} - \frac{x^3}{3} - 6x \right]_1^2 + \left[2x^2 - \frac{x^3}{3} \right]_2^4 \\[2mm]
&= \left(14 - \frac{8}{3} - 12 - \frac{7}{2} + \frac{1}{3} + 6 \right) + \left(32 - \frac{64}{3} - 8 + \frac{8}{3} \right) \\[2mm]
&= \frac{15}{2}.
\end{aligned}
$$

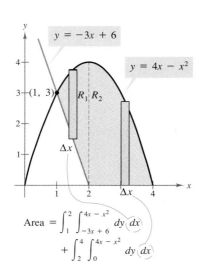

$$\text{Area} = \int_1^2 \int_{-3x+6}^{4x-x^2} dy\,dx$$
$$+ \int_2^4 \int_0^{4x-x^2} dy\,dx$$

FIGURE 14.7

REMARK   In Examples 3–6, be sure you see the benefit of sketching the region of integration. We strongly recommend that you develop the habit of making sketches to help determine the limits of integration for all iterated integrals in this chapter.

At this point you may be wondering why you would need iterated integrals. After all, you already know how to use conventional integration to find the area of a region in the plane. (For instance, compare the solution of Example 4 in this section with that given in Example 3 in Section 6.1.) The need for iterated integrals will become clear in the next section. In this section, we have chosen to give primary attention to procedures for finding the limits of integration of the region of an iterated integral, and the following exercise set is designed to develop skill in this important procedure.

EXERCISES for Section 14.1

In Exercises 1–10, evaluate the integral.

1. $\int_0^x (2x - y)\, dy$

2. $\int_x^{x^2} \frac{y}{x}\, dy$

3. $\int_1^{2y} \frac{y}{x}\, dx$

4. $\int_0^{\cos y} y\, dx$

5. $\int_0^{\sqrt{4-x^2}} x^2 y\, dy$

6. $\int_{x^2}^{\sqrt{x}} (x^2 + y^2)\, dy$

7. $\int_{e^y}^y \frac{y \ln x}{x}\, dx$

8. $\int_{-\sqrt{1-y^2}}^{\sqrt{1-y^2}} (x^2 + y^2)\, dx$

$\quad + y^2)\, dx$

9. $\int_0^{x^3} ye^{-y/x}\, dy$

10. $\int_y^{\pi/2} \sin^3 x \cos y\, dx$

In Exercises 11–20, evaluate the iterated integral.

11. $\int_0^1 \int_0^2 (x + y)\, dy\, dx$

12. $\int_0^1 \int_0^x \sqrt{1 - x^2}\, dy\, dx$

13. $\int_1^2 \int_0^4 (x^2 - 2y^2 + 1)\, dx\, dy$

14. $\int_0^1 \int_y^{2y} (1 + 2x^2 + 2y^2)\, dx\, dy$

15. $\int_0^1 \int_0^{\sqrt{1-y^2}} (x + y)\, dx\, dy$

16. $\int_0^2 \int_{3y^2-6y}^{2y-y^2} 3y\, dx\, dy$

17. $\int_0^2 \int_0^{\sqrt{4-y^2}} \frac{2}{\sqrt{4 - y^2}}\, dx\, dy$

18. $\int_0^{\pi/2} \int_0^{2\cos\theta} r\, dr\, d\theta$

19. $\int_0^{\pi/2} \int_0^{\sin\theta} \theta r\, dr\, d\theta$

20. $\int_0^{\pi/4} \int_0^{\cos\theta} 3r^2 \sin\theta\, dr\, d\theta$

In Exercises 21–24, evaluate the improper iterated integral.

21. $\int_1^\infty \int_0^{1/x} y\, dy\, dx$

22. $\int_0^3 \int_0^\infty \frac{x^2}{1 + y^2}\, dy\, dx$

23. $\int_0^\infty \int_0^\infty xye^{-(x^2+y^2)}\, dx\, dy$

24. $\int_1^\infty \int_1^\infty \frac{1}{xy}\, dx\, dy$

In Exercises 25–28, sketch the region R of integration and switch the order of integration.

25. $\int_0^4 \int_0^y f(x, y)\, dx\, dy$

26. $\int_0^4 \int_{\sqrt{y}}^2 f(x, y)\, dx\, dy$

27. $\int_{-\pi/2}^{\pi/2} \int_0^{\cos x} f(x, y)\, dy\, dx$

28. $\int_{-1}^1 \int_{x^2}^1 f(x, y)\, dy\, dx$

In Exercises 29–36, sketch the region R whose area is given by the iterated integral. Then switch the order of integration and show that both orders yield the same area.

29. $\int_0^1 \int_0^2 dy\, dx$

30. $\int_1^2 \int_2^4 dx\, dy$

31. $\int_0^1 \int_{-\sqrt{1-y^2}}^{\sqrt{1-y^2}} dx\, dy$

32. $\int_0^2 \int_0^x dy\, dx + \int_2^4 \int_0^{4-x} dy\, dx$

33. $\int_0^2 \int_{x/2}^1 dy\, dx$

34. $\int_0^4 \int_{\sqrt{x}}^2 dy\, dx$

35. $\int_0^1 \int_{y^2}^{\sqrt[3]{y}} dx\, dy$

36. $\int_{-2}^2 \int_0^{4-y^2} dx\, dy$

In Exercises 37–42, use an iterated integral to find the area of the region.

37.

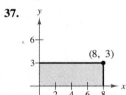

38.

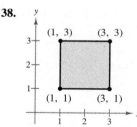

39.

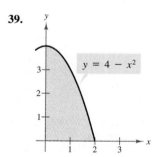

40.

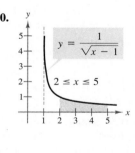

41.

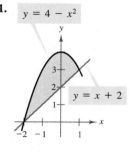

42.

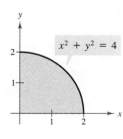

In Exercises 43–48, use an iterated integral to find the area of the region bounded by the graphs of the equations.

43. $\sqrt{x} + \sqrt{y} = 2$, $x = 0$, $y = 0$

44. $y = x^{3/2}$, $y = x$

45. $2x - 3y = 0$, $x + y = 5$, $y = 0$

46. $xy = 9$, $y = x$, $y = 0$, $x = 9$

47. $\dfrac{x^2}{a^2} + \dfrac{y^2}{b^2} = 1$

48. $y = x$, $y = 2x$, $x = 2$

In Exercises 49–52, evaluate the iterated integral. (Note that it is necessary to switch the order of integration.)

49. $\displaystyle\int_0^2 \int_x^2 x\sqrt{1 + y^3}\,dy\,dx$

50. $\displaystyle\int_0^2 \int_x^2 e^{-y^2}\,dy\,dx$

51. $\displaystyle\int_0^1 \int_y^1 \sin x^2\,dx\,dy$

52. $\displaystyle\int_0^2 \int_{y^2}^4 \sqrt{x}\sin x\,dx\,dy$

*C **In Exercises 53–56, use a computer to evaluate the iterated integral.**

53. $\displaystyle\int_0^2 \int_{x^2}^{2x} (x^3 + 3y^2)\,dy\,dx$

54. $\displaystyle\int_0^1 \int_y^{2y} \sin(x + y)\,dx\,dy$

55. $\displaystyle\int_0^4 \int_0^y \dfrac{2}{(x + 1)(y + 1)}\,dx\,dy$

56. $\displaystyle\int_0^a \int_0^{a-x} (x^2 + y^2)\,dy\,dx$

C **In Exercises 57 and 58, use a computer to approximate the iterated integral.**

57. $\displaystyle\int_0^2 \int_0^{4-x^2} e^{xy}\,dy\,dx$

58. $\displaystyle\int_0^2 \int_x^2 \sqrt{16 - x^3 - y^3}\,dy\,dx$

True or False **In Exercises 59 and 60, determine whether the statement is true or false. If it is false, explain why or give an example that shows it is false.**

59. $\displaystyle\int_a^b \int_c^d f(x, y)\,dy\,dx = \int_c^d \int_a^b f(x, y)\,dx\,dy$

60. $\displaystyle\int_0^1 \int_0^x f(x, y)\,dy\,dx = \int_0^1 \int_0^y f(x, y)\,dx\,dy$

Areas of Simple Closed Curves **In Exercises 61–66, match the closed curve with its area. (These exercises were adapted from the article "The Surveyor's Area Formula" by Bart Braden in the September, 1986 issue of the *College Mathematics Journal*.)**

61. Ellipse: $(0 \le t \le 2\pi)$
$x = b\cos t$
$y = a\sin t$

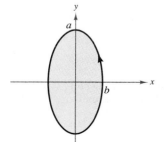

62. Astroid: $(0 \le t \le 2\pi)$
$x = a\cos^3 t$
$y = a\sin^3 t$

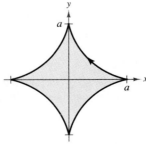

63. Cardioid: $(0 \le t \le 2\pi)$
$x = 2a\cos t - a\cos 2t$
$y = 2a\sin t - a\sin 2t$

64. Deltoid: $(0 \le t \le 2\pi)$
$x = 2a\cos t + a\cos 2t$
$y = 2a\sin t - a\sin 2t$

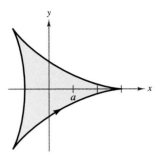

65. Hourglass: $(0 \le t \le 2\pi)$
$x = a\sin 2t$
$y = b\sin t$

66. Teardrop: $(0 \le t \le 2\pi)$
$x = 2a\cos t - a\sin 2t$
$y = b\sin t$

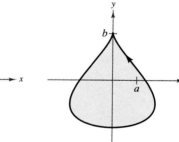

a. $\dfrac{8}{3}ab$ **b.** $\dfrac{3}{8}\pi a^2$ **c.** $2\pi a^2$

d. πab **e.** $2\pi ab$ **f.** $6\pi a^2$

---

*A C indicates an exercise in which you are instructed to use graphing technology or a symbolic computer algebra system. The solutions of other exercises may also be facilitated by appropriate technology.

14.2 Double Integrals and Volume of a Solid Region • Properties of Double Integrals • Evaluation of Double Integrals

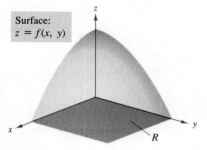

Surface:
$z = f(x, y)$

FIGURE 14.8

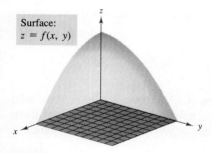

Surface:
$z = f(x, y)$

FIGURE 14.9
The inner partition of region R.

Double Integrals and Volume of a Solid Region

You already know that a definite integral over an *interval* uses a limit process to assign measure to quantities such as area, volume, arc length, and mass. In this section, we use a similar process to define the **double integral** of a function of two variables over a *region in the plane*.

Consider a continuous function f such that $f(x, y) \geq 0$ for all (x, y) in a region R in the xy-plane. The goal is to find the volume of the solid region lying between the surface given by $z = f(x, y)$ and the xy-plane, as shown in Figure 14.8. You can begin by superimposing a rectangular grid over the region, as shown in Figure 14.9. The rectangles lying entirely within R form an **inner partition,** Δ, whose **norm** $\| \Delta \|$ is defined as the length of the longest diagonal of the n rectangles. Next, choose a point (x_i, y_i) in each rectangle and form the rectangular prism whose height is $f(x_i, y_i)$, as shown in Figure 14.10. Because the area of the ith rectangle is $\Delta A_i = \Delta x_i \Delta y_i$, it follows that the volume of the ith prism is

$$f(x_i, y_i) \, \Delta A_i = f(x_i, y_i) \, \Delta x_i \, \Delta y_i \qquad \text{Volume of } i\text{th prism}$$

and you can approximate the volume of the solid region by the Riemann sum of the volumes of all n prisms,

$$\sum_{i=1}^{n} f(x_i, y_i) \, \Delta x_i \, \Delta y_i \qquad \text{Riemann sum}$$

as shown in Figure 14.11. This approximation can be improved by tightening the mesh of the grid to form smaller and smaller rectangles, as shown in Example 1.

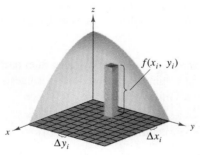

$f(x_i, y_i)$

Δy_i Δx_i

FIGURE 14.10

FIGURE 14.11
Volume approximated by rectangular prisms.

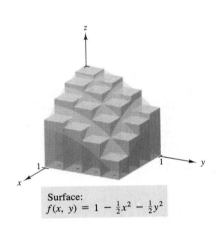

Surface:
$f(x, y) = 1 - \frac{1}{2}x^2 - \frac{1}{2}y^2$

FIGURE 14.12

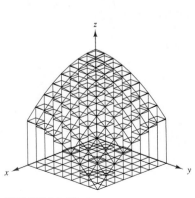

FIGURE 14.13

EXAMPLE 1   Approximating the Volume of a Solid

Approximate the volume of the solid lying between the paraboloid

$$f(x, y) = 1 - \frac{1}{2}x^2 - \frac{1}{2}y^2$$

and the square region R given by $0 \leq x \leq 1, 0 \leq y \leq 1$. Use a partition made up of squares whose edges have a length of $\frac{1}{4}$.

Solution   Begin by forming the specified partition of R. For this partition, it is convenient to choose the centers of the subregions as the points at which to evaluate $f(x, y)$.

$(\frac{1}{8}, \frac{1}{8})$	$(\frac{1}{8}, \frac{3}{8})$	$(\frac{1}{8}, \frac{5}{8})$	$(\frac{1}{8}, \frac{7}{8})$
$(\frac{3}{8}, \frac{1}{8})$	$(\frac{3}{8}, \frac{3}{8})$	$(\frac{3}{8}, \frac{5}{8})$	$(\frac{3}{8}, \frac{7}{8})$
$(\frac{5}{8}, \frac{1}{8})$	$(\frac{5}{8}, \frac{3}{8})$	$(\frac{5}{8}, \frac{5}{8})$	$(\frac{5}{8}, \frac{7}{8})$
$(\frac{7}{8}, \frac{1}{8})$	$(\frac{7}{8}, \frac{3}{8})$	$(\frac{7}{8}, \frac{5}{8})$	$(\frac{7}{8}, \frac{7}{8})$

Because the area of each square is $\Delta x_i \Delta y_i = \frac{1}{16}$, you can approximate the volume by the sum

$$\sum_{i=1}^{16} f(x_i, y_i) \Delta x_i \Delta y_i = \sum_{i=1}^{16} \left(1 - \frac{1}{2}x_i^2 - \frac{1}{2}y_i^2\right)\left(\frac{1}{16}\right) \approx 0.672.$$

This approximation is shown graphically in Figure 14.12. The exact volume of the solid is $\frac{2}{3}$ (see Example 2). You can obtain a better approximation by using a finer partition. For example, with a partition of squares with sides of length $\frac{1}{10}$, the approximation is 0.668.

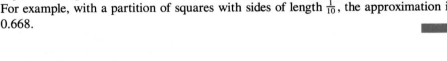

REMARK   Some three-dimensional graphing utilities are capable of sketching figures such as that shown in Figure 14.12. For instance, the sketch shown in Figure 14.13 was drawn with a computer program. In this sketch, note that each of the rectangular prisms lies within the solid region.

In Example 1, note that by using finer partitions, you can obtain better approximations of the volume. This observation suggests that you could obtain the exact volume by taking a limit. That is,

$$\text{Volume} = \lim_{\|\Delta\| \to 0} \sum_{i=1}^{n} f(x_i, y_i) \Delta x_i \Delta y_i.$$

The precise meaning of this limit is that the limit is equal to L if for every $\varepsilon > 0$ there exists a $\delta > 0$ such that

$$\left| L - \sum_{i=1}^{n} f(x_i, y_i) \Delta x_i \Delta y_i \right| < \varepsilon$$

for all partitions Δ of the plane region R (that satisfy $\|\Delta\| < \delta$) and for all possible choices of x_i and y_i in the ith region.

Using the limit of a Riemann sum to define volume is a special case of using the limit to define a **double integral**. The general case, however, does not require that the function be positive or continuous.

REMARK Having defined a double integral, we will occasionally refer to a definite integral as a **single integral.**

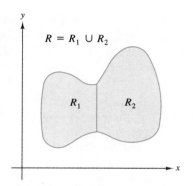

FIGURE 14.14

Two regions are nonoverlapping if their intersection is a set that has an area of 0. In this figure, the area of the line segment that is common to R_1 and R_2 is 0.

Definition of Double Integral

If f is defined on a closed, bounded region R in the xy-plane, then the **double integral of f over R** is given by

$$\iint_R f(x, y)\, dA = \lim_{\|\Delta\| \to 0} \sum_{i=1}^{n} f(x_i, y_i)\, \Delta x_i\, \Delta y_i$$

provided the limit exists. If the limit exists, then f is **integrable** over R.

Sufficient conditions for the double integral of f on the region R to exist are that R can be written as the union of a finite number of nonoverlapping (see Figure 14.14) subregions that are vertically or horizontally simple *and* that f is continuous on the region R.

A double integral can be used to find the volume of a solid region that lies between the xy-plane and the surface given by $z = f(x, y)$.

Volume of a Solid Region

If f is integrable over a plane region R and $f(x, y) \geq 0$ for all (x, y) in R, then the volume of the solid region that lies above R and below the graph of f is defined as

$$V = \iint_R f(x, y)\, dA.$$

Properties of Double Integrals

Double integrals share many properties of single integrals.

THEOREM 14.1 Properties of Double Integrals

Let f and g be continuous over a closed, bounded plane region R, and let c be a constant.

1. $\displaystyle \iint_R c f(x, y)\, dA = c \iint_R f(x, y)\, dA$

2. $\displaystyle \iint_R [f(x, y) \pm g(x, y)]\, dA = \iint_R f(x, y)\, dA \pm \iint_R g(x, y)\, dA$

3. $\displaystyle \iint_R f(x, y)\, dA \geq 0, \quad \text{if } f(x, y) \geq 0$

4. $\displaystyle \iint_R f(x, y)\, dA \geq \iint_R g(x, y)\, dA, \quad \text{if } f(x, y) \geq g(x, y)$

5. $\displaystyle \iint_R f(x, y)\, dA = \iint_{R_1} f(x, y)\, dA + \iint_{R_2} f(x, y)\, dA$

where R is the union of two nonoverlapping subregions R_1 and R_2.

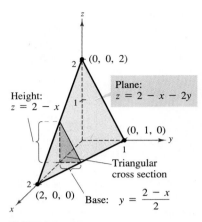

Height:
$z = 2 - x$

Plane:
$z = 2 - x - 2y$

(0, 0, 2)

(0, 1, 0)

Triangular cross section

(2, 0, 0)   Base: $y = \dfrac{2 - x}{2}$

FIGURE 14.15

Volume: $\displaystyle\int_0^2 A(x)\,dx$

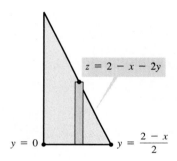

$z = 2 - x - 2y$

$y = 0$ $y = \dfrac{2 - x}{2}$

FIGURE 14.16
Triangular cross section

Evaluation of Double Integrals

Normally, the first step in evaluating a double integral is to rewrite it as an iterated integral. To show how this is done, we use a geometric model of a double integral as the volume of a solid.

Consider the solid region bounded by the plane $z = f(x, y) = 2 - x - 2y$ and the three coordinate planes, as shown in Figure 14.15. Each vertical cross section taken parallel to the yz-plane is a triangular region whose base has a length of $y = (2 - x)/2$ and whose height is $z = 2 - x$. This implies that for a fixed value of x, the area of the triangular cross section is

$$A(x) = \frac{1}{2}(\text{base})(\text{height}) = \frac{1}{2}\left(\frac{2 - x}{2}\right)(2 - x) = \frac{(2 - x)^2}{4}.$$

By the formula for the volume of a solid with known cross sections (Section 6.2), the volume of the solid is

$$\text{Volume} = \int_a^b A(x)\,dx = \int_0^2 \frac{(2 - x)^2}{4}\,dx = -\frac{(2 - x)^3}{12}\bigg]_0^2 = \frac{8}{12} = \frac{2}{3}.$$

This procedure works no matter how $A(x)$ is obtained. In particular, you can find $A(x)$ by integration, as indicated in Figure 14.16. That is, you consider x to be constant, and integrate $z = 2 - x - 2y$ from 0 to $(2 - x)/2$ to obtain

$$\begin{aligned}
A(x) &= \int_0^{(2-x)/2} (2 - x - 2y)\,dy \\
&= (2 - x)y - y^2 \bigg]_0^{(2-x)/2} \\
&= \frac{(2 - x)^2}{4}.
\end{aligned}$$

Combining these results, you have the *iterated integral*

$$\text{Volume} = \iint_R f(x, y)\,dA = \int_0^2 \int_0^{(2-x)/2} (2 - x - 2y)\,dy\,dx.$$

To better understand this procedure, it helps to imagine the integration as two sweeping motions. For the inner integration, a vertical line sweeps out the area of a cross section. For the outer integration, the triangular cross section sweeps out the volume, as shown in Figure 14.17.

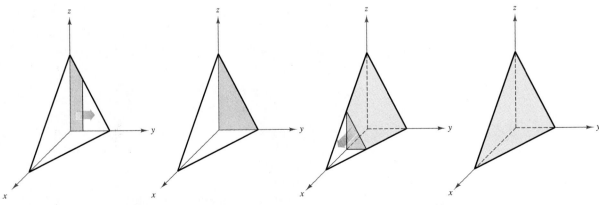

Integrate with respect to y to
obtain the area of the cross section.

Integrate with respect to x to
obtain the volume of the solid.

FIGURE 14.17

The following theorem was proved by the Italian mathematician Guido Fubini (1879–1943). The theorem states that if R is a vertically or horizontally simple region and f is continuous on R, then the double integral of f on R is equal to an iterated integral.

THEOREM 14.2   Fubini's Theorem

Let f be continuous on a plane region R.

1. If R is defined by $a \le x \le b$ and $g_1(x) \le y \le g_2(x)$, where g_1 and g_2 are continuous on $[a, b]$, then

$$\iint_R f(x, y)\, dA = \int_a^b \int_{g_1(x)}^{g_2(x)} f(x, y)\, dy\, dx.$$

2. If R is defined by $c \le y \le d$ and $h_1(y) \le x \le h_2(y)$, where h_1 and h_2 are continuous on $[c, d]$, then

$$\iint_R f(x, y)\, dA = \int_c^d \int_{h_1(y)}^{h_2(y)} f(x, y)\, dx\, dy.$$

EXAMPLE 2   Evaluating a Double Integral as an Iterated Integral

Evaluate

$$\iint_R \left(1 - \frac{1}{2}x^2 - \frac{1}{2}y^2\right) dA$$

where R is the region given by $0 \le x \le 1,\, 0 \le y \le 1$.

Solution   Because the region R is a simple square, it is both vertically and horizontally simple, and you can use either order of integration. Suppose you choose $dy\, dx$ by placing a vertical representative rectangle in the region, as shown in Figure 14.18. This produces the following.

$$\iint_R \left(1 - \frac{1}{2}x^2 - \frac{1}{2}y^2\right) dA = \int_0^1 \int_0^1 \left(1 - \frac{1}{2}x^2 - \frac{1}{2}y^2\right) dy\, dx$$

$$= \int_0^1 \left[\left(1 - \frac{1}{2}x^2\right)y - \frac{y^3}{6}\right]_0^1 dx$$

$$= \int_0^1 \left(\frac{5}{6} - \frac{1}{2}x^2\right) dx = \left[\frac{5}{6}x - \frac{x^3}{6}\right]_0^1 = \frac{2}{3}$$

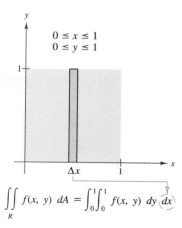

$0 \le x \le 1$
$0 \le y \le 1$

$$\iint_R f(x, y)\, dA = \int_0^1 \int_0^1 f(x, y)\, dy\, dx$$

FIGURE 14.18
The volume of the solid region is $\frac{2}{3}$.

REMARK   The double integral evaluated in Example 2 represents the volume of the solid region approximated in Example 1. Note that the approximation obtained in Example 1 is quite good (0.672 vs. $\frac{2}{3}$), even though we used a partition consisting of only 16 squares. The error resulted because we used the centers of the square subregions as the points in the approximation. This is comparable to the Midpoint Rule approximation of a single integral.

EXAMPLE 5   Volume of a Region Bounded by Two Surfaces

Find the volume of the solid region R bounded above by the paraboloid $z = 1 - x^2 - y^2$ and below by the plane $z = 1 - y$, as shown in Figure 14.22.

Solution   Equating z-values, you can determine that the intersection of the two surfaces occurs on the right circular cylinder given by

$$1 - y = 1 - x^2 - y^2 \quad \longrightarrow \quad x^2 = y - y^2.$$

Because the volume of R is the difference between the volume under the paraboloid and the volume under the plane, you have

$$\text{Volume} = \int_0^1 \int_{-\sqrt{y-y^2}}^{\sqrt{y-y^2}} (1 - x^2 - y^2)\, dx\, dy - \int_0^1 \int_{-\sqrt{y-y^2}}^{\sqrt{y-y^2}} (1 - y)\, dx\, dy$$

$$= \int_0^1 \int_{-\sqrt{y-y^2}}^{\sqrt{y-y^2}} (y - y^2 - x^2)\, dx\, dy$$

$$= \int_0^1 \left[(y - y^2)x - \frac{x^3}{3} \right]_{-\sqrt{y-y^2}}^{\sqrt{y-y^2}} dy$$

$$= \frac{4}{3} \int_0^1 (y - y^2)^{3/2}\, dy$$

$$= \left(\frac{4}{3} \right)\left(\frac{1}{8} \right) \int_0^1 [1 - (2y - 1)^2]^{3/2}\, dy$$

$$= \frac{1}{6} \int_{-\pi/2}^{\pi/2} \frac{\cos^4 \theta}{2}\, d\theta \qquad\qquad 2y - 1 = \sin\theta$$

$$= \frac{1}{6} \int_0^{\pi/2} \cos^4 \theta\, d\theta = \left(\frac{1}{6} \right)\left(\frac{3\pi}{16} \right)$$

$$= \frac{\pi}{32}. \qquad\qquad\qquad \text{Wallis's Formula}$$

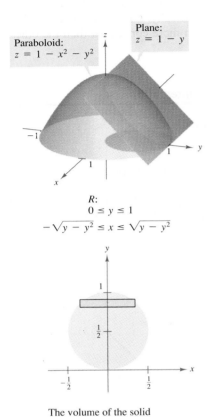

Paraboloid:
$z = 1 - x^2 - y^2$

Plane:
$z = 1 - y$

R:
$0 \le y \le 1$
$-\sqrt{y - y^2} \le x \le \sqrt{y - y^2}$

The volume of the solid region is $\pi/32$.

FIGURE 14.22

EXERCISES for Section 14.2

In Exercises 1–4, approximate the integral

$$\int_R \int f(x, y)\, dA$$

by dividing the rectangle R with vertices $(0, 0)$, $(4, 0)$, $(4, 2)$, and $(0, 2)$ into eight equal squares and finding the sum

$$\sum_{i=1}^{8} f(x_i, y_i)\, \Delta x_i\, \Delta y_i$$

where (x_i, y_i) is the center of the ith square. Evaluate the double integral and compare it with the approximation.

1. $\displaystyle \int_0^4 \int_0^2 (x + y)\, dy\, dx$ **2.** $\displaystyle \int_0^4 \int_0^2 xy\, dy\, dx$

3. $\displaystyle \int_0^4 \int_0^2 (x^2 + y^2)\, dy\, dx$ **4.** $\displaystyle \int_0^4 \int_0^2 \frac{1}{(x + 1)(y + 1)}\, dy\, dx$

5. Let R be a region in the xy-plane whose area is B. If $f(x, y) = k$ for every point (x, y) in R, then what is the value of

$$\int_R \int f(x, y)\, dA?$$

6. Let R represent a county in the northern part of the United States, and let $f(x, y)$ represent the total annual snowfall at the point (x, y) in R. Give an interpretation of each of the following.

a. $\displaystyle \int_R \int f(x, y)\, dA$ **b.** $\displaystyle \frac{\int_R \int f(x, y)\, dA}{\int_R \int dA}$

In Exercises 7–12, sketch the region R and evaluate the double integral

$$\int_R \int f(x,y)\, dA.$$

7. $\displaystyle \int_0^2 \int_0^1 (1 + 2x + 2y)\, dy\, dx$

8. $\displaystyle \int_0^\pi \int_0^{\pi/2} \sin^2 x \cos^2 y\, dy\, dx$

9. $\displaystyle \int_0^6 \int_{y/2}^3 (x + y)\, dx\, dy$

10. $\displaystyle \int_0^1 \int_y^{\sqrt{y}} x^2 y^2\, dx\, dy$

11. $\displaystyle \int_{-a}^a \int_{-\sqrt{a^2-x^2}}^{\sqrt{a^2-x^2}} (x + y)\, dy\, dx$

12. $\displaystyle \int_0^1 \int_{y-1}^0 e^{x+y}\, dx\, dy + \int_0^1 \int_0^{1-y} e^{x+y}\, dx\, dy$

In Exercises 13–18, set up the integral for both orders of integration, and use the more convenient order to evaluate the integral over the region R.

13. $\displaystyle \int_R \int xy\, dA$
R: rectangle with vertices $(0, 0)$, $(0, 5)$, $(3, 5)$, and $(3, 0)$

14. $\displaystyle \int_R \int \sin x \sin y\, dA$
R: rectangle with vertices $(-\pi, 0)$, $(\pi, 0)$, $(\pi, \pi/2)$, and $(-\pi, \pi/2)$

15. $\displaystyle \int_R \int \frac{y}{x^2 + y^2}\, dA$
R: triangle bounded by $y = x$, $y = 2x$, $x = 2$

16. $\displaystyle \int_R \int \frac{y}{1 + x^2}\, dA$
R: region bounded by $y = 0$, $y = \sqrt{x}$, $x = 4$

17. $\displaystyle \int_R \int x\, dA$
R: sector of a circle in the first quadrant bounded by $y = \sqrt{25 - x^2}$, $3x - 4y = 0$, $y = 0$

18. $\displaystyle \int_R \int (x^2 + y^2)\, dA$
R: semicircle bounded by $y = \sqrt{4 - x^2}$, $y = 0$

In Exercises 19–28, use a double integral to find the volume of the specified solid.

19.

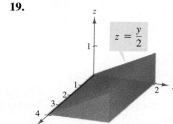

$0 \le x \le 4$
$0 \le y \le 2$

20.

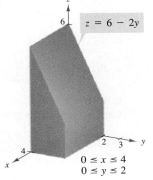

$0 \le x \le 4$
$0 \le y \le 2$

21.

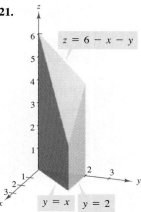

22.

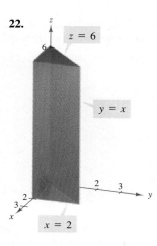

23.

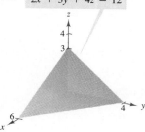

$2x + 3y + 4z = 12$

24.

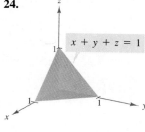

25.

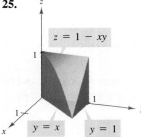

26.

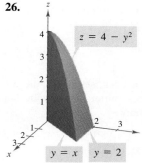

27. Improper integral

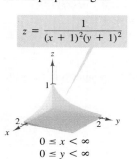

$0 \le x < \infty$
$0 \le y < \infty$

28. Improper integral

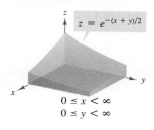

$0 \le x < \infty$
$0 \le y < \infty$

C In Exercises 29 and 30, use a symbolic integration utility to find the volume of the solid region.

29.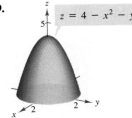

30.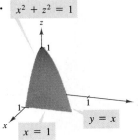

In Exercises 31–38, use a double integral to find the volume of the solid bounded by the graphs of the equations.

31. $z = xy, z = 0, y = x, x = 1$ (first octant)

32. $y = 0, z = 0, y = x, z = x, x = 0, x = 5$

33. $z = 0, z = x^2, x = 0, x = 2, y = 0, y = 4$

34. $x^2 + y^2 + z^2 = r^2$

35. $x^2 + z^2 = 1, y^2 + z^2 = 1$ (first octant)

36. $y = 1 - x^2, z = 1 - x^2$ (first octant)

37. $z = x + y, x^2 + y^2 = 4$ (first octant)

38. $z = \dfrac{1}{1 + y^2}, x = 0, x = 2, y \geq 0$

Wallis's Formula   In Exercises 39 and 40, use Wallis's Formula as an aid in finding the volume of the solid bounded by the graph of the equations.

39. $z = x^2 + y^2, x^2 + y^2 = 4, z = 0$

40. $z = \sin^2 x, z = 0, 0 \leq x \leq \pi, 0 \leq y \leq 5$

C In Exercises 41–44, use a symbolic integration utility to find the volume of the solid bounded by the graphs of the equations.

41. $z = 4 - x^2 - y^2, z = 0$

42. $x^2 = 9 - y, z^2 = 9 - y$ (first octant)

43. $z = \dfrac{2}{1 + x^2 + y^2}, z = 0, y = 0, x = 0, y = -0.5x + 1$

44. $z = \ln(1 + x + y), z = 0, y = 0, x = 0, x = 4 - \sqrt{y}$

45. If f is a continuous function such that $0 \leq f(x, y) \leq 1$ over a region R of area 1, prove that

$$0 \leq \int\int_R f(x, y)\, dA \leq 1.$$

46. Find the volume of the solid in the first octant bounded by the coordinate planes and the plane

$$\frac{x}{a} + \frac{y}{b} + \frac{z}{c} = 1$$

where $a > 0, b > 0,$ and $c > 0.$

In Exercises 47–50, evaluate the iterated integral. (Note that it is necessary to switch the order of integration.)

47. $\displaystyle\int_0^1 \int_{y/2}^{1/2} e^{-x^2}\, dx\, dy$

48. $\displaystyle\int_0^1 \int_0^{\arccos y} \sin x \sqrt{1 + \sin^2 x}\, dx\, dy$

49. $\displaystyle\int_0^{\ln 10} \int_{e^x}^{10} \frac{1}{\ln y}\, dy\, dx$

50. $\displaystyle\int_0^2 \int_{x^2}^4 \sqrt{y} \cos y\, dy\, dx$

In Exercises 51–54, find the average value of $f(x, y)$ over the region R where

$$\text{Average} = \frac{1}{A}\int\int_R f(x, y)\, dA$$

and where A is the area of $R.$

51. $f(x, y) = x$
   R: rectangle with vertices $(0, 0), (4, 0), (4, 2),$ and $(0, 2)$

52. $f(x, y) = xy$
   R: rectangle with vertices $(0, 0), (4, 0), (4, 2),$ and $(0, 2)$

53. $f(x, y) = x^2 + y^2$
   R: square with vertices $(0, 0), (2, 0), (2, 2),$ and $(0, 2)$

54. $f(x, y) = e^{x+y}$
   R: triangle with vertices $(0, 0), (0, 1),$ and $(1, 1)$

55. *Average Production*   The Cobb-Douglas production function for a company is

$$f(x, y) = 100x^{0.6}y^{0.4}.$$

Estimate the average production level if the number of units of labor varies between 200 and 250 and the number of units of capital varies between 300 and 325.

C 56. *Average Profit*   A firm's profit in marketing two products is

$$P = 192x + 576y - x^2 - 5y^2 - 2xy - 5000$$

where x and y represent the number of units of each product. Use a computer algebra system to evaluate the double integral yielding the average weekly profit if x varies between 40 and 50 units and y varies between 45 and 60 units.

Probability   A joint density function of the continuous random variables x and y is a function $f(x, y)$ satisfying the following properties.

a. $f(x, y) \geq 0$ for all (x, y)

b. $\displaystyle\int_{-\infty}^{\infty} \int_{-\infty}^{\infty} f(x, y)\, dA = 1$

c. $P[(x, y) \in R] = \displaystyle\int\int_R f(x, y)\, dA$

In Exercises 57–60, show that the function is a joint density function and find the required probability.

57. $f(x, y) = \begin{cases} \frac{1}{10}, & 0 \leq x \leq 5, 0 \leq y \leq 2 \\ 0, & \text{elsewhere} \end{cases}$
   $P(0 \leq x \leq 2, 1 \leq y \leq 2)$

58. $f(x, y) = \begin{cases} \frac{1}{4}xy, & 0 \le x \le 2, 0 \le y \le 2 \\ 0, & \text{elsewhere} \end{cases}$

$P(0 \le x \le 1, 1 \le y \le 2)$

59. $f(x, y) = \begin{cases} \frac{1}{27}(9 - x - y), & 0 \le x \le 3, 3 \le y \le 6 \\ 0, & \text{elsewhere} \end{cases}$

$P(0 \le x \le 1, 4 \le y \le 6)$

60. $f(x, y) = \begin{cases} e^{-(x-y)}, & x \ge 0, y \ge 0 \\ 0, & \text{elsewhere} \end{cases}$

$P(0 \le x \le 1, x \le y \le 1)$

61. *Center of Pressure on a Sail* Perform the required integrations to verify that the center of pressure on a triangular sail with vertices at $(0, 0)$, $(2, 1)$, and $(0, 5)$ is $(x_p, y_p) = (\frac{7}{12}, \frac{31}{12})$, where

$$x_p = \frac{\displaystyle\iint_R xy\,dA}{\displaystyle\iint_R y\,dA} \quad \text{and} \quad y_p = \frac{\displaystyle\iint_R y^2\,dA}{\displaystyle\iint_R y\,dA}.$$

C **62.** *Center of Pressure on a Sail* Repeat Exercise 61 for a sail with vertices at $(0, 0)$, $(3, 1)$, and $(0, 7)$. Use a computer algebra system to perform the required double integrations.

C **63.** Consider a continuous function $f(x, y)$ over the rectangular region R with vertices $(0, 0)$, $(a, 0)$, (a, b), and $(0, b)$. Partition the intervals $[0, a]$ and $[0, b]$ into m and n subintervals, respectively, so that the subintervals in a given direction are of equal length. Write a computer program to compute the sum

$$\sum_{i=1}^{m}\sum_{j=1}^{n} f(x_i, y_j)\,\Delta x_i\,\Delta y_j \approx \int_0^a \int_0^b f(x, y)\,dA$$

where (x_i, y_j) is the center of a representative rectangle in R.

C **64.** Consider the double integral

$$\int_0^1 \int_0^2 \sin\sqrt{x + y}\,dy\,dx.$$

a. Use a computer algebra system to approximate the double integral.

b. Use the program from Exercise 63 to approximate the integral when $m = 4$ and $n = 8$.

In Exercises 65 and 66, determine which value best approximates the volume of the solid between the *xy*-plane and the function over the region. (Make your selection on the basis of a sketch of the solid and *not* by performing any calculations.)

65. $f(x, y) = 4x$

R: square with vertices $(0, 0)$, $(4, 0)$, $(4, 4)$, and $(0, 4)$

a. -200　　**b.** 600　　**c.** 50　　**d.** 125　　**e.** 1000

66. $f(x, y) = \sqrt{x^2 + y^2}$

R: circle bounded by $x^2 + y^2 = 9$

a. 50　　**b.** 500　　**c.** -500　　**d.** 5　　**e.** 5000

True or False **In Exercises 67 and 68, determine whether the statement is true or false. If it is false, explain why or give an example that shows it is false.**

67. The volume of the sphere $x^2 + y^2 + z^2 = 1$ is given by the integral

$$V = 8 \int_0^1 \int_0^1 \sqrt{1 - x^2 - y^2}\,dx\,dy.$$

68. If $f(x, y) \le g(x, y)$ for all (x, y) in R, and both f and g are continuous over R, then

$$\iint_R f(x, y)\,dA \le \iint_R g(x, y)\,dA.$$

69. *Essay* From 1963 to 1986, the volume of the Great Salt Lake approximately tripled while its top surface area approximately doubled. Read the article "Relations Between Surface Area and Volume in Lakes" by Daniel Cass and Gerald Wildenberg in the November, 1990 issue of the *College Mathematics Journal*. Then give examples of solids that have "water levels" a and b such that $V(b) = 3V(a)$ and $A(b) = 2A(a)$, as indicated in the figure.

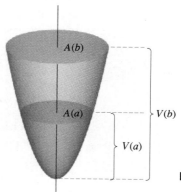

FIGURE FOR 69

70. Find $\displaystyle\int_0^\infty \frac{e^{-x} - e^{-2x}}{x}\,dx.$

$$\left[\text{Hint: Evaluate } \int_1^2 e^{-xy}\,dy.\right]$$

71. Let $f(x) = \displaystyle\int_1^x e^{t^2}\,dt$. Find the average value of f on the interval $[0, 1]$.

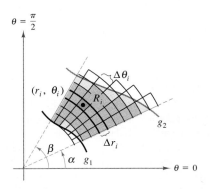

FIGURE 14.23
Area of R_i: $\Delta A_i = r_i \Delta r_i \Delta \theta_i$

Double Integrals in Polar Coordinates

Some double integrals are *much* easier to evaluate in polar form than in rectangular form. This is especially true for regions such as circles, cardioids, and petal curves, and for integrands that involve $x^2 + y^2$.

To define a double integral of a continuous function $z = f(r, \theta)$ in polar coordinates, consider a region R bounded by the graphs of $r = g_1(\theta)$ and $r = g_2(\theta)$ and by the lines $\theta = \alpha$ and $\theta = \beta$. On R, superimpose a polar grid made of rays and circular arcs, as shown in Figure 14.23. The polar sectors R_i lying entirely within R form an **inner polar partition**, Δ, whose **norm** $\| \Delta \|$ is the length of the longest diagonal of the n polar sectors. Recall from the development of area in polar coordinates that if you choose a point (r_i, θ_i) in R_i such that r_i is the average radius of R_i, then the area of R_i is

$$\Delta A_i = r_i \Delta r_i \Delta \theta_i \qquad \text{Area of } R_i$$

where θ is measured in radians (see Exercise 39). To define a double integral in the polar coordinate system, you can form the Riemann sum $\Sigma f(r_i, \theta_i) r_i \Delta r_i \Delta \theta_i$ and take the limit as $\| \Delta \| \to 0$.

Double Integral in Polar Coordinates

If f is a continuous function of r and θ on a closed bounded plane region R, then the **double integral of f over R** in polar coordinates is given by

$$\int_R \int f(r, \theta) \, dA = \lim_{\| \Delta \| \to 0} \sum_{i=1}^{n} f(r_i, \theta_i) r_i \Delta r_i \Delta \theta_i = \int_R \int f(r, \theta) r \, dr \, d\theta.$$

REMARK In polar coordinates, note that $dA = r \, dr \, d\theta$ or $dA = r \, d\theta \, dr$.

The region R is restricted to two basic types, **r-simple** regions and **θ-simple** regions, as shown in Figure 14.24.

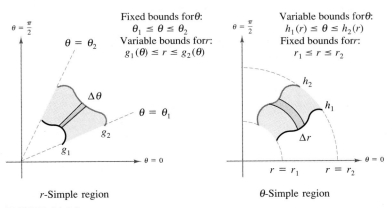

r-Simple region   θ-Simple region

FIGURE 14.24

You can evaluate a double integral in polar form with an iterated integral, as stated in the following polar form of Fubini's Theorem.

THEOREM 14.3   Polar Form of Fubini's Theorem

Let f be continuous on a plane region R.

1. If R is defined by $\theta_1 \leq \theta \leq \theta_2$ and $g_1(\theta) \leq r \leq g_2(\theta)$, where g_1 and g_2 are continuous on $[\theta_1, \theta_2]$, then

$$\iint_R f(r, \theta)\, dA = \int_{\theta_1}^{\theta_2} \int_{g_1(\theta)}^{g_2(\theta)} f(r, \theta)\, r\, dr\, d\theta.$$

2. If R is defined by $r_1 \leq r \leq r_2$ and $h_1(r) \leq \theta \leq h_2(r)$, where h_1 and h_2 are continuous on $[r_1, r_2]$, then

$$\iint_R f(r, \theta)\, dA = \int_{r_1}^{r_2} \int_{h_1(r)}^{h_2(r)} f(r, \theta)\, r\, d\theta\, dr.$$

REMARK   Note that each integrand in Theorem 14.3 contains a factor r. This arises from the area of the ith polar sector $\Delta A_i = r_i \Delta r_i \Delta \theta_i$.

EXAMPLE 1   Evaluating a Double Polar Integral

Evaluate

$$\iint_R \sin\theta\, dA$$

where R is the first-quadrant region lying inside the circle given by $r = 4\cos\theta$ and outside the circle given by $r = 2$.

Solution   In Figure 14.25, you can see that R is an r-simple region, and you can sketch a representative sector whose bounds yield the following limits of integration.

$$0 \leq \theta \leq \frac{\pi}{3} \qquad \text{Fixed bounds on } \theta$$

$$2 \leq r \leq 4\cos\theta \qquad \text{Variable bounds on } r$$

Thus, you obtain

$$\iint_R \sin\theta\, dA = \int_0^{\pi/3} \int_2^{4\cos\theta} (\sin\theta)\, r\, dr\, d\theta$$

$$= \int_0^{\pi/3} (\sin\theta)\, \frac{r^2}{2} \Big]_2^{4\cos\theta}\, d\theta$$

$$= \frac{1}{2} \int_0^{\pi/3} (\sin\theta)(16\cos^2\theta - 4)\, d\theta$$

$$= 2 \int_0^{\pi/3} [4\cos^2\theta(\sin\theta) - \sin\theta]\, d\theta$$

$$= 2 \left[-\frac{4\cos^3\theta}{3} + \cos\theta \right]_0^{\pi/3}$$

$$= 2 \left[\left(-\frac{4}{3}\left(\frac{1}{2}\right)^3 + \frac{1}{2} \right) - \left(-\frac{4}{3} + 1 \right) \right]$$

$$= \frac{4}{3}.$$

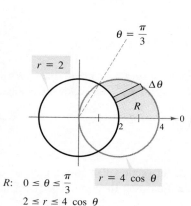

$\theta = \dfrac{\pi}{3}$

$r = 2$

$\Delta\theta$

R

$r = 4\cos\theta$

$R: \quad 0 \leq \theta \leq \dfrac{\pi}{3}$

$\quad 2 \leq r \leq 4\cos\theta$

FIGURE 14.25
R is an r-simple region.

EXAMPLE 2   Finding Areas of Polar Regions

Use a double integral to find the area enclosed by the graph of $r = 3\cos 3\theta$.

Solution   Let R be one petal of the curve shown in Figure 14.26. This region is r-simple, and the boundaries are as follows.

$$-\frac{\pi}{6} \le \theta \le \frac{\pi}{6} \qquad \text{Fixed bounds on } \theta$$

$$0 \le r \le 3\cos 3\theta \qquad \text{Variable bounds on } r$$

Thus, the area of one petal is

$$\frac{1}{3}A = \int_R\int dA = \int_{-\pi/6}^{\pi/6}\int_0^{3\cos 3\theta} r\,dr\,d\theta$$

$$= \int_{-\pi/6}^{\pi/6} \frac{r^2}{2}\bigg]_0^{3\cos 3\theta} d\theta$$

$$= \frac{9}{2}\int_{-\pi/6}^{\pi/6} \cos^2 3\theta\,d\theta$$

$$= \frac{9}{4}\int_{-\pi/6}^{\pi/6} (1 + \cos 6\theta)\,d\theta$$

$$= \frac{9}{4}\left[\theta + \frac{1}{6}\sin 6\theta\right]_{-\pi/6}^{\pi/6}$$

$$= \frac{3\pi}{4}.$$

Therefore, the total area is $A = 9\pi/4$.

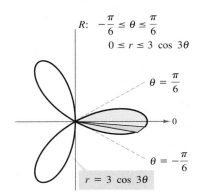

$R: \ -\dfrac{\pi}{6} \le \theta \le \dfrac{\pi}{6}$

$0 \le r \le 3\ \cos 3\theta$

$\theta = \dfrac{\pi}{6}$

$\theta = -\dfrac{\pi}{6}$

$r = 3\ \cos 3\theta$

FIGURE 14.26
The area of R is $3\pi/4$, and the total area is $9\pi/4$.

TECHNOLOGY   Any symbolic integration utility that can handle double integrals in rectangular coordinates can also handle double integrals in polar coordinates. The reason this is true is that once you have formed the iterated integral, its value is not changed by using different variables. In other words, if you use a symbolic integrator to evaluate

$$\int_{-\pi/6}^{\pi/6}\int_0^{3\cos 3y} x\,dx\,dy$$

you should obtain the same value that was obtained in Example 2.

Change of Variables to Polar Form

You will now see the reason for introducing double integrals in polar form. With sufficient restrictions on a function f and a region R, you can make the following change of variables.

$$x = r\cos\theta, \qquad y = r\sin\theta$$
$$r^2 = x^2 + y^2, \qquad dA = r\,dr\,d\theta$$

This change of variables converts a double integral in rectangular coordinates to a double integral in polar coordinates, as stated in the following theorem. The proof of this theorem is discussed in Section 14.8.

> **THEOREM 14.4   Change of Variables to Polar Form**
>
> Let R be a plane region consisting of all points $(x, y) = (r\cos\theta, r\sin\theta)$ satisfying the condition
>
> $$0 \le g_1(\theta) \le r \le g_2(\theta), \qquad \theta_1 \le \theta \le \theta_2$$
>
> where $0 < (\theta_2 - \theta_1) \le 2\pi$. If g_1 and g_2 are continuous on $[\theta_1, \theta_2]$ and f is continuous on R, then
>
> $$\iint_R f(x, y)\, dA = \int_{\theta_1}^{\theta_2}\int_{g_1(\theta)}^{g_2(\theta)} f(r\cos\theta, r\sin\theta)r\, dr\, d\theta.$$

If $z = f(x, y)$ is nonnegative on R, then the integral in Theorem 14.4 can be interpreted as the *volume* of the solid region between the graph of f and the region R. We use this interpretation in our next example.

EXAMPLE 3   Change of Variables to Polar Coordinates

Use polar coordinates to find the volume of the solid region bounded above by the hemisphere

$$z = \sqrt{16 - x^2 - y^2} \qquad \text{Hemisphere forms upper surface}$$

and below by the circular region R given by

$$x^2 + y^2 = 4 \qquad \text{Circular region forms lower surface}$$

as shown in Figure 14.27.

Solution   In Figure 14.27, you can see that R has the bounds

$$-\sqrt{4 - y^2} \le x \le \sqrt{4 - y^2}, \qquad -2 \le y \le 2$$

and that $0 \le z \le \sqrt{16 - x^2 - y^2}$. In polar coordinates the bounds are

$$0 \le r \le 2 \quad \text{and} \quad 0 \le \theta \le 2\pi$$

with height $z = \sqrt{16 - x^2 - y^2} = \sqrt{16 - r^2}$. Consequently, the volume V is given by

$$
\begin{aligned}
V = \iint_R f(x, y)\, dA &= \int_0^{2\pi}\int_0^2 \sqrt{16 - r^2}\, r\, dr\, d\theta \\
&= -\frac{1}{3}\int_0^{2\pi} (16 - r^2)^{3/2}\Big]_0^2\, d\theta \\
&= -\frac{1}{3}\int_0^{2\pi} \left(24\sqrt{3} - 64\right) d\theta \\
&= -\frac{8}{3}(3\sqrt{3} - 8)\theta\Big]_0^{2\pi} \\
&= \frac{16\pi}{3}\left(8 - 3\sqrt{3}\right) \\
&\approx 46.98.
\end{aligned}
$$

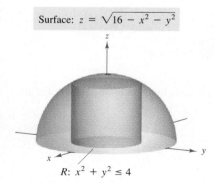

Surface: $z = \sqrt{16 - x^2 - y^2}$

$R: x^2 + y^2 \le 4$

FIGURE 14.27

REMARK   To see the benefit of polar coordinates in Example 3, you should try to evaluate the corresponding rectangular double integral

$$\int_{-2}^{2}\int_{-\sqrt{4-y^2}}^{\sqrt{4-y^2}} \sqrt{16 - x^2 - y^2}\, dx\, dy.$$

R: $1 \leq r \leq \sqrt{5}$
     $0 \leq \theta \leq 2\pi$

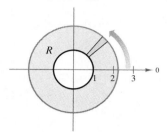

FIGURE 14.28
r-Simple region:
$dA = r\, dr\, d\theta$.

R: $1 \leq r \leq \sqrt{5}$
     $0 \leq \theta \leq 2\pi$

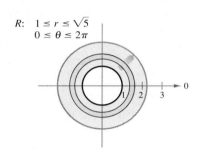

FIGURE 14.29
θ-Simple region:
$dA = r\, d\theta\, dr$.

EXAMPLE 4   Change of Variables to Polar Coordinates

Let R be the annular region lying between the two circles $x^2 + y^2 = 1$ and $x^2 + y^2 = 5$, as shown in Figure 14.28. Evaluate the integral

$$\int_R \int (x^2 + y)\, dA.$$

Solution   The polar boundaries are $1 \leq r \leq \sqrt{5}$ and $0 \leq \theta \leq 2\pi$. Thus, you have

$$\int_R \int (x^2 + y)\, dA = \int_0^{2\pi} \int_1^{\sqrt{5}} (r^2\cos^2\theta + r\sin\theta) r\, dr\, d\theta.$$

For the sake of illustration, we change the order of integration, as indicated in Figure 14.29, and obtain

$$\int_R \int (x^2 + y)\, dA = \int_1^{\sqrt{5}} \int_0^{2\pi} r^2(r\cos^2\theta + \sin\theta)\, d\theta\, dr$$

$$= \int_1^{\sqrt{5}} r^2 \left[\int_0^{2\pi} \left(\frac{r}{2} + \frac{r\cos 2\theta}{2} + \sin\theta \right) d\theta \right] dr$$

$$= \int_1^{\sqrt{5}} r^2 \left[\frac{r\theta}{2} + \frac{r\sin 2\theta}{4} - \cos\theta \right]_0^{2\pi} dr$$

$$= \int_1^{\sqrt{5}} r^2(\pi r)\, dr = \pi \frac{r^4}{4} \Big]_1^{\sqrt{5}}$$

$$= 6\pi.$$

Try integrating with $dA = r\, dr\, d\theta$ to see which order is more convenient.

TECHNOLOGY
Laboratory Guide
Lab 14.3

EXERCISES for Section 14.3

In Exercises 1–6, evaluate the double integral $\int_R \int f(r,\theta)\, dA$, and sketch the region R.

1. $\displaystyle \int_0^{2\pi} \int_0^6 3r^2\sin\theta\, dr\, d\theta$

2. $\displaystyle \int_0^{\pi/4} \int_0^4 r^2\sin\theta\cos\theta\, dr\, d\theta$

3. $\displaystyle \int_0^{\pi/2} \int_2^3 \sqrt{9 - r^2}\, r\, dr\, d\theta$

4. $\displaystyle \int_0^{\pi/2} \int_0^3 re^{-r^2}\, dr\, d\theta$

5. $\displaystyle \int_0^{\pi/2} \int_0^{1+\sin\theta} \theta\, dr\, d\theta$

6. $\displaystyle \int_0^{\pi/2} \int_0^{1-\cos\theta} \sin\theta\, dr\, d\theta$

In Exercises 7–12, use a double integral to find the area of the indicated region.

7. $r = 6\cos\theta$

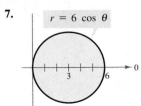

8. $r = 2$ $r = 4$

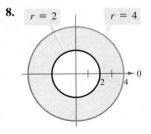

9.

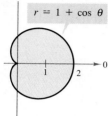

$r = 1 + \cos \theta$

10.

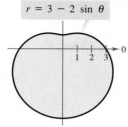

$r = 3 - 2 \sin \theta$

11.

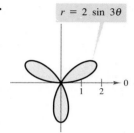

$r = 2 \sin 3\theta$

12.

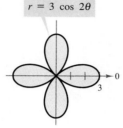

$r = 3 \cos 2\theta$

In Exercises 13–18, evaluate the double integral by changing to polar coordinates.

13. $\displaystyle\int_0^a \int_0^{\sqrt{a^2-y^2}} y \, dx \, dy$

14. $\displaystyle\int_0^a \int_0^{\sqrt{a^2-x^2}} x \, dy \, dx$

15. $\displaystyle\int_0^3 \int_0^{\sqrt{9-x^2}} (x^2 + y^2)^{3/2} \, dy \, dx$

16. $\displaystyle\int_0^2 \int_y^{\sqrt{8-y^2}} \sqrt{x^2 + y^2} \, dx \, dy$

17. $\displaystyle\int_0^2 \int_0^{\sqrt{2x-x^2}} xy \, dy \, dx$

18. $\displaystyle\int_0^4 \int_0^{\sqrt{4y-y^2}} x^2 \, dx \, dy$

In Exercises 19 and 20, combine the sum of the two double integrals into a single double integral by using polar coordinates. Evaluate the resulting double integral.

19. $\displaystyle\int_0^2 \int_0^x \sqrt{x^2 + y^2} \, dy \, dx + \int_2^{2\sqrt{2}} \int_0^{\sqrt{8-x^2}} \sqrt{x^2 + y^2} \, dy \, dx$

20. $\displaystyle\int_0^{5\sqrt{2}/2} \int_0^x xy \, dy \, dx + \int_{5\sqrt{2}/2}^5 \int_0^{\sqrt{25-x^2}} xy \, dy \, dx$

In Exercises 21–24, use polar coordinates to evaluate the double integral $\int_R \int f(x,y) \, dA$.

21. $f(x, y) = x + y$
    $R: x^2 + y^2 \le 4, \, 0 \le x, \, 0 \le y$

22. $f(x, y) = e^{-(x^2+y^2)}$
    $R: x^2 + y^2 \le 4, \, 0 \le x, \, 0 \le y$

23. $f(x, y) = \arctan \dfrac{y}{x}$
    $R: x^2 + y^2 \ge 1, \, x^2 + y^2 \le 4, \, 0 \le y \le x$

24. $f(x, y) = 9 - x^2 - y^2$
    $R: x^2 + y^2 \le 9, \, 0 \le x, \, 0 \le y$

Volume   **In Exercises 25–30, use a double integral in polar coordinates to find the volume of the solid bounded by the graphs of the equations.**

25. $z = xy$, $x^2 + y^2 = 1$ (first octant)

26. $z = x^2 + y^2 + 1$, $z = 0$, $x^2 + y^2 = 4$

27. $z = \sqrt{x^2 + y^2}$, $z = 0$, $x^2 + y^2 = 25$

28. $z = \sqrt{x^2 + y^2}$, $z = 0$, $x^2 + y^2 \ge 4$, $x^2 + y^2 \le 16$

29. Inside the hemisphere $z = \sqrt{16 - x^2 - y^2}$ and inside the cylinder $x^2 + y^2 - 4x = 0$

30. Inside the hemisphere $z = \sqrt{16 - x^2 - y^2}$ and outside the cylinder $x^2 + y^2 = 1$

31. *Volume*   Find a so that the volume inside the hemisphere $z = \sqrt{16 - x^2 - y^2}$ and outside the cylinder $x^2 + y^2 = a^2$ is one-half the volume of the hemisphere.

32. *Volume*   Use a double integral in polar coordinates to find the volume of a sphere of radius a.

33. *Probability*   The integral

$$I = \int_{-\infty}^{\infty} e^{-x^2/2} \, dx$$

is important in calculating probabilities when using the normal probability distribution.

a. Use polar coordinates to evaluate the double integral

$$I^2 = \left(\int_{-\infty}^{\infty} e^{-x^2/2} \, dx \right)\left(\int_{-\infty}^{\infty} e^{-y^2/2} \, dy \right)$$

$$= \int_{-\infty}^{\infty} \int_{-\infty}^{\infty} e^{-(x^2+y^2)/2} \, dA.$$

b. Use the result of part a to determine I.

FOR FURTHER INFORMATION   For more information on this problem, see the article "Integrating e^{-x^2} Without Polar Coordinates" by William Dunham in the January, 1988 issue of *Mathematics Teacher*.

34. Use the result of Exercise 33 and change of variables to evaluate the following integrals. No integration is required.

a. $\displaystyle\int_{-\infty}^{\infty} e^{-x^2} \, dx$ **b.** $\displaystyle\int_{-\infty}^{\infty} e^{-4x^2} \, dx$

35. *Population*   The population density of a city is approximated by the model

$$f(x, y) = 4000 e^{-0.01(x^2+y^2)}, \qquad x^2 + y^2 \le 49$$

where x and y are measured in miles. Integrate the density function over the specified circular region to approximate the population of the city.

36. *Probability*   Find k so that the function

$$f(x, y) = \begin{cases} ke^{-(x^2+y^2)}, & x \ge 0, \, y \ge 0 \\ 0, & \text{elsewhere} \end{cases}$$

is a probability density function.

37. Consider the region bounded by the graphs of $y = 2$, $y = 4$, $y = x$, and $y = \sqrt{3}x$ and the double integral $\int_R \int f \, dA$. Determine the limits of integration if the region R is divided into
   a. horizontal representative elements.
   b. vertical representative elements.
   c. polar sectors.

38. Repeat Exercise 37 for a region R bounded by the graphs of the equation $(x - 2)^2 + y^2 = 4$.

39. Show that the area of the polar sector R (see figure) is

$$\text{Area} = r \Delta r \Delta \theta$$

where $r = (r_1 + r_2)/2$ is the average radius of R.

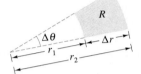

FIGURE FOR 39

40. Let R be the region in the first quadrant bounded by the curves $x^2 + y^2 = 1$ and $x^2 + y^2 = 4$. Find

$$\int_R \int \ln(x^2 + y^2) \, dA.$$

41. Find the "volume" of the "four-dimensional sphere" $x^2 + y^2 + z^2 + w^2 = a^2$, by calculating

$$16 \int_0^a \int_0^{\sqrt{a^2 - x^2}} \int_0^{\sqrt{a^2 - x^2 - y^2}} \int_0^{\sqrt{a^2 - x^2 - y^2 - z^2}} dw \, dz \, dy \, dx.$$

SECTION 14.4 Center of Mass and Moments of Inertia

Mass • Moments and Center of Mass • Moments of Inertia

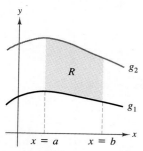

FIGURE 14.30
Lamina of constant density.

Mass

In Section 6.7, we discussed several applications of integration involving a lamina of *constant* density ρ. For example, if the lamina corresponding to the region R, as shown in Figure 14.30, has a constant density ρ, then the mass of the lamina is given by

$$\text{Mass} = \rho A = \rho \int_R\int dA = \int_R\int \rho\, dA. \qquad \text{Constant density}$$

The use of a double integral suggests a natural extension of the formula for finding the mass of a lamina of *variable* density, where the density at (x, y) is given by the **density function ρ.**

Definition of Mass of a Planar Lamina of Variable Density

If ρ is a continuous density function on the lamina corresponding to a plane region R, then the mass m of the lamina is given by

$$m = \int_R\int \rho(x, y)\, dA. \qquad \text{Variable density}$$

REMARK Density is normally expressed as mass per unit volume. For a planar lamina, however, density is mass per unit surface area.

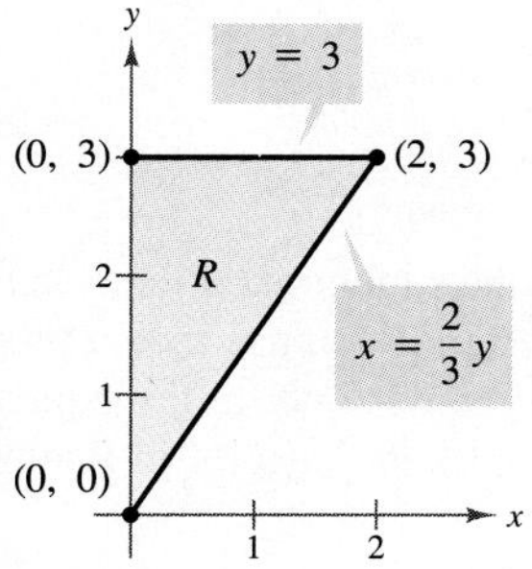

FIGURE 14.31
Lamina of variable density.

REMARK In Figure 14.31, note that the planar lamina is shaded so that the darkest shading corresponds to the densest part.

EXAMPLE 1 Finding the Mass of a Planar Lamina

Find the mass of the triangular lamina with vertices $(0, 0)$, $(0, 3)$, and $(2, 3)$, given that the density at (x, y) is $\rho(x, y) = 2x + y$.

Solution As shown in Figure 14.31, region R has the boundaries $x = 0$, $y = 3$, and $y = 3x/2$ (or $x = 2y/3$). Therefore, the mass of the lamina is

$$\begin{aligned} m = \int_R\int (2x + y)\, dA &= \int_0^3 \int_0^{2y/3} (2x + y)\, dx\, dy \\ &= \int_0^3 \Big[x^2 + xy\Big]_0^{2y/3} dy \\ &= \frac{10}{9}\int_0^3 y^2\, dy = \frac{10}{9}\frac{y^3}{3}\Big]_0^3 = 10. \end{aligned}$$

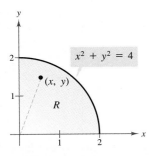

FIGURE 14.32
Density at (x, y):
$\rho(x, y) = k\sqrt{x^2 + y^2}$.

EXAMPLE 2   Finding Mass by Polar Coordinates

Find the mass of the lamina corresponding to the first-quadrant portion of the circle $x^2 + y^2 = 4$, where the density at the point (x, y) is proportional to the distance between the point and the origin, as shown in Figure 14.32.

Solution   At any point (x, y), the density of the lamina is

$$\rho(x, y) = k\sqrt{(x - 0)^2 + (y - 0)^2}$$
$$= k\sqrt{x^2 + y^2}.$$

Because $0 \le x \le 2$ and $0 \le y \le \sqrt{4 - x^2}$, the mass is given by

$$m = \int\!\!\int_R k\sqrt{x^2 + y^2}\, dA$$
$$= \int_0^2 \int_0^{\sqrt{4-x^2}} k\sqrt{x^2 + y^2}\, dy\, dx.$$

To simplify the integration, you can change to polar coordinates, using the bounds $0 \le \theta \le \pi/2$ and $0 \le r \le 2$. Thus, the mass is

$$m = \int\!\!\int_R k\sqrt{x^2 + y^2}\, dA = \int_0^{\pi/2} \int_0^2 k\sqrt{r^2}\, r\, dr\, d\theta$$
$$= \int_0^{\pi/2} \int_0^2 kr^2\, dr\, d\theta$$
$$= \int_0^{\pi/2} \frac{kr^3}{3} \Big]_0^2 d\theta$$
$$= \frac{8k}{3} \int_0^{\pi/2} d\theta$$
$$= \frac{8k}{3} \theta \Big]_0^{\pi/2}$$
$$= \frac{4\pi k}{3}.$$

⋮ **TECHNOLOGY**   On many occasions in this text, we have mentioned the benefits of
⋮ computer programs that perform symbolic integration. Even if you use such a program
⋮ regularly, you should remember that its greatest benefit comes only in the hands of a
⋮ knowledgeable user. For instance, notice how much simpler the integral in Example 2
⋮ becomes when it is converted to polar form.

Rectangular form	Polar form
$\int_0^2 \int_0^{\sqrt{4-x^2}} k\sqrt{x^2 + y^2}\, dy\, dx$	$\int_0^{\pi/2} \int_0^2 kr^2\, dr\, d\theta$

⋮ If you have access to software that performs symbolic integration, try using it to
⋮ evaluate both integrals. Some software programs cannot handle the first integral, but
⋮ any program that can handle double integrals can evaluate the second integral.

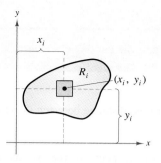

FIGURE 14.33

$M_x = (\text{mass})(y_i)$

$M_y = (\text{mass})(x_i)$

Moments and Center of Mass

For a lamina of variable density, moments of mass are defined in a manner similar to that used for the uniform density case. For a partition Δ of a lamina corresponding to a plane region R, consider the ith rectangle R_i of area ΔA_i, as shown in Figure 14.33. Assume that the mass of R_i is concentrated at one of its interior points (x_i, y_i). The moment of mass of R_i with respect to the x-axis can be approximated by

$$(\text{mass})(y_i) \approx [\rho(x_i, y_i)\,\Delta A_i](y_i).$$

Similarly, the moment of mass with respect to the y-axis can be approximated by

$$(\text{mass})(x_i) \approx [\rho(x_i, y_i)\,\Delta A_i](x_i).$$

By forming the Riemann sum of all such products and taking the limit as the norm of Δ approaches 0, you obtain the following definitions of moments of mass with respect to the x- and y-axes.

Moments and Center of Mass of a Variable Density Planar Lamina

Let ρ be a continuous density function on the planar lamina R. The **moments of mass** with respect to the x- and y-axes are

$$M_x = \iint_R y\rho(x, y)\,dA \quad \text{and} \quad M_y = \iint_R x\rho(x, y)\,dA.$$

If m is the mass of the lamina, then the **center of mass** is

$$(\bar{x}, \bar{y}) = \left(\frac{M_y}{m}, \frac{M_x}{m}\right).$$

If R represents a simple plane region rather than a lamina, the point $(\bar{x}, \bar{y})$ is called the **centroid** of the region.

For some planar laminas, you can determine the center of mass (or one of its coordinates) using symmetry rather than using integration. For instance, consider the laminas shown in Figure 14.34. Using symmetry, you can see that $\bar{x} = 0$ for the first lamina and $\bar{y} = 0$ for the second lamina.

$R:\ 0 \le x \le 1$
$-\sqrt{1 - x^2} \le y \le \sqrt{1 - x^2}$

$R:\ -\sqrt{1 - y^2} \le x \le \sqrt{1 - y^2}$
$0 \le y \le 1$

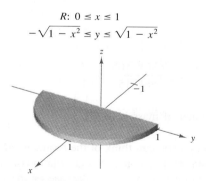

Symmetric with respect to the x-axis

Symmetric with respect to the y-axis

FIGURE 14.34

$$= \frac{k}{4}\int_{-2} y \bigg]_0 \quad dx$$

$$= \frac{k}{4}\int_{-2}^{2} (256 - 256x^2 + 96x^4 - 16x^6 + x^8)\,dx$$

$$= \frac{k}{4}\left[256x - \frac{256x^3}{3} + \frac{96x^5}{5} - \frac{16x^7}{7} + \frac{x^9}{9}\right]_{-2}^{2} = \frac{32{,}768k}{315}.$$

EXAMPLE 3   Finding the Center of Mass

Find the center of mass of the lamina corresponding to the parabolic region

The moment of inertia I of a revolving lamina can be used to measure its kinetic energy. For example, suppose a planar lamina is revolving about a line with an **angular speed** of ω radians per second, as shown in Figure 14.37. The kinetic energy of the revolving lamina is

$$E = \frac{1}{2}I\omega^2. \qquad \text{Kinetic energy for rotational motion}$$

On the other hand, the kinetic energy of a mass m moving in a straight line at a velocity v is

$$E = \frac{1}{2}mv^2. \qquad \text{Kinetic energy for linear motion}$$

Thus, the kinetic energy of a mass moving in a straight line is proportional to its mass, but the kinetic energy of a mass revolving about an axis is proportional to its moment of inertia.

The **radius of gyration** $\bar{\bar{r}}$ of a revolving mass m with moment of inertia I is defined to be

$$\bar{\bar{r}} = \sqrt{\frac{I}{m}}. \qquad \text{Radius of gyration}$$

If the entire mass were located at a distance $\bar{\bar{r}}$ from its axis of revolution, it would have the same moment of inertia and, consequently, the same kinetic energy. For instance, the radius of gyration of the lamina in Example 4 about the x-axis is given by

$$\bar{\bar{y}} = \sqrt{\frac{I_x}{m}} = \sqrt{\frac{32{,}768k/315}{256k/15}} = \sqrt{\frac{128}{21}} \approx 2.47.$$

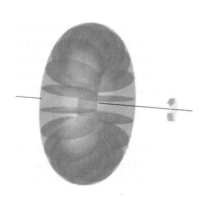

FIGURE 14.37
Planar lamina revolving at ω radians per second.

EXAMPLE 5   Finding the Radius of Gyration

Find the radius of gyration about the y-axis for the lamina corresponding to the region $R: 0 \le y \le \sin x,\ 0 \le x \le \pi$, where the density at (x, y) is given by $\rho(x, y) = x$.

Solution   The region R is shown in Figure 14.38. By integrating $\rho(x, y) = x$ over the region R, you can determine that the mass of the region is π. The moment of inertia about the y-axis is

$$I_y = \int_0^\pi \int_0^{\sin x} x^3 \, dy \, dx$$

$$= \int_0^\pi x^3 y \Big]_0^{\sin x} dx$$

$$= \int_0^\pi x^3 \sin x \, dx$$

$$= \left[(3x^2 - 6)(\sin x) - (x^3 - 6x)(\cos x) \right]_0^\pi$$

$$= \pi^3 - 6\pi.$$

Thus, the radius of gyration about the y-axis is

$$\bar{\bar{x}} = \sqrt{\frac{I_y}{m}} = \sqrt{\frac{\pi^3 - 6\pi}{\pi}} = \sqrt{\pi^2 - 6} \approx 1.97.$$

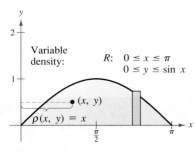

FIGURE 14.38
The radius of gyration about the y-axis is approximately 1.97.

EXERCISES for Section 14.4

In Exercises 1–4, find the mass and center of mass of the lamina for the specified densities.

1. R: rectangle with vertices $(0, 0)$, $(a, 0)$, $(0, b)$, and (a, b)
   a. $\rho = k$ **b.** $\rho = ky$

2. R: rectangle with vertices $(0, 0)$, $(a, 0)$, $(0, b)$, and (a, b)
   a. $\rho = kxy$ **b.** $\rho = k(x^2 + y^2)$

3. R: triangle with vertices $(0, 0)$, $(b/2, h)$, and $(b, 0)$
   a. $\rho = k$ **b.** $\rho = ky$

4. R: triangle with vertices $(0, 0)$, $(0, a)$, and $(a, 0)$
   a. $\rho = k$ **b.** $\rho = x^2 + y^2$

In Exercises 5–16, find the mass and center of mass of the lamina bounded by the graphs of the given equations for the specified density or densities. (*Hint:* Some of the integrals are simpler in polar coordinates.)

5. $y = \sqrt{a^2 - x^2}$, $y = 0$
   a. $\rho = k$ **b.** $\rho = k(a - y)y$

6. $x^2 + y^2 = a^2$, $0 \le x$, $0 \le y$
   a. $\rho = k$ **b.** $\rho = k(x^2 + y^2)$

7. $y = \sqrt{x}$, $y = 0$, $x = 4$, $\rho = kxy$

8. $y = x^2$, $y = 0$, $x = 4$, $\rho = kx$

9. $y = \dfrac{1}{1 + x^2}$, $y = 0$, $x = -1$, $x = 1$, $\rho = k$

10. $xy = 4$, $x = 1$, $x = 4$, $\rho = kx^2$

11. $x = 16 - y^2$, $x = 0$, $\rho = kx$

12. $y = 9 - x^2$, $y = 0$, $\rho = ky^2$

13. $y = \sin \dfrac{\pi x}{L}$, $y = 0$, $x = 0$, $x = L$, $\rho = ky$

14. $y = \cos \dfrac{\pi x}{L}$, $y = 0$, $x = 0$, $x = \dfrac{L}{2}$, $\rho = k$

15. $y = \sqrt{a^2 - x^2}$, $0 \le y \le x$, $\rho = k$

16. $y = \sqrt{a^2 - x^2}$, $y = 0$, $y = x$, $\rho = k\sqrt{x^2 + y^2}$

C In Exercises 17–20, use a symbolic integration utility to find the mass and center of mass of the lamina bounded by the graphs of the given equations for the specified density.

17. $y = e^{-x}$, $y = 0$, $x = 0$, $x = 2$, $\rho = ky$

18. $y = \ln x$, $y = 0$, $z = 1$, $x = e$, $\rho = \dfrac{k}{x}$

19. $r = 2 \cos 3\theta$, $-\dfrac{\pi}{6} \le \theta \le \dfrac{\pi}{6}$, $\rho = k$

20. $r = 1 + \cos \theta$, $\rho = k$

In Exercises 21–26, verify the given moment(s) of inertia and find $\overline{\overline{x}}$ and $\overline{\overline{y}}$. Assume each lamina has a density of $\rho = 1$. (These regions are common shapes used in engineering.)

21. Rectangle

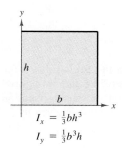

$I_x = \frac{1}{3} bh^3$
$I_y = \frac{1}{3} b^3 h$

22. Right triangle

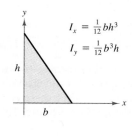

$I_x = \frac{1}{12} bh^3$
$I_y = \frac{1}{12} b^3 h$

23. Circle

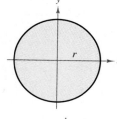

$I_0 = \frac{1}{2} \pi r^4$

24. Semicircle

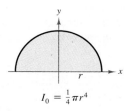

$I_0 = \frac{1}{4} \pi r^4$

25. Quarter circle

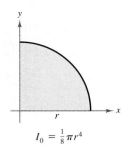

$I_0 = \frac{1}{8} \pi r^4$

26. Ellipse

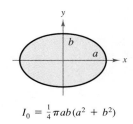

$I_0 = \frac{1}{4} \pi ab(a^2 + b^2)$

C In Exercises 27–34, find I_x, I_y, I_0, $\overline{\overline{x}}$, and $\overline{\overline{y}}$ for the lamina bounded by the graphs of the given equations. Use a symbolic integration utility to evaluate the double integrals.

27. $y = 0$, $y = b$, $x = 0$, $x = a$, $\rho = ky$

28. $y = \sqrt{a^2 - x^2}$, $y = 0$, $\rho = ky$

29. $y = 4 - x^2$, $y = 0$, $x > 0$, $\rho = kx$

30. $y = x$, $y = x^2$, $\rho = kxy$

31. $y = \sqrt{x}$, $y = 0$, $x = 4$, $\rho = kxy$

32. $y = x^2$, $y^2 = x$, $\rho = x^2 + y^2$

33. $y = x^2$, $y^2 = x$, $\rho = kx$

34. $y = x^3$, $y = 4x$, $\rho = ky$

C In Exercises 35–40, find the moment of inertia I, about the specified line, of the lamina bounded by the graphs of the equations. Use a symbolic integration utility to evaluate the double integrals.

35. $x^2 + y^2 = b^2$, $\rho = k$, line: $x = a(a > b)$

36. $y = 0$, $y = 2$, $x = 0$, $x = 4$, $\rho = k$, line: $x = 6$

37. $y = \sqrt{x}$, $y = 0$, $x = 4$, $\rho = kx$, line: $x = 6$

38. $y = \sqrt{a^2 - x^2}$, $y = 0$, $\rho = ky$, line: $y = a$

39. $y = \sqrt{a^2 - x^2}$, $y = 0$, $0 \le x$, $\rho = k(a - y)$, line: $y = a$

40. $y = 4 - x^2$, $y = 0$, $\rho = k$, line: $y = 2$

Hydraulics In Exercises 41–44, determine the location of the horizontal axis y_a at which a vertical gate in a dam is required to be hinged so that there is no moment causing rotation under the specified loading. The model for y_a is given by

$$y_a = \bar{y} - \frac{I_{\bar{y}}}{hA}$$

where $\bar{y}$ is the y-coordinate of the centroid of the gate, $I_{\bar{y}}$ is the moment of inertia of the gate about the line $y = \bar{y}$, h is the depth of the centroid below the surface of the water, and A is the area of the gate.

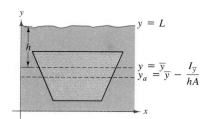

41.

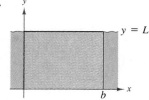

42.

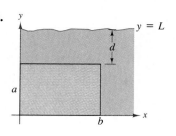

43.

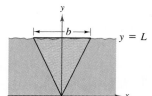

44.

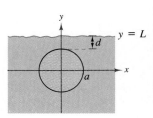

45. Prove the following Theorem of Pappus.

Let R be a region in a plane and let L be a line in the same plane such that L does not intersect the interior of R. If r is the distance between the centroid of R and the line, then the volume V of the solid of revolution formed by revolving R about the line is given by

$$V = 2\pi rA$$

where A is the area of R.

Surface Area

At this point you know a great deal about the solid region lying between a surface and a closed and bounded region R in the xy-plane, as shown in Figure 14.39. For example, you know how to find: the extrema of f on R (Section 13.8), the area of the base R of the solid (Section 14.1), the volume of the solid (Section 14.2), and the centroid of the base R (Section 14.4).

In this section, you will learn how to find the upper **surface area** of the solid. Later, you will learn how to find the centroid of the solid (Section 14.6) and the lateral surface area (Section 15.2).

To begin, consider a surface S given by $z = f(x, y)$ defined over a region R. Assume that R is closed and bounded and that f has continuous first partial derivatives. To find the surface area, construct an inner partition of R consisting of n rectangles, where the area of the ith rectangle R_i is $\Delta A_i = \Delta x_i \Delta y_i$, as shown in Figure 14.40. In each R_i, let (x_i, y_i) be the point that is closest to the origin. At the point $(x_i, y_i, z_i) = (x_i, y_i, f(x_i, y_i))$ on the surface S, construct a tangent plane T_i. The area of the portion of the tangent plane that lies directly above R_i is approximately equal to the area of the surface lying directly above R_i. That is, $\Delta T_i \approx \Delta S_i$. Hence, the surface area of S is given by $\Sigma \Delta S_i \approx \Sigma \Delta T_i$.

To find the area of the parallelogram ΔT_i, note that its sides are given by the vectors

$$\mathbf{u} = \Delta x_i \mathbf{i} + f_x(x_i, y_i) \Delta x_i \mathbf{k} \quad \text{and} \quad \mathbf{v} = \Delta y_i \mathbf{j} + f_y(x_i, y_i) \Delta y_i \mathbf{k}.$$

From Theorem 11.8, the area of ΔT_i is given by $\| \mathbf{u} \times \mathbf{v} \|$, where

$$\mathbf{u} \times \mathbf{v} = \begin{vmatrix} \mathbf{i} & \mathbf{j} & \mathbf{k} \\ \Delta x_i & 0 & f_x(x_i, y_i) \Delta x_i \\ 0 & \Delta y_i & f_y(x_i, y_i) \Delta y_i \end{vmatrix}$$

$$= -f_x(x_i, y_i) \Delta x_i \Delta y_i \mathbf{i} - f_y(x_i, y_i) \Delta x_i \Delta y_i \mathbf{j} + \Delta x_i \Delta y_i \mathbf{k}$$

$$= (-f_x(x_i, y_i)\mathbf{i} - f_y(x_i, y_i)\mathbf{j} + \mathbf{k}) \Delta A_i.$$

Thus, the area of ΔT_i is

$$\| \mathbf{u} \times \mathbf{v} \| = \sqrt{[f_x(x_i, y_i)]^2 + [f_y(x_i, y_i)]^2 + 1} \, \Delta A_i$$

and

$$\text{Surface area of } S \approx \sum_{i=1}^{n} \Delta S_i \approx \sum_{i=1}^{n} \sqrt{1 + [f_x(x_i, y_i)]^2 + [f_y(x_i, y_i)]^2} \, \Delta A_i.$$

This suggests the following definition of surface area.

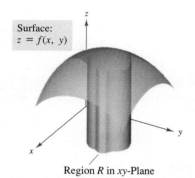

Surface:
$z = f(x, y)$

Region R in xy-Plane

FIGURE 14.39

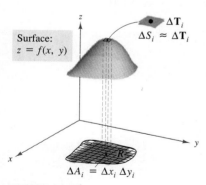

Surface:
$z = f(x, y)$

ΔT_i

$\Delta S_i \approx \Delta T_i$

$\Delta A_i = \Delta x_i \Delta y_i$

FIGURE 14.40

Definition of Surface Area

If f and its first partial derivatives are continuous on the closed region R in the xy-plane, then the **area of the surface** $z = f(x, y)$ over R is given by

$$\text{Surface area} = \iint_R dS = \iint_R \sqrt{1 + [f_x(x, y)]^2 + [f_y(x, y)]^2}\, dA.$$

As an aid to remembering the double integral for surface area, it is helpful to note its similarity to the integral for arc length.

Length on x-axis $\displaystyle\int_a^b dx$

Arc length in xy-plane $\displaystyle\int_a^b ds = \int_a^b \sqrt{1 + [f'(x)]^2}\, dx$

Area in xy-plane $\displaystyle\iint_R dA$

Surface area in space $\displaystyle\iint_R dS = \iint_R \sqrt{1 + [f_x(x, y)]^2 + [f_y(x, y)]^2}\, dA$

Like integrals for arc length, integrals for surface area are often very difficult to evaluate. However, one type that is easily evaluated is demonstrated in the next example.

EXAMPLE 1   The Surface Area of a Plane Region

Find the surface area of that portion of the plane $z = 2 - x - y$ that lies above the circle $x^2 + y^2 = 1$ in the first quadrant, as shown in Figure 14.41.

Solution   Because $f_x(x, y) = -1$ and $f_y(x, y) = -1$, the surface area is given by

$$S = \iint_R \sqrt{1 + [f_x(x, y)]^2 + [f_y(x, y)]^2}\, dA$$

$$= \iint_R \sqrt{3}\, dA$$

$$= \sqrt{3} \iint_R dA.$$

Note that the integral on the right is simply $\sqrt{3}$ times the area of the region R. Thus, the area of S is

$$S = \sqrt{3}\, (\text{area of } R)$$

$$= \sqrt{3}\left(\frac{\pi}{4}\right)$$

$$= \frac{\sqrt{3}\,\pi}{4}.$$

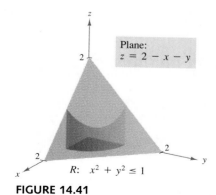

Plane:
$z = 2 - x - y$

$R:\ x^2 + y^2 \le 1$

FIGURE 14.41
The surface area of the portion of the plane that lies above the quarter circle is $\sqrt{3}\pi/4$.

Surface:
$f(x, y) = 1 - x^2 + y$

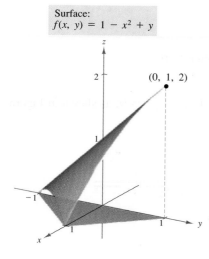

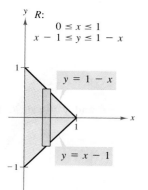

R:
$0 \leq x \leq 1$
$x - 1 \leq y \leq 1 - x$

$y = 1 - x$

$y = x - 1$

FIGURE 14.42

EXAMPLE 2   Finding Surface Area

Find the area of that portion of the surface $f(x, y) = 1 - x^2 + y$ that lies above the triangular region with vertices $(1, 0, 0)$, $(0, -1, 0)$, and $(0, 1, 0)$, as shown in Figure 14.42.

Solution   Because $f_x(x, y) = -2x$ and $f_y(x, y) = 1$, you have

$$S = \int_R \int \sqrt{1 + [f_x(x, y)]^2 + [f_y(x, y)]^2} \, dA$$

$$= \int_R \int \sqrt{1 + 4x^2 + 1} \, dA.$$

In Figure 14.42, you can see that the bounds for R are $0 \leq x \leq 1$ and $x - 1 \leq y \leq 1 - x$. Thus, the integral becomes

$$S = \int_0^1 \int_{x-1}^{1-x} \sqrt{2 + 4x^2} \, dy \, dx$$

$$= \int_0^1 y\sqrt{2 + 4x^2} \Big]_{x-1}^{1-x} \, dx$$

$$= \int_0^1 \left(2\sqrt{2 + 4x^2} - 2x\sqrt{2 + 4x^2}\right) dx$$

$$= \left[x\sqrt{2 + 4x^2} + \ln\left(2x + \sqrt{2 + 4x^2}\right) - \frac{(2 + 4x^2)^{3/2}}{6}\right]_0^1$$

$$= \sqrt{6} + \ln\left(2 + \sqrt{6}\right) - \sqrt{6} - \ln\sqrt{2} + \frac{1}{3}\sqrt{2}$$

$$\approx 1.618.$$

EXAMPLE 3   Change of Variables to Polar Coordinates

Find the surface area of the paraboloid $z = 1 + x^2 + y^2$ that lies above the unit circle, as shown in Figure 14.43.

Solution   Because $f_x(x, y) = 2x$ and $f_y(x, y) = 2y$, you have

$$S = \int_R \int \sqrt{1 + [f_x(x, y)]^2 + [f_y(x, y)]^2} \, dA$$

$$= \int_R \int \sqrt{1 + 4x^2 + 4y^2} \, dA.$$

You can convert to polar coordinates by letting $x = r\cos\theta$ and $y = r\sin\theta$. Then, because the region R is bounded by $0 \leq r \leq 1$ and $0 \leq \theta \leq 2\pi$, you have

$$S = \int_0^{2\pi} \int_0^1 \sqrt{1 + 4r^2} \, r \, dr \, d\theta = \int_0^{2\pi} \frac{1}{12}(1 + 4r^2)^{3/2} \Big]_0^1 d\theta$$

$$= \int_0^{2\pi} \frac{5\sqrt{5} - 1}{12} \, d\theta$$

$$= \frac{\pi(5\sqrt{5} - 1)}{6}$$

$$\approx 5.33.$$

Paraboloid:
$z = 1 + x^2 + y^2$

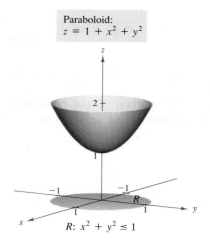

$R: x^2 + y^2 \leq 1$

FIGURE 14.43
The surface area of the portion of the paraboloid that lies above the unit circle is approximately 5.33.

EXERCISES for Section 14.5

In Exercises 1–14, find the area of the surface given by $z = f(x, y)$ over the region R. (*Hint:* Some of the integrals are simpler in polar coordinates.)

1. $f(x, y) = 2x + 2y$
R: triangle with vertices $(0, 0)$, $(2, 0)$, and $(0, 2)$

2. $f(x, y) = 10 + 2x - 3y$
R: square with vertices $(0, 0)$, $(2, 0)$, $(0, 2)$ and $(2, 2)$

3. $f(x, y) = 8 + 2x + 2y$
$R = \{(x, y): x^2 + y^2 \le 4\}$

4. $f(x, y) = 10 + 2x - 3y$
$R = \{(x, y): x^2 + y^2 \le 9\}$

5. $f(x, y) = 9 - x^2$
R: square with vertices $(0, 0)$, $(3, 0)$, $(0, 3)$, and $(3, 3)$

6. $f(x, y) = y^2$
R: square with vertices $(0, 0)$, $(3, 0)$, $(0, 3)$, and $(3, 3)$

7. $f(x, y) = 2 + x^{3/2}$
R: rectangle with vertices $(0, 0)$, $(0, 4)$, $(3, 4)$, and $(3, 0)$

8. $f(x, y) = 2 + \frac{2}{3}x^{3/2}$
$R = \{(x, y): 0 \le x \le 1, 0 \le y \le 1 - x\}$

9. $f(x, y) = \ln|\sec x|$
$R = \left\{(x, y): 0 \le x \le \dfrac{\pi}{4}, 0 \le y \le \tan x\right\}$

10. $f(x, y) = 4 + x^2 - y^2$
$R = \{(x, y): x^2 + y^2 \le 1\}$

11. $f(x, y) = \sqrt{x^2 + y^2}$
$R = \{(x, y): 0 \le f(x, y) \le 1\}$

12. $f(x, y) = xy$
$R = \{(x, y): x^2 + y^2 \le 16\}$

13. $f(x, y) = \sqrt{a^2 - x^2 - y^2}$
$R = \{(x, y): x^2 + y^2 \le b^2, b < a\}$

14. $f(x, y) = \sqrt{a^2 - x^2 - y^2}$
$R = \{(x, y): x^2 + y^2 \le a^2\}$

In Exercises 15–18, find the area of the surface.

15. The portion of the plane $z = 24 - 3x - 2y$ in the first octant.

16. The portion of the paraboloid $z = 16 - x^2 - y^2$ in the first octant.

17. The portion of the sphere $x^2 + y^2 + z^2 = 25$ inside the cylinder $x^2 + y^2 = 9$.

18. The portion of the cone $z = \sqrt{x^2 + y^2}$ inside the cylinder $x^2 + y^2 = 1$.

C In Exercises 19–24, write a double integral that represents the surface area of $z = f(x, y)$ over the region R. Use a symbolic integration utility to evaluate the double integral.

19. $f(x, y) = 2y + x^2$
R: triangle with vertices $(0, 0)$, $(1, 0)$, and $(1, 1)$

20. $f(x, y) = 2x + y^2$
R: triangle with vertices $(0, 0)$, $(2, 0)$, and $(2, 2)$

21. $f(x, y) = 4 - x^2 - y^2$
$R = \{(x, y): 0 \le f(x, y)\}$

22. $f(x, y) = x^2 + y^2$
$R = \{(x, y): 0 \le f(x, y) \le 16\}$

23. $f(x, y) = 4 - x^2 - y^2$
$R = \{(x, y): 0 \le x \le 1, 0 \le y \le 1\}$

24. $f(x, y) = \frac{2}{3}x^{3/2} + \cos x$
$R = \{(x, y): 0 \le x \le 1, 0 \le y \le 1\}$

C In Exercises 25 and 26, approximate the double integral that gives the surface area on the graph of f over the region $R = \{(x, y): 0 \le x \le 1, 0 \le y \le 1\}$. Perform the first integration by hand. Then use Simpson's Rule with $n = 10$ to approximate the resulting single integral.

25. $f(x, y) = e^x$ **26.** $f(x, y) = \frac{2}{5}y^{5/2}$

In Exercises 27–32, set up the double integral that gives the area of the surface on the graph of f over the region R.

27. $f(x, y) = x^3 - 3xy + y^3$
R: square with vertices $(1, 1)$, $(-1, 1)$, $(-1, -1)$, and $(1, -1)$

28. $f(x, y) = e^{-x}\sin y$
$R = \{(x, y): 0 \le x \le 4, 0 \le y \le x\}$

29. $f(x, y) = e^{-x}\sin y$
$R = \{(x, y): x^2 + y^2 \le 4\}$

30. $f(x, y) = x^2 - 3xy - y^2$
$R = \{(x, y): 0 \le x \le 4, 0 \le y \le x\}$

31. $f(x, y) = e^{xy}$
$R = \{(x, y): 0 \le x \le 4, 0 \le y \le 10\}$

32. $f(x, y) = \cos(x^2 + y^2)$
$R = \left\{(x, y): x^2 + y^2 \le \dfrac{\pi}{2}\right\}$

33. Find the surface area of the solid of intersection of the cylinders $x^2 + z^2 = 1$ and $y^2 + z^2 = 1$ (see figure).

34. Show that the surface area of the cone
$$z = k\sqrt{x^2 + y^2}, \quad k > 0$$
over the circular region $x^2 + y^2 \le r^2$ in the xy-plane is $\pi r^2\sqrt{k^2 + 1}$, as shown in the figure.

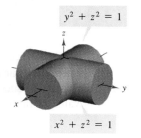

$y^2 + z^2 = 1$

$x^2 + z^2 = 1$

FIGURE FOR 33

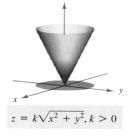

$z = k\sqrt{x^2 + y^2}, k > 0$

FIGURE FOR 34

35. *Building Design* A new auditorium is built with a founda-tion in the shape of $\frac{1}{4}$ of a circle of radius 50 feet. Therefore, it forms a region R bounded by the graph of $x^2 + y^2 = 50^2$ with $x \geq 0$ and $y \geq 0$. The equations for the floor and ceil-ing are given by the following.

$$z = \frac{x + y}{5} \qquad \text{Floor: incline plane}$$

$$z = 20 + \frac{xy}{100} \qquad \text{Ceiling}$$

a. Calculate the volume of the room. This is needed to determine the heating and cooling requirements.
b. Find the surface area of the ceiling.

36. *Product Design* A company produces a spherical object whose radius is 25 centimeters. A hole, with radius 4 centime-ters, is drilled through the center of the object. Find
a. the volume of the object.
b. the outer surface area of the object.

37. The angle between a plane P and the xy-plane is θ, where $0 \leq \theta < \pi/2$. The projection of a rectangular region in P onto the xy-plane is a rectangle whose sides have lengths of Δx and Δy, as shown in the figure. Prove that the area of the rectangular region in P is $\sec \theta \, \Delta x \, \Delta y$.

Area: $\sec \theta \, \Delta x \Delta y$

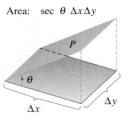

Area in xy-plane: $\Delta x \Delta y$

FIGURE FOR 37

38. *Capillary Action* A well-known property of liquids is that they will rise in narrow vertical channels–this property is called "capillary action." The figure shows two plates, which form a narrow wedge, in a container of liquid. The upper surface of the liquid follows a hyperbolic shape given by

$$z = \frac{k}{\sqrt{x^2 + y^2}}$$

where x, y, and z are measured in inches. The constant k depends on the angle of the wedge, the type of liquid, and the material that comprises the flat plates.

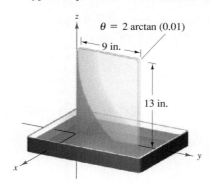

a. Find the volume of the liquid that has risen in the wedge. (Assume $k = 1$.)
b. Find the horizontal surface area of the liquid that has risen in the wedge.
(This problem was adapted from the article "Capillary Phenomena" by Thomas B. Greenslade, Jr. in the May, 1992 issue of the *Physics Teacher*.)

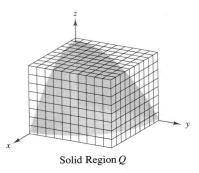

Solid Region Q

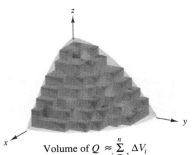

Volume of $Q \approx \sum\limits_{i=1}^{n} \Delta V_i$

FIGURE 14.48

Triple Integrals

The procedure used to define a **triple integral** follows that used for double integrals. Consider a function f of three variables that is continuous over a bounded solid region Q. Then, encompass Q with a network of boxes and form the **inner partition** consisting of all boxes lying entirely within Q, as shown in Figure 14.48. The volume of the ith box is

$$\Delta V_i = \Delta x_i \Delta y_i \Delta z_i. \qquad \text{Volume of } i\text{th box}$$

The **norm** $\|\Delta\|$ of the partition is the length of the longest diagonal of the n boxes in the partition. Choose a point (x_i, y_i, z_i) in each box and form the Riemann sum

$$\sum_{i=1}^{n} f(x_i, y_i, z_i)\, \Delta V_i.$$

Taking the limit as $\|\Delta\| \to 0$ leads to the following definition.

Definition of Triple Integral

If f is continuous over a bounded solid region Q, then the **triple integral of f over Q** is defined as

$$\iiint\limits_{Q} f(x, y, z)\, dV = \lim_{\|\Delta\| \to 0} \sum_{i=1}^{n} f(x_i, y_i, z_i)\, \Delta V_i$$

provided the limit exists. The **volume** of the solid region Q is given by

$$\text{Volume of } Q = \iiint\limits_{Q} dV.$$

Each of the properties of double integrals in Theorem 14.1 can be restated in terms of triple integrals

1. $\displaystyle \iiint\limits_{Q} c f(x, y, z)\, dV = c \iiint\limits_{Q} f(x, y, z)\, dV$

2. $\displaystyle \iiint\limits_{Q} [f(x, y, z) \pm g(x, y, z)]\, dV = \iiint\limits_{Q} f(x, y, z)\, dV \pm \iiint\limits_{Q} g(x, y, z)\, dV$

3. $\displaystyle \iiint\limits_{Q} f(x, y, z)\, dV = \iiint\limits_{Q_1} f(x, y, z)\, dV + \iiint\limits_{Q_2} f(x, y, z)\, dV$

where Q is the union of two nonoverlapping solid subregions Q_1 and Q_2.

If the solid region Q is simple, the triple integral $\iiint f(x, y, z) \, dV$ can be evaluated with an iterated integral using one of the six possible orders of integration:

$$dx \, dy \, dz \qquad dy \, dx \, dz \qquad dz \, dx \, dy$$
$$dx \, dz \, dy \qquad dy \, dz \, dx \qquad dz \, dy \, dx.$$

The following version of Fubini's Theorem describes a region that is considered simple with respect to the order $dz \, dy \, dx$. Similar descriptions can be given for the other five orders.

THEOREM 14.5   Evaluation by Iterated Integrals

Let f be continuous on a solid region Q defined by

$$a \leq x \leq b, \qquad h_1(x) \leq y \leq h_2(x), \qquad g_1(x, y) \leq z \leq g_2(x, y)$$

where h_1, h_2, g_1, and g_2 are continuous functions. Then,

$$\iiint_Q f(x, y, z) \, dV = \int_a^b \int_{h_1(x)}^{h_2(x)} \int_{g_1(x,y)}^{g_2(x,y)} f(x, y, z) \, dz \, dy \, dx.$$

To evaluate a triple iterated integral in the order $dz \, dy \, dx$, hold *both* x and y constant for the innermost integration. Then, hold x constant for the second integration. This is demonstrated in Example 1.

EXAMPLE 1   Evaluating a Triple Iterated Integral

Evaluate the triple iterated integral

$$\int_0^2 \int_0^x \int_0^{x+y} e^x(y + 2z) \, dz \, dy \, dx.$$

Solution   For the first integration, hold x and y constant and integrate with respect to z.

$$\int_0^2 \int_0^x \int_0^{x+y} e^x(y + 2z) \, dz \, dy \, dx = \int_0^2 \int_0^x e^x(yz + z^2) \Big]_0^{x+y} dy \, dx$$

$$= \int_0^2 \int_0^x e^x(x^2 + 3xy + 2y^2) \, dy \, dx$$

For the second integration, hold x constant and integrate with respect to y.

$$\int_0^2 \int_0^x e^x(x^2 + 3xy + 2y^2) \, dy \, dx = \int_0^2 \left[e^x\left(x^2 y + \frac{3xy^2}{2} + \frac{2y^3}{3}\right)\right]_0^x dx$$

$$= \frac{19}{6} \int_0^2 x^3 e^x \, dx$$

$$= \frac{19}{6}\left[e^x(x^3 - 3x^2 + 6x - 6)\right]_0^2$$

$$= 19\left(\frac{e^2}{3} + 1\right)$$

REMARK Example 1 demonstrates the integration order $dz \, dy \, dx$. For other orders, you can follow a similar procedure. For instance, to evaluate a triple iterated integral in the order $dx \, dy \, dz$, hold both y and z constant for the innermost integration and integrate with respect to x. Then, for the second integration, hold z constant and integrate with respect to y. Finally, for the third integration, integrate with respect to z.

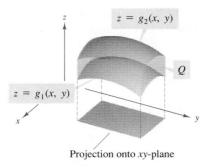

FIGURE 14.49

Solid region Q lies between two surfaces.

To find the limits for a particular order of integration, it is generally advisable to first determine the innermost limits, which may be functions of the outer two variables. Then, by projecting the solid Q onto the coordinate plane of the outer two variables, you can determine their limits of integration by the methods used for double integrals. For instance, to evaluate

$$\iiint_Q f(x, y, z)\, dz\, dy\, dx$$

first determine the limits for z, and then the integral has the form

$$\iint \left[\int_{g_1(x,y)}^{g_2(x,y)} f(x, y, z)\, dz \right] dy\, dx.$$

By projecting the solid Q onto the xy-plane, you can determine the limits for x and y as we did for double integrals, as shown in Figure 14.49.

EXAMPLE 2   Using a Triple Integral to Find Volume

Find the volume of the ellipsoidal solid given by $4x^2 + 4y^2 + z^2 = 16$.

Solution   Because x, y, and z play similar roles in the equation, the order of integration is probably immaterial, and we arbitrarily choose $dz\,dy\,dx$. Moreover, you can simplify the calculation by considering only that portion of the ellipsoid lying in the first octant, as shown in Figure 14.50. From the order $dz\,dy\,dx$, you first determine the bounds for z:

$$0 \le z \le 2\sqrt{4 - x^2 - y^2}.$$

In Figure 14.51, you can see that the boundaries for x and y are $0 \le x \le 2$ and $0 \le y \le \sqrt{4 - x^2}$, so the volume of the ellipsoid is

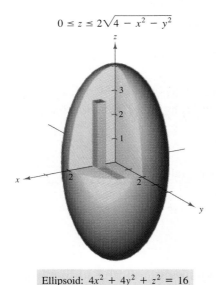

$0 \le z \le 2\sqrt{4 - x^2 - y^2}$

Ellipsoid: $4x^2 + 4y^2 + z^2 = 16$

FIGURE 14.50

The volume of the ellipsoid is $64\pi/3$.

$$V = \iiint_Q dV$$

$$= 8 \int_0^2 \int_0^{\sqrt{4-x^2}} \int_0^{2\sqrt{4-x^2-y^2}} dz\, dy\, dx$$

$$= 8 \int_0^2 \int_0^{\sqrt{4-x^2}} z \Big]_0^{2\sqrt{4-x^2-y^2}} dy\, dx$$

$$= 16 \int_0^2 \int_0^{\sqrt{4-x^2}} \sqrt{(4 - x^2) - y^2}\, dy\, dx$$

$$= 8 \int_0^2 \left[y\sqrt{4 - x^2 - y^2} + (4 - x^2)\arcsin\left(\frac{y}{\sqrt{4 - x^2}}\right) \right]_0^{\sqrt{4-x^2}} dx$$

$$= 8 \int_0^2 (4 - x^2)\left(\frac{\pi}{2}\right) dx$$

$$= 4\pi \left[4x - \frac{x^3}{3} \right]_0^2$$

$$= 4\pi \left[\left(8 - \frac{8}{3}\right) - (0 - 0) \right]$$

$$= \frac{64\pi}{3}.$$

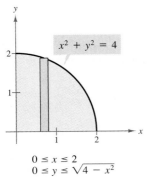

$x^2 + y^2 = 4$

$0 \le x \le 2$
$0 \le y \le \sqrt{4 - x^2}$

FIGURE 14.51

The solid region Q has a triangular base and top with rectangular vertical sides.

Example 2 is unusual in that all six possible orders of integration produce integrals of comparable difficulty. Try setting up some other possible orders of integration to find the volume of the ellipsoid. For instance, the order $dx\,dy\,dz$ yields the integral

$$V = 8 \int_0^4 \int_0^{\sqrt{16-z^2}/2} \int_0^{\sqrt{16-4y^2-z^2}/2} dx\,dy\,dz.$$

If you solve this integral, you will obtain the same volume obtained in Example 2. This is always the case—the order of integration does not affect the value of the integral. However, the order of integration often does affect the complexity of the integral. In Example 3, the given order of integration is not convenient, and we change the order to simplify the problem.

EXAMPLE 3   Changing the Order of Integration

Evaluate $\displaystyle\int_0^{\sqrt{\pi/2}} \int_x^{\sqrt{\pi/2}} \int_1^3 \sin y^2\,dz\,dy\,dx.$

Solution   Note that after one integration in the given order, you would encounter the integral $2\int \sin(y^2)\,dy$, which is not an elementary function. To avoid this problem, change the order of integration to $dz\,dx\,dy$, so that y is the outer variable. The solid region Q is given by

$$0 \le x \le \sqrt{\frac{\pi}{2}}, \qquad x \le y \le \sqrt{\frac{\pi}{2}}, \qquad 1 \le z \le 3$$

as shown in Figure 14.52, and the projection of Q in the xy-plane yields the bounds

$$0 \le y \le \sqrt{\frac{\pi}{2}} \quad \text{and} \quad 0 \le x \le y.$$

Therefore, you have

$$V = \iiint_Q dV$$

$$= \int_0^{\sqrt{\pi/2}} \int_0^y \int_1^3 \sin(y^2)\,dz\,dx\,dy$$

$$= \int_0^{\sqrt{\pi/2}} \int_0^y z\sin(y^2) \Big]_1^3 dx\,dy$$

$$= 2 \int_0^{\sqrt{\pi/2}} \int_0^y \sin(y^2)\,dx\,dy$$

$$= 2 \int_0^{\sqrt{\pi/2}} x\sin(y^2) \Big]_0^y dy$$

$$= 2 \int_0^{\sqrt{\pi/2}} y\sin(y^2)\,dy$$

$$= -\cos(y^2) \Big]_0^{\sqrt{\pi/2}}$$

$$= 1.$$

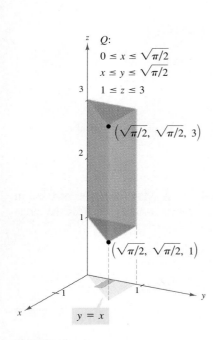

FIGURE 14.52
The volume of the solid region Q is 1.

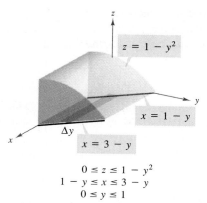

$$z = 1 - y^2$$

$$x = 1 - y$$

$$x = 3 - y$$

$$0 \le z \le 1 - y^2$$
$$1 - y \le x \le 3 - y$$
$$0 \le y \le 1$$

FIGURE 14.53

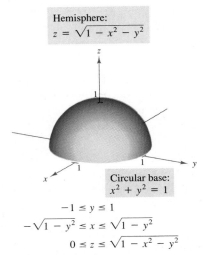

Hemisphere:
$$z = \sqrt{1 - x^2 - y^2}$$

Circular base:
$$x^2 + y^2 = 1$$

$$-1 \le y \le 1$$
$$-\sqrt{1 - y^2} \le x \le \sqrt{1 - y^2}$$
$$0 \le z \le \sqrt{1 - x^2 - y^2}$$

FIGURE 14.54

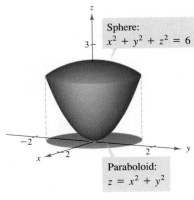

Sphere:
$$x^2 + y^2 + z^2 = 6$$

Paraboloid:
$$z = x^2 + y^2$$

$$x^2 + y^2 \le z \le \sqrt{6 - x^2 - y^2}$$
$$-\sqrt{2 - x^2} \le y \le \sqrt{2 - x^2}$$
$$-\sqrt{2} \le x \le \sqrt{2}$$

FIGURE 14.55

EXAMPLE 4   Determining the Limits of Integration

Set up a triple integral for the volume of each solid region.

a. The region in the first octant bounded above by the cylinder $z = 1 - y^2$ and lying between the vertical planes $x + y = 1$ and $x + y = 3$.

b. The upper hemisphere given by $z = \sqrt{1 - x^2 - y^2}$.

c. The region bounded below by the paraboloid $z = x^2 + y^2$ and above by the sphere $x^2 + y^2 + z^2 = 6$.

Solution

a. In Figure 14.53, note that the solid is bounded below by the xy-plane ($z = 0$) and above by the cylinder $z = 1 - y^2$. Therefore,

$$0 \le z \le 1 - y^2. \qquad \text{\small Bounds for } z$$

Projecting the region onto the xy-plane produces a parallelogram. Because two sides of the parallelogram are parallel to the x-axis, you have the following bounds:

$$1 - y \le x \le 3 - y \quad \text{and} \quad 0 \le y \le 1.$$

Therefore, the volume of the region is given by

$$V = \iiint_Q dV = \int_0^1 \int_{1-y}^{3-y} \int_0^{1-y^2} dz\,dx\,dy.$$

b. For the upper hemisphere given by $z = \sqrt{1 - x^2 - y^2}$, you have

$$0 \le z \le \sqrt{1 - x^2 - y^2}. \qquad \text{\small Bounds for } z$$

In Figure 14.54, note that the projection of the hemisphere onto the xy-plane is the circle given by $x^2 + y^2 = 1$, and you can use either order $dx\,dy$ or $dy\,dx$. Choosing the first produces

$$-\sqrt{1 - y^2} \le x \le \sqrt{1 - y^2} \quad \text{and} \quad -1 \le y \le 1$$

which implies that the volume of the region is given by

$$V = \iiint_Q dV = \int_{-1}^1 \int_{-\sqrt{1-y^2}}^{\sqrt{1-y^2}} \int_0^{\sqrt{1-x^2-y^2}} dz\,dx\,dy.$$

c. For the region bounded below by the paraboloid $z = x^2 + y^2$ and above by the sphere $x^2 + y^2 + z^2 = 6$, you have

$$x^2 + y^2 \le z \le \sqrt{6 - x^2 - y^2}. \qquad \text{\small Bounds for } z$$

The sphere and the paraboloid intersect when $z = 2$. Moreover, you can see in Figure 14.55 that the projection of the solid region onto the xy-plane is the circle given by $x^2 + y^2 = 2$. Using the order $dy\,dx$ produces

$$-\sqrt{2 - x^2} \le y \le \sqrt{2 - x^2} \quad \text{and} \quad -\sqrt{2} \le x \le \sqrt{2}$$

which implies that the volume of the region is given by

$$V = \iiint_Q dV = \int_{-\sqrt{2}}^{\sqrt{2}} \int_{-\sqrt{2-x^2}}^{\sqrt{2-x^2}} \int_{x^2+y^2}^{\sqrt{6-x^2-y^2}} dz\,dy\,dx.$$

Center of Mass and Moments of Inertia

In the remainder of this section, we discuss two applications of triple integrals that are important in engineering. Consider a solid region Q whose density at (x, y, z) is given by the **density function** ρ. The **center of mass** of a solid region Q of mass m is given by $(\bar{x}, \bar{y}, \bar{z})$, where

$$m = \iiint\limits_Q \rho(x, y, z)\, dV \qquad M_{xz} = \iiint\limits_Q y\rho(x, y, z)\, dV$$

$$M_{yz} = \iiint\limits_Q x\rho(x, y, z)\, dV \qquad M_{xy} = \iiint\limits_Q z\rho(x, y, z)\, dV$$

and

$$\bar{x} = \frac{M_{yz}}{m}, \qquad \bar{y} = \frac{M_{xz}}{m}, \qquad \bar{z} = \frac{M_{xy}}{m}.$$

The quantities M_{yz}, M_{xz}, and M_{xy} are called the **first moments** of the region Q about the yz-, xz-, and xy-planes, respectively.

The first moments for solid regions are taken about a plane, whereas the second moments for solids are taken about a line. The **second moments** (or **moments of inertia**) about the x-, y- and z-axes are as follows.

$$I_x = \iiint\limits_Q (y^2 + z^2)\rho(x, y, z)\, dV \qquad \text{Moment of inertia about } x\text{-axis}$$

$$I_y = \iiint\limits_Q (x^2 + z^2)\rho(x, y, z)\, dV \qquad \text{Moment of inertia about } y\text{-axis}$$

$$I_z = \iiint\limits_Q (x^2 + y^2)\rho(x, y, z)\, dV \qquad \text{Moment of inertia about } z\text{-axis}$$

For problems requiring the calculation of all three moments, considerable effort can be saved by applying the additive property of triple integrals and writing

$$I_x = I_{xz} + I_{xy}, \quad I_y = I_{yz} + I_{xy}, \quad \text{and} \quad I_z = I_{yz} + I_{xz}$$

where I_{xy}, I_{xz}, and I_{yz} are as follows.

$$I_{xy} = \iiint\limits_Q z^2 \rho(x, y, z)\, dV$$

$$I_{xz} = \iiint\limits_Q y^2 \rho(x, y, z)\, dV$$

$$I_{yz} = \iiint\limits_Q x^2 \rho(x, y, z)\, dV$$

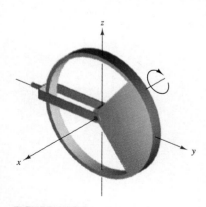

FIGURE 14.56

REMARK   In engineering and physics, the moment of inertia of a mass is used to find the time required for a mass to reach a given speed of rotation about an axis, as indicated in Figure 14.56. The greater the moment of inertia, the longer a force must be applied for the mass to reach the given speed.

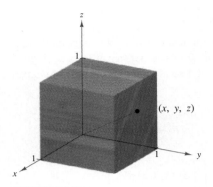

FIGURE 14.57
Variable density:
$\rho(x, y, z) = k(x^2 + y^2 + z^2).$

EXAMPLE 5   Finding the Center of Mass of a Solid Region

Find the center of mass of the unit cube shown in Figure 14.57, given that the density at the point (x, y, z) is proportional to the square of its distance from the origin.

Solution   Because the density at (x, y, z) is proportional to the square of the distance between $(0, 0, 0)$ and (x, y, z), you have

$$\rho(x, y, z) = k(x^2 + y^2 + z^2).$$

You can use this density function to find the mass of the cube. Because of the symmetry of the region, any order of integration will produce an integral of comparable difficulty.

$$m = \int_0^1 \int_0^1 \int_0^1 k(x^2 + y^2 + z^2)\,dz\,dy\,dx$$

$$= k \int_0^1 \int_0^1 \left[(x^2 + y^2)z + \frac{z^3}{3} \right]_0^1 dy\,dx$$

$$= k \int_0^1 \int_0^1 \left(x^2 + y^2 + \frac{1}{3} \right) dy\,dx$$

$$= k \int_0^1 \left[\left(x^2 + \frac{1}{3} \right) y + \frac{y^3}{3} \right]_0^1 dx$$

$$= k \int_0^1 \left(x^2 + \frac{2}{3} \right) dx$$

$$= k \left[\frac{x^3}{3} + \frac{2x}{3} \right]_0^1$$

$$= k$$

The first moment about the yz-plane is

$$M_{yz} = k \int_0^1 \int_0^1 \int_0^1 x(x^2 + y^2 + z^2)\,dz\,dy\,dx$$

$$= k \int_0^1 x \left[\int_0^1 \int_0^1 (x^2 + y^2 + z^2)\,dz\,dy \right] dx.$$

Note that x can be factored out of the two inner integrals, because it is constant with respect to y and z. After factoring, the two inner integrals are the same as for the mass m. Hence, you have

$$M_{yz} = k \int_0^1 x \left(x^2 + \frac{2}{3} \right) dx$$

$$= k \left[\frac{x^4}{4} + \frac{x^2}{3} \right]_0^1$$

$$= \frac{7k}{12}.$$

Therefore,

$$\bar{x} = \frac{M_{yz}}{m} = \frac{7k/12}{k} = \frac{7}{12}.$$

Finally, from the nature of ρ and the symmetry of x, y, and z in this solid region, you have $\bar{x} = \bar{y} = \bar{z}$, and the center of mass is $\left(\frac{7}{12}, \frac{7}{12}, \frac{7}{12} \right)$.

EXAMPLE 6   **Moments of Inertia for a Solid Region**

Find the moments of inertia about the x- and y-axes for the solid region lying between the hemisphere

$$z = \sqrt{4 - x^2 - y^2}$$

and the xy-plane, given that the density at (x, y, z) is proportional to the distance between (x, y, z) and the xy-plane.

Solution   The density of the region is given by $\rho(x, y, z) = kz$. Considering the symmetry of this problem, you know that $I_x = I_y$, and you need to compute only one moment, say I_x. From Figure 14.58, choose the order $dz\, dy\, dx$ and write

$$I_x = \iiint\limits_Q (y^2 + z^2)\rho(x, y, z)\, dV$$

$$= \int_{-2}^{2} \int_{-\sqrt{4-x^2}}^{\sqrt{4-x^2}} \int_{0}^{\sqrt{4-x^2-y^2}} (y^2 + z^2)(kz)\, dz\, dy\, dx$$

$$= k \int_{-2}^{2} \int_{-\sqrt{4-x^2}}^{\sqrt{4-x^2}} \left[\frac{y^2 z^2}{2} + \frac{z^4}{4} \right]_0^{\sqrt{4-x^2-y^2}} dy\, dx$$

$$= k \int_{-2}^{2} \int_{-\sqrt{4-x^2}}^{\sqrt{4-x^2}} \left[\frac{y^2(4 - x^2 - y^2)}{2} + \frac{(4 - x^2 - y^2)^2}{4} \right] dy\, dx$$

$$= \frac{k}{4} \int_{-2}^{2} \int_{-\sqrt{4-x^2}}^{\sqrt{4-x^2}} [(4 - x^2)^2 - y^4]\, dy\, dx$$

$$= \frac{k}{4} \int_{-2}^{2} \left[(4 - x^2)^2 y - \frac{y^5}{5} \right]_{-\sqrt{4-x^2}}^{\sqrt{4-x^2}} dx$$

$$= \frac{k}{4} \int_{-2}^{2} \frac{8}{5}(4 - x^2)^{5/2}\, dx$$

$$= \frac{4k}{5} \int_{0}^{2} (4 - x^2)^{5/2}\, dx \qquad x = 2\sin\theta$$

$$= \frac{4k}{5} \int_{0}^{\pi/2} 64\cos^6\theta\, d\theta$$

$$= \left(\frac{256k}{5} \right) \left(\frac{5\pi}{32} \right) \qquad \text{Wallis's Formula}$$

$$= 8k\pi.$$

Thus, $I_x = 8k\pi$, and $I_y = 8k\pi$.

$-2 \le x \le 2$
$-\sqrt{4 - x^2} \le y \le \sqrt{4 - x^2}$
$0 \le z \le \sqrt{4 - x^2 - y^2}$

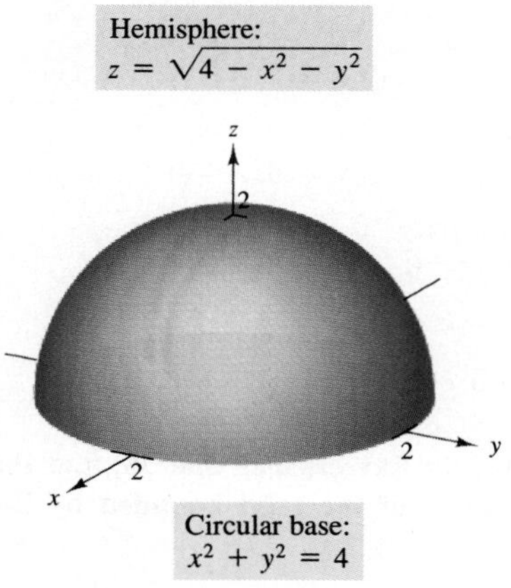

Hemisphere:
$z = \sqrt{4 - x^2 - y^2}$

Circular base:
$x^2 + y^2 = 4$

FIGURE 14.58
Variable density:
$\rho(x, y, z) = kz$

REMARK   In Example 6, notice that the moments of inertia about the x- and y-axes are equal to each other. The moment about the z-axis, however, is different. Does it seem that the moment of inertia about the z-axis should be less or greater than the moments calculated in Example 6? By performing the calculations, you can determine that $I_z = \frac{16}{3}\pi$. This tells you that the solid shown in Figure 14.58 has a greater resistance to rotation about the x- or y-axis than about the z-axis.

EXERCISES for Section 14.6

In Exercises 1–8, evaluate the triple integral.

1. $\displaystyle\int_0^3 \int_0^2 \int_0^1 (x + y + z)\, dx\, dy\, dz$

2. $\displaystyle\int_{-1}^1 \int_{-1}^1 \int_{-1}^1 x^2 y^2 z^2\, dx\, dy\, dz$

3. $\displaystyle\int_0^1 \int_0^x \int_0^{xy} x\, dz\, dy\, dx$

4. $\displaystyle\int_0^4 \int_0^\pi \int_0^{1-x} x\sin y\, dz\, dy\, dx$

5. $\displaystyle\int_1^4 \int_0^1 \int_0^x 2ze^{-x^2}\, dy\, dx\, dz$

6. $\displaystyle\int_1^4 \int_1^{e^2} \int_0^{1/xz} \ln z\, dy\, dz\, dx$

7. $\displaystyle\int_0^9 \int_0^{y/3} \int_0^{\sqrt{y^2-9x^2}} z\, dz\, dx\, dy$

8. $\displaystyle\int_0^{\pi/2} \int_0^{y/2} \int_0^{1/y} \sin y\, dz\, dx\, dy$

C In Exercises 9 and 10, use a symbolic integration utility to evaluate the triple integral.

9. $\displaystyle\int_0^2 \int_{-\sqrt{4-x^2}}^{\sqrt{4-x^2}} \int_0^{x^2} x\, dz\, dy\, dx$

10. $\displaystyle\int_0^{\sqrt{2}} \int_0^{\sqrt{2-x^2}} \int_{2x^2+y^2}^{4-y^2} y\, dz\, dy\, dx$

C In Exercises 11 and 12, use a symbolic integration utility to approximate the triple integral.

11. $\displaystyle\int_0^2 \int_0^{\sqrt{4-x^2}} \int_1^4 \frac{x^2 \sin y}{z}\, dz\, dy\, dx$

12. $\displaystyle\int_0^3 \int_0^{2-(2y/3)} \int_0^{6-2y-3z} ze^{-x^2 y^2}\, dx\, dz\, dy$

In Exercises 13–16, sketch the solid whose volume is given by the triple integral, and rewrite the integral with the specified order of integration.

13. $\displaystyle\int_0^4 \int_0^{(4-x)/2} \int_0^{(12-3x-6y)/4} dz\, dy\, dx$

Rewrite using the order $dy\, dx\, dz$.

14. $\displaystyle\int_0^4 \int_0^{\sqrt{16-x^2}} \int_0^{10-x-y} dz\, dy\, dx$

Rewrite using the order $dz\, dx\, dy$.

15. $\displaystyle\int_0^1 \int_y^1 \int_0^{\sqrt{1-y^2}} dz\, dx\, dy$

Rewrite using the order $dz\, dy\, dx$.

16. $\displaystyle\int_0^2 \int_{2x}^4 \int_0^{\sqrt{y^2-4x^2}} dz\, dy\, dx$

Rewrite using the order $dx\, dy\, dz$.

In Exercises 17 and 18, list the six possible orders of integration for the triple integral

$$\iiint_Q xyz\, dV$$

over the solid Q.

17. $Q = \{(x, y, z): 0 \le x \le 1, 0 \le y \le x, 0 \le z \le 3\}$

18. $Q = \{(x, y, z): 0 \le x \le 2, x^2 \le y \le 4, 0 \le z \le 2 - x\}$

Volume In Exercises 19–24, use a triple integral to find the volume of the solid bounded by the graphs of the given equations.

19. $x = 4 - y^2, z = 0, z = x$

20. $z = xy, z = 0, x = 0, x = 1, y = 0, y = 1$

21. $x^2 + y^2 + z^2 = a^2$

22. $z = 9 - x^2 - y^2, z = 0$

23. $z = 4 - x^2, y = 4 - x^2$ (first octant)

24. $z = 9 - x^2, y = -x + 2, y = 0, z = 0, x \ge 0$

Mass and Center of Mass In Exercises 25–28, find the mass and the indicated coordinates of the center of mass of the solid of specified density bounded by the graphs of the equations.

25. Find $\bar{x}$ using $\rho(x, y, z) = k$.
$Q: 2x + 3y + 6z = 12, x = 0, y = 0, z = 0$

26. Find $\bar{y}$ using $\rho(x, y, z) = ky$.
$Q: 2x + 3y + 6z = 12, x = 0, y = 0, z = 0$

27. Find $\bar{z}$ using $\rho(x, y, z) = kx$.
$Q: z = 4 - x, z = 0, y = 0, y = 4, x = 0$

28. Find $\bar{y}$ using $\rho(x, y, z) = k$.
$Q: \dfrac{x}{a} + \dfrac{y}{b} + \dfrac{z}{c} = 1 \ (a, b, c > 0), x = 0, y = 0, z = 0$

Mass and Center of Mass In Exercises 29 and 30, find the mass and the center of mass of the solid bounded by the graphs of the given equations.

29. $x = 0, x = b, y = 0, y = b, z = 0, z = b,$
$\rho(x, y, z) = kxy$

30. $x = 0, x = a, y = 0, y = b, z = 0, z = c, \rho(x, y, z) = kz$

C *Centroid* In Exercises 31–36, find the centroid of the solid region bounded by the graphs of the given equations or described by the figure. Use a symbolic integration utility to evaluate the triple integrals. (Assume uniform density and find the center of mass.)

31. $z = \dfrac{h}{r}\sqrt{x^2 + y^2}, z = h$

32. $y = \sqrt{4 - x^2}, z = y, z = 0$

33. $z = \sqrt{4^2 - x^2 - y^2}, z = 0$

34. $z = \dfrac{1}{y^2 + 1}$, $z = 0$, $x = -2$, $x = 2$, $y = 0$, $y = 1$

35.

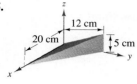

36.

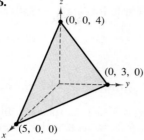

C *Moments of Inertia*   In Exercises 37–40, find I_x, I_y, and I_z for the indicated solid of specified density. Use a symbolic integration utility to evaluate the triple integrals.

37. a. $\rho = k$ **38. a.** $\rho(x, y, z) = k$
   b. $\rho = kxyz$ **b.** $\rho(x, y, z) = k(x^2 + y^2)$

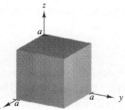   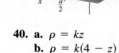

39. a. $\rho(x, y, z) = k$ **40. a.** $\rho = kz$
   b. $\rho = ky$ **b.** $\rho = k(4 - z)$

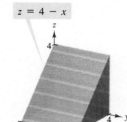   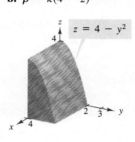

C *Moments of Inertia*   In Exercises 41 and 42, verify the moments of inertia for the solids of uniform density. Use a symbolic integration utility to evaluate the triple integrals.

41. $I_x = I_z = \frac{1}{12} m(3a^2 + L^2)$
   $I_y = \frac{1}{2} ma^2$

42. $I_x = \frac{1}{12} m(a^2 + b^2)$
   $I_y = \frac{1}{12} m(b^2 + c^2)$
   $I_z = \frac{1}{12} m(a^2 + c^2)$

   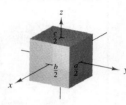

FIGURE FOR 41   **FIGURE FOR 42**
Right Circular Cylinder

Moment of Inertia   In Exercises 43 and 44, set up a triple integral that gives the moment of inertia about the z-axis of the solid Q of density ρ.

43. $Q = \{(x, y, z): -1 \le x \le 1, -1 \le y \le 1,$
   $0 \le z \le 1 - x\}$
   $\rho = \sqrt{x^2 + y^2 + z^2}$

44. $Q = \{(x, y, z): x^2 + y^2 \le 1, 0 \le z \le 4 - x^2 - y^2\}$
   $\rho = kx^2$

Triple Integrals in Cylindrical and Spherical Coordinates

Triple Integrals in Cylindrical Coordinates • Triple Integrals in Spherical Coordinates

PIERRE SIMON DE LAPLACE

One of the first to use a cylindrical coordinate system was the French mathematician Pierre Simon de Laplace (1749–1827). Laplace has been called the "Newton of France," and he published many important works in mechanics, differential equations, and probability.

Triple Integrals in Cylindrical Coordinates

Many common solid regions such as spheres, ellipsoids, cones, and paraboloids can yield difficult triple integrals in rectangular coordinates. In fact, it is precisely this difficulty that led to the introduction of nonrectangular coordinate systems. In this section, you will learn how to use *cylindrical* and *spherical* coordinates to evaluate triple integrals.

Recall from Section 11.7 that the rectangular conversion equations for cylindrical coordinates are

$$x = r\cos\theta, \quad y = r\sin\theta, \quad \text{and} \quad z = z.$$

In this coordinate system, the simplest solid region is a cylindrical block determined by

$$r_1 \le r \le r_2, \quad \theta_1 \le \theta \le \theta_2, \quad \text{and} \quad z_1 \le z \le z_2$$

as shown in Figure 14.59.

To obtain the cylindrical coordinate form of a triple integral, let f be a continuous function of r, θ, and z defined over a bounded solid region Q. Then, encompass the solid by a network of cylindrical blocks and form the **inner partition** Δ, consisting of all blocks lying entirely within Q. The **norm** $\|\Delta\|$ of the partition is the length of the longest diagonal of the n blocks in Δ. If you choose a point (r_i, θ_i, z_i) in the ith block such that r_i is the average radius of the block, then the block's volume is

$$\Delta V_i = (\text{area of base})(\text{height}) = (r_i \Delta r_i \Delta\theta_i)\,\Delta z_i.$$

Forming the sum

$$\sum_{i=1}^{n} f(r_i, \theta_i, z_i) r_i\, \Delta r_i\, \Delta\theta_i\, \Delta z_i$$

and taking the limit as $\|\Delta\| \to 0$ suggests the following definition.

Triple Integral in Cylindrical Coordinates

If f is a continuous function of r, θ, and z on a bounded solid region Q, then in cylindrical coordinates the **triple integral of f over Q** is

$$\iiint\limits_{Q} f(r, \theta, z)\, dV = \lim_{\|\Delta\| \to 0} \sum_{i=1}^{n} f(r_i, \theta_i, z_i) r_i\, \Delta r_i\, \Delta\theta_i\, \Delta z_i.$$

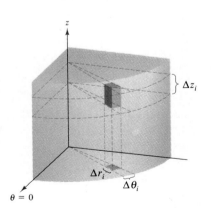

FIGURE 14.59
Volume of cylindrical block:
$\Delta V_i = r_i \Delta r_i \Delta\theta_i \Delta z_i.$

You can evaluate a triple integral in cylindrical coordinates, provided that the solid region Q is simple with respect to one of the six possible orders of integration. For example, if the region is bounded above and below by $h_1(r, \theta) \leq z \leq h_2(r, \theta)$, then you can write

$$\iiint_Q f(r, \theta, z)\, dV = \iint_R \left[\int_{h_1(r,\theta)}^{h_2(r,\theta)} f(r, \theta, z)\, dz \right] r\, dr\, d\theta$$

where the double integral over R is evaluated in polar coordinates. (That is, R is a plane region that is either r-simple or θ-simple, as discussed in Section 14.3.) If R is r-simple, then the iterated form is

$$\int_{\theta_1}^{\theta_2} \int_{g_1(\theta)}^{g_2(\theta)} \int_{h_1(r,\theta)}^{h_2(r,\theta)} f(r, \theta, z)\, r\, dz\, dr\, d\theta.$$

To visualize a particular order of integration, it helps to view the iterated integral in terms of three sweeping motions—each adding another dimension to the solid. For instance, in the order $dr\, d\theta\, dz$, the first integration occurs in the r-direction as a point sweeps out a ray. Then, as θ increases, the line sweeps out a sector. Finally, as z increases, the sector sweeps out a solid wedge, as shown in Figure 14.60.

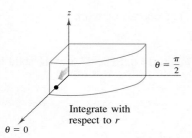

Integrate with respect to r

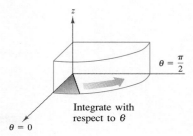

Integrate with respect to θ

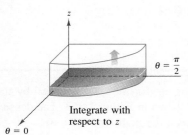

Integrate with respect to z

FIGURE 14.60

EXAMPLE 1   Finding Volume by Cylindrical Coordinates

Find the volume of the solid region Q cut from the sphere $x^2 + y^2 + z^2 = 4$ by the cylinder $r = 2 \sin \theta$, as shown in Figure 14.61.

Solution   Because $x^2 + y^2 + z^2 = r^2 + z^2 = 4$, the bounds on z are

$$-\sqrt{4 - r^2} \leq z \leq \sqrt{4 - r^2}.$$

Let R be the circular projection of the solid onto the $r\theta$-plane. Then the bounds on R are $0 \leq r \leq 2 \sin \theta$ and $0 \leq \theta \leq \pi$. Thus, the volume of Q is

$$
\begin{aligned}
V &= \int_0^\pi \int_0^{2\sin\theta} \int_{-\sqrt{4-r^2}}^{\sqrt{4-r^2}} r\, dz\, dr\, d\theta \\
&= \int_0^\pi \int_0^{2\sin\theta} rz \Big]_{-\sqrt{4-r^2}}^{\sqrt{4-r^2}} dr\, d\theta \\
&= 2\int_0^{\pi/2} \int_0^{2\sin\theta} 2r\sqrt{4-r^2}\, dr\, d\theta \\
&= 2\int_0^{\pi/2} -\frac{2}{3}(4-r^2)^{3/2} \Big]_0^{2\sin\theta} d\theta \\
&= \frac{4}{3}\int_0^{\pi/2} \left[8 - 8\cos^3\theta \right] d\theta \\
&= \frac{32}{3}\int_0^{\pi/2} \left[1 - (\cos\theta)(1 - \sin^2\theta) \right] d\theta \\
&= \frac{32}{3}\left[\theta - \sin\theta + \frac{\sin^3\theta}{3} \right]_0^{\pi/2} \\
&= \frac{16}{9}(3\pi - 4).
\end{aligned}
$$

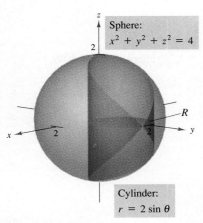

Sphere:
$x^2 + y^2 + z^2 = 4$

Cylinder:
$r = 2\sin\theta$

FIGURE 14.61
The volume of the solid region Q is $\frac{16}{9}(3\pi - 4)$.

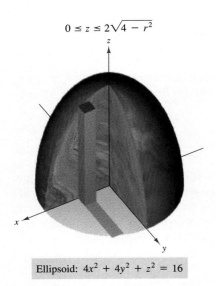

$0 \leq z \leq 2\sqrt{4 - r^2}$

Ellipsoid: $4x^2 + 4y^2 + z^2 = 16$

FIGURE 14.62
The mass of the ellipsoidal solid is $16\pi k$.

EXAMPLE 2   Finding Mass by Cylindrical Coordinates

Find the mass of the ellipsoidal solid Q given by $4x^2 + 4y^2 + z^2 = 16$, lying above the xy-plane. The density at a point in the solid is proportional to the distance between the point and the xy-plane.

Solution   The density function $\rho(r, \theta, z) = kz$. The bounds on z are

$$0 \leq z \leq \sqrt{16 - 4x^2 - 4y^2} = 2\sqrt{4 - r^2}$$

where $0 \leq r \leq 2$ and $0 \leq \theta \leq 2\pi$, as shown in Figure 14.62. The mass of the solid is

$$m = \int_0^{2\pi} \int_0^2 \int_0^{\sqrt{16-4r^2}} kzr \, dz \, dr \, d\theta$$

$$= \frac{k}{2} \int_0^{2\pi} \int_0^2 z^2 r \Big]_0^{\sqrt{16-4r^2}} dr \, d\theta$$

$$= \frac{k}{2} \int_0^{2\pi} \int_0^2 (16r - 4r^3) \, dr \, d\theta$$

$$= \frac{k}{2} \int_0^{2\pi} \left[8r^2 - r^4 \right]_0^2 d\theta$$

$$= 8k \int_0^{2\pi} d\theta = 16\pi k.$$

EXAMPLE 3   Finding a Moment of Inertia

Find the moment of inertia about the axis of symmetry of the solid bounded by the paraboloid $z = x^2 + y^2$ and the plane $z = 4$, as shown in Figure 14.63. The density at each point is proportional to the distance between the point and the z-axis.

Solution   Because the z-axis is the axis of symmetry, and $\rho(x, y, z) = k\sqrt{x^2 + y^2}$, it follows that

$$I_z = \iiint\limits_Q k(x^2 + y^2)\sqrt{x^2 + y^2} \, dV.$$

In cylindrical coordinates, $0 \leq r \leq \sqrt{x^2 + y^2} = \sqrt{z}$. Therefore, you have

$$I_z = k \int_0^4 \int_0^{2\pi} \int_0^{\sqrt{z}} r^2(r) r \, dr \, d\theta \, dz$$

$$= k \int_0^4 \int_0^{2\pi} \frac{r^5}{5} \Big]_0^{\sqrt{z}} d\theta \, dz$$

$$= k \int_0^4 \int_0^{2\pi} \frac{z^{5/2}}{5} \, d\theta \, dz$$

$$= k \int_0^4 \frac{z^{5/2}}{5} (2\pi) \, dz$$

$$= k \left[\left(\frac{2\pi}{5} \right) \left(\frac{2}{7} \right) z^{7/2} \right]_0^4 = \frac{512k\pi}{35}.$$

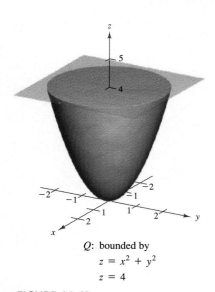

Q: bounded by
$z = x^2 + y^2$
$z = 4$

FIGURE 14.63
The moment of inertia about the z-axis is $(512k\pi)/(35)$.

Triple Integrals in Spherical Coordinates

Recall from Section 11.7 that the rectangular conversion equations for spherical coordinates are

$$x = \rho \sin\phi \cos\theta, \quad y = \rho \sin\phi \sin\theta, \quad \text{and} \quad z = \rho \cos\phi.$$

For solids in spherical coordinates, the fundamental element of volume is a spherical block determined by $\rho_1 \le \rho \le \rho_2$, $\theta_1 \le \theta \le \theta_2$, and $\phi_1 \le \phi \le \phi_2$, as shown in Figure 14.64. If (ρ, θ, ϕ) is a point in the interior of such a block, then the volume of the block can be approximated as follows.

$$\Delta V \approx \rho^2 \sin\phi \, \Delta\rho \, \Delta\theta \, \Delta\phi$$

Using the usual inner partition–summation–limit process, you can develop the following version of a triple integral in spherical coordinates.

Triple Integral in Spherical Coordinates

If f is a continuous function of ρ, θ, and ϕ on a bounded solid region Q, then in spherical coordinates the **triple integral of f over Q** is

$$\iiint\limits_{Q} f(\rho, \theta, \phi) \, dV = \lim_{\|\Delta\| \to 0} \sum_{i=1}^{n} f(\rho_i, \theta_i, \phi_i) \rho_i^2 \sin\phi_i \, \Delta\rho_i \, \Delta\theta_i \, \Delta\phi_i.$$

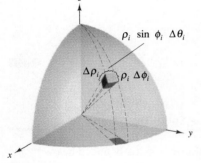

FIGURE 14.64
Spherical block:
$\Delta V_i \approx \rho_i^2 \sin\phi_i \, \Delta\rho_i \, \Delta\theta_i \, \Delta\phi_i.$

REMARK The Greek letter ρ used in spherical coordinates is not related to density. Rather, it is the three-dimensional analog of the r used in polar coordinates. For problems involving spherical coordinates and a density function, we will use a different symbol to denote density.

Like triple integrals in cylindrical coordinates, triple integrals in spherical coordinates are evaluated with iterated integrals. As with cylindrical coordinates, you can visualize a particular order of integration by viewing the iterated integral in terms of three sweeping motions—each adding another dimension to the solid. For instance, the iterated integral

$$\int_{0}^{2\pi} \int_{0}^{\pi/4} \int_{0}^{3} \rho^2 \sin\phi \, d\rho \, d\phi \, d\theta$$

(which is used Example 4) is illustrated in Figure 14.65.

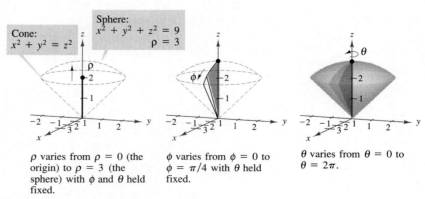

Cone:
$x^2 + y^2 = z^2$

Sphere:
$x^2 + y^2 + z^2 = 9$
$\rho = 3$

ρ varies from $\rho = 0$ (the origin) to $\rho = 3$ (the sphere) with ϕ and θ held fixed.

ϕ varies from $\phi = 0$ to $\phi = \pi/4$ with θ held fixed.

θ varies from $\theta = 0$ to $\theta = 2\pi$.

FIGURE 14.65

EXAMPLE 4   Finding Volume in Spherical Coordinates

Find the volume of the solid region Q bounded below by the upper nappe of the cone $z^2 = x^2 + y^2$ and above by the sphere $x^2 + y^2 + z^2 = 9$, as shown in Figure 14.66.

Solution   In spherical coordinates, the equation of the sphere is

$$\rho^2 = x^2 + y^2 + z^2 = 9 \quad \longrightarrow \quad \rho = 3.$$

Furthermore, the sphere and cone intersect when

$$(x^2 + y^2) + z^2 = (z^2) + z^2 = 9 \quad \longrightarrow \quad z = \frac{3}{\sqrt{2}}$$

and, because $z = \rho \cos \phi$, it follows that

$$\left(\frac{3}{\sqrt{2}}\right)\left(\frac{1}{3}\right) = \cos \phi \quad \longrightarrow \quad \phi = \frac{\pi}{4}.$$

Consequently, you can use the integration order $d\rho \, d\phi \, d\theta$, where $0 \le \rho \le 3$, $0 \le \phi \le \pi/4$, and $0 \le \theta \le 2\pi$. The volume is

$$V = \iiint_Q dV = \int_0^{2\pi} \int_0^{\pi/4} \int_0^3 \rho^2 \sin\phi \, d\rho \, d\phi \, d\theta$$

$$= \int_0^{2\pi} \int_0^{\pi/4} 9 \sin\phi \, d\phi \, d\theta$$

$$= 9 \int_0^{2\pi} -\cos \phi \Big]_0^{\pi/4} d\theta$$

$$= 9 \int_0^{2\pi} \left(1 - \frac{\sqrt{2}}{2}\right) d\theta = 9\pi(2 - \sqrt{2}) \approx 16.56.$$

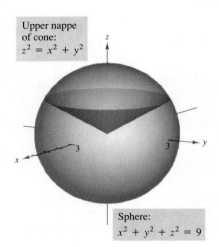

Upper nappe
of cone:
$z^2 = x^2 + y^2$

Sphere:
$x^2 + y^2 + z^2 = 9$

FIGURE 14.66

EXAMPLE 5   Finding the Center of Mass of a Solid Region

Find the center of mass of the solid region Q of uniform density, bounded below by the upper nappe of the cone $z^2 = x^2 + y^2$ and above by the sphere $x^2 + y^2 + z^2 = 9$.

Solution   Because the density is uniform, you can consider the density at the point (x, y, z) to be k. By symmetry, the center of mass lies on the z-axis, and we need only calculate $\bar{z} = M_{xy}/m$, where $m = kV = 9k\pi(2 - \sqrt{2})$ from Example 4. Because $z = \rho \cos \phi$, it follows that

$$M_{xy} = \iiint_Q kz \, dV = k \int_0^3 \int_0^{2\pi} \int_0^{\pi/4} (\rho \cos \phi)\rho^2 \sin \phi \, d\phi \, d\theta \, d\rho$$

$$= k \int_0^3 \int_0^{2\pi} \rho^3 \frac{\sin^2 \phi}{2} \Big]_0^{\pi/4} d\theta \, d\rho$$

$$= \frac{k}{4} \int_0^3 \int_0^{2\pi} \rho^3 \, d\theta \, d\rho = \frac{k\pi}{2} \int_0^3 \rho^3 \, d\rho = \frac{81k\pi}{8}.$$

Therefore,

$$\bar{z} = \frac{M_{xy}}{m} = \frac{81k\pi/8}{9k\pi(2 - \sqrt{2})} = \frac{9(2 + \sqrt{2})}{16} \approx 1.92$$

and the center of mass is approximately $(0, 0, 1.92)$.

EXERCISES for Section 14.7

In Exercises 1–6, evaluate the triple integral.

1. $\displaystyle\int_0^4 \int_0^{\pi/2} \int_0^2 r\cos\theta \, dr \, d\theta \, dz$

2. $\displaystyle\int_0^{\pi/4} \int_0^2 \int_0^{2-r} rz \, dz \, dr \, d\theta$

3. $\displaystyle\int_0^{\pi/2} \int_0^{2\cos^2\theta} \int_0^{4-r^2} r\sin\theta \, dz \, dr \, d\theta$

4. $\displaystyle\int_0^{\pi/2} \int_0^{\pi} \int_0^2 e^{-\rho^3}\rho^2 \, d\rho \, d\theta \, d\phi$

5. $\displaystyle\int_0^{2\pi} \int_0^{\pi/4} \int_0^{\cos\phi} \rho^2 \sin\phi \, d\rho \, d\phi \, d\theta$

6. $\displaystyle\int_0^{\pi/4} \int_0^{\pi/4} \int_0^{\cos\theta} \rho^2 \sin\phi \cos\phi \, d\rho \, d\theta \, d\phi$

C In Exercises 7 and 8, use a symbolic integration utility to evaluate the triple integral.

7. $\displaystyle\int_0^4 \int_0^z \int_0^{\pi/2} re^r \, d\theta \, dr \, dz$

8. $\displaystyle\int_0^{\pi/2} \int_0^{\pi} \int_0^{\sin\theta} (2\cos\phi)\rho^2 \, d\rho \, d\theta \, d\phi$

In Exercises 9–12, sketch the solid region whose volume is given by the integral, and evaluate the integral.

9. $\displaystyle\int_0^{\pi/2} \int_0^3 \int_0^{e^{-r^2}} r \, dz \, dr \, d\theta$

10. $\displaystyle\int_0^{2\pi} \int_0^{\sqrt{3}} \int_0^{3-r^2} r \, dz \, dr \, d\theta$

11. $\displaystyle\int_0^{2\pi} \int_{\pi/6}^{\pi/2} \int_0^4 \rho^2 \sin\phi \, d\rho \, d\phi \, d\theta$

12. $\displaystyle\int_0^{2\pi} \int_0^{\pi} \int_2^5 \rho^2 \sin\phi \, d\rho \, d\phi \, d\theta$

In Exercises 13–16, convert the integral from rectangular coordinates to both cylindrical and spherical coordinates, and evaluate the simplest integral.

13. $\displaystyle\int_{-2}^2 \int_{-\sqrt{4-x^2}}^{\sqrt{4-x^2}} \int_{x^2+y^2}^4 x \, dz \, dy \, dx$

14. $\displaystyle\int_0^2 \int_0^{\sqrt{4-x^2}} \int_0^{\sqrt{16-x^2-y^2}} \sqrt{x^2+y^2} \, dz \, dy \, dx$

15. $\displaystyle\int_{-a}^a \int_{-\sqrt{a^2-x^2}}^{\sqrt{a^2-x^2}} \int_a^{a+\sqrt{a^2-x^2-y^2}} x \, dz \, dy \, dx$

16. $\displaystyle\int_0^1 \int_0^{\sqrt{1-x^2}} \int_0^{\sqrt{1-x^2-y^2}} \sqrt{x^2+y^2+z^2} \, dz \, dy \, dx$

In Exercises 17–22, use cylindrical coordinates to find the indicated characteristic of the cone (see figure).

17. *Volume* Find the volume of the cone.

18. *Centroid* Find the centroid of the cone.

C 19. *Center of Mass* Find the center of mass of the cone, assuming that its density at any point is proportional to the distance between the point and the axis of the cone. Use a symbolic integration utility to evaluate the triple integral.

C 20. *Center of Mass* Find the center of mass of the cone, assuming that its density at any point is proportional to the distance between the point and the base. Use a symbolic integration utility to evaluate the triple integral.

21. *Moment of Inertia* Assume that the cone has uniform density, and show that the moment of inertia about the z-axis is

$$I_z = \frac{3}{10}mr_0^2.$$

22. *Moment of Inertia* Assume that the density is given by

$$\rho(x, y, z) = k(x^2 + y^2)$$

and find the moment of inertia about the z-axis.

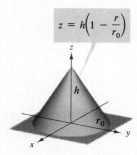

$$z = h\left(1 - \frac{r}{r_0}\right)$$

FIGURE FOR 17–22

***Moment of Inertia* In Exercises 23 and 24, use cylindrical coordinates to verify the given formula for the moment of inertia of the solid of uniform density.**

23. Cylindrical shell: $I_z = \frac{1}{2}m(a^2 + b^2)$

$$0 < a \leq r \leq b, \; 0 \leq z \leq h$$

C 24. Right circular cylinder: $I_z = \frac{3}{2}ma^2$

$$r = 2a\sin\theta, \; 0 \leq z \leq h$$

Use a computer algebra system to evaluate the triple integral.

***Volume* In Exercises 25–28, use cylindrical coordinates to find the volume of the solid.**

25. Solid inside both $x^2 + y^2 + z^2 = a^2$

and $\left(x - \dfrac{a}{2}\right)^2 + y^2 = \left(\dfrac{a}{2}\right)^2$

26. Solid inside $x^2 + y^2 + z^2 = 16$ and outside $z = \sqrt{x^2 + y^2}$

27. *Volume*   Find the volume of the solid bounded by the graphs of the sphere $r^2 + z^2 = a^2$ and the cylinder $r = a \cos \theta$.

28. *Volume*   Find the volume of the solid inside the sphere $x^2 + y^2 + z^2 = 4$ and above the cone $z^2 = x^2 + y^2$.

C *Volume*   **In Exercises 29 and 30, use spherical coordinates to find the volume of the solid.**

29. The torus given by $\rho = 4 \sin \phi$. Use a symbolic integration utility to evaluate the triple integral.

30. The solid between the spheres $x^2 + y^2 + z^2 = a^2$ and $x^2 + y^2 + z^2 = b^2$, $b > a$, and inside the cone $z^2 = x^2 + y^2$

Mass   **In Exercises 31 and 32, use spherical coordinates to find the mass of the sphere $x^2 + y^2 + z^2 = a^2$ with the specified density.**

31. The density at any point is proportional to the distance between the point and the origin.

32. The density at any point is proportional to the distance of the point from the z-axis.

Center of Mass   **In Exercises 33 and 34, use spherical coordinates to find the center of mass of the solid of uniform density.**

33. Hemispherical solid of radius r

34. Solid lying between two concentric hemispheres of radii r and R, where $r < R$

Moment of Inertia   **In Exercises 35 and 36, use spherical coordinates to find the moment of inertia about the z-axis of the solid of uniform density.**

35. Solid bounded by the hemisphere $\rho = \cos \phi$, $\pi/4 \le \phi \le \pi/2$, and the cone $\phi = \pi/4$

36. Solid lying between two concentric hemispheres of radii r and R, where $r < R$

Wrinkled and Bumpy Spheres   **In Exercises 37 and 38, find the volume of the wrinkled sphere or bumpy sphere. These solids are used as models for tumors. (For more information on this, see the article "Heat Therapy for Tumors" by Leah Edelstine-Keshet in the Summer, 1991 issue of the *UMAP Journal*.)**

37. Wrinkled sphere
$\rho = 1 + 0.2 \sin 8\theta \sin \phi$
$(0 \le \theta \le 2\pi, 0 \le \phi \le \pi)$

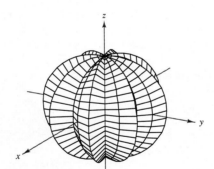

38. Bumpy sphere
$\rho = 1 + 0.2 \sin 8\theta \sin 4\phi$
$(0 \le \theta \le 2\pi, 0 \le \phi \le \pi)$

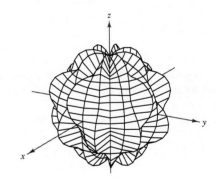

SECTION
14.8 Change of Variables: Jacobians

Jacobians • Change of Variables for Double Integrals

CARL GUSTAV JACOBI

The Jacobian is named after the German mathematician Carl Gustav Jacobi (1804–1851). Jacobi is known for his work in many areas of mathematics, but his interest in integration stemmed from the problem of finding the circumference of an ellipse.

Jacobians

For the single integral

$$\int_a^b f(x)\,dx$$

you can change variables by letting $x = g(u)$, so that $dx = g'(u)\,du$, and obtain

$$\int_a^b f(x)\,dx = \int_c^d f(g(u))g'(u)\,du$$

where $a = g(c)$ and $b = g(d)$. Note that the change of variables process introduces an additional factor $g'(u)$ into the integrand. This also occurs in the case of double integrals.

$$\iint_R f(x, y)\,dA = \iint_S f(g(u,v), h(u,v)) \underbrace{\left| \frac{\partial x}{\partial u} \frac{\partial y}{\partial v} - \frac{\partial y}{\partial u} \frac{\partial x}{\partial v} \right|}_{\text{Jacobian}} du\,dv$$

where the change of variables $x = g(u, v)$ and $y = h(u, v)$ introduces a factor called the **Jacobian** of x and y with respect to u and v. In defining the Jacobian, it is convenient to use the following determinant notation.

Definition of the Jacobian

If $x = g(u, v)$ and $y = h(u, v)$, then the **Jacobian** of x and y with respect to u and v, denoted by $\partial(x, y)/\partial(u, v)$, is

$$\frac{\partial(x, y)}{\partial(u, v)} = \begin{vmatrix} \dfrac{\partial x}{\partial u} & \dfrac{\partial x}{\partial v} \\[2mm] \dfrac{\partial y}{\partial u} & \dfrac{\partial y}{\partial v} \end{vmatrix} = \frac{\partial x}{\partial u} \frac{\partial y}{\partial v} - \frac{\partial y}{\partial u} \frac{\partial x}{\partial v}.$$

EXAMPLE 1   The Jacobian for Rectangular-to-Polar Conversion

Find the Jacobian for the change of variables defined by

$$x = r\cos\theta \quad \text{and} \quad y = r\sin\theta.$$

Solution   From the definition of a Jacobian, you obtain

$$\frac{\partial(x, y)}{\partial(r, \theta)} = \begin{vmatrix} \dfrac{\partial x}{\partial r} & \dfrac{\partial x}{\partial \theta} \\[2mm] \dfrac{\partial y}{\partial r} & \dfrac{\partial y}{\partial \theta} \end{vmatrix} = \begin{vmatrix} \cos\theta & -r\sin\theta \\ \sin\theta & r\cos\theta \end{vmatrix} = r\cos^2\theta + r\sin^2\theta = r.$$

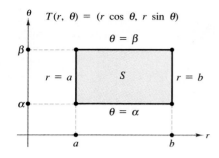

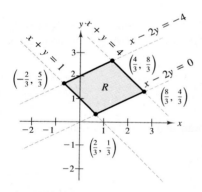

FIGURE 14.67
S in the $r\theta$-plane corresponds to R in the xy-plane.

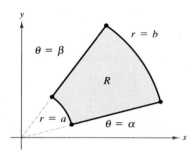

FIGURE 14.68
Region R in the xy-plane.

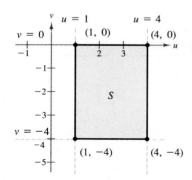

FIGURE 14.69
Region S in the uv-plane.

Example 1 points out that the change of variables from rectangular to polar coordinates for a double integral can be written as

$$\iint_R f(x, y)\, dA = \iint_S f(r\cos\theta, r\sin\theta) r\, dr\, d\theta, \quad r > 0$$

$$= \iint_S f(r\cos\theta, r\sin\theta) \left|\frac{\partial(x, y)}{\partial(r, \theta)}\right|\, dr\, d\theta$$

where S is the region in the $r\theta$-plane that corresponds to the region R in the xy-plane, as shown in Figure 14.67.

In general, a change of variables is given by a one-to-one **transformation** T from a region S in the uv-plane to a region R in the xy-plane, to be given by

$$T(u, v) = (x, y)$$
$$= (g(u, v), h(u, v))$$

where g and h have continuous first partial derivatives in the region S. Note that the point (u, v) lies in S and the point (x, y) lies in R. In most cases, you are hunting for a transformation for which the region S is simpler than the region R.

EXAMPLE 2   Finding a Change of Variables to Simplify a Region

Let R be the region bounded by the lines

$$x - 2y = 0, \quad x - 2y = -4, \quad x + y = 4, \quad \text{and} \quad x + y = 1$$

as shown in Figure 14.68. Find a transformation T from a region S to R such that S is a rectangular region (with sides parallel to the u- or v-axis).

Solution   To begin, let $u = x + y$ and $v = x - 2y$. Solving this system of equations for x and y produces $T(u, v) = (x, y)$, where

$$x = \frac{1}{3}(2u + v) \quad \text{and} \quad y = \frac{1}{3}(u - v).$$

The four boundaries for R in the xy-plane give rise to the following bounds for S in the uv-plane.

Bounds in xy-plane		*Bounds in uv-plane*
$x + y = 1$	$\longrightarrow$	$u = 1$
$x + y = 4$	$\longrightarrow$	$u = 4$
$x - 2y = 0$	$\longrightarrow$	$v = 0$
$x - 2y = -4$	$\longrightarrow$	$v = -4$

The region S is shown in Figure 14.69. Note that the transformation T maps the vertices of the region S onto the vertices of the region R.

$$T(1, 0) = \left(\frac{1}{3}[2(1) + 0], \frac{1}{3}[1 - 0]\right) = \left(\frac{2}{3}, \frac{1}{3}\right)$$

$$T(4, 0) = \left(\frac{1}{3}[2(4) + 0], \frac{1}{3}[4 - 0]\right) = \left(\frac{8}{3}, \frac{4}{3}\right)$$

$$T(1, -4) = \left(\frac{1}{3}[2(1) - 4], \frac{1}{3}[1 - (-4)]\right) = \left(-\frac{2}{3}, \frac{5}{3}\right)$$

$$T(4, -4) = \left(\frac{1}{3}[2(4) - 4], \frac{1}{3}[4 - (-4)]\right) = \left(\frac{4}{3}, \frac{8}{3}\right)$$

Change of Variables for Double Integrals

> **THEOREM 14.6   Change of Variables for Double Integrals**
>
> Let R and S be regions in the xy- and uv-planes that are related by the equations $x = g(u, v)$ and $y = h(u, v)$ such that each point in R is the image of a unique point in S. If f is continuous on R, g and h have continuous partial derivatives on S, and $\partial(x, y)/\partial(u, v)$ is nonzero on S, then
>
> $$\iint_R f(x, y)\, dA = \iint_S f(g(u, v), h(u, v)) \left| \frac{\partial(x, y)}{\partial(u, v)} \right| du\, dv.$$

Proof   Consider the case in which S is a rectangular region in the uv-plane with vertices (u, v), $(u + \Delta u, v)$, $(u + \Delta u, v + \Delta v)$, and $(u, v + \Delta v)$, as shown in Figure 14.70. The images of these vertices in the xy-plane are shown in Figure 14.71. If Δu and Δv are small, then the continuity of g and h implies that R is approximately a parallelogram determined by the vectors $\overrightarrow{MN}$ and $\overrightarrow{MQ}$. Thus, the area of R is $\Delta A \approx \| \overrightarrow{MN} \times \overrightarrow{MQ} \|$. Moreover, for small Δu and Δv, the partial derivatives of g and h with respect to u can be approximated by

$$g_u(u, v) \approx \frac{g(u + \Delta u, v) - g(u, v)}{\Delta u}$$

and

$$h_u(u, v) \approx \frac{h(u + \Delta u, v) - h(u, v)}{\Delta u}.$$

Consequently,

$$\overrightarrow{MN} = [g(u + \Delta u, v) - g(u, v)]\mathbf{i} + [h(u + \Delta u, v) - h(u, v)]\mathbf{j}$$
$$\approx [g_u(u, v)\, \Delta u]\mathbf{i} + [h_u(u, v)\, \Delta u]\mathbf{j} = \frac{\partial x}{\partial u}\Delta u\, \mathbf{i} + \frac{\partial y}{\partial u}\Delta u\, \mathbf{j}.$$

Similarly, you can approximate $\overrightarrow{MQ}$ by $\dfrac{\partial x}{\partial v}\Delta v\, \mathbf{i} + \dfrac{\partial y}{\partial v}\Delta v\, \mathbf{j}$, which implies that

$$\overrightarrow{MN} \times \overrightarrow{MQ} \approx \begin{vmatrix} \mathbf{i} & \mathbf{j} & \mathbf{k} \\ \dfrac{\partial x}{\partial u}\Delta u & \dfrac{\partial y}{\partial u}\Delta u & 0 \\ \dfrac{\partial x}{\partial v}\Delta v & \dfrac{\partial y}{\partial v}\Delta v & 0 \end{vmatrix} = \begin{vmatrix} \dfrac{\partial x}{\partial u} & \dfrac{\partial y}{\partial u} \\ \dfrac{\partial x}{\partial v} & \dfrac{\partial y}{\partial v} \end{vmatrix} \Delta u\, \Delta v\, \mathbf{k}.$$

It follows that, in Jacobian notation,

$$\Delta A \approx \| \overrightarrow{MN} \times \overrightarrow{MQ} \| \approx \left| \frac{\partial(x, y)}{\partial(u, v)} \right| \Delta u\, \Delta v.$$

Because this approximation improves as Δu and Δv approach 0, the limiting case can be written as

$$dA \approx \| \overrightarrow{MN} \times \overrightarrow{MQ} \| \approx \left| \frac{\partial(x, y)}{\partial(u, v)} \right| du\, dv.$$

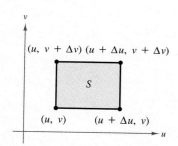

FIGURE 14.70
Area of $S = \Delta u \Delta v$
$\Delta u > 0$, $\Delta v > 0$.

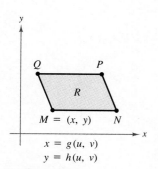

$$x = g(u, v)$$
$$y = h(u, v)$$

FIGURE 14.71
$M = (g(u, v), h(u, v))$
$N = (g(u + \Delta u, v), h(u + \Delta u, v))$
$P = (g(u + \Delta u, v + \Delta v),$
$\quad h(u + \Delta u, v + \Delta v))$
$Q = (g(u, v + \Delta v), h(u, v + \Delta v))$

The next two examples show how a change of variables can simplify the integration process. The simplification can occur in various ways. You can make a change of variables to simplify either the *region R* or the *integrand f(x, y)*, or both.

EXAMPLE 3   Using a Change of Variables to Simplify a Region

Let R be the region bounded by the lines

$$x - 2y = 0, \quad x - 2y = -4, \quad x + y = 4, \quad \text{and} \quad x + y = 1$$

as shown in Figure 14.72. Evaluate the double integral

$$\int_R\int 3xy \, dA.$$

Solution   From Example 2, you can use the following change of variables.

$$y = \frac{1}{3}(u - v) \quad \text{and} \quad x = \frac{1}{3}(2u + v)$$

The partial derivatives of x and y are

$$\frac{\partial x}{\partial u} = \frac{2}{3}, \quad \frac{\partial x}{\partial v} = \frac{1}{3}, \quad \frac{\partial y}{\partial u} = \frac{1}{3}, \quad \text{and} \quad \frac{\partial y}{\partial v} = -\frac{1}{3}$$

which implies that the Jacobian is

$$\frac{\partial(x, y)}{\partial(u, v)} = \begin{vmatrix} \dfrac{\partial x}{\partial u} & \dfrac{\partial x}{\partial v} \\[2mm] \dfrac{\partial y}{\partial u} & \dfrac{\partial y}{\partial v} \end{vmatrix}$$

$$= \begin{vmatrix} \dfrac{2}{3} & \dfrac{1}{3} \\[2mm] \dfrac{1}{3} & -\dfrac{1}{3} \end{vmatrix}$$

$$= -\frac{2}{9} - \frac{1}{9} = -\frac{1}{3}.$$

Therefore, by Theorem 14.6, you obtain

$$\int_R\int 3xy \, dA = \int_S\int 3\left[\frac{1}{3}(2u + v)\frac{1}{3}(u - v)\right] \left|\frac{\partial(x, y)}{\partial(u, v)}\right| dv \, du$$

$$= \int_1^4 \int_{-4}^0 \frac{1}{9}(2u^2 - uv - v^2) \, dv \, du$$

$$= \frac{1}{9}\int_1^4 \left[2u^2v - \frac{uv^2}{2} - \frac{v^3}{3}\right]_{-4}^0 du$$

$$= \frac{1}{9}\int_1^4 \left(8u^2 + 8u - \frac{64}{3}\right) du$$

$$= \frac{1}{9}\left[\frac{8u^3}{3} + 4u^2 - \frac{64}{3}u\right]_1^4$$

$$= \frac{164}{9}.$$

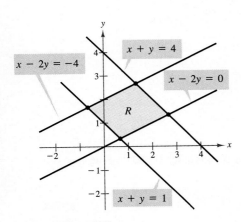

FIGURE 14.72

EXAMPLE 4   **Using a Change of Variables to Simplify an Integrand**

Let R be the region bounded by the square with vertices $(0, 1)$, $(1, 2)$, $(2, 1)$, and $(1, 0)$. Evaluate the integral

$$\iint_R (x + y)^2 \sin^2(x - y)\, dA.$$

Solution   Note that the sides of R lie on the lines $x + y = 1$, $x - y = 1$, $x + y = 3$, and $x - y = -1$, as shown in Figure 14.73. Letting $u = x + y$ and $v = x - y$, you can determine the bounds for region S in the uv-plane to be

$$1 \le u \le 3 \quad \text{and} \quad -1 \le v \le 1$$

as shown in Figure 14.74. Solving for x and y in terms of u and v produces

$$x = \frac{1}{2}(u + v) \quad \text{and} \quad y = \frac{1}{2}(u - v).$$

The partial derivatives of x and y are

$$\frac{\partial x}{\partial u} = \frac{1}{2}, \quad \frac{\partial x}{\partial v} = \frac{1}{2}, \quad \frac{\partial y}{\partial u} = \frac{1}{2}, \quad \text{and} \quad \frac{\partial y}{\partial v} = -\frac{1}{2}$$

which implies that the Jacobian is

$$\frac{\partial(x, y)}{\partial(u, v)} = \begin{vmatrix} \dfrac{\partial x}{\partial u} & \dfrac{\partial x}{\partial v} \\[2mm] \dfrac{\partial y}{\partial u} & \dfrac{\partial y}{\partial v} \end{vmatrix} = \begin{vmatrix} \dfrac{1}{2} & \dfrac{1}{2} \\[2mm] \dfrac{1}{2} & -\dfrac{1}{2} \end{vmatrix}$$

$$= -\frac{1}{4} - \frac{1}{4} = -\frac{1}{2}.$$

By Theorem 14.6, it follows that

$$\iint_R (x + y)^2 \sin^2(x - y)\, dA = \int_{-1}^{1} \int_{1}^{3} u^2 \sin^2 v \left(\frac{1}{2}\right) du\, dv$$

$$= \frac{1}{2} \int_{-1}^{1} (\sin^2 v) \frac{u^3}{3} \Big]_{1}^{3} dv$$

$$= \frac{13}{3} \int_{-1}^{1} \sin^2 v\, dv$$

$$= \frac{13}{6} \int_{-1}^{1} (1 - \cos 2v)\, dv$$

$$= \frac{13}{6} \left[v - \frac{1}{2} \sin 2v \right]_{-1}^{1}$$

$$= \frac{13}{6} \left[2 - \frac{1}{2} \sin 2 + \frac{1}{2} \sin(-2) \right]$$

$$= \frac{13}{6} (2 - \sin 2)$$

$$\approx 2.363.$$

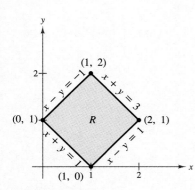

FIGURE 14.73
Region R in the xy-plane.

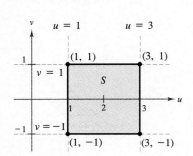

FIGURE 14.74
Region S in the uv-plane.

In each of the change-of-variable examples in this section, the region S has been a rectangle with sides parallel to the u- or v-axis. Occasionally, a change of variables can be used for other types of regions. For instance, Figure 14.75 shows a change of variables from a circular region S to an elliptical region R.

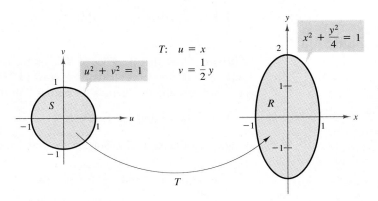

FIGURE 14.75
The change of variables from a circular region to an elliptical region.

EXERCISES for Section 14.8

In Exercises 1–8, find the Jacobian $\partial(x,y)/\partial(u,v)$ for the indicated change of variables.

1. $x = -\frac{1}{2}(u - v)$, $y = \frac{1}{2}(u + v)$

2. $x = au + bv$, $y = cu + dv$

3. $x = u - v^2$, $y = u + v$

4. $x = u - uv$, $y = uv$

5. $x = u\cos\theta - v\sin\theta$, $y = u\sin\theta + v\cos\theta$

6. $x = u + a$, $y = v + a$

7. $x = e^u \sin v$, $y = e^u \cos v$

8. $x = \dfrac{u}{v}$, $y = u + v$

In Exercises 9 and 10, sketch the image S in the uv-plane of the region R in the xy-plane using the given transformations.

9. $x = 3u + 2v$
$y = 3v$

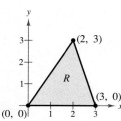

10. $x = 4u + v$
$y = u + 2v$

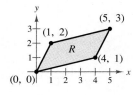

In Exercises 11–16, use the indicated change of variables to evaluate the double integral.

11. $\displaystyle\int\!\!\int_R 48xy\,dx\,dy$
$x = \frac{1}{2}(u + v)$
$y = \frac{1}{2}(u - v)$

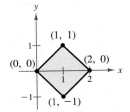

12. $\displaystyle\int\!\!\int_R 4(x^2 + y^2)\,dx\,dy$
$x = \frac{1}{2}(u + v)$
$y = \frac{1}{2}(u - v)$

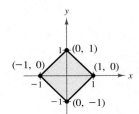

13. $\displaystyle\int\!\!\int_R 4(x + y)e^{x-y}\,dy\,dx$
$x = \frac{1}{2}(u + v)$
$y = \frac{1}{2}(u - v)$

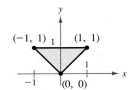

14. $\displaystyle\int\!\!\int_R y(x - y)\,dx\,dy$
$x = u + v$
$y = u$

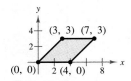

15. $\displaystyle\iint_R \frac{\sqrt{x+y}}{x}\,dy\,dx$

$x = u,\ y = uv$

R: triangle with vertices $(1, 0)$, $(4, 0)$, and $(4, 4)$

16. $\displaystyle\iint_R y\sin xy\,dy\,dx$

$x = \dfrac{u}{v},\ y = v$

R: region bounded by the graphs of $xy = 1$, $xy = 4$, $y = 1$, and $y = 4$

Volume   In Exercises 17–22, use a change of variables to find the volume of the solid region lying below the surface $z = f(x, y)$ and above the plane region R.

17. $f(x, y) = (x + y)e^{x-y}$

R: region bounded by the square with vertices $(4, 0)$, $(6, 2)$, $(4, 4)$, and $(2, 2)$

18. $f(x, y) = (x + y)^2\sin^2(x - y)$

R: region bounded by the square with vertices $(\pi, 0)$, $(3\pi/2, \pi/2)$, (π, π), and $(\pi/2, \pi/2)$

19. $f(x, y) = \sqrt{(x - y)(x + 4y)}$

R: region bounded by the parallelogram with vertices $(0, 0)$, $(1, 1)$, $(5, 0)$, and $(4, -1)$

20. $f(x, y) = (3x + 2y)^2\sqrt{2y - x}$

R: region bounded by the parallelogram with vertices $(0, 0)$, $(-2, 3)$, $(2, 5)$, and $(4, 2)$

21. $f(x, y) = \sqrt{x + y}$

R: region bounded by the triangle with vertices $(0, 0)$, $(a, 0)$, and $(0, a)$, where $0 < a$

22. $f(x, y) = \dfrac{xy}{1 + x^2 y^2}$

R: region bounded by the graphs of $xy = 1$, $xy = 4$, $x = 1$, $x = 4$. (*Hint:* Let $x = u,\ y = v/u$.)

23. Consider the region R in the xy-plane bounded by the ellipse

$$\frac{x^2}{a^2} + \frac{y^2}{b^2} = 1$$

and the transformation $x = au$ and $y = bv$.

a. Sketch the graph of the region R and its image S under the specified transformation.

b. Find $\partial(x, y)/\partial(u, v)$.

c. Find the area of the ellipse.

24. ***Volume***   Use the result of Exercise 23 to find the volume of each dome-shaped solid lying below the surface $z = f(x, y)$ and above the elliptical region R. [*Hint:* After making the change of variables specified by the results of Exercise 23, make a second change of variables to polar coordinates.]

a. $f(x, y) = 16 - x^2 - y^2$

$R: \dfrac{x^2}{16} + \dfrac{y^2}{9} \le 1$

b. $f(x, y) = A\cos\left(\dfrac{\pi}{2}\sqrt{\dfrac{x^2}{a^2} + \dfrac{y^2}{b^2}}\right)$

$R: \dfrac{x^2}{a^2} + \dfrac{y^2}{b^2} \le 1$

In Exercises 25–28, find the Jacobian $\partial(x, y, z)/\partial(u, v, w)$ for the indicated change of variables. If $x = f(u, v, w)$, $y = g(u, v, w)$, and $z = h(u, v, w)$, then the Jacobian of $x, y,$ and z with respect to $u, v,$ and w is

$$\frac{\partial(x, y, z)}{\partial(u, v, w)} = \begin{vmatrix} \dfrac{\partial x}{\partial u} & \dfrac{\partial x}{\partial v} & \dfrac{\partial x}{\partial w} \\[2mm] \dfrac{\partial y}{\partial u} & \dfrac{\partial y}{\partial v} & \dfrac{\partial y}{\partial w} \\[2mm] \dfrac{\partial z}{\partial u} & \dfrac{\partial z}{\partial v} & \dfrac{\partial z}{\partial w} \end{vmatrix}.$$

25. $x = u(1 - v),\ y = uv(1 - w),\ z = uvw$

26. $x = 4u - v,\ y = 4v - w,\ z = u + w$

27. *Spherical coordinates*
$x = \rho\sin\phi\cos\theta,\ y = \rho\sin\phi\sin\theta,\ z = \rho\cos\phi$

28. *Cylindrical coordinates*
$x = r\cos\theta,\ y = r\sin\theta,\ z = z$

REVIEW EXERCISES for Chapter 14

In Exercises 1 and 2, evaluate the integral.

1. $\displaystyle\int_1^{x^2} x\ln y\,dy$

2. $\displaystyle\int_y^{2y} (x^2 + y^2)\,dx$

In Exercises 3–12, evaluate the multiple integral. Change the coordinate system when convenient.

3. $\displaystyle\int_0^1\int_0^{1+x} (3x + 2y)\,dy\,dx$

4. $\displaystyle\int_0^2\int_{x^2}^{2x} (x^2 + 2y)\,dy\,dx$

5. $\displaystyle\int_0^3\int_0^{\sqrt{9-x^2}} 4x\,dy\,dx$

6. $\displaystyle\int_0^{\sqrt{3}}\int_{2-\sqrt{4-y^2}}^{2+\sqrt{4-y^2}} dx\,dy$

7. $\displaystyle\int_0^h\int_0^x \sqrt{x^2 + y^2}\,dy\,dx$

8. $\displaystyle\int_0^4\int_0^{\sqrt{16-y^2}} (x^2 + y^2)\,dx\,dy$

9. $\displaystyle\int_{-3}^3\int_{-\sqrt{9-x^2}}^{\sqrt{9-x^2}}\int_{x^2+y^2}^9 \sqrt{x^2 + y^2}\,dz\,dy\,dx$

10. $\displaystyle\int_{-2}^2\int_{-\sqrt{4-x^2}}^{\sqrt{4-x^2}}\int_0^{(x^2+y^2)/2} (x^2 + y^2)\,dz\,dy\,dx$

11. $\displaystyle\int_0^a\int_0^b\int_0^c (x^2 + y^2 + z^2)\,dx\,dy\,dz$

12. $\int_0^5 \int_0^{\sqrt{25-x^2}} \int_0^{\sqrt{25-x^2-y^2}} \frac{1}{1+x^2+y^2+z^2} \, dz \, dy \, dx$

C In Exercises 13–16, use a computer algebra system to evaluate the multiple integral.

13. $\int_{-2}^4 \int_{y^2/4}^{(4+y)/2} (x-y) \, dx \, dy$

14. $\int_{-2}^2 \int_0^{4-y^2} (8x-2y^2) \, dx \, dy$

15. $\int_{-1}^1 \int_{-\sqrt{1-x^2}}^{\sqrt{1-x^2}} \int_{-\sqrt{1-x^2-y^2}}^{\sqrt{1-x^2-y^2}} (x^2+y^2) \, dz \, dy \, dx$

16. $\int_0^2 \int_0^{\sqrt{4-x^2}} \int_0^{\sqrt{4-x^2-y^2}} xyz \, dz \, dy \, dx$

In Exercises 17–24, write the limits for the double integral

$$\int_R \int f(x,y) \, dA$$

for both orders of integration. Compute the area of R by letting $f(x,y) = 1$ and integrating.

17. Triangle: vertices $(0, 0)$, $(3, 0)$, and $(0, 1)$

18. Triangle: vertices $(0, 0)$, $(3, 0)$, and $(2, 2)$

19. The larger area between the graphs of $x^2 + y^2 = 25$ and $x = 3$

20. Region bounded by the graphs of $y = 6x - x^2$ and $y = x^2 - 2x$

21. Region enclosed by the graph of $y^2 = x^2 - x^4$

22. Region bounded by the graphs of $x = y^2 + 1$, $x = 0$, $y = 0$, and $y = 2$

23. Region bounded by the graphs of $x = y + 3$ and $x = y^2 + 1$

24. Region bounded by the graphs of $x = -y$ and $x = 2y - y^2$

Volume   In Exercises 25–30, use a multiple integral and a convenient coordinate system to find the volume of the solid.

25. Solid bounded by the graphs of $z = x^2 - y + 4$, $z = 0$, $x = 0$, and $x = 4$

26. Solid bounded by the graphs of $z = x + y$, $z = 0$, $x = 0$, $x = 3$, and $y = x$

27. Solid bounded by the graphs of $z = 0$ and $z = h$, outside the cylinder $x^2 + y^2 = 1$ and inside the hyperboloid $x^2 + y^2 - z^2 = 1$

28. Solid that remains after drilling a hole of radius b through the center of a sphere of radius R $(b < R)$

29. Solid inside the graphs of $r = 2\cos\theta$ and $r^2 + z^2 = 4$

30. Solid inside the graphs of $r^2 + z = 16$ and $r = 2\sin\theta$

Probability   In Exercises 31 and 32, find k so that the function is a joint density function and find the required probability, where $P(a \le x \le b, c \le y \le d) = \int_c^d \int_a^b f(x,y) \, dx \, dy$.

31. $f(x,y) = \begin{cases} kxye^{-(x+y)}, & x \ge 0, y \ge 0 \\ 0, & \text{elsewhere} \end{cases}$
  $P(0 \le x \le 1, 0 \le y \le 1)$

32. $f(x,y) = \begin{cases} kxy, & 0 \le x \le 1, 0 \le y \le x \\ 0, & \text{elsewhere} \end{cases}$
  $P(0 \le x \le 0.5, 0 \le y \le 0.25)$

C *Mass and Center of Mass*   In Exercises 33 and 34, find the mass and center of mass of the lamina bounded by the graphs of the equations of specified density. Use a symbolic integration utility to evaluate the multiple integrals.

33. $y = 2x$, $y = 2x^3$ (first quadrant)
  a. $\rho = kxy$ **b.** $\rho = k(x^2 + y^2)$

34. $y = \dfrac{h}{2}\left(2 - \dfrac{x}{L} - \dfrac{x^2}{L^2}\right)$ (first quadrant)
  $\rho = k$

C *Surface Area*   In Exercises 35 and 36, find the area of the surface on the function $f(x,y)$ over the region R.

35. $f(x,y) = 16 - x^2 - y^2$
  $R = \{(x,y): x^2 + y^2 \le 16\}$

36. $f(x,y) = 16 - x - y^2$
  $R = \{(x,y): 0 \le x \le 2, 0 \le y \le x\}$
  Use a symbolic integration utility to evaluate the multiple integral.

Center of Mass   In Exercises 37–40, find the center of mass of the solid of uniform density bounded by the graphs of the given equations.

37. Solid inside the hemisphere $\rho = \cos\phi$, $\pi/4 \le \phi \le \pi/2$, and outside the cone $\phi = \pi/4$

38. Wedge: $x^2 + y^2 = a^2$, $z = cy(0 < c)$, $0 \le y$, $0 \le z$

39. $x^2 + y^2 + z^2 = a^2$ (first octant)

40. $x^2 + y^2 + z^2 = 25$, $z = 4$ (the larger solid)

Moment of Inertia   In Exercises 41 and 42, find the moment of inertia I_z of the solid of specified density.

41. The solid of uniform density inside the paraboloid $z = 16 - x^2 - y^2$ and outside the cylinder $x^2 + y^2 = 9$, $z \ge 0$.

42. $x^2 + y^2 + z^2 = a^2$, density is proportional to the distance from the center

In Exercises 43 and 44, give a geometric interpretation of the triple integral.

43. $\displaystyle\int_0^{2\pi}\int_{-\pi/2}^{\pi/2}\int_0^{6\sin\phi}\rho^2\sin\phi\,d\rho\,d\phi\,d\theta$

44. $\displaystyle\int_0^{\pi}\int_0^2\int_0^{1+r^2}r\,dz\,dr\,d\theta$

True or False   In Exercises 45–48, determine whether the statement is true or false. If it is false, explain why or give an example that shows it is false.

45. $\displaystyle\int_a^b\int_c^d f(x)g(y)\,dy\,dx=\left[\int_a^b f(x)\,dx\right]\left[\int_c^d g(y)\,dy\right]$

46. If f is continuous over R_1 and R_2 and $\int_{R_1}\!\!\int dA=\int_{R_2}\!\!\int dA$, then $\int_{R_1}\!\!\int f(x,y)\,dA=\int_{R_1}\!\!\int f(x,y)\,dA.$

47. $\displaystyle\int_{-1}^1\int_{-1}^1\cos(x^2+y^2)\,dx\,dy=4\int_0^1\int_0^1\cos(x^2+y^2)\,dx\,dy$

48. $\displaystyle\int_0^1\int_0^1\frac{1}{1+x^2+y^2}\,dx\,dy<\frac{\pi}{4}$

Chapter 13

Vector Analysis

Vector Fields

In Chapter 12, you studied vector-valued functions—functions that assign a vector to a *real number*. There you saw that vector-valued functions of a real number are useful in representing curves and motion along a curve. In this chapter, you will study two other types of vector-valued functions—functions that assign a vector to a *point in the plane* or to a *point in space*. Such functions are called **vector fields,** and they are useful in representing various types of **force fields** and **velocity fields.**

Definition of a Vector Field

Let M and N be functions of two variables x and y, defined on a plane region R. The function $\mathbf{F}$ defined by

$$\mathbf{F}(x, y) = M\mathbf{i} + N\mathbf{j} \qquad \text{Plane}$$

is called a **vector field over R.**

Let M, N, and P be functions of three variables x, y, and z, defined on a solid region Q in space. The function $\mathbf{F}$ defined by

$$\mathbf{F}(x, y, z) = M\mathbf{i} + N\mathbf{j} + P\mathbf{k} \qquad \text{Space}$$

is called a **vector field over Q.**

From this definition, you see that the *gradient* is one example of a vector field. For example, if

$$f(x, y) = x^2 + y^2$$

then the gradient of f

$$\nabla f(x, y) = f_x(x, y)\mathbf{i} + f_y(x, y)\mathbf{j}$$
$$= 2x\mathbf{i} + 2y\mathbf{j} \qquad \text{Vector field in the plane}$$

is a vector field in the plane. Similarly, if

$$f(x, y, z) = x^2 + y^2 + z^2$$

then the gradient of f

$$\nabla f(x, y, z) = f_x(x, y, z)\mathbf{i} + f_y(x, y, z)\mathbf{j} + f_z(x, y, z)\mathbf{k}$$
$$= 2x\mathbf{i} + 2y\mathbf{j} + 2z\mathbf{k} \qquad \text{Vector field in space}$$

is a vector field in space.

◄ *The velocity of swirling water can be modeled by a velocity field, as discussed in Section 15.8, Example 3.*

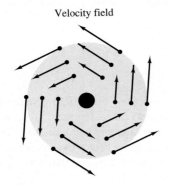

FIGURE 15.1
Rotating wheel

FIGURE 15.2
Air-flow vector field

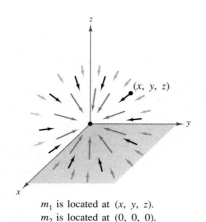

m_1 is located at (x, y, z).
m_2 is located at $(0, 0, 0)$.

FIGURE 15.3
Gravitational force field

Some common *physical* examples of vector fields are **velocity fields, gravitational fields,** and **electric force fields.**

1. *Velocity fields* describe the motion of a system of particles in the plane or in space. For instance, Figure 15.1 shows the vector field determined by a wheel rotating on an axle. Notice that the velocity vectors are determined by the location of their initial points—the farther a point is from the axle, the greater its velocity. Velocity fields are also determined by the flow of liquids through a container or by the flow of air currents around a moving object, as shown in Figure 15.2.

2. *Gravitational fields* are defined by **Newton's Law of Gravitation,** which states that the force of attraction exerted on a particle of mass m_1 located at (x, y, z) by a particle of mass m_2 located at $(0, 0, 0)$ is given by

$$\mathbf{F}(x, y, z) = \frac{-Gm_1m_2}{x^2 + y^2 + z^2}\mathbf{u}$$

where G is the gravitational constant and $\mathbf{u}$ is the unit vector in the direction from the origin to (x, y, z). In Figure 15.3, you can see that the gravitational field $\mathbf{F}$ has the properties that $\mathbf{F}(x, y, z)$ always points toward the origin, and that the magnitude of $\mathbf{F}(x, y, z)$ is the same at all points equidistant from the origin. A vector field with these two properties is called a **central force field.** Using the position vector $\mathbf{r} = x\mathbf{i} + y\mathbf{j} + z\mathbf{k}$ for the point (x, y, z), we can express the gravitational field $\mathbf{F}$ as

$$\mathbf{F}(x, y, z) = \frac{-Gm_1m_2}{\|\mathbf{r}\|^2} \cdot \frac{\mathbf{r}}{\|\mathbf{r}\|} = \frac{-Gm_1m_2}{\|\mathbf{r}\|^2}\mathbf{u}.$$

3. *Electric force fields* are defined by **Coulomb's Law,** which states that the force exerted on a particle with electric charge q_1 located at (x, y, z) by a particle with electric charge q_2 located at $(0, 0, 0)$ is given by

$$\mathbf{F}(x, y, z) = \frac{cq_1q_2}{\|\mathbf{r}\|^2}\mathbf{u}$$

where $\mathbf{r} = x\mathbf{i} + y\mathbf{j} + z\mathbf{k}$, $\mathbf{u} = \mathbf{r}/\|\mathbf{r}\|$, and c is a constant that depends on the choice of units for $\|\mathbf{r}\|$, q_1, and q_2.

Note that an electric force field has the same form as a gravitational field. That is, $\mathbf{F}(x, y, z) = (k/\|\mathbf{r}\|^2)\mathbf{u}$. Such a force field is called an **inverse square field.**

Definition of Inverse Square Field

Let $\mathbf{r}(t) = x(t)\mathbf{i} + y(t)\mathbf{j} + z(t)\mathbf{k}$ be the position vector. The vector field $\mathbf{F}$ is an **inverse square field** if

$$\mathbf{F}(x, y, z) = \frac{k}{\|\mathbf{r}\|^2}\mathbf{u}$$

where k is a real number and $\mathbf{u} = \mathbf{r}/\|\mathbf{r}\|$ is a unit vector in the direction of $\mathbf{r}$.

Because vector fields consist of infinitely many vectors, it is not possible to actually create a sketch of the field. Instead, when you sketch a vector field, your goal is to sketch representative vectors that help you visualize the field.

EXAMPLE 1   Sketching a Vector Field

Sketch some vectors in the vector field given by

$$\mathbf{F}(x, y) = -y\mathbf{i} + x\mathbf{j}.$$

Solution   You could plot vectors at several random points in the plane. However, it is more enlightening to plot vectors of equal magnitude. This corresponds to finding level curves in scalar fields. In this case, vectors of equal magnitude lie on circles.

$$\|\mathbf{F}\| = c \qquad \text{Vectors of length } c$$
$$\sqrt{x^2 + y^2} = c$$
$$x^2 + y^2 = c^2 \qquad \text{Equation of circle}$$

To begin making the sketch, choose a value for c and plot several vectors on the resulting circle. For instance, the following vectors occur on the unit circle.

Point	Vector
$(1, 0)$	$\mathbf{F}(1, 0) = \mathbf{j}$
$(0, 1)$	$\mathbf{F}(0, 1) = -\mathbf{i}$
$(-1, 0)$	$\mathbf{F}(-1, 0) = -\mathbf{j}$
$(0, -1)$	$\mathbf{F}(0, -1) = \mathbf{i}$

These and several other vectors in the vector field are shown in Figure 15.4. Note in the figure that this vector field is similar to that illustrated by the rotating wheel shown in Figure 15.1.

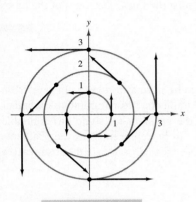

Vector field:
$\mathbf{F}(x, y) = -y\mathbf{i} + x\mathbf{j}$

FIGURE 15.4

EXAMPLE 2   Sketching a Vector Field

Sketch some vectors in the vector field given by

$$\mathbf{F}(x, y) = 2x\mathbf{i} + y\mathbf{j}.$$

Solution   For this vector field, vectors of equal length lie on ellipses given by

$$\|\mathbf{F}\| = \sqrt{(2x)^2 + (y)^2} = c \;\longrightarrow\; 4x^2 + y^2 = c^2.$$

For $c = 1$, sketch several vectors $2x\mathbf{i} + y\mathbf{j}$ of magnitude 1 at points on the ellipse given by

$$4x^2 + y^2 = 1.$$

For $c = 2$, sketch several vectors $2x\mathbf{i} + y\mathbf{j}$ of magnitude 2 at points on the ellipse given by

$$4x^2 + y^2 = 4.$$

These vectors are shown in Figure 15.5.

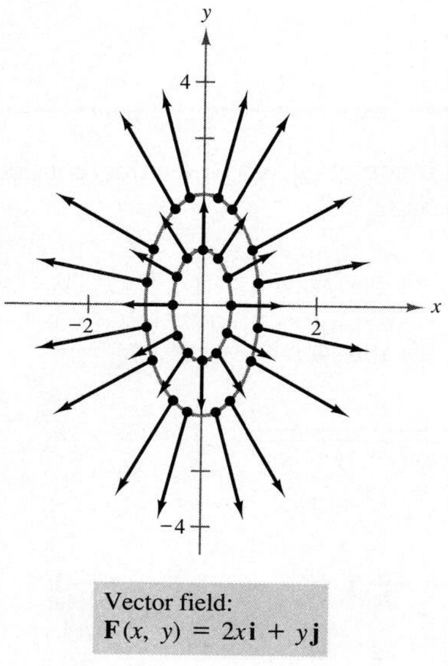

Vector field:
$\mathbf{F}(x, y) = 2x\mathbf{i} + y\mathbf{j}$

FIGURE 15.5

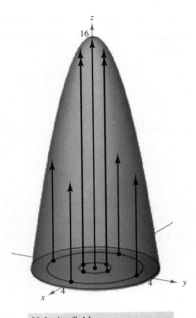

Velocity field:
$\mathbf{v}(x,\ y,\ z) = (16 - x^2 - y^2)\mathbf{k}$

FIGURE 15.6

EXAMPLE 3   Sketching a Velocity Field

Sketch some vectors in the velocity field given by

$$\mathbf{v}(x, y, z) = (16 - x^2 - y^2)\mathbf{k}$$

where $x^2 + y^2 \leq 16$.

Solution   You can imagine that $\mathbf{v}$ describes the velocity of a liquid flowing through a tube of radius 4. Vectors near the z-axis are longer than those near the edge of the tube. For instance, at the point $(0, 0, 0)$, the velocity vector is $\mathbf{v}(0, 0, 0) = 16\mathbf{k}$, whereas at the point $(0, 3, 0)$, the velocity vector is $\mathbf{v}(0, 3, 0) = 7\mathbf{k}$. Figure 15.6 shows these and several other vectors for the velocity field. From the figure, you can see that the speed of the liquid is greater near the center of the tube than near the edges of the tube.

Conservative Vector Fields

Notice in Figure 15.5 that all the vectors appear to be normal to the level curve from which they emanate. Because this is a property of gradients, it is natural to ask whether the vector field given by $\mathbf{F}(x, y) = 2x\mathbf{i} + y\mathbf{j}$ is the *gradient* for some differentiable function f. The answer is that some vector fields can be represented as the gradients of differentiable functions and some cannot—those that can are called **conservative** vector fields.

Definition of Conservative Vector Field

A vector field $\mathbf{F}$ is called **conservative** if there exists a differentiable function f such that $\mathbf{F} = \nabla f$. The function f is called the **potential function** for $\mathbf{F}$.

EXAMPLE 4   Conservative Vector Fields

a. The vector field given by $\mathbf{F}(x, y) = 2x\mathbf{i} + y\mathbf{j}$ is conservative. To see this, consider the potential function $f(x, y) = x^2 + \frac{1}{2}y^2$. Because

$$\nabla f = 2x\mathbf{i} + y\mathbf{j} = \mathbf{F}$$

it follows that $\mathbf{F}$ is conservative.

b. Every inverse square field is conservative. To see this, let

$$\mathbf{F}(x, y, z) = \frac{k}{\|\mathbf{r}\|^2}\mathbf{u} \quad \text{and} \quad f(x, y, z) = \frac{-k}{\sqrt{x^2 + y^2 + z^2}}$$

where $\mathbf{u} = \mathbf{r}/\|\mathbf{r}\|$. Because

$$\nabla f = \frac{kx}{(x^2 + y^2 + z^2)^{3/2}}\mathbf{i} + \frac{ky}{(x^2 + y^2 + z^2)^{3/2}}\mathbf{j} + \frac{kz}{(x^2 + y^2 + z^2)^{3/2}}\mathbf{k}$$

$$= \frac{k}{x^2 + y^2 + z^2}\left(\frac{x\mathbf{i} + y\mathbf{j} + z\mathbf{k}}{\sqrt{x^2 + y^2 + z^2}}\right) = \frac{k}{\|\mathbf{r}\|^2}\frac{\mathbf{r}}{\|\mathbf{r}\|} = \frac{k}{\|\mathbf{r}\|^2}\mathbf{u}$$

it follows that $\mathbf{F}$ is conservative.

As can be seen in Example 4b, many important vector fields, including gravitational fields, magnetic fields, and electric force fields, are conservative. Most of the terminology in this chapter comes from physics. For example, the term "conservative" is derived from the classic physical law regarding the conservation of energy. This law states that the sum of the kinetic energy and the potential energy of a particle moving in a conservative force field is constant. (The kinetic energy of a particle is the energy due to its motion, and the potential energy is the energy due to its position in the force field.)

The following important theorem gives a necessary and sufficient condition for a vector field *in the plane* to be conservative.

THEOREM 15.1   Test for Conservative Vector Field in the Plane

Let M and N have continuous first partial derivatives on an open disc R. The vector field given by $\mathbf{F}(x, y) = M\,\mathbf{i} + N\,\mathbf{j}$ is conservative if and only if

$$\frac{\partial N}{\partial x} = \frac{\partial M}{\partial y}.$$

Proof   To prove that the given condition is necessary for $\mathbf{F}$ to be conservative, we suppose there exists a potential function f such that

$$\mathbf{F}(x, y) = \nabla f(x, y) = M\,\mathbf{i} + N\,\mathbf{j}.$$

Then, we have

$$f_x(x, y) = M \quad \longrightarrow \quad f_{xy}(x, y) = \frac{\partial M}{\partial y}$$

$$f_y(x, y) = N \quad \longrightarrow \quad f_{yx}(x, y) = \frac{\partial N}{\partial x}$$

and, by the equivalence of the mixed partials f_{xy} and f_{yx}, we conclude that $\partial N/\partial x = \partial M/\partial y$ for all (x, y) in R. The sufficiency of the condition is proved in Section 15.4.

REMARK   Theorem 15.1 requires that the domain of $\mathbf{F}$ be an open disc. If R is simply an open region, then the given condition is necessary but not sufficient to produce a conservative vector field.

EXAMPLE 5   Testing for Conservative Vector Fields in the Plane

a. The vector field given by $\mathbf{F}(x, y) = x^2 y\,\mathbf{i} + xy\,\mathbf{j}$ *is not* conservative because

$$\frac{\partial M}{\partial y} = \frac{\partial}{\partial y}[x^2 y] = x^2 \quad \text{and} \quad \frac{\partial N}{\partial x} = \frac{\partial}{\partial x}[xy] = y.$$

b. The vector field given by $\mathbf{F}(x, y) = 2x\,\mathbf{i} + y\,\mathbf{j}$ *is* conservative because

$$\frac{\partial M}{\partial y} = \frac{\partial}{\partial y}[2x] = 0 \quad \text{and} \quad \frac{\partial N}{\partial x} = \frac{\partial}{\partial x}[y] = 0.$$

Theorem 15.1 tells you whether a vector field is conservative. It does not tell you how to find a potential function of **F**. The problem is comparable to antidifferentiation. Sometimes you will be able to find a potential function by simple inspection. For instance, in Example 4 we observed that

$$f(x, y) = x^2 + \frac{1}{2}y^2$$

has the property that $\nabla f(x, y) = 2x\,\mathbf{i} + y\,\mathbf{j}$. We will discuss techniques for finding potential functions in detail in Chapter 16 (in the section on exact differential equations). For now, we outline the procedure by way of an example.

EXAMPLE 6   Finding a Potential Function for F(x, y)

Find a potential function for

$$\mathbf{F}(x, y) = 2xy\,\mathbf{i} + (x^2 - y)\mathbf{j}.$$

Solution   From Theorem 15.1, it follows that **F** is conservative because

$$\frac{\partial}{\partial y}[2xy] = 2x \quad \text{and} \quad \frac{\partial}{\partial x}[x^2 - y] = 2x.$$

If f is a function whose gradient is equal to $\mathbf{F}(x, y)$, then $\nabla f(x, y) = 2xy\,\mathbf{i} + (x^2 - y)\mathbf{j}$ which implies that

$$f_x(x, y) = 2xy \quad \text{and} \quad f_y(x, y) = x^2 - y.$$

To reconstruct the function f from these two partial derivatives, integrate $f_x(x, y)$ with respect to x and $f_y(x, y)$ with respect to y, as follows.

$$f(x, y) = \int f_x(x, y)\, dx = \int 2xy\, dx = x^2 y + g(y)$$

$$f(x, y) = \int f_y(x, y)\, dy = \int (x^2 - y)\, dy = x^2 y - \frac{y^2}{2} + h(x)$$

Note that $g(y)$ is constant with respect to x and $h(x)$ is constant with respect to y. To find a single expression that represents $f(x, y)$, let $g(y) = -\frac{1}{2}y^2 + K$ and $h(x) = K$. Then, you can write

$$f(x, y) = x^2 y + g(y) + K$$

$$= x^2 y - \frac{y^2}{2} + K.$$

You can check this result by forming the gradient of f—it should be equal to the original function **F**.

REMARK   Note that the solution in Example 6 is comparable to that given by an indefinite integral. That is, the solution represents a family of potential functions, any two of which differ by a constant. To find a unique solution, you would have to be given an initial condition satisfied by the potential function.

Curl of a Vector Field

Theorem 15.1 has a counterpart for vector fields in space. Before stating that result, we define the **curl of a vector field** in space.

Definition of Curl of a Vector Field

The **curl** of $\mathbf{F}(x, y, z) = M\mathbf{i} + N\mathbf{j} + P\mathbf{k}$ is

$$\text{curl } \mathbf{F}(x, y, z) = \nabla \times \mathbf{F}(x, y, z)$$
$$= \left(\frac{\partial P}{\partial y} - \frac{\partial N}{\partial z}\right)\mathbf{i} - \left(\frac{\partial P}{\partial x} - \frac{\partial M}{\partial z}\right)\mathbf{j} + \left(\frac{\partial N}{\partial x} - \frac{\partial M}{\partial y}\right)\mathbf{k}.$$

REMARK   If **curl F** = **0**, then we say that **F** is **irrotational.**

The cross-product notation used for curl comes from viewing the gradient ∇f as the result of the **differential operator** ∇ acting on the function f. In this context, you can use the following determinant form as an aid in remembering the formula for curl.

$$\text{curl } \mathbf{F}(x, y, z) = \nabla \times \mathbf{F}(x, y, z)$$

$$= \begin{vmatrix} \mathbf{i} & \mathbf{j} & \mathbf{k} \\ \dfrac{\partial}{\partial x} & \dfrac{\partial}{\partial y} & \dfrac{\partial}{\partial z} \\ M & N & P \end{vmatrix}$$

$$= \left(\frac{\partial P}{\partial y} - \frac{\partial N}{\partial z}\right)\mathbf{i} - \left(\frac{\partial P}{\partial x} - \frac{\partial M}{\partial z}\right)\mathbf{j} + \left(\frac{\partial N}{\partial x} - \frac{\partial M}{\partial y}\right)\mathbf{k}$$

EXAMPLE 7   Finding the Curl of a Vector Field

Find **curl F** for the vector field given by

$$\mathbf{F}(x, y, z) = 2xy\,\mathbf{i} + (x^2 + z^2)\mathbf{j} + 2zy\,\mathbf{k}.$$

Solution   The curl of **F** is given by

$$\text{curl } \mathbf{F}(x, y, z) = \nabla \times \mathbf{F}(x, y, z)$$

$$= \begin{vmatrix} \mathbf{i} & \mathbf{j} & \mathbf{k} \\ \dfrac{\partial}{\partial x} & \dfrac{\partial}{\partial y} & \dfrac{\partial}{\partial z} \\ 2xy & x^2 + z^2 & 2zy \end{vmatrix}$$

$$= \begin{vmatrix} \dfrac{\partial}{\partial y} & \dfrac{\partial}{\partial z} \\ x^2 + z^2 & 2zy \end{vmatrix}\mathbf{i} - \begin{vmatrix} \dfrac{\partial}{\partial x} & \dfrac{\partial}{\partial z} \\ 2xy & 2zy \end{vmatrix}\mathbf{j} + \begin{vmatrix} \dfrac{\partial}{\partial x} & \dfrac{\partial}{\partial y} \\ 2xy & x^2 + z^2 \end{vmatrix}\mathbf{k}$$

$$= (2z - 2z)\mathbf{i} - (0 - 0)\mathbf{j} + (2x - 2x)\mathbf{k}$$
$$= \mathbf{0}.$$

Later in this chapter, we will assign a physical interpretation to the curl of a vector field. But for now, the primary use we make of curl is in the following test for conservative vector fields in space. The test states that for a vector field whose domain is all of three-dimensional space (or an open sphere), the curl is **0** at every point in the domain if and only if **F** is conservative. The proof is similar to that given in Theorem 15.1.

THEOREM 15.2   Test for Conservative Vector Field in Space

Suppose M, N, and P have continuous first partial derivatives in an open sphere Q in space. The vector field given by $\mathbf{F}(x, y, z) = M\mathbf{i} + N\mathbf{j} + P\mathbf{k}$ is conservative if and only if

   curl $\mathbf{F}(x, y, z) = \mathbf{0}$.

That is, **F** is conservative if and only if

$$\frac{\partial P}{\partial y} = \frac{\partial N}{\partial z}, \quad \frac{\partial P}{\partial x} = \frac{\partial M}{\partial z}, \quad \text{and} \quad \frac{\partial N}{\partial x} = \frac{\partial M}{\partial y}.$$

From Theorem 15.2, you can see that the vector field given in Example 7 is conservative because **curl** $\mathbf{F}(x, y, z) = \mathbf{0}$. Try showing that the vector field $\mathbf{F}(x, y, z) = x^3 y^2 z\mathbf{i} + x^2 z\mathbf{j} + x^2 y\mathbf{k}$ is not conservative—you can do this by showing that its curl is **curl** $\mathbf{F}(x, y, z) = (x^3 y^2 - 2xy)\mathbf{j} + (2xz - 2x^3 yz)\mathbf{k} \neq \mathbf{0}$.

For vector fields in space that pass the test for being conservative, you can find a potential function by following the same pattern used in the plane (as demonstrated in Example 6).

EXAMPLE 8   Finding a Potential Function for $\mathbf{F}(x, y, z)$

Find a potential function for $\mathbf{F}(x, y, z) = 2xy\mathbf{i} + (x^2 + z^2)\mathbf{j} + 2zy\mathbf{k}$.

Solution   From Example 7, you know that the vector field given by **F** is conservative. If f is a function such that $\mathbf{F}(x, y, z) = \nabla f(x, y, z)$, then

$$f_x(x, y, z) = 2xy, \quad f_y(x, y, z) = x^2 + z^2, \quad \text{and} \quad f_z(x, y, z) = 2zy$$

and by integrating with respect to x, y, and z separately, you obtain

$$f(x, y, z) = \int M\,dx = \int 2xy\,dx = x^2 y + g(y, z)$$

$$f(x, y, z) = \int N\,dy = \int (x^2 + z^2)\,dy = x^2 y + z^2 y + h(x, z)$$

$$f(x, y, z) = \int P\,dz = \int 2zy\,dz = z^2 y + k(x, y).$$

Comparing these three versions of $f(x, y, z)$, you can conclude that

$$g(y, z) = z^2 y, \quad h(x, z) = 0, \quad \text{and} \quad k(x, y) = x^2 y.$$

Therefore, $f(x, y, z)$ is given by

$$f(x, y, z) = x^2 y + z^2 y + K.$$

REMARK   Examples 6 and 8 are illustrations of a type of problem called *recovering a function from its gradient*. We will discuss other methods for solving this type of problem in Chapter 16. One popular method gives an interplay between successive "partial integrations" and partial differentiations.

Divergence of a Vector Field

You have seen that the curl of a vector field $\mathbf{F}$ is itself a vector field. Another important function defined on a vector field is **divergence,** which is a scalar function.

REMARK Divergence can be viewed as a type of derivative of $\mathbf{F}$ in that, for vector fields representing velocities of moving particles, the divergence measures the rate of particle flow per unit volume at a point. In hydrodynamics (the study of fluid motion) a velocity field that is divergence free is called **incompressible.** In the study of electricity and magnetism, a vector field that is divergence free is called **solenoidal.**

Definition of Divergence of a Vector Field

The **divergence** of $\mathbf{F}(x, y) = M\mathbf{i} + N\mathbf{j}$ is

$$\operatorname{div} \mathbf{F}(x, y) = \nabla \cdot \mathbf{F}(x, y) = \frac{\partial M}{\partial x} + \frac{\partial N}{\partial y}. \qquad \text{Plane}$$

The **divergence** of $\mathbf{F}(x, y, z) = M\mathbf{i} + N\mathbf{j} + P\mathbf{k}$ is

$$\operatorname{div} \mathbf{F}(x, y, z) = \nabla \cdot \mathbf{F}(x, y, z) = \frac{\partial M}{\partial x} + \frac{\partial N}{\partial y} + \frac{\partial P}{\partial z}. \qquad \text{Space}$$

If $\operatorname{div} \mathbf{F} = 0$, then $\mathbf{F}$ is said to be **divergence free.**

The dot-product notation used for divergence comes from considering ∇ as a **differential operator,** as follows.

$$\nabla \cdot \mathbf{F}(x, y, z) = \left[\left(\frac{\partial}{\partial x} \right)\mathbf{i} + \left(\frac{\partial}{\partial y} \right)\mathbf{j} + \left(\frac{\partial}{\partial z} \right)\mathbf{k} \right] \cdot (M\mathbf{i} + N\mathbf{j} + P\mathbf{k})$$

$$= \frac{\partial M}{\partial x} + \frac{\partial N}{\partial y} + \frac{\partial P}{\partial z}$$

EXAMPLE 9   Finding the Divergence of a Vector Field

Find the divergence at $(2, 1, -1)$ for the vector field

$$\mathbf{F}(x, y, z) = x^3 y^2 z\mathbf{i} + x^2 z\mathbf{j} + x^2 y\mathbf{k}.$$

Solution   The divergence of $\mathbf{F}$ is

$$\operatorname{div} \mathbf{F}(x, y, z) = \frac{\partial}{\partial x}[x^3 y^2 z] + \frac{\partial}{\partial y}[x^2 z] + \frac{\partial}{\partial z}[x^2 y] = 3x^2 y^2 z.$$

At the point $(2, 1, -1)$, the divergence is

$$\operatorname{div} \mathbf{F}(2, 1, -1) = 3(2^2)(1^2)(-1) = -12.$$

There are many important properties of the divergence and curl of a vector field $\mathbf{F}$ (see Exercises 59–65). One that is used often is described in Theorem 15.3. You are asked to prove this theorem in Exercise 66.

THEOREM 15.3   Relationship Between Divergence and Curl

If $\mathbf{F}(x, y, z) = M\mathbf{i} + N\mathbf{i} + P\mathbf{k}$ is a vector field and M, N, and P have continuous second partial derivatives, then

$$\operatorname{div} (\mathbf{curl\ F}) = 0.$$

EXERCISES for Section 15.1

In Exercises 1–14, sketch several representative vectors in the vector field.

1. $\mathbf{F}(x, y) = \mathbf{i} + \mathbf{j}$

2. $\mathbf{F}(x, y) = 2\mathbf{i}$

3. $\mathbf{F}(x, y) = x\mathbf{j}$

4. $\mathbf{F}(x, y) = y\mathbf{i}$

5. $\mathbf{F}(x, y) = x\mathbf{i} + y\mathbf{j}$

6. $\mathbf{F}(x, y) = -x\mathbf{i} + y\mathbf{j}$

7. $\mathbf{F}(x, y) = x\mathbf{i} + 3y\mathbf{j}$

8. $\mathbf{F}(x, y) = y\mathbf{i} - x\mathbf{j}$

9. $\mathbf{F}(x, y, z) = 3y\mathbf{j}$

10. $\mathbf{F}(x, y) = x\mathbf{i}$

11. $\mathbf{F}(x, y) = 4x\mathbf{i} + y\mathbf{j}$

12. $\mathbf{F}(x, y) = \mathbf{i} + (x^2 + y^2)\mathbf{j}$

13. $\mathbf{F}(x, y, z) = \mathbf{i} + \mathbf{j} + \mathbf{k}$

14. $\mathbf{F}(x, y, z) = x\mathbf{i} + y\mathbf{j} + z\mathbf{k}$

In Exercises 15–20, find the gradient vector field for the scalar function. (That is, find the conservative vector field for the given potential function.)

15. $f(x, y) = 5x^2 + 3xy + 10y^2$

16. $f(x, y) = \sin 3x \cos 4y$

17. $f(x, y, z) = z - ye^{x^2}$

18. $f(x, y, z) = \dfrac{y}{z} + \dfrac{z}{x} - \dfrac{xz}{y}$

19. $g(x, y, z) = xy \ln(x + y)$

20. $g(x, y, z) = x \arcsin yz$

In Exercises 21–28, determine whether the vector field is conservative. If it is, find a potential function for the vector field.

21. $\mathbf{F}(x, y) = 2xy\mathbf{i} + x^2\mathbf{j}$

22. $\mathbf{F}(x, y) = \dfrac{1}{y^2}(y\mathbf{i} - 2x\mathbf{j})$

23. $\mathbf{F}(x, y) = xe^{x^2y}(2y\mathbf{i} + x\mathbf{j})$

24. $\mathbf{F}(x, y) = 2xy^3\mathbf{i} + 3y^2x^2\mathbf{j}$

25. $\mathbf{F}(x, y) = \dfrac{x\mathbf{i} + y\mathbf{j}}{x^2 + y^2}$

26. $\mathbf{F}(x, y) = \dfrac{2y}{x}\mathbf{i} - \dfrac{x^2}{y^2}\mathbf{j}$

27. $\mathbf{F}(x, y) = e^x(\cos y\,\mathbf{i} + \sin y\,\mathbf{j})$

28. $\mathbf{F}(x, y) = \dfrac{2x\mathbf{i} + 2y\mathbf{j}}{(x^2 + y^2)^2}$

In Exercises 29–32, find the curl of the vector field F at the indicated point.

Vector field	Point
29. $\mathbf{F}(x, y, z) = xyz\mathbf{i} + y\mathbf{j} + z\mathbf{k}$	$(1, 2, 1)$
30. $\mathbf{F}(x, y, z) = x^2z\mathbf{i} - 2xz\mathbf{j} + yz\mathbf{k}$	$(2, -1, 3)$
31. $\mathbf{F}(x, y, z) = e^x \sin y\mathbf{i} - e^x \cos y\mathbf{j}$	$(0, 0, 3)$
32. $\mathbf{F}(x, y, z) = e^{-xyz}(\mathbf{i} + \mathbf{j} + \mathbf{k})$	$(3, 2, 0)$

In Exercises 33–36, find the curl of the vector field F.

33. $\mathbf{F}(x, y, z) = \arctan\dfrac{x}{y}\mathbf{i} + \ln\sqrt{x^2 + y^2}\mathbf{j} + \mathbf{k}$

34. $\mathbf{F}(x, y, z) = \dfrac{yz}{y - z}\mathbf{i} + \dfrac{xz}{x - z}\mathbf{j} + \dfrac{xy}{x - y}\mathbf{k}$

35. $\mathbf{F}(x, y, z) = \sin(x - y)\mathbf{i} + \sin(y - z)\mathbf{j} + \sin(z - x)\mathbf{k}$

36. $\mathbf{F}(x, y, z) = \sqrt{x^2 + y^2 + z^2}\,(\mathbf{i} + \mathbf{j} + \mathbf{k})$

In Exercises 37–42, determine whether the vector field F is conservative. If it is, find a potential function for the vector field.

37. $\mathbf{F}(x, y, z) = \sin y\mathbf{i} - x\cos y\mathbf{j} + \mathbf{k}$

38. $\mathbf{F}(x, y, z) = e^z(y\mathbf{i} + x\mathbf{j} + \mathbf{k})$

39. $\mathbf{F}(x, y, z) = e^z(y\mathbf{i} + x\mathbf{j} + xy\mathbf{k})$

40. $\mathbf{F}(x, y, z) = 3x^2y^2z\mathbf{i} + 2x^3yz\mathbf{j} + x^3y^2\mathbf{k}$

41. $\mathbf{F}(x, y, z) = \dfrac{1}{y}\mathbf{i} - \dfrac{x}{y^2}\mathbf{j} + (2z - 1)\mathbf{k}$

42. $\mathbf{F}(x, y, z) = \dfrac{x}{x^2 + y^2}\mathbf{i} + \dfrac{y}{x^2 + y^2}\mathbf{j} + \mathbf{k}$

In Exercises 43 and 44, find curl $(\mathbf{F} \times \mathbf{G})$.

43. $\mathbf{F}(x, y, z) = \mathbf{i} + 2x\mathbf{j} + 3y\mathbf{k}$
$\mathbf{G}(x, y, z) = x\mathbf{i} - y\mathbf{j} + z\mathbf{k}$

44. $\mathbf{F}(x, y, z) = x\mathbf{i} - z\mathbf{k}$
$\mathbf{G}(x, y, z) = x^2\mathbf{i} + y\mathbf{j} + z^2\mathbf{k}$

In Exercises 45 and 46, find curl (curl $\mathbf{F}$) $= \nabla \times (\nabla \times \mathbf{F})$.

45. $\mathbf{F}(x, y, z) = xyz\mathbf{i} + y\mathbf{j} + z\mathbf{k}$

46. $\mathbf{F}(x, y, z) = x^2z\mathbf{i} - 2xz\mathbf{j} + yz\mathbf{k}$

In Exercises 47–50, find the divergence of the vector field F.

47. $\mathbf{F}(x, y) = 6x^2\mathbf{i} - xy^2\mathbf{j}$

48. $\mathbf{F}(x, y) = xe^x\mathbf{i} + ye^y\mathbf{j}$

49. $\mathbf{F}(x, y, z) = \sin x\mathbf{i} + \cos y\mathbf{j} + z^2\mathbf{k}$

50. $\mathbf{F}(x, y, z) = \ln(x^2 + y^2)\mathbf{i} + xy\mathbf{j} + \ln(y^2 + z^2)\mathbf{k}$

In Exercises 51–54, find the divergence of the vector field F at the indicated point.

Vector field	Point
51. $\mathbf{F}(x, y, z) = xyz\mathbf{i} + y\mathbf{j} + z\mathbf{k}$	$(1, 2, 1)$
52. $\mathbf{F}(x, y, z) = x^2z\mathbf{i} - 2xz\mathbf{j} + yz\mathbf{k}$	$(2, -1, 3)$
53. $\mathbf{F}(x, y, z) = e^x \sin y\mathbf{i} - e^x \cos y\mathbf{j}$	$(0, 0, 3)$
54. $\mathbf{F}(x, y, z) = e^{-xyz}(\mathbf{i} + \mathbf{j} + \mathbf{k})$	$(3, 2, 0)$

In Exercises 55 and 56, find div$(\mathbf{F} \times \mathbf{G})$.

55. $\mathbf{F}(x, y, z) = \mathbf{i} + 2x\mathbf{j} + 3y\mathbf{k}$
$\mathbf{G}(x, y, z) = x\mathbf{i} - y\mathbf{j} + z\mathbf{k}$

56. $\mathbf{F}(x,y,z) = x\mathbf{i} - z\mathbf{k}$
$\mathbf{G}(x,y,z) = x^2\mathbf{i} + y\mathbf{j} + z^2\mathbf{k}$

In Exercises 57 and 58, find

   div (curl **F**) $= \nabla \cdot (\nabla \times \mathbf{F})$.

57. $\mathbf{F}(x,y,z) = xyz\mathbf{i} + y\mathbf{j} + z\mathbf{k}$

58. $\mathbf{F}(x,y,z) = x^2z\mathbf{i} - 2xz\mathbf{j} + yz\mathbf{k}$

In Exercises 59–65, prove the given property for vector fields F and G and scalar function f. (Assume the required partial derivatives are continuous.)

59. curl (**F** + **G**) = curl **F** + curl **G**

60. curl $(\nabla f) = \nabla \times (\nabla f) = \mathbf{0}$

61. div (**F** + **G**) = div **F** + div **G**

62. div (**F** × **G**) = (curl **F**)·**G** − **F**·(curl **G**)

63. $\nabla \times [\nabla f + (\nabla \times \mathbf{F})] = \nabla \times (\nabla \times \mathbf{F})$

64. $\nabla \times (f\mathbf{F}) = f(\nabla \times \mathbf{F}) + (\nabla f) \times \mathbf{F}$

65. div $(f\mathbf{F}) = f$ div $\mathbf{F} + \nabla f \cdot \mathbf{F}$

66. Prove Theorem 15.3.

In Exercises 67–70, let $\mathbf{F}(x,y,z) = x\mathbf{i} + y\mathbf{j} + z\mathbf{k}$, **and** $f(x,y,z) = \| \mathbf{F}(x,y,z) \|$.

67. Show that $\nabla(\ln f) = \dfrac{\mathbf{F}}{f^2}$.

68. Show that $\nabla\left(\dfrac{1}{f}\right) = -\dfrac{\mathbf{F}}{f^3}$.

69. Show that $\nabla f^n = nf^{n-2}\mathbf{F}$.

70. The **Laplacian** is the differential operator

$$\nabla^2 = \nabla \cdot \nabla = \frac{\partial^2}{\partial x^2} + \frac{\partial^2}{\partial y^2} + \frac{\partial^2}{\partial z^2}$$

and Laplace's equation is

$$\nabla^2 w = \frac{\partial^2 w}{\partial x^2} + \frac{\partial^2 w}{\partial y^2} + \frac{\partial^2 w}{\partial z^2} = 0.$$

Any function that satisfies this equation is called **harmonic.** Show that the function $1/f$ is harmonic.

71. *Magnetic Field*   A cross section of the earth's magnetic field can be represented as a vector field in which the center of the earth is located at the origin and the positive y-axis points in the direction of the magnetic north pole. The equation for this field is

$$\mathbf{F}(x,y) = M(x,y)\mathbf{i} + N(x,y)\mathbf{j}$$

$$= \frac{m}{(x^2 + y^2)^{5/2}}[3xy\,\mathbf{i} + (2y^2 - x^2)\mathbf{j}]$$

where m is the magnetic moment of the earth. Show that this vector field is conservative.

JOSIAH WILLARD GIBBS

Many physicists and mathematicians have contributed to the theory and applications described in this chapter—Newton, Gauss, Laplace, Hamilton, Maxwell, and many others. However, the use of vector analysis to describe the results is primarily due to the American mathematical physicist Josiah Willard Gibbs (1839–1903).

Piecewise Smooth Curves

A classical property of gravitational fields is that, subject to certain physical constraints, the work done by gravity on an object moving between two points in the field is independent of the path taken by the object. One of the constraints is that the **path** must be a piecewise smooth curve. Recall that a plane curve C given by

$$\mathbf{r}(t) = x(t)\mathbf{i} + y(t)\mathbf{j}, \qquad a \leq t \leq b$$

is **smooth** if dx/dt and dy/dt are continuous on $[a, b]$ and not simultaneously 0 on (a, b). Similarly, a space curve C given by

$$\mathbf{r}(t) = x(t)\mathbf{i} + y(t)\mathbf{j} + z(t)\mathbf{k}, \qquad a \leq t \leq b$$

is **smooth** if dx/dt, dy/dt, and dz/dt are continuous on $[a, b]$ and not simultaneously 0 on (a, b). A curve C is **piecewise smooth** if the interval $[a, b]$ can be partitioned into a finite number of subintervals, on each of which C is smooth.

EXAMPLE 1   Finding a Piecewise Smooth Parametrization

Find a piecewise smooth parametrization of the graph C shown in Figure 15.7.

Solution   Because C consists of three line segments C_1, C_2, and C_3, you can construct a smooth parametrization for each and piece them together by making the last t-value in C_i correspond to the first t-value in C_{i+1} as follows.

$$
\begin{aligned}
C_1 &: x(t) = 0, & y(t) &= 2t, & z(t) &= 0, & 0 &\leq t \leq 1 \\
C_2 &: x(t) = t - 1, & y(t) &= 2, & z(t) &= 0, & 1 &\leq t \leq 2 \\
C_3 &: x(t) = 1, & y(t) &= 2, & z(t) &= t - 2, & 2 &\leq t \leq 3
\end{aligned}
$$

Therefore, C is given by

$$
\mathbf{r}(t) = \begin{cases}
2t\,\mathbf{j}, & 0 \leq t \leq 1 \\
(t - 1)\mathbf{i} + 2\mathbf{j}, & 1 \leq t \leq 2 \\
\mathbf{i} + 2\mathbf{j} + (t - 2)\mathbf{k}, & 2 \leq t \leq 3.
\end{cases}
$$

Because C_1, C_2, and C_3 are smooth, it follows that C is piecewise smooth. ▬

Recall that the parametrization of a curve induces an **orientation** to the curve. For instance, in Example 1 the curve is oriented so that the positive direction is from $(0, 0, 0)$, following the curve to $(1, 2, 1)$. Try finding a parametrization that induces the opposite orientation.

FIGURE 15.7
The graph C is piecewise smooth.

Line Integrals

Up to this point in the text, you have studied various types of integrals. For a single integral

$$\int_a^b f(x)\, dx \qquad \text{Integrate over interval } [a,b]$$

you integrated over the interval $[a, b]$. Similarly for a double integral

$$\iint_R f(x, y)\, dA \qquad \text{Integrate over region } R$$

you integrated over the region R in the plane. In this section, you will study a new type of integral called a **line integral**

$$\int_C f(x, y)\, ds \qquad \text{Integrate over curve } C$$

for which you integrate over a piecewise smooth curve C. (The terminology is somewhat unfortunate—this type of integral might be better described as a "curve integral.")

To introduce the concept of a line integral, consider the mass of a wire of finite length, given by a curve C in space. The density (mass per unit length) of the wire at the point (x, y, z) is given by $f(x, y, z)$. Partition the curve C by the points $P_0, P_1, \ldots, P_n$, producing n subarcs, as shown in Figure 15.8. The length of the ith subarc is given by Δs_i. Next, choose a point (x_i, y_i, z_i) in each subarc. If the length of each subarc is small, then the total mass of the wire can be approximated by the sum

$$\text{Mass of wire} \approx \sum_{i=1}^{n} f(x_i, y_i, z_i)\, \Delta s_i.$$

If you let $\|\Delta\|$ denote the length of the longest subarc and let $\|\Delta\|$ approach 0, it seems reasonable that the limit of this sum approaches the mass of the wire. This leads to the following definition.

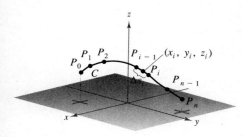

FIGURE 15.8
Partition of curve C

Definition of Line Integral

If f is defined in a region containing a smooth curve C of finite length, then the **line integral of f along C** is given by

$$\int_C f(x, y)\, ds = \lim_{\|\Delta\| \to 0} \sum_{i=1}^{n} f(x_i, y_i)\, \Delta s_i \qquad \text{Plane}$$

or

$$\int_C f(x, y, z)\, ds = \lim_{\|\Delta\| \to 0} \sum_{i=1}^{n} f(x_i, y_i, z_i)\, \Delta s_i \qquad \text{Space}$$

provided this limit exists.

As with the integrals in Chapter 14, evaluation of a line integral is best accomplished by converting to a definite integral. It can be shown that if f is *continuous*, then the above limit exists and is the same for all smooth parametrizations of C.

To evaluate a line integral over a plane curve C given by $\mathbf{r}(t) = x(t)\mathbf{i} + y(t)\mathbf{j}$, use the fact that

$$ds = \|\mathbf{r}'(t)\| \, dt = \sqrt{[x'(t)]^2 + [y'(t)]^2} \, dt.$$

A similar formula holds for a space curve, as indicated in the following theorem.

THEOREM 15.4   Evaluation of a Line Integral as a Definite Integral

Let f be continuous in a region containing a smooth curve C. If C is given by $\mathbf{r}(t) = x(t)\mathbf{i} + y(t)\mathbf{j}$, where $a \le t \le b$, then

$$\int_C f(x, y) \, ds = \int_a^b f(x(t), y(t)) \sqrt{[x'(t)]^2 + [y'(t)]^2} \, dt.$$

If C is given by $\mathbf{r}(t) = x(t)\mathbf{i} + y(t)\mathbf{j} + z(t)\mathbf{k}$, where $a \le t \le b$, then

$$\int_C f(x, y, z) \, ds = \int_a^b f(x(t), y(t), z(t)) \sqrt{[x'(t)]^2 + [y'(t)]^2 + [z'(t)]^2} \, dt.$$

Note that if $f(x, y, z) = 1$, then the line integral gives the arc length of the curve C, as defined in Section 12.5. That is,

$$\int_C 1 \, ds = \int_a^b \|\mathbf{r}'(t)\| \, dt = \text{length of curve } C.$$

REMARK   The value of the line integral in Example 2 does not depend on the parametrization of the line segment C (any smooth parametrization will produce the same value). To convince yourself of this, try some other parametrizations, such as $x = 1 + 2t$, $y = 2 + 4t$, $z = 1 + 2t$, $-\frac{1}{2} \le t \le 0$, or $x = -t$, $y = -2t$, $z = -t$, $-1 \le t \le 0$.

EXAMPLE 2   Evaluating a Line Integral

Evaluate

$$\int_C (x^2 - y + 3z) \, ds$$

where C is the line segment shown in Figure 15.9.

Solution   Begin by writing a parametric form of the equation of a line:

$$x = t, \quad y = 2t, \quad \text{and} \quad z = t, \quad 0 \le t \le 1.$$

Hence, $x'(t) = 1$, $y'(t) = 2$, and $z'(t) = 1$, which implies that

$$\sqrt{[x'(t)]^2 + [y'(t)]^2 + [z'(t)]^2} = \sqrt{1^2 + 2^2 + 1^2} = \sqrt{6}.$$

Thus, the line integral takes the following form.

$$\int_C (x^2 - y + 3z) \, ds = \int_0^1 (t^2 - 2t + 3t)\sqrt{6} \, dt$$

$$= \sqrt{6} \int_0^1 (t^2 + t) \, dt$$

$$= \sqrt{6} \left[\frac{t^3}{3} + \frac{t^2}{2} \right]_0^1$$

$$= \frac{5\sqrt{6}}{6}$$

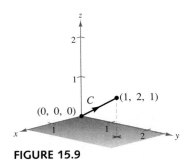

FIGURE 15.9

Suppose C is a path composed of smooth curves $C_1, C_2, \ldots, C_n$. If f is continuous on C, then it can be shown that

$$\int_C f(x, y) \, ds = \int_{C_1} f(x, y) \, ds + \int_{C_2} f(x, y) \, ds + \cdots + \int_{C_n} f(x, y) \, ds.$$

This property is used in Example 3.

EXAMPLE 3   Evaluating a Line Integral Over a Path

Evaluate the line integral

$$\int_C x \, ds$$

where C is the piecewise smooth curve shown in Figure 15.10.

Solution   Begin by integrating up the line $y = x$, using the following parametrization.

$$C_1: x = t, \ y = t, \qquad 0 \le t \le 1.$$

For this curve, $\mathbf{r}(t) = t\mathbf{i} + t\mathbf{j}$, which implies that $x'(t) = 1$ and $y'(t) = 1$. Thus, $\sqrt{[x'(t)]^2 + [y'(t)]^2} = \sqrt{2}$, and you have

$$\int_{C_1} x \, ds = \int_0^1 t\sqrt{2} \, dt = \frac{\sqrt{2}}{2} t^2 \Big]_0^1 = \frac{\sqrt{2}}{2}.$$

Next integrate down the parabola $y = x^2$, using the parametrization

$$C_2: x = 1 - t, \ y = (1 - t)^2, \qquad 0 \le t \le 1.$$

For this curve, $\mathbf{r}(t) = (1 - t)\mathbf{i} + (1 - t)^2 \mathbf{j}$, which implies that $x'(t) = -1$ and $y'(t) = -2(1 - t)$. Thus,

$$\sqrt{[x'(t)]^2 + [y'(t)]^2} = \sqrt{1 + 4(1 - t)^2},$$

and you have

$$\int_{C_2} x \, ds = \int_0^1 (1 - t)\sqrt{1 + 4(1 - t)^2} \, dt$$

$$= -\frac{1}{8}\left[\frac{2}{3}[1 + 4(1 - t)^2]^{3/2}\right]_0^1$$

$$= \frac{1}{12}(5^{3/2} - 1).$$

Consequently,

$$\int_C x \, ds = \int_{C_1} x \, ds + \int_{C_2} x \, ds = \frac{\sqrt{2}}{2} + \frac{1}{12}(5^{3/2} - 1) \approx 1.56.$$

For parametrizations given by $\mathbf{r}(t) = x(t)\mathbf{i} + y(t)\mathbf{j} + z(t)\mathbf{k}$, it is helpful to remember the form of ds as

$$ds = \|\mathbf{r}'(t)\| \, dt = \sqrt{[x'(t)]^2 + [y'(t)]^2 + [z'(t)]^2} \, dt.$$

This is demonstrated in Example 4.

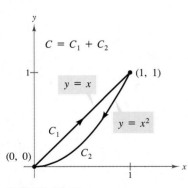

FIGURE 15.10

EXAMPLE 4　Evaluating a Line Integral

Evaluate $\displaystyle\int_C (x + 2)\,ds$, where C is the curve represented by

$$\mathbf{r}(t) = t\,\mathbf{i} + \frac{4}{3}t^{3/2}\mathbf{j} + \frac{1}{2}t^2\mathbf{k}, \qquad 0 \le t \le 2.$$

Solution　Because $\mathbf{r}'(t) = \mathbf{i} + 2t^{1/2}\mathbf{j} + t\,\mathbf{k}$, and

$$\|\mathbf{r}'(t)\| = \sqrt{[x'(t)]^2 + [y'(t)]^2 + [z'(t)]^2} = \sqrt{1 + 4t + t^2}$$

it follows that

$$
\begin{aligned}
\int_C (x + 2)\,ds &= \int_0^2 (t + 2)\sqrt{1 + 4t + t^2}\,dt \\
&= \frac{1}{2}\int_0^2 2(t + 2)(1 + 4t + t^2)^{1/2}\,dt \\
&= \frac{1}{3}\left[(1 + 4t + t^2)^{3/2}\right]_0^2 \\
&= \frac{1}{3}\left(13\sqrt{13} - 1\right) \\
&\approx 15.29.
\end{aligned}
$$

The next example shows how a line integral can be used to find the mass of a spring whose density varies. In Figure 15.11, note that the density of this spring increases as the spring spirals up the z-axis.

EXAMPLE 5　Finding the Mass of a Spring

Find the mass of a spring in the shape of the circular helix

$$\mathbf{r}(t) = \frac{1}{\sqrt{2}}(\cos t\,\mathbf{i} + \sin t\,\mathbf{j} + t\,\mathbf{k}), \qquad 0 \le t \le 6\pi$$

where the density of the wire is $\rho(x, y, z) = 1 + z$, as shown in Figure 15.11.

Solution　Because

$$\|\mathbf{r}'(t)\| = \frac{1}{\sqrt{2}}\sqrt{(-\sin t)^2 + (\cos t)^2 + (1)^2} = 1$$

it follows that the mass of the spring is

$$
\begin{aligned}
\text{Mass} &= \int_C (1 + z)\,ds = \int_0^{6\pi}\left(1 + \frac{t}{\sqrt{2}}\right)dt \\
&= \left[t + \frac{t^2}{2\sqrt{2}}\right]_0^{6\pi} \\
&= 6\pi\left(1 + \frac{3\pi}{\sqrt{2}}\right) \\
&\approx 144.47.
\end{aligned}
$$

Density:
$\rho(x, y, z) = 1 + z$

$\mathbf{r}(t) = \dfrac{1}{\sqrt{2}}(\cos t\,\mathbf{i} + \sin t\,\mathbf{j} + t\,\mathbf{k})$

FIGURE 15.11
The mass of the spring is
approximately 144.47.

Inverse Square Force Field **F**

Vectors Along a Parabolic
Path in the Force Field **F**

FIGURE 15.12

Line Integrals of Vector Fields

One of the most important physical applications of line integrals is that of finding the **work** done on an object moving in a force field. For example, Figure 15.12 shows an inverse square field similar to the gravitational field of the sun. Note that the magnitude of the force along a circular path about the center is constant, whereas the magnitude of the force along a parabolic path varies from point to point.

To see how a line integral can be used to find work done in a force field **F**, consider an object moving along a path C in the field, as shown in Figure 15.13. To determine the work done by the force, you need consider only that part of the force that is acting in the same direction as that in which the object is moving (or the opposite direction). This means that at each point on C, you can consider the projection $\mathbf{F} \cdot \mathbf{T}$ of the force vector **F** onto the unit tangent vector **T**. On a small subarc of length Δs_i, the increment of work is

$$\Delta W_i = \text{(force)(distance)}$$
$$\approx \left[\mathbf{F}(x_i, y_i, z_i) \cdot \mathbf{T}(x_i, y_i, z_i) \right] \Delta s_i$$

where (x_i, y_i, z_i) is a point in the ith subarc. Consequently, the total work done is given by the following integral.

$$W = \int_C \mathbf{F}(x, y, z) \cdot \mathbf{T}(x, y, z) \, ds$$

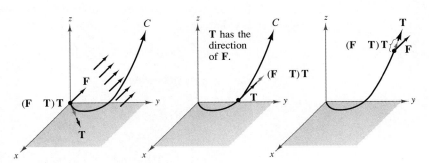

FIGURE 15.13
At each point of C, the force in the direction of motion is $(\mathbf{F} \cdot \mathbf{T})\mathbf{T}$.

This line integral appears in other contexts and is the basis of the following definition of the **line integral of a vector field.** Note in the definition that

$$\mathbf{F} \cdot \mathbf{T} \, ds = \mathbf{F} \cdot \frac{\mathbf{r}'(t)}{\| \mathbf{r}'(t) \|} \, \| \mathbf{r}'(t) \| \, dt = \mathbf{F} \cdot \mathbf{r}'(t) \, dt = \mathbf{F} \cdot d\mathbf{r}.$$

Definition of Line Integral of a Vector Field

Let **F** be a continuous vector field defined on a smooth curve C given by $\mathbf{r}(t)$. The **line integral** of **F** on C is given by

$$\int_C \mathbf{F} \cdot d\mathbf{r} = \int_C \mathbf{F} \cdot \mathbf{T} \, ds = \int_a^b \mathbf{F}(x(t), y(t), z(t)) \cdot \mathbf{r}'(t) \, dt.$$

EXAMPLE 6   Work Done by a Force

Find the work done by the force field

$$\mathbf{F}(x, y, z) = -\frac{1}{2}x\mathbf{i} - \frac{1}{2}y\mathbf{j} + \frac{1}{4}\mathbf{k} \qquad \text{Force field, } \mathbf{F}$$

on a particle as it moves along the helix given by

$$\mathbf{r}(t) = \cos t\,\mathbf{i} + \sin t\,\mathbf{j} + t\,\mathbf{k} \qquad \text{Space curve, } C$$

from the point $(1, 0, 0)$ to $(-1, 0, 3\pi)$, as shown in Figure 15.14.

Solution   Because

$$\begin{aligned}
\mathbf{r}(t) &= x(t)\mathbf{i} + y(t)\mathbf{j} + z(t)\mathbf{k} \\
&= \cos t\,\mathbf{i} + \sin t\,\mathbf{j} + t\,\mathbf{k}
\end{aligned}$$

it follows that $x(t) = \cos t$, $y(t) = \sin t$, and $z(t) = t$. Thus, the force field can be written as

$$\mathbf{F}(x(t), y(t), z(t)) = -\frac{1}{2}\cos t\,\mathbf{i} - \frac{1}{2}\sin t\,\mathbf{j} + \frac{1}{4}\mathbf{k}.$$

To find the work done by the force field in moving a particle along the curve C, use the fact that

$$\mathbf{r}'(t) = -\sin t\,\mathbf{i} + \cos t\,\mathbf{j} + \mathbf{k}$$

and write the following.

$$\begin{aligned}
W &= \int_C \mathbf{F} \cdot d\mathbf{r} \\
&= \int_a^b \mathbf{F}(x(t), y(t), z(t)) \cdot \mathbf{r}'(t)\, dt \\
&= \int_0^{3\pi} \left(-\frac{1}{2}\cos t\,\mathbf{i} - \frac{1}{2}\sin t\,\mathbf{j} + \frac{1}{4}\mathbf{k} \right) \cdot (-\sin t\,\mathbf{i} + \cos t\,\mathbf{j} + \mathbf{k})\, dt \\
&= \int_0^{3\pi} \left(\frac{1}{2}\sin t\cos t - \frac{1}{2}\sin t\cos t + \frac{1}{4} \right) dt \\
&= \int_0^{3\pi} \frac{1}{4}\, dt \\
&= \left[\frac{1}{4}t \right]_0^{3\pi} \\
&= \frac{3\pi}{4}
\end{aligned}$$

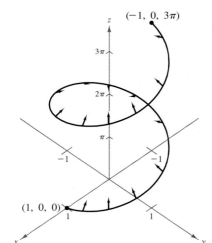

FIGURE 15.14

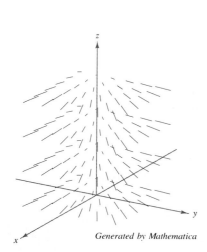

Generated by Mathematica

FIGURE 15.15
This computer-generated view of the force field in Example 6 indicates that each vector in the force field points toward the z-axis.

REMARK   In Example 6, note that the x- and y-components of the force field end up contributing nothing to the total work. This occurs because *in this particular example* the z-component of the force field is the only portion of the force that is acting in the same (or opposite) direction in which the particle is moving (see Figure 15.15).

For line integrals of vector functions, the orientation of the curve C is important. If the orientation of the curve is reversed, then the unit tangent vector $\mathbf{T}(t)$ is changed to $-\mathbf{T}(t)$, and you obtain

$$\int_{-C} \mathbf{F} \cdot d\mathbf{r} = -\int_{C} \mathbf{F} \cdot d\mathbf{r}.$$

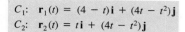

C_1: $\mathbf{r}_1(t) = (4 - t)\mathbf{i} + (4t - t^2)\mathbf{j}$
C_2: $\mathbf{r}_2(t) = t\mathbf{i} + (4t - t^2)\mathbf{j}$

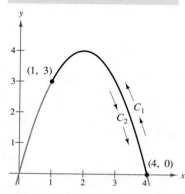

FIGURE 15.16

REMARK   Although the value of the line integral in Example 7 does depend on the orientation of C, it does not depend on the parametrization of C. To see this, let C_3 be represented by

$\mathbf{r}_3 = (t + 2)\mathbf{i} + (4 - t^2)\mathbf{j}$

where $-1 \leq t \leq 2$. The graph of this curve is the same parabolic segment shown in Figure 15.16. Does the value of the line integral over C_3 agree with the value over C_1 or C_2? Why?

EXAMPLE 7   Orientation and Parametrization of a Curve

Let $\mathbf{F}(x, y) = y\mathbf{i} + x^2\mathbf{j}$ and evaluate the line integral $\int_C \mathbf{F} \cdot d\mathbf{r}$ for each of the following parabolic curves (see Figure 15.16).

a. C_1: $\mathbf{r}_1(t) = (4 - t)\mathbf{i} + (4t - t^2)\mathbf{j}$, $0 \leq t \leq 3$
b. C_2: $\mathbf{r}_2(t) = t\mathbf{i} + (4t - t^2)\mathbf{j}$, $1 \leq t \leq 4$

Solution

a. Because $\mathbf{r}_1'(t) = -\mathbf{i} + (4 - 2t)\mathbf{j}$ and

$$\mathbf{F}(x(t), y(t)) = (4t - t^2)\mathbf{i} + (4 - t)^2\mathbf{j}$$

the line integral is

$$\int_{C_1} \mathbf{F} \cdot d\mathbf{r} = \int_0^3 [(4t - t^2)\mathbf{i} + (4 - t)^2\mathbf{j}] \cdot [-\mathbf{i} + (4 - 2t)\mathbf{j}] \, dt$$

$$= \int_0^3 (-4t + t^2 + 64 - 64t + 20t^2 - 2t^3) \, dt$$

$$= \int_0^3 (-2t^3 + 21t^2 - 68t + 64) \, dt$$

$$= \left[-\frac{t^4}{2} + 7t^3 - 34t^2 + 64t \right]_0^3$$

$$= \frac{69}{2}.$$

b. Because $\mathbf{r}_2'(t) = \mathbf{i} + (4 - 2t)\mathbf{j}$ and

$$\mathbf{F}(x(t), y(t)) = (4t - t^2)\mathbf{i} + t^2\mathbf{j}$$

the line integral is

$$\int_{C_2} \mathbf{F} \cdot d\mathbf{r} = \int_1^4 [(4t - t^2)\mathbf{i} + t^2\mathbf{j}] \cdot [\mathbf{i} + (4 - 2t)\mathbf{j}] \, dt$$

$$= \int_1^4 (4t - t^2 + 4t^2 - 2t^3) \, dt$$

$$= \int_1^4 (-2t^3 + 3t^2 + 4t) \, dt$$

$$= \left[-\frac{t^4}{2} + t^3 + 2t^2 \right]_1^4$$

$$= -\frac{69}{2}.$$

The answer in part b is the negative of that in part a because C_1 and C_2 represent opposite orientations of the same parabolic segment.

REMARK   The orientation of C affects the value of the differential form of a line integral. Specifically, if $-C$ has the opposite orientation as C, then

$$\int_{-C} M\,dx + N\,dy = -\int_{C} M\,dx + N\,dy.$$

Thus, of the three line integral forms presented in this section, the orientation of C does not affect the form $\int_{C} f(x, y)\,ds$, but it does affect the vector form and the differential form.

A second commonly used form of line integral is derived from the vector field notation used in the previous section. If $\mathbf{F}$ is a vector field of the form $\mathbf{F}(x, y) = M\mathbf{i} + N\mathbf{j}$, and C is given by $\mathbf{r}(t) = x(t)\mathbf{i} + y(t)\mathbf{j}$, then $\mathbf{F} \cdot d\mathbf{r}$ is often written as $M\,dx + N\,dy$.

$$\int_{C} \mathbf{F} \cdot d\mathbf{r} = \int_{C} \mathbf{F} \cdot \frac{d\mathbf{r}}{dt}\,dt = \int_{a}^{b} (M\mathbf{i} + N\mathbf{j}) \cdot (x'(t)\mathbf{i} + y'(t)\mathbf{j})\,dt$$

$$= \int_{a}^{b} \left(M\frac{dx}{dt} + N\frac{dy}{dt} \right) dt$$

$$= \int_{C} (M\,dx + N\,dy)$$

This **differential form** can be extended to three variables. The parentheses are often omitted, as follows.

$$\int_{C} M\,dx + N\,dy \quad \text{and} \quad \int_{C} M\,dx + N\,dy + P\,dz$$

Notice how this differential notation is used in Example 8.

EXAMPLE 8   Evaluating a Line Integral in Differential Form

Let C be the circle of radius 3 given by

$$\mathbf{r}(t) = 3\cos t\,\mathbf{i} + 3\sin t\,\mathbf{j}, \qquad 0 \le t \le 2\pi$$

(see Figure 15.17) and evaluate the line integral

$$\int_{C} y^3\,dx + (x^3 + 3xy^2)\,dy.$$

Solution   Because $x = 3\cos t$ and $y = 3\sin t$, you have $dx = -3\sin t\,dt$ and $dy = 3\cos t\,dt$. Thus, the line integral is

$$\int_{C} M\,dx + N\,dy$$

$$= \int_{C} y^3\,dx + (x^3 + 3xy^2)\,dy$$

$$= \int_{0}^{2\pi} [(27\sin^3 t)(-3\sin t) + (27\cos^3 t + 81\cos t \sin^2 t)(3\cos t)]\,dt$$

$$= 81\int_{0}^{2\pi} (\cos^4 t - \sin^4 t + 3\cos^2 t \sin^2 t)\,dt$$

$$= 81\int_{0}^{2\pi} \left(\cos^2 t - \sin^2 t + \frac{3}{4}\sin^2 2t \right) dt$$

$$= 81\int_{0}^{2\pi} \left[\cos 2t + \frac{3}{4}\left(\frac{1 - \cos 4t}{2} \right) \right] dt$$

$$= 81\left[\frac{\sin 2t}{2} + \frac{3}{8}t - \frac{3\sin 4t}{32} \right]_{0}^{2\pi}$$

$$= \frac{243\pi}{4}.$$

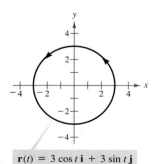

$\mathbf{r}(t) = 3\cos t\,\mathbf{i} + 3\sin t\,\mathbf{j}$

FIGURE 15.17

For curves represented by $y = g(x), a \leq x \leq b$, you can let $x = t$ and obtain the parametric form

$$x = t \quad \text{and} \quad y = g(t), \qquad a \leq t \leq b.$$

Because $dx = dt$ for this form, you have the option of evaluating the line integral in the variable x or t. This is demonstrated in Example 9.

EXAMPLE 9   Evaluating a Line Integral in Differential Form

Evaluate

$$\int_C y\,dx + x^2\,dy$$

where C is the parabolic arc given by $y = 4x - x^2$ from $(4, 0)$ to $(1, 3)$, as shown in Figure 15.18.

Solution   Rather than converting to the parameter t, you can simply retain the variable x and write

$$y = 4x - x^2 \rightarrow dy = (4 - 2x)\,dx.$$

Then, in the direction from $(4, 0)$ to $(1, 3)$, the line integral is

$$\int_C y\,dx + x^2\,dy = \int_4^1 [(4x - x^2)\,dx + x^2(4 - 2x)\,dx]$$

$$= \int_4^1 (4x + 3x^2 - 2x^3)\,dx$$

$$= \left[2x^2 + x^3 - \frac{x^4}{2} \right]_4^1$$

$$= \frac{69}{2}.$$

(See Example 7.)

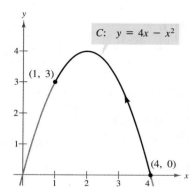

FIGURE 15.18
The line integral over C from $(4, 0)$ to $(1, 3)$ is $\dfrac{69}{2}$.

$C: \quad y = 4x - x^2$

EXERCISES for Section 15.2

TECHNOLOGY
Laboratory Guide
Labs 15.1–15.2

In Exercises 1–6, find a piecewise smooth parametrization of the path C.

1.

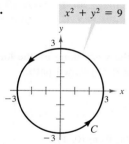

$x^2 + y^2 = 9$

2.

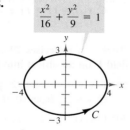

$\dfrac{x^2}{16} + \dfrac{y^2}{9} = 1$

3.

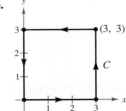

4.

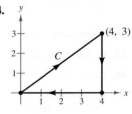

59. *Engine Design*   A tractor engine has a steel component with a circular base modeled by the vector-valued function $\mathbf{r}(t) = 2\cos t\,\mathbf{i} + 2\sin t\,\mathbf{j}$. Its height is given by $z = 1 + y^2$. All measurements of the component are given in centimeters.
   a. Find the lateral surface area of the component.
   b. If the component is in the form of a shell of thickness 0.2 centimeter, use the result of part a to approximate the amount of steel used in its manufacture.
   c. Make a sketch of the component.

60. *Building Design*   The ceiling of a building has a height above the floor given by $z = 20 + \frac{1}{4}x$, and one of the walls follows a path given by $y = x^{3/2}$. Find the surface area of the wall if $0 \le x \le 40$. (All measurements are given in feet.)

Estimation   **In Exercises 61 and 62, determine which value best approximates the lateral surface area over the curve C in the xy-plane and under the surface $z = f(x, y)$. (Make your selection on the basis of a sketch of the surface and *not* by performing any calculations.)**

61. $f(x, y) = y$
   C: $y = x^2$ from $(0, 0)$ to $(2, 4)$
   a. 2   **b.** 4   **c.** 8   **d.** 16

62. $f(x, y) = e^{xy}$
   C: line from $(0, 0)$ to $(2, 2)$
   a. 54   **b.** 25   **c.** -250 **d.** 75   **e.** 100

True or False   **In Exercises 63–66, determine whether the statement is true or false. If it is false, explain why or give an example that shows it is false.**

63. If C is given by $x(t) = t$, $y(t) = t$, $0 \le t \le 1$, then

$$\int_C xy\,ds = \int_0^1 t^2\,dt.$$

64. If $C_2 = -C_1$, then $\displaystyle\int_{C_1} f(x, y)\,ds + \int_{C_2} f(x, y)\,ds = 0$.

65. The vector functions $\mathbf{r}_1 = t\,\mathbf{i} + t^2\,\mathbf{j}$, $0 \le t \le 1$, and $\mathbf{r}_2 = (1 - t)\,\mathbf{i} + (1 - t)^2\,\mathbf{j}$, $0 \le t \le 1$, define the same curve.

66. If $\displaystyle\int_C \mathbf{F} \cdot \mathbf{T}\,ds = 0$, then $\mathbf{F}$ and $\mathbf{T}$ are orthogonal.

Conservative Vector Fields and Independence of Path

15.3   Fundamental Theorem of Line Integrals • Independence of Path • Conservation of Energy

Fundamental Theorem of Line Integrals

In the previous section, we pointed out that in a gravitational field the work done by gravity on an object moving between two points in the field is independent of the path taken by the object. In this section, you will study an important generalization of this result—it is called the **Fundamental Theorem of Line Integrals.**

We begin with an example in which the line integral of a *conservative vector field* is evaluated over three different paths.

EXAMPLE 1   Line Integral of a Conservative Vector Field

Find the work done by the force field

$$\mathbf{F}(x, y) = \frac{1}{2}xy\,\mathbf{i} + \frac{1}{4}x^2\,\mathbf{j}$$

on a particle that moves from (0, 0) to (1, 1) along the following paths.

a. C_1: $y = x$ **b.** C_2: $x = y^2$ **c.** C_3: $y = x^3$

Solution   (See Figure 15.19.)

a. Let $\mathbf{r}(t) = t\,\mathbf{i} + t\,\mathbf{j}$ for $0 \le t \le 1$, so that

$$d\mathbf{r} = (\mathbf{i} + \mathbf{j})\,dt \quad \text{and} \quad \mathbf{F}(x, y) = \frac{1}{2}t^2\,\mathbf{i} + \frac{1}{4}t^2\,\mathbf{j}.$$

Then, the work done is

$$W = \int_{C_1} \mathbf{F} \cdot d\mathbf{r} = \int_0^1 \frac{3}{4}t^2\,dt = \frac{1}{4}t^3 \bigg]_0^1 = \frac{1}{4}.$$

b. Let $\mathbf{r}(t) = t\,\mathbf{i} + \sqrt{t}\,\mathbf{j}$ for $0 \le t \le 1$, so that

$$d\mathbf{r} = \left(\mathbf{i} + \frac{1}{2\sqrt{t}}\mathbf{j}\right)dt \quad \text{and} \quad \mathbf{F}(x, y) = \frac{1}{2}t^{3/2}\,\mathbf{i} + \frac{1}{4}t^2\,\mathbf{j}.$$

Then, the work done is

$$W = \int_{C_2} \mathbf{F} \cdot d\mathbf{r} = \int_0^1 \frac{5}{8}t^{3/2}\,dt = \frac{1}{4}t^{5/2} \bigg]_0^1 = \frac{1}{4}.$$

c. Let $\mathbf{r}(t) = \frac{1}{2}t\,\mathbf{i} + \frac{1}{8}t^3\,\mathbf{j}$ for $0 \le t \le 2$, so that

$$d\mathbf{r} = \left(\frac{1}{2}\mathbf{i} + \frac{3}{8}t^2\,\mathbf{j}\right)dt \quad \text{and} \quad \mathbf{F}(x, y) = \frac{1}{32}t^4\,\mathbf{i} + \frac{1}{16}t^2\,\mathbf{j}.$$

Then, the work done is

$$W = \int_{C_3} \mathbf{F} \cdot d\mathbf{r} = \int_0^2 \frac{5}{128}t^4\,dt = \frac{1}{128}t^5 \bigg]_0^2 = \frac{1}{4}.$$

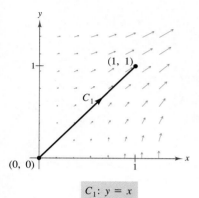

C_1: $y = x$

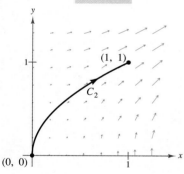

C_2: $x = y^2$

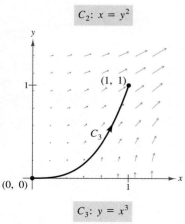

C_3: $y = x^3$

FIGURE 15.19
The work done by a conservative vector field is the same for all paths.

In Example 1, note that the vector field $\mathbf{F}(x, y) = \frac{1}{2}xy\,\mathbf{i} + \frac{1}{4}x^2\,\mathbf{j}$ is conservative because $\mathbf{F}(x, y) = \nabla f(x, y)$, where $f(x, y) = \frac{1}{4}x^2 y$. In such cases, the following theorem states that the value of $\int_C \mathbf{F} \cdot d\mathbf{r}$ is given by

$$\int_C \mathbf{F} \cdot d\mathbf{r} = f(x(1), y(1)) - f(x(0), y(0)) = \frac{1}{4} - 0 = \frac{1}{4}.$$

THEOREM 15.5   Fundamental Theorem of Line Integrals

Let C be a piecewise smooth curve lying in an open region R and given by

$$\mathbf{r}(t) = x(t)\mathbf{i} + y(t)\mathbf{j}, \qquad a \le t \le b.$$

If $\mathbf{F}(x, y) = M\mathbf{i} + N\mathbf{j}$ is conservative in R, and M and N are continuous in R, then

$$\int_C \mathbf{F} \cdot d\mathbf{r} = \int_C \nabla f \cdot d\mathbf{r} = f(x(b), y(b)) - f(x(a), y(a))$$

where f is a potential function of $\mathbf{F}$. That is, $\mathbf{F}(x, y) = \nabla f(x, y)$.

Proof   We provide a proof only for a smooth curve. For piecewise smooth curves, the procedure is carried out separately on each smooth portion. Because

$$\mathbf{F}(x, y) = \nabla f(x, y) = f_x(x, y)\mathbf{i} + f_y(x, y)\mathbf{j},$$

it follows that

$$\int_C \mathbf{F} \cdot d\mathbf{r} = \int_a^b \mathbf{F} \cdot \frac{d\mathbf{r}}{dt}\, dt = \int_a^b \left[f_x(x, y)\frac{dx}{dt} + f_y(x, y)\frac{dy}{dt} \right] dt$$

and, by the Chain Rule (Theorem 13.6), you have

$$\int_C \mathbf{F} \cdot d\mathbf{r} = \int_a^b \frac{d}{dt}[f(x(t), y(t))]\, dt = f(x(b), y(b)) - f(x(a), y(a)).$$

The last step is an application of the Fundamental Theorem of Calculus.

In space, the Fundamental Theorem of Line Integrals takes the following form. Let C be a piecewise smooth curve lying in an open region Q and given by $\mathbf{r}(t) = x(t)\mathbf{i} + y(t)\mathbf{j} + z(t)\mathbf{k}$, $a \le t \le b$. If $\mathbf{F}(x, y, z) = M\mathbf{i} + N\mathbf{j} + P\mathbf{k}$ is conservative and M, N, and P are continuous, then

$$\int_C \mathbf{F} \cdot d\mathbf{r} = \int_C \nabla f \cdot d\mathbf{r}$$
$$= f(x(b), y(b), z(b)) - f(x(a), y(a), z(a))$$

where $\mathbf{F}(x, y, z) = \nabla f(x, y, z)$.

The Fundamental Theorem of Line Integrals states that if the vector field $\mathbf{F}$ is conservative, then the line integral between any two points is simply the difference in the values of the *potential* function f at these points.

EXAMPLE 2   Using the Fundamental Theorem of Line Integrals

Evaluate $\int_C \mathbf{F} \cdot d\mathbf{r}$, where C is a piecewise smooth curve from $(-1, 4)$ to $(1, 2)$ and

$$\mathbf{F}(x, y) = 2xy\,\mathbf{i} + (x^2 - y)\mathbf{j}.$$

(See Figure 15.20.)

Solution   From Example 6 of Section 15.1, you know that $\mathbf{F}$ is the gradient of f where

$$f(x, y) = x^2y - \frac{1}{2}y^2 + K.$$

Consequently, $\mathbf{F}$ is conservative, and by the Fundamental Theorem of Line Integrals, it follows that

$$\int_C \mathbf{F} \cdot d\mathbf{r} = f(1, 2) - f(-1, 4)$$

$$= \left[1^2(2) - \frac{1}{2}(2^2) \right] - \left[(-1)^2(4) - \frac{1}{2}(4^2) \right]$$

$$= 4.$$

Note that it is unnecessary to include a constant K as part of f, because it is canceled by subtraction.

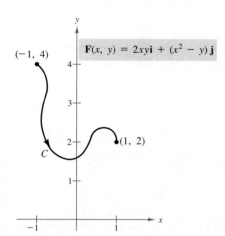

$\mathbf{F}(x, y) = 2xy\mathbf{i} + (x^2 - y)\mathbf{j}$

FIGURE 15.20
Using the Fundamental Theorem of Line Integrals, $\int_C \mathbf{F} \cdot d\mathbf{r} = 4$.

EXAMPLE 3   Using the Fundamental Theorem of Line Integrals

Evaluate $\int_C \mathbf{F} \cdot d\mathbf{r}$, where C is a piecewise smooth curve from $(1, 1, 0)$ to $(0, 2, 3)$ and

$$\mathbf{F}(x, y, z) = 2xy\,\mathbf{i} + (x^2 + z^2)\mathbf{j} + 2zy\,\mathbf{k}.$$

(See Figure 15.21.)

Solution   From Example 8 of Section 15.1, you know that $\mathbf{F}$ is the gradient of f where

$$f(x, y, z) = x^2y + z^2y.$$

Consequently, $\mathbf{F}$ is conservative, and by the Fundamental Theorem of Line Integrals, it follows that

$$\int_C \mathbf{F} \cdot d\mathbf{r} = f(0, 2, 3) - f(1, 1, 0)$$

$$= [(0)^2(2) + (3^2)(2)] - [1^2(1) + (0^2)(1)]$$

$$= 17.$$

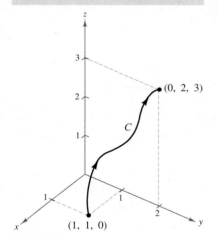

$\mathbf{F}(x, y, z) = 2xy\,\mathbf{i} + (x^2 + z^2)\mathbf{j} + 2zy\,\mathbf{k}$

FIGURE 15.21
Using the Fundamental Theorem of Line Integrals, $\int_C \mathbf{F} \cdot d\mathbf{r} = 17$.

REMARK   In Examples 2 and 3, be sure you see that the value of the line integral is the same for any smooth curve C that has the given initial and terminal points. For instance, in Example 3, try evaluating the line integral for the curve given by

$$\mathbf{r}(t) = (1 - t)\mathbf{i} + (1 + t)\mathbf{j} + 3t\,\mathbf{k}.$$

You should obtain

$$\int_C \mathbf{F} \cdot d\mathbf{r} = \int_0^1 (30t^2 + 16t - 1)\,dt = 17.$$

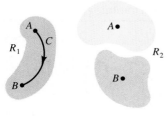

R_1 is connected. R_2 is not
connected.

FIGURE 15.22

Independence of Path

From the Fundamental Theorem of Line Integrals, it is clear that if **F** is continuous and conservative in an open region R, then the value of $\int_C \mathbf{F} \cdot d\mathbf{r}$ is the same for every piecewise smooth curve C from one fixed point in R to another fixed point in R. This result is described by saying that the line integral $\int_C \mathbf{F} \cdot d\mathbf{r}$ is **independent of path** in the region R.

A region in the plane (or in space) is **connected** if any two points in the region can be joined by a piecewise smooth curve lying entirely within the region, as shown in Figure 15.22. In open regions that are *connected*, the path independence of $\int_C \mathbf{F} \cdot d\mathbf{r}$ is equivalent to the condition that **F** is conservative.

THEOREM 15.6   Independence of Path and Conservative Vector Fields

If **F** is continuous on an open connected region, then the line integral

$$\int_C \mathbf{F} \cdot d\mathbf{r}$$

is independent of path if and only if **F** is conservative.

Proof   If **F** is conservative, then by the Fundamental Theorem of Line Integrals the line integral is independent of path. We establish the converse for a plane region R. Let $\mathbf{F}(x, y) = M\mathbf{i} + N\mathbf{j}$, and let (x_0, y_0) be a fixed point in R. If (x, y) is any point in R, then choose a piecewise smooth curve C running from (x_0, y_0) to (x, y), and define f by

$$f(x, y) = \int_C \mathbf{F} \cdot d\mathbf{r} = \int_C M\,dx + N\,dy.$$

The existence of C in R is guaranteed by the fact that R is connected. You can show that f is a potential function of **F** by considering two different paths between (x_0, y_0) and (x, y). For the *first* path, choose (x_1, y) in R such that $x \neq x_1$. This is possible because R is open. Then choose C_1 and C_2, as shown in Figure 15.23. Using the independence of path, it follows that

$$f(x, y) = \int_C M\,dx + N\,dy = \int_{C_1} M\,dx + N\,dy + \int_{C_2} M\,dx + N\,dy.$$

Because the first integral does not depend on x, and $dy = 0$ in the second integral, you have

$$f(x, y) = g(y) + \int_{C_2} M\,dx$$

and it follows that the partial derivative of f with respect to x is $f_x(x, y) = M$. For the *second* path, choose a point (x, y_1). Using reasoning similar to that used for the first path, you can conclude that $f_y(x, y) = N$. Therefore,

$$\nabla f(x, y) = f_x(x, y)\mathbf{i} + f_y(x, y)\mathbf{j} = M\mathbf{i} + N\mathbf{j} = \mathbf{F}(x, y)$$

and it follows that **F** is conservative.

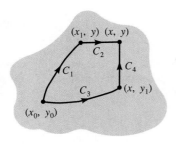

FIGURE 15.23

EXAMPLE 4   Finding Work in a Conservative Force Field

For the force field given by

$$\mathbf{F}(x, y, z) = e^x \cos y \, \mathbf{i} - e^x \sin y \, \mathbf{j} + 2\mathbf{k}$$

show that $\int_C \mathbf{F} \cdot d\mathbf{r}$ is independent of path, and calculate the work done by $\mathbf{F}$ on an object moving along a curve C from $(0, \pi/2, 1)$ to $(1, \pi, 3)$.

Solution   Writing the force field in the form $\mathbf{F}(x, y, z) = M\mathbf{i} + N\mathbf{j} + P\mathbf{k}$, you have $M = e^x \cos y$, $N = -e^x \sin y$, and $P = 2$, and it follows that

$$\frac{\partial P}{\partial y} = 0 = \frac{\partial N}{\partial z}$$

$$\frac{\partial P}{\partial x} = 0 = \frac{\partial M}{\partial z}$$

$$\frac{\partial N}{\partial x} = -e^x \sin y = \frac{\partial M}{\partial y}.$$

Hence, $\mathbf{F}$ is conservative. If f is a potential function of $\mathbf{F}$, then

$$f_x(x, y, z) = e^x \cos y$$
$$f_y(x, y, z) = -e^x \sin y$$
$$f_z(x, y, z) = 2.$$

By integrating with respect to x, y, and z separately, we obtain

$$f(x, y, z) = \int f_x(x, y, z) \, dx = \int e^x \cos y \, dx = e^x \cos y + g(y, z)$$

$$f(x, y, z) = \int f_y(x, y, z) \, dy = \int -e^x \sin y \, dy = e^x \cos y + h(x, z)$$

$$f(x, y, z) = \int f_z(x, y, z) \, dz = \int 2 \, dz = 2z + k(x, y).$$

By comparing these three versions of $f(x, y, z)$, you conclude that

$$f(x, y, z) = e^x \cos y + 2z + K.$$

Therefore, the work done by $\mathbf{F}$ along *any* curve C from $(0, \pi/2, 1)$ to $(1, \pi, 3)$ is

$$W = \int_C \mathbf{F} \cdot d\mathbf{r} = \left[e^x \cos y + 2z \right]_{(0, \pi/2, 1)}^{(1, \pi, 3)}$$
$$= (-e + 6) - (0 + 2)$$
$$= 4 - e.$$

How much work would be done if the object in Example 4 moved from the point $(0, \pi/2, 1)$ to $(1, \pi, 3)$ and then back to the starting point $(0, \pi/2, 1)$? The Fundamental Theorem of Line Integrals states that there is zero work done. Remember that, by definition, work can be negative. Hence, by the time the object gets back to its starting point, the amount of work that registers positively is canceled out by the amount of work that registers negatively.

A curve C, given by $\mathbf{r}(t)$ for $a \le t \le b$, is **closed** if $\mathbf{r}(a) = \mathbf{r}(b)$. By the Fundamental Theorem of Line Integrals, you can conclude that if $\mathbf{F}$ is continuous and conservative on an open region R, then the line integral over every closed curve C is 0.

THEOREM 15.7   Equivalent Conditions

Let $\mathbf{F}(x, y, z) = M\mathbf{i} + N\mathbf{j} + P\mathbf{k}$ have continuous first partial derivatives in an open connected region R, and let C be a piecewise smooth curve in R. The following conditions are equivalent.

1. $\mathbf{F}$ is conservative. That is, $\mathbf{F} = \nabla f$ for some function f.

2. $\displaystyle\int_C \mathbf{F} \cdot d\mathbf{r}$ is independent of path.

3. $\displaystyle\int_C \mathbf{F} \cdot d\mathbf{r} = 0$ for every *closed* curve C in R.

REMARK   Theorem 15.7 gives you options for evaluating a line integral involving a conservative vector field. You can use a potential function, or it might be more convenient to choose a particularly simple path, such as a straight line.

EXAMPLE 5   Evaluating a Line Integral

Evaluate $\int_{C_1} \mathbf{F} \cdot d\mathbf{r}$, where $\mathbf{F}(x, y) = (y^3 + 1)\mathbf{i} + (3xy^2 + 1)\mathbf{j}$ and C_1 is the semicircular path from $(0, 0)$ to $(2, 0)$, as shown in Figure 15.24.

Solution   You have the following three options.

a. You can use the method of the previous section to evaluate the line integral along the *given curve*. To do this, you can use the parametrization $\mathbf{r}(t) = (1 - \cos t)\mathbf{i} + \sin t\,\mathbf{j}$, where $0 \le t \le \pi$. For this parametrization, it follows that $d\mathbf{r} = \mathbf{r}'(t)\,dt = (\sin t\,\mathbf{i} + \cos t\,\mathbf{j})\,dt$, and

$$\int_{C_1} \mathbf{F} \cdot d\mathbf{r} = \int_0^\pi (\sin t + \sin^4 t + \cos t + 3\sin^2 t\cos t - 3\cos^2 t\sin^2 t)\,dt.$$

This integral ought to dampen your enthusiasm for this option.

b. You can try to find a *potential function* and evaluate the line integral by the Fundamental Theorem of Line Integrals. Using the technique demonstrated in Example 4, you can find the potential function to be $f(x, y) = xy^3 + x + y + K$, and, by the Fundamental Theorem,

$$W = \int_{C_1} \mathbf{F} \cdot d\mathbf{r} = f(2, 0) - f(0, 0) = 2.$$

c. Knowing that $\mathbf{F}$ is conservative, you have a third option. Because the value of the line integral is independent of path, you can replace the semicircular path with a *simpler path*. Suppose you choose the straight line path C_2 from $(0, 0)$ to $(2, 0)$. Then, $\mathbf{r}(t) = t\mathbf{i}$, where $0 \le t \le 2$. Thus, $d\mathbf{r} = \mathbf{i}\,dt$ and $\mathbf{F}(x, y) = (y^3 + 1)\mathbf{i} + (3xy^2 + 1)\mathbf{j} = \mathbf{i} + \mathbf{j}$, so that

$$\int_{C_1} \mathbf{F} \cdot d\mathbf{r} = \int_{C_2} \mathbf{F} \cdot d\mathbf{r} = \int_0^2 1\,dt = t\Big]_0^2 = 2.$$

Of the three options, obviously the third one is the easiest.

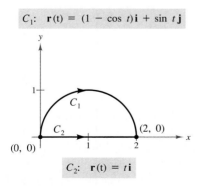

C_1: $\mathbf{r}(t) = (1 - \cos t)\mathbf{i} + \sin t\,\mathbf{j}$

C_2: $\mathbf{r}(t) = t\mathbf{i}$

FIGURE 15.24

MICHAEL FARADAY

Several philosophers of science have considered Faraday's law of conservation of energy to be the greatest generalization ever conceived by humankind. Many physicists have contributed to our knowledge of this law. Two early and influential ones were James Prescott Joule (1818–1889) and Hermann Ludwig Helmholtz (1821–1894).

Conservation of Energy

In 1840, the English physicist Michael Faraday (1791–1867) wrote, "Nowhere is there a pure creation or production of power without a corresponding exhaustion of something to supply it." This statement represents the first formulation of one of the most important laws of physics—the **Law of Conservation of Energy.** In modern terminology, the law is stated as follows: *In a conservative force field, the sum of the potential and kinetic energies of an object remains constant from point to point.*

You can use the Fundamental Theorem of Line Integrals to derive this law. From physics, the **kinetic energy** of a particle of mass m and speed v is $k = \frac{1}{2}mv^2$. The **potential energy** p of a particle at point (x, y, z) in a conservative vector field $\mathbf{F}$ is defined as

$$p(x, y, z) = -f(x, y, z)$$

where f is the potential function for $\mathbf{F}$. Consequently, the work done by $\mathbf{F}$ along a smooth curve C from A to B is

$$W = \int_C \mathbf{F} \cdot d\mathbf{r} = f(x, y, z) \Big]_A^B = -p(x, y, z) \Big]_A^B = p(A) - p(B)$$

as indicated in Figure 15.25. In other words, work W is equal to the difference in the potential energies of A and B. Now, suppose that $\mathbf{r}(t)$ is the position vector for a particle moving along C from $A = \mathbf{r}(a)$ to $B = \mathbf{r}(b)$. At any time t, the particle's velocity, acceleration, and speed are $\mathbf{v}(t) = \mathbf{r}'(t)$, $\mathbf{a}(t) = \mathbf{r}''(t)$, and $v(t) = \|\mathbf{v}(t)\|$, respectively. Thus, by Newton's Second Law of Motion, $\mathbf{F} = m\mathbf{a}(t) = m(\mathbf{v}'(t))$, and the work done by $\mathbf{F}$ is

$$
\begin{aligned}
W = \int_C \mathbf{F} \cdot d\mathbf{r} &= \int_a^b \mathbf{F} \cdot \mathbf{r}'(t)\, dt \\
&= \int_a^b \mathbf{F} \cdot \mathbf{v}(t)\, dt = \int_a^b [m\mathbf{v}'(t)] \cdot \mathbf{v}(t)\, dt \\
&= \int_a^b m[\mathbf{v}'(t) \cdot \mathbf{v}(t)]\, dt \\
&= \frac{m}{2} \int_a^b \frac{d}{dt}[\mathbf{v}(t) \cdot \mathbf{v}(t)]\, dt \\
&= \frac{m}{2} \int_a^b \frac{d}{dt}[\|\mathbf{v}(t)\|^2]\, dt = \frac{m}{2} \|\mathbf{v}(t)\|^2 \Big]_a^b \\
&= \frac{m}{2} [v(t)]^2 \Big]_a^b = \frac{1}{2}m[v(b)]^2 - \frac{1}{2}m[v(a)]^2 \\
&= k(B) - k(A).
\end{aligned}
$$

Equating these two results for W produces

$$p(A) - p(B) = k(B) - k(A)$$
$$p(A) + k(A) = p(B) + k(B)$$

which implies that the sum of the potential and kinetic energies remains constant from point to point.

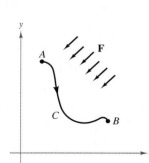

FIGURE 15.25

The work done by $\mathbf{F}$ along C is

$$W = \int_C \mathbf{F} \cdot d\mathbf{r} = p(A) - p(B).$$

TECHNOLOGY
Laboratory Guide
Labs 15.3–15.4

In Exercises 1–4, show that the value of $\int_C \mathbf{F} \cdot d\mathbf{r}$ is the same for both parametric representations of C.

1. $\mathbf{F}(x, y) = x^2\mathbf{i} + xy\mathbf{j}$
  a. $\mathbf{r}_1(t) = t\mathbf{i} + t^2\mathbf{j}$, $0 \le t \le 1$
  b. $\mathbf{r}_2(\theta) = \sin\theta\,\mathbf{i} + \sin^2\theta\,\mathbf{j}$, $0 \le \theta \le \dfrac{\pi}{2}$

2. $\mathbf{F}(x, y) = (x^2 + y^2)\mathbf{i} - x\mathbf{j}$
  a. $\mathbf{r}_1(t) = t\mathbf{i} + \sqrt{t}\,\mathbf{j}$, $0 \le t \le 4$
  b. $\mathbf{r}_2(w) = w^2\mathbf{i} + w\mathbf{j}$, $0 \le w \le 2$

3. $\mathbf{F}(x, y) = y\mathbf{i} - x\mathbf{j}$
  a. $\mathbf{r}_1(\theta) = \sec\theta\,\mathbf{i} + \tan\theta\,\mathbf{j}$, $0 \le \theta \le \dfrac{\pi}{3}$
  b. $\mathbf{r}_2(t) = \sqrt{t+1}\,\mathbf{i} + \sqrt{t}\,\mathbf{j}$, $0 \le t \le 3$

4. $\mathbf{F}(x, y) = y\mathbf{i} + x^2\mathbf{j}$
  a. $\mathbf{r}_1(t) = (2 + t)\mathbf{i} + (3 - t)\mathbf{j}$, $0 \le t \le 3$
  b. $\mathbf{r}_2(w) = (2 + \ln w)\mathbf{i} + (3 - \ln w)\mathbf{j}$, $1 \le w \le e^3$

In Exercises 5–18, find the value of the line integral $\int_C \mathbf{F} \cdot d\mathbf{r}$. (Hint: If F is conservative, the integration may be easier on an alternative path.)

5. $\mathbf{F}(x, y) = 2xy\mathbf{i} + x^2\mathbf{j}$
  a. $\mathbf{r}_1(t) = t\mathbf{i} + t^2\mathbf{j}$, $0 \le t \le 1$
  b. $\mathbf{r}_2(t) = t\mathbf{i} + t^3\mathbf{j}$, $0 \le t \le 1$

6. $\mathbf{F}(x, y) = ye^{xy}\mathbf{i} + xe^{xy}\mathbf{j}$
  a. $\mathbf{r}_1(t) = t\mathbf{i} - \frac{3}{2}(t - 2)\mathbf{j}$, $0 \le t \le 2$
  b. Line segments from $(0, 3)$ to $(0, 0)$, and then from $(0, 0)$ to $(2, 0)$

7. $\mathbf{F}(x, y) = y\mathbf{i} - x\mathbf{j}$
  a. $\mathbf{r}_1(t) = t\mathbf{i} + t\mathbf{j}$, $0 \le t \le 1$
  b. $\mathbf{r}_2(t) = t\mathbf{i} + t^2\mathbf{j}$, $0 \le t \le 1$
  c. $\mathbf{r}_3(t) = t\mathbf{i} + t^3\mathbf{j}$, $0 \le t \le 1$

8. $\mathbf{F}(x, y) = xy^2\mathbf{i} + 2x^2y\mathbf{j}$
  a. $\mathbf{r}_1(t) = t\mathbf{i} + \dfrac{1}{t}\mathbf{j}$, $1 \le t \le 3$
  b. $\mathbf{r}_2(t) = (t + 1)\mathbf{i} - \frac{1}{3}(t - 3)\mathbf{j}$, $0 \le t \le 2$

9. $\displaystyle\int_C y^2\,dx + 2xy\,dy$

a.

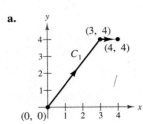

b.

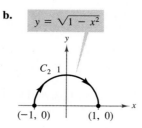

c.

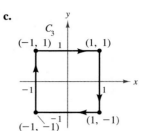

d.

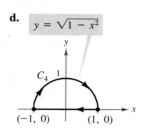

10. $\displaystyle\int_C (2x - 3y + 1)\,dx - (3x + y - 5)\,dy$

a.

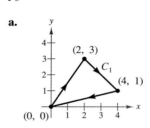

b.

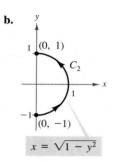

c.

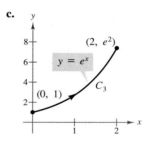

d.

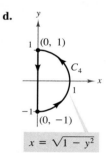

11. $\displaystyle\int_C 2xy\,dx + (x^2 + y^2)\,dy$
  a. C: ellipse $\dfrac{x^2}{25} + \dfrac{y^2}{16} = 1$ from $(5, 0)$ to $(0, 4)$
  b. C: parabola $y = 4 - x^2$ from $(2, 0)$ to $(0, 4)$

12. $\displaystyle\int_C (x^2 + y^2)\,dx + 2xy\,dy$
  a. $\mathbf{r}_1(t) = t^3\mathbf{i} + t^2\mathbf{j}$, $0 \le t \le 2$
  b. $\mathbf{r}_2(t) = 2\cos t\,\mathbf{i} + 2\sin t\,\mathbf{j}$, $0 \le t \le \dfrac{\pi}{2}$

13. $\mathbf{F}(x, y, z) = yz\mathbf{i} + xz\mathbf{j} + xy\mathbf{k}$
  a. $\mathbf{r}_1(t) = t\mathbf{i} + 2\mathbf{j} + t\mathbf{k}$, $0 \le t \le 4$
  b. $\mathbf{r}_2(t) = t^2\mathbf{i} + t\mathbf{j} + t^2\mathbf{k}$, $0 \le t \le 2$

14. $\mathbf{F}(x, y, z) = \mathbf{i} + z\mathbf{j} + y\mathbf{k}$
  a. $\mathbf{r}_1(t) = \cos t\,\mathbf{i} + \sin t\,\mathbf{j} + t^2\mathbf{k}$, $0 \le t \le \pi$
  b. $\mathbf{r}_2(t) = (1 - 2t)\mathbf{i} + \pi^2 t\mathbf{k}$, $0 \le t \le 1$

15. $\mathbf{F}(x, y, z) = (2y + x)\mathbf{i} + (x^2 - z)\mathbf{j} + (2y - 4z)\mathbf{k}$
   a. $\mathbf{r}_1(t) = t\,\mathbf{i} + t^2\mathbf{j} + \mathbf{k}, \quad 0 \le t \le 1$
   b. $\mathbf{r}_2(t) = t\,\mathbf{i} + t\,\mathbf{j} + (2t - 1)^2\mathbf{k}, \quad 0 \le t \le 1$

16. $\mathbf{F}(x, y, z) = -y\mathbf{i} + x\mathbf{j} + 3xz^2\mathbf{k}$
   a. $\mathbf{r}_1(t) = \cos t\,\mathbf{i} + \sin t\,\mathbf{j} + t\,\mathbf{k}, \quad 0 \le t \le \pi$
   b. $\mathbf{r}_2(t) = (1 - 2t)\mathbf{i} + \pi t\,\mathbf{k}, \quad 0 \le t \le 1$

17. $\mathbf{F}(x, y, z) = e^z(y\mathbf{i} + x\mathbf{j} + xy\mathbf{k})$
   a. $\mathbf{r}_1(t) = 4\cos t\,\mathbf{i} + 4\sin t\,\mathbf{j} + 3\mathbf{k}, \quad 0 \le t \le \pi$
   b. $\mathbf{r}_2(t) = (4 - 8t)\mathbf{i} + 3\mathbf{k}, \quad 0 \le t \le 1$

18. $\mathbf{F}(x, y, z) = y\sin z\,\mathbf{i} + x\sin z\,\mathbf{j} + xy\cos x\,\mathbf{k}$
   a. $\mathbf{r}_1(t) = t^2\mathbf{i} + t^2\mathbf{j}, \quad 0 \le t \le 2$
   b. $\mathbf{r}_2(t) = 4t\,\mathbf{i} + 4t\,\mathbf{j}, \quad 0 \le t \le 1$

In Exercises 19–28, evaluate the given line integral using the Fundamental Theorem of Line Integrals.

19. $\displaystyle\int_C (y\mathbf{i} + x\mathbf{j}) \cdot d\mathbf{r}$

   C: smooth curve from $(0, 0)$ to $(3, 8)$

20. $\displaystyle\int_C [2(x + y)\mathbf{i} + 2(x + y)\mathbf{j}] \cdot d\mathbf{r}$

   C: smooth curve from $(-1, 1)$ to $(3, 2)$

21. $\displaystyle\int_C \cos x \sin y\,dx + \sin x \cos y\,dy$

   C: smooth curve from $(0, -\pi)$ to $\left(\dfrac{3\pi}{2}, \dfrac{\pi}{2}\right)$

22. $\displaystyle\int_C \frac{y\,dx - x\,dy}{x^2 + y^2}$

   C: smooth curve from $(1, 1)$ to $\left(2\sqrt{3}, 2\right)$

23. $\displaystyle\int_C e^x \sin y\,dx + e^x \cos y\,dy$

   C: cycloid $x = \theta - \sin\theta$, $y = 1 - \cos\theta$ from $(0, 0)$ to $(2\pi, 0)$

24. $\displaystyle\int_C \frac{2x}{(x^2 + y^2)^2}\,dx + \frac{2y}{(x^2 + y^2)^2}\,dy$

   C: circle $(x - 4)^2 + (y - 5)^2 = 9$ clockwise from $(7, 5)$ to $(1, 5)$

25. $\displaystyle\int_C (z + 2y)\,dx + (2x - z)\,dy + (x - y)\,dz$

   a. C: line segment from $(0, 0, 0)$ to $(1, 1, 1)$
   b. C: line segments from $(0, 0, 0)$ to $(0, 0, 1)$ to $(1, 1, 1)$
   c. C: line segments from $(0, 0, 0)$ to $(1, 0, 0)$ to $(1, 1, 0)$ to $(1, 1, 1)$

26. Repeat Exercise 25 using the integral

   $\displaystyle\int_C zy\,dx + xz\,dy + xy\,dz.$

27. $\displaystyle\int_C -\sin x\,dx + z\,dy + y\,dz$

   C: smooth curve from $(0, 0, 0)$ to $\left(\dfrac{\pi}{2}, 3, 4\right)$

28. $\displaystyle\int_C 6x\,dx - 4z\,dy - (4y - 20z)\,dz$

   C: smooth curve from $(0, 0, 0)$ to $(3, 4, 0)$

Work   In Exercises 29 and 30, find the work done by the force field F in moving an object from P to Q.

29. $\mathbf{F}(x, y) = 9x^2y^2\mathbf{i} + (6x^3y - 1)\mathbf{j}$
   $P = (0, 0), Q = (5, 9)$

30. $\mathbf{F}(x, y) = \dfrac{2x}{y}\mathbf{i} - \dfrac{x^2}{y^2}\mathbf{j}$
   $P = (-1, 1), Q = (3, 2)$

31. *Work*   A stone weighing 1 pound is attached to the end of a 2-foot string and is whirled horizontally with one end held fixed. It makes one revolution per second. Find the work done by the force $\mathbf{F}$ that keeps the stone moving in a circular path. (*Hint:* Use Force = (Mass)(Centripetal Acceleration).)

32. *Work*   If $\mathbf{F}(x, y, z) = a_1\mathbf{i} + a_2\mathbf{j} + a_3\mathbf{k}$ is a constant force vector field, show that the work done in moving a particle along any path from P to Q is

   $W = \mathbf{F} \cdot \overrightarrow{PQ}.$

33. *Kinetic and Potential Energy*   The kinetic energy of an object moving through a conservative force field is decreasing at a rate of 10 units per minute. At what rate is the potential energy changing?

34. *Work*   To allow a way of escape for workers in a hazardous job 50 meters above ground level, a slide wire has been installed. It runs from their position to a point on the ground 50 meters from the base of the installation where they are located. Show that the work done by the gravitational force field for a 150-pound man moving the length of the slide wire is the same for the following two paths.

   a. $\mathbf{r}(t) = t\,\mathbf{i} + (50 - t)\mathbf{j}$
   b. $\mathbf{r}(t) = t\,\mathbf{i} + \dfrac{1}{50}(50 - t)^2\mathbf{j}$

35. *Work*   Can you find a path for the slide wire in Exercise 34 such that the work done by the gravitational force field would differ from the amounts of work done for the two paths given? Explain why or why not.

36. Let $\mathbf{F}(x, y) = \dfrac{y}{x^2 + y^2}\mathbf{i} - \dfrac{x}{x^2 + y^2}\mathbf{j}$.
   a. Show that

   $$\frac{\partial N}{\partial x} = \frac{\partial M}{\partial y}$$

   where

   $$M = \frac{y}{x^2 + y^2}$$

   and

   $$N = \frac{-x}{x^2 + y^2}.$$

   b. If $\mathbf{r}(t) = \cos t\,\mathbf{i} + \sin t\,\mathbf{j}$, for $0 \le t \le \pi$, find $\int_C \mathbf{F} \cdot d\mathbf{r}$.
   c. If $\mathbf{r}(t) = \cos t\,\mathbf{i} - \sin t\,\mathbf{j}$, for $0 \le t \le \pi$, find $\int_C \mathbf{F} \cdot d\mathbf{r}$.

d. If $\mathbf{r}(t) = \cos t\,\mathbf{i} + \sin t\,\mathbf{j}$, for $0 \le t \le 2\pi$, find $\int_C \mathbf{F} \cdot d\mathbf{r}$. Why doesn't this contradict Theorem 15.7?

e. Show that

$$\nabla\left(\arctan\frac{x}{y}\right) = \mathbf{F}.$$

True or False   **In Exercises 37–40, determine whether the statement is true or false. If it is false, explain why or give an example that shows it is false.**

37. If C_1, C_2, and C_3 have the same initial and terminal points and $\int_{C_1} \mathbf{F} \cdot d\mathbf{r}_1 = \int_{C_2} \mathbf{F} \cdot d\mathbf{r}_2$, then $\int_{C_1} \mathbf{F} \cdot d\mathbf{r}_1 = \int_{C_3} \mathbf{F} \cdot d\mathbf{r}_3$.

38. If $\mathbf{F} = y\,\mathbf{i} + x\,\mathbf{j}$ and C is given by $\mathbf{r}(t) = (4\sin t)\mathbf{i} + (3\cos t)\mathbf{j}$, $0 \le t \le \pi$, then $\int_C \mathbf{F} \cdot d\mathbf{r} = 0$.

39. If $\mathbf{F}$ is conservative in a region R bounded by a simple closed path, and C lies within R, then $\int_C \mathbf{F} \cdot d\mathbf{r}$ is path-independent.

40. If $\mathbf{F} = M\,\mathbf{i} + N\,\mathbf{j}$ and $\partial M/\partial x = \partial N/\partial y$, then $\mathbf{F}$ is conservative.

41. f is called harmonic if

$$\frac{\partial^2 f}{\partial x^2} + \frac{\partial^2 f}{\partial y^2} = 0.$$

Prove that if f is harmonic, then

$$\int_C \left(\frac{\partial f}{\partial y}\,dx - \frac{\partial f}{\partial x}\,dy\right) = 0$$

where C is a smooth closed curve in the plane.

15.4

Green's Theorem • Alternative Forms of Green's Theorem

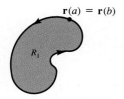

Simply Connected

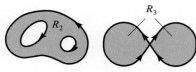

Not Simply Connected

FIGURE 15.26

Green's Theorem

In this section, you will study **Green's Theorem**, named after the English mathematician George Green (1793–1841). This theorem states that the value of a double integral over a *simply connected* plane region R is determined by the value of a line integral around the boundary of R.

A curve C given by $\mathbf{r}(t) = x(t)\mathbf{i} + y(t)\mathbf{j}$, where $a \le t \le b$, is **simple** if it does not cross itself—that is, $\mathbf{r}(c) \neq \mathbf{r}(d)$ for all c and d in the open interval (a, b). A plane region R is **simply connected** if its boundary consists of *one* simple closed curve, as shown in Figure 15.26.

THEOREM 15.8   Green's Theorem

Let R be a simply connected region with a piecewise smooth boundary C, oriented counterclockwise (that is, C is traversed *once* so that the region R always lies to the *left*). If M and N have continuous partial derivatives in an open region containing R, then

$$\int_C M\,dx + N\,dy = \iint_R \left(\frac{\partial N}{\partial x} - \frac{\partial M}{\partial y} \right) dA.$$

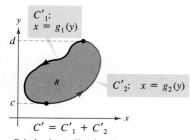

FIGURE 15.27

Proof   We give a proof only for a region that is both vertically simple and horizontally simple, as shown in Figure 15.27.

$$\int_C M\,dx = \int_{C_1} M\,dx + \int_{C_2} M\,dx$$
$$= \int_a^b M(x, f_1(x))\,dx + \int_b^a M(x, f_2(x))\,dx$$
$$= \int_a^b [M(x, f_1(x)) - M(x, f_2(x))]\,dx$$

On the other hand,

$$\iint_R \frac{\partial M}{\partial y}\,dA = \int_a^b \int_{f_1(x)}^{f_2(x)} \frac{\partial M}{\partial y}\,dy\,dx = \int_a^b M(x, y) \Big]_{f_1(x)}^{f_2(x)}\,dx$$
$$= \int_a^b [M(x, f_2(x)) - M(x, f_1(x))]\,dx.$$

Consequently, $\int_C M\,dx = -\int_R \int \partial M/\partial y\,dA$. Similarly, you can use $g_1(y)$ and $g_2(y)$ to show that $\int_C N\,dy = \int_R \int \partial N/\partial x\,dA$. By adding the integrals $\int_C M\,dx$ and $\int_C N\,dy$, you obtain the conclusion stated in the theorem.

EXAMPLE 1   Using Green's Theorem

Use Green's Theorem to evaluate the line integral

$$\int_C y^3\, dx + (x^3 + 3xy^2)\, dy$$

where C is the path from $(0, 0)$ to $(1, 1)$ along the graph of $y = x^3$ and from $(1, 1)$ to $(0, 0)$ along the graph of $y = x$, as shown in Figure 15.28.

Solution   Because $M = y^3$ and $N = x^3 + 3xy^2$, it follows that

$$\frac{\partial N}{\partial x} = 3x^2 + 3y^2 \quad \text{and} \quad \frac{\partial M}{\partial y} = 3y^2.$$

Applying Green's Theorem, you then have

$$\int_C y^3\, dx + (x^3 + 3xy^2)\, dy = \int\int_R \left(\frac{\partial N}{\partial x} - \frac{\partial M}{\partial y} \right) dA$$

$$= \int_0^1 \int_{x^3}^{x} [(3x^2 + 3y^2) - 3y^2]\, dy\, dx$$

$$= \int_0^1 \int_{x^3}^{x} 3x^2\, dy\, dx$$

$$= \int_0^1 \left. 3x^2 y \right]_{x^3}^{x} dx$$

$$= \int_0^1 (3x^3 - 3x^5)\, dx$$

$$= \left[\frac{3x^4}{4} - \frac{x^6}{2} \right]_0^1$$

$$= \frac{1}{4}.$$

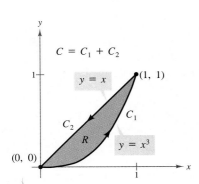

FIGURE 15.28
C is simple and closed, and the region
R always lies to the left of C.

Green's Theorem cannot be applied to every line integral. Among other restrictions stated in Theorem 15.8, the curve C must be simple and closed. When Green's Theorem does apply, however, it can save time. To see this, try using the techniques described in Section 15.2 to evaluate the line integral in Example 1. To do this, you would need to write the line integral as

$$\int_C y^3\, dx + (x^3 + 3xy^2)\, dy$$

$$= \int_{C_1} y^3\, dx + (x^3 + 3xy^2)\, dy + \int_{C_2} y^3\, dx + (x^3 + 3xy^2)\, dy$$

where C_1 is the cubic path given by

$$\mathbf{r}(t) = t\mathbf{i} + t^3\mathbf{j}$$

from $t = 0$ to $t = 1$, and C_2 is the line segment given by

$$\mathbf{r}(t) = (1 - t)\mathbf{i} + (1 - t)\mathbf{j}$$

from $t = 0$ to $t = 1$.

EXAMPLE 2   Using Green's Theorem to Calculate Work

While subject to the force $\mathbf{F}(x, y) = y^3\mathbf{i} + (x^3 + 3xy^2)\mathbf{j}$, a particle travels once around the circle of radius 3 shown in Figure 15.29. Use Green's Theorem to find the work done by $\mathbf{F}$.

Solution   From Example 1, you know by Green's Theorem that

$$\int_C y^3\,dx + (x^3 + 3xy^2)\,dy = \iint_R 3x^2\,dA.$$

In polar coordinates, using $x = r\cos\theta$ and $dA = r\,dr\,d\theta$, the work done is

$$
\begin{aligned}
W = \iint_R 3x^2\,dA &= \int_0^{2\pi}\int_0^3 3(r\cos\theta)^2 r\,dr\,d\theta \\
&= 3\int_0^{2\pi}\int_0^3 r^3\cos^2\theta\,dr\,d\theta \\
&= 3\int_0^{2\pi} \frac{r^4}{4}\cos^2\theta\,\Big]_0^3\,d\theta \\
&= 3\int_0^{2\pi} \frac{81}{4}\cos^2\theta\,d\theta \\
&= \frac{243}{8}\int_0^{2\pi}(1 + \cos 2\theta)\,d\theta \\
&= \frac{243}{8}\left[\theta + \frac{\sin 2\theta}{2}\right]_0^{2\pi} \\
&= \frac{243\pi}{4}.
\end{aligned}
$$

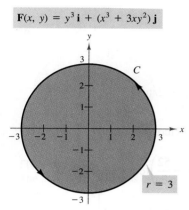

$\mathbf{F}(x, y) = y^3\mathbf{i} + (x^3 + 3xy^2)\mathbf{j}$

$r = 3$

FIGURE 15.29

The work done by $\mathbf{F}$ as a particle travels once around the circle is $\dfrac{243\pi}{4}$.

When evaluating line integrals over closed curves, remember that, for conservative vector fields (those for which $\partial N/\partial x = \partial M/\partial y$), the value of the line integral is 0. This is easily seen from the statement of Green's Theorem:

$$\int_C M\,dx + N\,dy = \iint_R\left(\frac{\partial N}{\partial x} - \frac{\partial M}{\partial y}\right)dA = 0.$$

EXAMPLE 3   Green's Theorem and Conservative Vector Fields

Evaluate the line integral

$$\int_C y^3\,dx + 3xy^2\,dy$$

where C is the path shown in Figure 15.30.

Solution   From this line integral, $M = y^3$ and $N = 3xy^2$. Thus, $\partial N/\partial x = 3y^2$ and $\partial M/\partial y = 3y^2$. This implies that the vector field $\mathbf{F} = M\mathbf{i} + N\mathbf{j}$ is conservative, and because C is closed, you can conclude that

$$\int_C y^3\,dx + 3xy^2\,dy = 0.$$

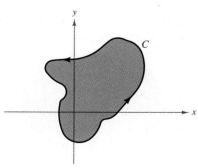

FIGURE 15.30
C is closed.

In Section 15.1, we presented a theorem that provided a necessary and sufficient condition for conservative vector fields. There, we proved the theorem in only one direction. We now outline the other direction, using Green's Theorem. Let $\mathbf{F}(x, y) = M\mathbf{i} + N\mathbf{j}$ be defined on an open disc R. We want to show that if M and N have continuous first partial derivatives and

$$\frac{\partial M}{\partial y} = \frac{\partial N}{\partial x}$$

then $\mathbf{F}$ is conservative. Suppose that C is a closed path forming the boundary of a connected region lying in R. Then, using the fact that $\partial M / \partial y = \partial N / \partial x$, we can apply Green's Theorem to conclude that

$$\int_C \mathbf{F} \cdot d\mathbf{r} = \int_C M\,dx + N\,dy = \iint_R \left(\frac{\partial N}{\partial x} - \frac{\partial M}{\partial y} \right) dA = 0.$$

This, in turn, is equivalent to showing that $\mathbf{F}$ is conservative (see Theorem 15.7).

Alternative Forms of Green's Theorem

We conclude this section with the derivation of two vector forms of Green's Theorem for regions in the plane. The extension of these vector forms to three dimensions is the basis for the discussion in the remaining sections of this chapter. If $\mathbf{F}$ is a vector field in the plane, you can write

$$\mathbf{F}(x, y) = M\mathbf{i} + N\mathbf{j} + 0\mathbf{k}$$

so that the curl of $\mathbf{F}$, as described in Section 15.1, is given by

$$\mathbf{curl}\ \mathbf{F} = \nabla \times \mathbf{F} = \begin{vmatrix} \mathbf{i} & \mathbf{j} & \mathbf{k} \\ \dfrac{\partial}{\partial x} & \dfrac{\partial}{\partial y} & \dfrac{\partial}{\partial z} \\ M & N & 0 \end{vmatrix}$$

$$= -\frac{\partial N}{\partial z}\mathbf{i} + \frac{\partial M}{\partial z}\mathbf{j} + \left(\frac{\partial N}{\partial x} - \frac{\partial M}{\partial y} \right)\mathbf{k}.$$

Consequently,

$$(\mathbf{curl}\ \mathbf{F}) \cdot \mathbf{k} = \left[-\frac{\partial N}{\partial z}\mathbf{i} + \frac{\partial M}{\partial z}\mathbf{j} + \left(\frac{\partial N}{\partial x} - \frac{\partial M}{\partial y} \right)\mathbf{k} \right] \cdot \mathbf{k}$$

$$= \frac{\partial N}{\partial x} - \frac{\partial M}{\partial y}.$$

With appropriate conditions on $\mathbf{F}$, C, and R, we can write Green's Theorem in the vector form

$$\int_C \mathbf{F} \cdot d\mathbf{r} = \iint_R \left(\frac{\partial N}{\partial x} - \frac{\partial M}{\partial y} \right) dA$$

$$= \iint_R (\mathbf{curl}\ \mathbf{F}) \cdot \mathbf{k}\, dA. \qquad \text{First alternative form}$$

The extension of this vector form of Green's Theorem to surfaces in space produces **Stokes's Theorem,** which is discussed in Section 15.8.

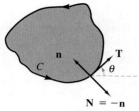

$\mathbf{T} = \cos\theta\mathbf{i} + \sin\theta\mathbf{j}$

$\mathbf{n} = \cos\left(\theta + \dfrac{\pi}{2}\right)\mathbf{i} + \sin\left(\theta + \dfrac{\pi}{2}\right)\mathbf{j}$

$\quad = -\sin\theta\mathbf{i} + \cos\theta\mathbf{j}$

$\mathbf{N} = \sin\theta\mathbf{i} - \cos\theta\mathbf{j}$

FIGURE 15.34

For the second vector form of Green's Theorem, assume the same conditions for **F**, C, and R. Using the arc length parameter s for C, we have $\mathbf{r}(s) = x(s)\mathbf{i} + y(s)\mathbf{j}$. Thus, a unit tangent vector **T** to curve C is given by

$$\mathbf{r}'(s) = \mathbf{T} = x'(s)\mathbf{i} + y'(s)\mathbf{j}.$$

In Figure 15.34, we can see that the *outward* unit normal vector **N** can then be written as

$$\mathbf{N} = y'(s)\mathbf{i} - x'(s)\mathbf{j}.$$

Consequently, for $\mathbf{F}(x, y) = M\mathbf{i} + N\mathbf{j}$, we can apply Green's Theorem to obtain

$$\int_C \mathbf{F} \cdot \mathbf{N}\, ds = \int_a^b (M\mathbf{i} + N\mathbf{j}) \cdot (y'(s)\mathbf{i} - x'(s)\mathbf{j})\, ds$$

$$= \int_a^b \left(M\frac{dy}{ds} - N\frac{dx}{ds}\right) ds$$

$$= \int_C M\, dy - N\, dx$$

$$= \int_C -N\, dx + M\, dy$$

$$= \int\!\!\int_R \left(\frac{\partial M}{\partial x} + \frac{\partial N}{\partial y}\right) dA \qquad \text{Green's Theorem}$$

$$= \int\!\!\int_R \operatorname{div} \mathbf{F}\, dA.$$

Therefore,

$$\int_C \mathbf{F} \cdot \mathbf{N}\, ds = \int\!\!\int_R \operatorname{div} \mathbf{F}\, dA. \qquad \text{Second alternative form}$$

The extension of this form to three dimensions is called the **Divergence Theorem,** which is discussed in Section 15.7. The physical interpretation of divergence and curl will be discussed in Sections 15.7 and 15.8.

EXERCISES for Section 15.4

TECHNOLOGY
Laboratory Guide
Labs 15.3–15.4

In Exercises 1–4, verify Green's Theorem by evaluating both integrals

$$\int_C y^2\, dx + x^2\, dy = \int\!\!\int_R \left(\frac{\partial N}{\partial x} - \frac{\partial M}{\partial y}\right) dA$$

for the specified path.

 1. C: boundary of the square with vertices $(0, 0)$, $(4, 0)$, $(4, 4)$, and $(0, 4)$

 2. C: boundary of the triangle with vertices $(0, 0)$, $(4, 0)$, and $(4, 4)$

 3. C: boundary of the region lying between the graphs of $y = x$ and $y = x^2/4$

 4. C: $x^2 + y^2 = 1$

C In Exercises 5 and 6, verify Green's Theorem by using a computer algebra system to evaluate both integrals

$$\int_C xe^y\, dx + e^x\, dy = \int\!\!\int_R \left(\frac{\partial N}{\partial x} - \frac{\partial M}{\partial y}\right) dA$$

for the specified path.

 5. C: $x^2 + y^2 = 4$

 6. C: boundary of the region bounded by the graphs of $y = x$, and $y = x^3$.

In Exercises 7–10, use Green's Theorem to evaluate the integral

$$\int_C (y - x)\, dx + (2x - y)\, dy$$

for the specified path.

7. C: boundary of the region lying between the graphs of $y = x$ and $y = x^2 - x$

8. C: $x = 2\cos\theta$, $y = \sin\theta$

9. C: boundary of the region lying inside the rectangle bounded by $x = -5$, $x = 5$, $y = -3$, and $y = 3$ and outside the square bounded by $x = -1$, $x = 1$, $y = -1$, and $y = 1$

10. C: boundary of the region lying inside the circle $x^2 + y^2 = 16$ and outside the circle $x^2 + y^2 = 1$

In Exercises 11–20, use Green's Theorem to evaluate the line integral.

11. $\displaystyle\int_C 2xy\, dx + (x + y)\, dy$

C: boundary of the region lying between the graphs of $y = 0$ and $y = 4 - x^2$

12. $\displaystyle\int_C y^2\, dx + xy\, dy$

C: boundary of the region bounded by the graphs of $y = 0$, $y = \sqrt{x}$, and $x = 4$

13. $\displaystyle\int_C (x^2 - y^2)\, dx + 2xy\, dy$

C: $x^2 + y^2 = a^2$

14. $\displaystyle\int_C (x^2 - y^2)\, dx + 2xy\, dy$

C: $r = 1 + \cos\theta$

15. $\displaystyle\int_C 2\arctan\frac{y}{x}\, dx + \ln(x^2 + y^2)\, dy$

C: $x = 4 + 2\cos\theta$, $y = 4 + \sin\theta$

16. $\displaystyle\int_C e^x \sin 2y\, dx + 2e^x \cos 2y\, dy$

C: $x^2 + y^2 = a^2$

17. $\displaystyle\int_C \sin x \cos y\, dx + (xy + \cos x \sin y)\, dy$

C: boundary of the region lying between the graphs of $y = x$ and $y = \sqrt{x}$

18. $\displaystyle\int_C (e^{-x^2/2} - y)\, dx + (e^{-y^2/2} + x)\, dy$

C: boundary of the region lying between the graphs of the circle $x = 5\cos\theta$, $y = 5\sin\theta$ and the ellipse $x = 2\cos\theta$, $y = \sin\theta$

19. $\displaystyle\int_C xy\, dx + (x + y)\, dy$

C: boundary of the region lying between the graphs of $x^2 + y^2 = 1$ and $x^2 + y^2 = 9$

20. $\displaystyle\int_C 3x^2 e^y\, dx + e^y\, dy$

C: boundary of the region lying between the squares with vertices $(1, 1), (-1, 1), (-1, -1)$, and $(1, -1)$, and $(2, 2)$, $(-2, 2), (-2, -2)$, and $(2, -2)$

Work **In Exercises 21–24, use Green's Theorem to calculate the work done by the force F on a particle that is moving counterclockwise around the closed path C.**

21. $\mathbf{F}(x, y) = xy\mathbf{i} + (x + y)\mathbf{j}$
C: $x^2 + y^2 = 4$

22. $\mathbf{F}(x, y) = (e^x - 3y)\mathbf{i} + (e^y + 6x)\mathbf{j}$
C: $r = 2\cos\theta$

23. $\mathbf{F}(x, y) = (x^{3/2} - 3y)\mathbf{i} + (6x + 5\sqrt{y})\mathbf{j}$
C: boundary of the triangle with vertices $(0, 0)$, $(5, 0)$, and $(0, 5)$

24. $\mathbf{F}(x, y) = (3x^2 + y)\mathbf{i} + 4xy^2\mathbf{j}$
C boundary of the region bounded by the graphs of $y = \sqrt{x}$, $y = 0$, and $x = 4$

Area **In Exercises 25–28, use a line integral to find the area of the region R.**

25. R: region bounded by the graph of $x^2 + y^2 = a^2$

26. R: triangle bounded by the graphs of $x = 0$, $2x - 3y = 0$, and $x + 3y = 9$

27. R: region bounded by the graphs of $y = 2x + 1$ and $y = 4 - x^2$

28. R: region inside the loop of the folium of Descartes bounded by the graph of

$$x = \frac{3t}{t^3 + 1}, \qquad y = \frac{3t^2}{t^3 + 1}.$$

In Exercises 29 and 30, use Green's Theorem to verify the line integral formulas.

29. *Centroid* The centroid of the region having area A bounded by the simple closed path C is

$$\bar{x} = \frac{1}{2A}\int_C x^2\, dy, \qquad \bar{y} = -\frac{1}{2A}\int_C y^2\, dx.$$

30. *Area* The area of a plane region bounded by the simple closed path C given in polar coordinates is

$$A = \frac{1}{2}\int_C r^2\, d\theta.$$

Centroid **In Exercises 31–34, use the result of Exercise 29 to find the centroid of the region.**

31. R: region bounded by the graphs of $y = 0$ and $y = 4 - x^2$

32. R: region bounded by the graphs of $y = \sqrt{a^2 - x^2}$ and $y = 0$

33. R: region bounded by the graphs of $y = x^3$ and $y = x$, $0 \le x \le 1$

34. R: triangle with vertices $(-a, 0)$, $(a, 0)$, and (b, c), where $-a \le b \le a$

Area   **In Exercises 35–38, use the result of Exercise 30 to find the area of the region bounded by the graph of the polar equation.**

35. $r = a(1 - \cos\theta)$ **36.** $r = a\cos 3\theta$

37. $r = 1 + 2\cos\theta$ **38.** $r = \dfrac{3}{2 - \cos\theta}$
(inner loop)

39. Let

$$I = \int_C \frac{y\,dx - x\,dy}{x^2 + y^2}$$

where C is a circle oriented counterclockwise. Show that $I = 0$ if C does not contain the origin. What is I if C contains the origin?

40. a. Let C be the line segment joining (x_1, y_1) and (x_2, y_2). Show that

$$\int_C -y\,dx + x\,dy = x_1 y_2 - x_2 y_1.$$

b. Let $(x_1, y_1), (x_2, y_2), \ldots, (x_n, y_n)$ be the vertices of a polygon. Prove that the area enclosed is

$$\frac{1}{2}[(x_1 y_2 - x_2 y_1) + (x_2 y_3 - x_3 y_2) + \cdots$$

$$+ (x_{n-1} y_n - x_n y_{n-1}) + (x_n y_1 - x_1 y_n)].$$

Area   **In Exercises 41 and 42, find the area enclosed by the polygon with the given vertices.**

41. Pentagon: $(0, 0), (2, 0), (3, 2), (1, 4), (-1, 1)$

42. Hexagon: $(0, 0), (2, 0), (3, 2), (2, 4), (0, 3), (-1, 1)$

43. Use Green's Theorem to prove that

$$\int_C f(x)\,dx + g(y)\,dy = 0$$

if f and g are differentiable functions and C is a piecewise smooth, simple closed path.

44. Let $\mathbf{F} = M\mathbf{i} + N\mathbf{j}$, where M and N have continuous first partial derivatives in a simply connected region R. Prove that if C is simple, smooth, and closed, and $N_x = M_y$, then

$$\int_C \mathbf{F} \cdot d\mathbf{r} = 0.$$

In Exercises 45 and 46, prove the identity where R is a simply connected region with boundary C. Also assume that the required partial derivatives of the scalar functions f and g are continuous. The expressions $D_N f$ and $D_N g$ are the derivatives in the direction of the outward normal vector N of C and are defined by

$$D_N f = \nabla f \cdot \mathbf{N}, \qquad D_N g = \nabla g \cdot \mathbf{N}.$$

45. Green's first identity:

$$\int_R \int (f\nabla^2 g + \nabla f \cdot \nabla g)\,dA = \int_C f D_N g\,ds$$

(*Hint:* Use the alternative form of Green's Theorem and the property

$$\text{div}\,(f\,\mathbf{G}) = f\,\text{div}\,\mathbf{G} + \nabla f \cdot \mathbf{G}.)$$

46. Green's second identity:

$$\int_R \int (f\nabla^2 g - g\nabla^2 f)\,dA = \int_C (f D_N g - g D_N f)\,ds$$

(*Hint:* Use Exercise 45 twice.)

15.5

Parametric Surfaces • Finding Parametric Equations for Surfaces • Normal Vectors and Tangent Planes • Area of a Parametric Surface

Parametric Surfaces

You already know how to represent a curve in the plane or in space by a set of parametric equations—or, equivalently, by a vector-valued function.

$$\mathbf{r}(t) = x(t)\mathbf{i} + y(t)\mathbf{j} \qquad \text{Plane curve}$$

$$\mathbf{r}(t) = x(t)\mathbf{i} + y(t)\mathbf{j} + z(t)\mathbf{k} \qquad \text{Space curve}$$

In this section, you will learn how to represent a surface in space by a set of parametric equations—or by a vector-valued function. For curves, note that the vector-valued function $\mathbf{r}$ is a function of a *single* parameter t. For surfaces, the vector-valued function is a function of *two* parameters u and v.

TECHNOLOGY Some computer graphing utilities are capable of sketching surfaces that are represented parametrically. If you have access to such software, try using it to sketch some of the surfaces in the examples and exercises in this section.

Definition of Parametric Surface

Let x, y, and z be functions of u and v that are continuous on a domain D in the uv-plane. The set of points (x, y, z) given by

$$\mathbf{r}(u, v) = x(u, v)\mathbf{i} + y(u, v)\mathbf{j} + z(u, v)\mathbf{k} \qquad \text{Parametric surface}$$

is called a **parametric surface.** The equations

$$x = x(u, v), \quad y = y(u, v), \quad \text{and} \quad z = z(u, v)$$

are the **parametric equations** for the surface.

If S is a parametric surface given by the vector-valued function $\mathbf{r}$, then S is traced out by the position vector $\mathbf{r}(u, v)$ as the point (u, v) moves throughout the domain D, as shown in Figure 15.35.

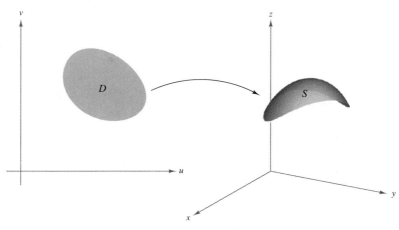

FIGURE 15.35

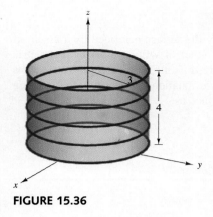

FIGURE 15.36

EXAMPLE 1　Sketching a Parametric Surface

Identify and sketch the parametric surface S given by

$$\mathbf{r}(u, v) = 3\cos u\,\mathbf{i} + 3\sin u\,\mathbf{j} + v\,\mathbf{k}$$

where $0 \le u \le 2\pi$ and $0 \le v \le 4$.

Solution　Because $x = 3\cos u$ and $y = 3\sin u$, you know that for each point (x, y, z) on the surface, x and y are related by the equation $x^2 + y^2 = 3^2$. In other words, each cross section of S taken parallel to the xy-plane is a circle of radius 3, centered on the z-axis. Because $z = v$, where $0 \le v \le 4$, you can see that the surface is a right circular cylinder of height 4. The radius of the cylinder is 3, and the z-axis forms the axis of the cylinder, as shown in Figure 15.36.

As with parametric representations of curves, parametric representations of surfaces are not unique. That is, there are many other sets of parametric equations that could be used to represent the surface shown in Figure 15.36.

EXAMPLE 2　Sketching a Parametric Surface

Identify and sketch the parametric surface S given by

$$\mathbf{r}(u, v) = \sin u \cos v\,\mathbf{i} + \sin u \sin v\,\mathbf{j} + \cos u\,\mathbf{k}$$

where $0 \le u \le \pi$ and $0 \le v \le 2\pi$.

Solution　To identify the surface, you can try to use trigonometric identities to eliminate the parameters. After some experimentation, you can discover that

$$
\begin{aligned}
x^2 + y^2 + z^2 &= (\sin u \cos v)^2 + (\sin u \sin v)^2 + (\cos u)^2 \\
&= \sin^2 u \cos^2 v + \sin^2 u \sin^2 v + \cos^2 u \\
&= \sin^2 u (\cos^2 v + \sin^2 v) + \cos^2 u \\
&= \sin^2 u + \cos^2 u \\
&= 1.
\end{aligned}
$$

Thus, each point on S lies on the unit sphere, centered at the origin, as shown in Figure 15.37. For fixed $u = d_i$, $\mathbf{r}(u, v)$ traces out latitude (or meridian) circles

$$x^2 + y^2 = \sin^2 d_i, \qquad 0 \le d_i \le \pi$$

that are parallel to the xy-plane, and for fixed $v = c_i$, $\mathbf{r}(u, v)$ traces out longitude (or great) circles.

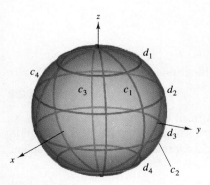

FIGURE 15.37

REMARK　To further convince yourself that the vector-valued function in Example 2 traces out the entire unit sphere, recall that the parametric equations

$$x = \rho \sin \phi \cos \theta, \quad y = \rho \sin \phi \sin \theta, \quad \text{and} \quad z = \rho \cos \phi$$

where $0 \le \theta \le 2\pi$ and $0 \le \phi \le \pi$, describe the conversion from rectangular to spherical coordinates, as discussed in Section 11.7.

Finding Parametric Equations for Surfaces

In Examples 1 and 2, you were asked to identify the surface described by a given set of parametric equations. The reverse problem—that of writing a set of parametric equations for a given surface—is generally more difficult. One such problem that is straightforward, however, is finding the parametric equations for a surface that is given by $z = f(x, y)$. You can parametrize such a surface as

$$\mathbf{r}(x, y) = x\mathbf{i} + y\mathbf{j} + f(x, y)\mathbf{k}.$$

EXAMPLE 3   Representing a Surface Parametrically

Write a set of parametric equations for the cone given by

$$z = \sqrt{x^2 + y^2}$$

as shown in Figure 15.38.

Solution   Because this surface is given in the form $z = f(x, y)$, you can let x and y be the parameters. Then the cone is represented by the vector-valued function

$$\mathbf{r}(x, y) = x\mathbf{i} + y\mathbf{j} + \sqrt{x^2 + y^2}\,\mathbf{k}$$

where (x, y) varies over the entire xy-plane.

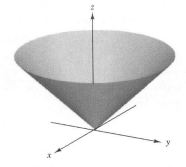

FIGURE 15.38

A second type of surface that is easily represented parametrically is a surface of revolution. For instance, to represent the surface formed by revolving the graph of $y = f(x)$, $a \le x \le b$, about the x-axis, use

$$x = u, \quad y = f(u)\cos v, \quad \text{and} \quad z = f(u)\sin v$$

where $a \le u \le b$ and $0 \le v \le 2\pi$.

EXAMPLE 4   Representing a Surface of Revolution Parametrically

Write a set of parametric equations for the surface of revolution obtained by revolving

$$f(x) = \frac{1}{x}, \qquad 1 \le x \le 10$$

about the x-axis.

Solution   Use the parameters u and v

$$x = u, \quad y = \frac{1}{u}\cos v, \quad \text{and} \quad z = \frac{1}{u}\sin v$$

where $1 \le u \le 10$ and $0 \le v \le 2\pi$. The resulting surface is a portion of *Gabriel's Horn*, as shown in Figure 15.39.

The surface of revolution in Example 4 is formed by revolving the graph of $y = f(x)$ about the x-axis. For other types of surfaces of revolution, a similar parametrization can be used. For instance, to parametrize the surface formed by revolving the graph of $x = f(z)$ about the z-axis, you can use

$$z = u, \quad x = f(u)\cos v, \quad \text{and} \quad y = f(u)\sin v.$$

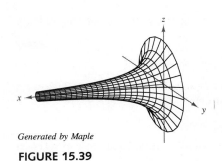

Generated by Maple

FIGURE 15.39

Normal Vectors and Tangent Planes

Let S be a parametric surface given by

$$\mathbf{r}(u, v) = x(u, v)\mathbf{i} + y(u, v)\mathbf{j} + z(u, v)\mathbf{k}$$

over an open region D such that x, y, and z have continuous partial derivatives on D. The **partial derivatives of r** with respect to u and v are defined as

$$\mathbf{r}_u = \frac{\partial x}{\partial u}(u, v)\mathbf{i} + \frac{\partial y}{\partial u}(u, v)\mathbf{j} + \frac{\partial z}{\partial u}(u, v)\mathbf{k}$$

and

$$\mathbf{r}_v = \frac{\partial x}{\partial v}(u, v)\mathbf{i} + \frac{\partial y}{\partial v}(u, v)\mathbf{j} + \frac{\partial z}{\partial v}(u, v)\mathbf{k}.$$

Each of these partial derivatives is a vector-valued function that can be interpreted geometrically in terms of tangent vectors. For instance, if $v = v_0$ is held constant, then $\mathbf{r}(u, v_0)$ is a vector-valued function of a single parameter and defines a curve C_1 that lies on the surface S. The tangent vector to C_1 at the point $(x(u_0, v_0), y(u_0, v_0), z(u_0, v_0))$ is given by

$$\mathbf{r}_u(u_0, v_0) = \frac{\partial x}{\partial u}(u_0, v_0)\mathbf{i} + \frac{\partial y}{\partial u}(u_0, v_0)\mathbf{j} + \frac{\partial z}{\partial u}(u_0, v_0)\mathbf{k}$$

as shown in Figure 15.40. In a similar way, if $u = u_0$ is held constant, then $\mathbf{r}(u_0, v)$ is a vector-valued function of a single parameter and defines a curve C_2 that lies on the surface S. The tangent vector to C_2 at the point $(x(u_0, v_0), y(u_0, v_0), z(u_0, v_0))$ is given by

$$\mathbf{r}_v(u_0, v_0) = \frac{\partial x}{\partial v}(u_0, v_0)\mathbf{i} + \frac{\partial y}{\partial v}(u_0, v_0)\mathbf{j} + \frac{\partial z}{\partial v}(u_0, v_0)\mathbf{k}.$$

If the normal vector $\mathbf{r}_u \times \mathbf{r}_v$ is not $\mathbf{0}$ for any (u, v) in D, then the surface S is called **smooth** and will have a tangent plane. Informally, a smooth surface is one that has no sharp points or cusps. For instance, spheres, ellipsoids, and paraboloids are smooth, whereas the cone given in Example 3 is not smooth.

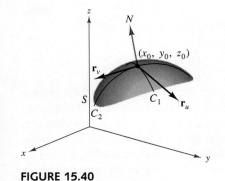

FIGURE 15.40

REMARK   Figure 15.40 shows the normal vector $\mathbf{r}_u \times \mathbf{r}_v$. The vector $\mathbf{r}_v \times \mathbf{r}_u$ is also normal to S and points in the opposite direction.

Normal Vector to a Smooth Parametric Surface

Let S be a smooth parametric surface
$$\mathbf{r}(u, v) = x(u, v)\mathbf{i} + y(u, v)\mathbf{j} + z(u, v)\mathbf{k}$$
defined over an open region D in the uv-plane. Let (u_0, v_0) be a point in D. A normal vector at the point
$$(x_0, y_0, z_0) = (x(u_0, v_0), y(u_0, v_0), z(u_0, v_0))$$
is given by

$$\mathbf{N} = \mathbf{r}_u(u_0, v_0) \times \mathbf{r}_v(u_0, v_0) = \begin{vmatrix} \mathbf{i} & \mathbf{j} & \mathbf{k} \\ \dfrac{\partial x}{\partial u} & \dfrac{\partial y}{\partial u} & \dfrac{\partial z}{\partial u} \\ \dfrac{\partial x}{\partial v} & \dfrac{\partial y}{\partial v} & \dfrac{\partial z}{\partial v} \end{vmatrix}.$$

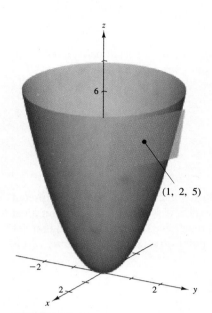

FIGURE 15.41

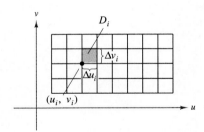

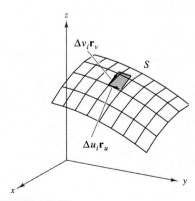

FIGURE 15.42

EXAMPLE 5   **Finding a Tangent Plane to a Parametric Surface**

Find an equation of the tangent plane to the paraboloid given by

$$\mathbf{r}(u, v) = u\mathbf{i} + v\mathbf{j} + (u^2 + v^2)\mathbf{k}$$

at the point $(1, 2, 5)$.

Solution   The point in the uv-plane that is mapped to the point $(x, y, z) = (1, 2, 5)$ is $(u, v) = (1, 2)$. The partial derivatives of $\mathbf{r}$ are

$$\mathbf{r}_u = \mathbf{i} + 2u\mathbf{k} \quad \text{and} \quad \mathbf{r}_v = \mathbf{j} + 2v\mathbf{k}.$$

The normal vector is given by

$$\mathbf{r}_u \times \mathbf{r}_v = \begin{vmatrix} \mathbf{i} & \mathbf{j} & \mathbf{k} \\ 1 & 0 & 2u \\ 0 & 1 & 2v \end{vmatrix} = -2u\mathbf{i} - 2v\mathbf{j} + \mathbf{k}$$

which implies that the normal vector at $(1, 2, 5)$ is $\mathbf{r}_u \times \mathbf{r}_v = -2\mathbf{i} - 4\mathbf{j} + \mathbf{k}$. Thus, an equation of the tangent plane at $(1, 2, 5)$ is

$$-2(x - 1) - 4(y - 2) + (z - 5) = 0$$
$$-2x - 4y + z = -5.$$

The tangent plane is shown in Figure 15.41.   ▬

Area of a Parametric Surface

To define the area of a parametric surface, you can use a development that is similar to that given in Section 14.5. Begin by constructing an inner partition of D consisting of n rectangles, where the area of the ith rectangle D_i is $\Delta A_i = \Delta u_i \Delta v_i$, as shown in Figure 15.42. In each D_i, let (u_i, v_i) be the point that is closest to the origin. At the point $(x_i, y_i, z_i) = (x(u_i, v_i), y(u_i, v_i), z(u_i, v_i))$ on the surface S, construct a tangent plane T_i. The area of the portion of S that corresponds to D_i, ΔT_i, can be approximated by a parallelogram in the tangent plane. That is, $\Delta T_i \approx \Delta S_i$. Hence, the surface area of S is given by $\Sigma \Delta S_i \approx \Sigma \Delta T_i$. The area of the parallelogram in the tangent plane is

$$\| \Delta u_i \mathbf{r}_u \times \Delta v_i \mathbf{r}_v \| = \| \mathbf{r}_u \times \mathbf{r}_v \| \Delta u_i \Delta v_i$$

which leads to the following definition.

Area of a Parametric Surface

Let S be a smooth parametric surface

$$\mathbf{r}(u, v) = x(u, v)\mathbf{i} + y(u, v)\mathbf{j} + z(u, v)\mathbf{k}$$

defined over an open region D in the uv-plane. If each point on the surface S corresponds to exactly one point in the domain D, then the **surface area** of S is given by

$$\text{Surface area} = \iint_S dS = \iint_D \| \mathbf{r}_u \times \mathbf{r}_v \| \, dA$$

where $\mathbf{r}_u = \dfrac{\partial x}{\partial u}\mathbf{i} + \dfrac{\partial y}{\partial u}\mathbf{j} + \dfrac{\partial z}{\partial u}\mathbf{k}$ and $\mathbf{r}_v = \dfrac{\partial x}{\partial v}\mathbf{i} + \dfrac{\partial y}{\partial v}\mathbf{j} + \dfrac{\partial z}{\partial v}\mathbf{k}$.

For a surface S given by $z = f(x, y)$, this formula for surface corresponds to that given in Section 14.5. To see this, you can parametrize the surface using the vector-valued function

$$\mathbf{r}(x, y) = x\mathbf{i} + y\mathbf{j} + f(x, y)\mathbf{k}$$

defined over the region R in the xy-plane. Using

$$\mathbf{r}_x = \mathbf{i} + f_x(x, y)\mathbf{k} \quad \text{and} \quad \mathbf{r}_y = \mathbf{j} + f_y(x, y)\mathbf{k}$$

you have

$$\mathbf{r}_x \times \mathbf{r}_y = \begin{vmatrix} \mathbf{i} & \mathbf{j} & \mathbf{k} \\ 1 & 0 & f_x(x, y) \\ 0 & 1 & f_y(x, y) \end{vmatrix} = -f_x(x, y)\mathbf{i} - f_y(x, y)\mathbf{j} + \mathbf{k}$$

and $\|\mathbf{r}_x \times \mathbf{r}_y\| = \sqrt{[f_x(x, y)]^2 + [f_y(x, y)]^2 + 1}$. This implies that the surface area of S is

$$\text{Surface area} = \iint_R \|\mathbf{r}_x \times \mathbf{r}_y\| \, dA$$

$$= \iint_R \sqrt{1 + [f_x(x, y)]^2 + [f_y(x, y)]^2} \, dA.$$

EXAMPLE 6   Finding Surface Area

REMARK The surface in Example 6 does not quite fulfill the hypothesis that each point on the surface corresponds to exactly one point in D. For this surface, $\mathbf{r}(u, 0) = \mathbf{r}(u, 2\pi)$ for any fixed value of u. However, because the overlap consists of only a semicircle (which has no area), you can still apply the formula for the area of a parametric surface.

Find the surface area of the unit sphere given by

$$\mathbf{r}(u, v) = \sin u \cos v \, \mathbf{i} + \sin u \sin v \, \mathbf{j} + \cos u \, \mathbf{k}$$

where the domain D is given by $0 \leq u \leq \pi$ and $0 \leq v \leq 2\pi$.

Solution   Begin by calculating $\mathbf{r}_u$ and $\mathbf{r}_v$.

$$\mathbf{r}_u = \cos u \cos v \, \mathbf{i} + \cos u \sin v \, \mathbf{j} - \sin u \, \mathbf{k}$$
$$\mathbf{r}_v = -\sin u \sin v \, \mathbf{i} + \sin u \cos v \, \mathbf{j}$$

The cross product of these two vectors is

$$\mathbf{r}_u \times \mathbf{r}_v = \begin{vmatrix} \mathbf{i} & \mathbf{j} & \mathbf{k} \\ \cos u \cos v & \cos u \sin v & -\sin u \\ -\sin u \sin v & \sin u \cos v & 0 \end{vmatrix}$$

$$= \sin^2 u \cos v \, \mathbf{i} + \sin^2 u \sin v \, \mathbf{j} + \sin u \cos u \, \mathbf{k}$$

which implies that

$$\|\mathbf{r}_u \times \mathbf{r}_v\| = \sqrt{(\sin^2 u \cos v)^2 + (\sin^2 u \sin v)^2 + (\sin u \cos u)^2}$$

$$= \sqrt{\sin^4 u + \sin^2 u \cos^2 u}$$

$$= \sqrt{\sin^2 u}$$

$$= \sin u. \qquad \sin u \geq 0 \text{ for } 0 \leq u \leq \pi$$

Finally, the surface area of the sphere is

$$A = \iint_D \|\mathbf{r}_u \times \mathbf{r}_v\| \, dA = \int_0^{2\pi} \int_0^{\pi} \sin u \, du \, dv$$

$$= \int_0^{2\pi} 2 \, dv = 4\pi.$$

EXAMPLE 7   Finding Surface Area

Find the surface area of the torus given by

$$\mathbf{r}(u, v) = (2 + \cos u)\cos v\,\mathbf{i} + (2 + \cos u)\sin v\,\mathbf{j} + \sin u\,\mathbf{k}$$

where the domain D is given by $0 \leq u \leq 2\pi$ and $0 \leq v \leq 2\pi$. (The torus is shown in Figure 15.43.)

Solution   Begin by calculating $\mathbf{r}_u$ and $\mathbf{r}_v$.

$$\mathbf{r}_u = -\sin u \cos v\,\mathbf{i} - \sin u \sin v\,\mathbf{j} + \cos u\,\mathbf{k}$$
$$\mathbf{r}_v = -(2 + \cos u)\sin v\,\mathbf{i} + (2 + \cos u)\cos v\,\mathbf{j}$$

The cross product of these two vectors is

$$\mathbf{r}_u \times \mathbf{r}_v = \begin{vmatrix} \mathbf{i} & \mathbf{j} & \mathbf{k} \\ -\sin u \cos v & -\sin u \sin v & \cos u \\ -(2 + \cos u)\sin v & (2 + \cos u)\cos v & 0 \end{vmatrix}$$
$$= -(2 + \cos u)[\cos v \cos u\,\mathbf{i} + \sin v \cos u\,\mathbf{j} + \sin u\,\mathbf{k}]$$

which implies that

$$\begin{aligned} \|\mathbf{r}_u \times \mathbf{r}_v\| &= (2 + \cos u)\sqrt{(\cos v \cos u)^2 + (\sin v \cos u)^2 + \sin^2 u} \\ &= (2 + \cos u)\sqrt{\cos^2 u\,(\cos^2 v + \sin^2 v) + \sin^2 u} \\ &= (2 + \cos u)\sqrt{\cos^2 u + \sin^2 u} \\ &= 2 + \cos u. \end{aligned}$$

Finally, the surface area of the torus is

$$\begin{aligned} A &= \int\int_D \|\mathbf{r}_u \times \mathbf{r}_v\|\,dA = \int_0^{2\pi}\int_0^{2\pi} (2 + \cos u)\,du\,dv \\ &= \int_0^{2\pi} 4\pi\,dv = 8\pi^2. \end{aligned}$$

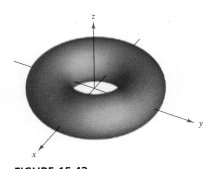

FIGURE 15.43

If the surface S is a surface of revolution, then you can show that the formula for surface area given in Section 6.4 is equivalent to the formula given in this section. For instance, suppose f is a nonnegative function such that f' is continuous over the interval $[a, b]$. Let S be the surface of revolution formed by revolving the graph of f, where $a \leq x \leq b$, about the x-axis. From Section 6.4, you know that the surface area is given by

$$\text{Surface area} = \int_a^b f(x)\sqrt{1 + [f'(x)]^2}\,dx.$$

To represent S parametrically, let $x = u$, $y = f(u)\cos v$, and $z = f(u)\sin v$, where $a \leq u \leq b$ and $0 \leq v \leq 2\pi$. Then,

$$\mathbf{r}(u, v) = u\,\mathbf{i} + f(u)\cos v\,\mathbf{j} + f(u)\sin v\,\mathbf{k}.$$

Try showing that the formula

$$\text{Surface area} = \int\int_D \|\mathbf{r}_u \times \mathbf{r}_v\|\,dA$$

is equivalent to the formula given above.

TECHNOLOGY
Laboratory Guide
Lab 15.5

In Exercises 1–4, match the vector-valued function with its graph. [The graphs are labeled (a), (b), (c), and (d).]

1. $\mathbf{r}(u, v) = u\mathbf{i} + v\mathbf{j} + uv\mathbf{k}$

2. $\mathbf{r}(u, v) = u\cos v\mathbf{i} + u\sin v\mathbf{j} + u\mathbf{k}$

3. $\mathbf{r}(u, v) = 2\cos v\cos u\mathbf{i} + 2\cos v\sin u\mathbf{j} + 2\sin v\mathbf{k}$

4. $\mathbf{r}(u, v) = 4\cos u\mathbf{i} + 4\sin u\mathbf{j} + v\mathbf{k}$

a.

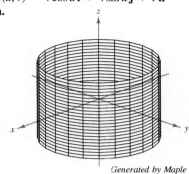

Generated by Maple

b.

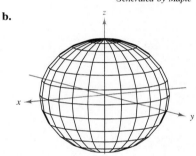

Generated by Maple

c.

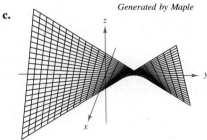

Generated by Maple

d.

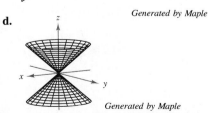

Generated by Maple

In Exercises 5–8, find the rectangular equation for the surface by eliminating the parameters from the vector-valued function, identify the surface, and sketch its graph.

5. $\mathbf{r}(u, v) = u\mathbf{i} + v\mathbf{j} + \dfrac{v}{2}\mathbf{k}$

6. $\mathbf{r}(u, v) = u\cos v\mathbf{i} + u\sin v\mathbf{j} + u^2\mathbf{k}$

7. $\mathbf{r}(u, v) = 2\cos u\mathbf{i} + v\mathbf{j} + 2\sin u\mathbf{k}$

8. $\mathbf{r}(u, v) = 5\cos v\cos u\mathbf{i} + 5\cos v\sin u\mathbf{j} + 5\sin v\mathbf{k}$

In Exercises 9–12, determine how the graph of the surface $s(u, v)$ differs from the graph of $\mathbf{r}(u, v) = u\cos v\mathbf{i} + u\sin v\mathbf{j} + u^2\mathbf{k}$, where $0 \le u \le 2$ and $0 \le v \le 2\pi$. (It is not necessary to graph s.)

9. $\mathbf{s}(u, v) = u\cos v\mathbf{i} + u\sin v\mathbf{j} - u^2\mathbf{k}$
$0 \le u \le 2, 0 \le v \le 2\pi$

10. $\mathbf{s}(u, v) = u\cos v\mathbf{i} + u^2\mathbf{j} + u\sin v\mathbf{k}$
$0 \le u \le 2, 0 \le v \le 2\pi$

11. $\mathbf{s}(u, v) = u\cos v\mathbf{i} + u\sin v\mathbf{j} + u^2\mathbf{k}$
$0 \le u \le 3, 0 \le v \le 2\pi$

12. $\mathbf{s}(u, v) = 4u\cos v\mathbf{i} + 4u\sin v\mathbf{j} + u^2\mathbf{k}$
$0 \le u \le 2, 0 \le v \le 2\pi$

C **In Exercises 13–18, use a graphing utility to graph the surface represented by the vector-valued function.**

13. $\mathbf{r}(u, v) = 2u\cos v\mathbf{i} + 2u\sin v\mathbf{j} + u^4\mathbf{k}$
$0 \le u \le 1, 0 \le v \le 2\pi$

14. $\mathbf{r}(u, v) = 2\cos v\cos u\mathbf{i} + 4\cos v\sin u\mathbf{j} + \sin v\mathbf{k}$
$0 \le u \le 2\pi, 0 \le v \le 2\pi$

15. $\mathbf{r}(u, v) = 2\sinh u\cos v\mathbf{i} + \sinh u\sin v\mathbf{j} + \cosh u\mathbf{k}$
$0 \le u \le 2, 0 \le v \le 2\pi$

16. $\mathbf{r}(u, v) = 2u\cos v\mathbf{i} + 2u\sin v\mathbf{j} + v\mathbf{k}$
$0 \le u \le 1, 0 \le v \le 3\pi$

17. $\mathbf{r}(u, v) = (u - \sin u)\cos v\mathbf{i} + (1 - \cos u)\sin v\mathbf{j} + u\mathbf{k}$
$0 \le u \le \pi, 0 \le v \le 2\pi$

18. $\mathbf{r}(u, v) = \cos^3 u\cos v\mathbf{i} + \sin^3 u\sin v\mathbf{j} + u\mathbf{k}$
$0 \le u \le \dfrac{\pi}{2}, 0 \le v \le 2\pi$

C **19.** Use a graphing utility to graph the torus

$$\mathbf{r}(u, v) = (a + b\cos v)\cos u\mathbf{i}$$
$$+ (a + b\cos v)\sin u\mathbf{j} + b\sin v\mathbf{k}$$

for each set of values for a and b and where $0 \le u \le 2\pi$ and $0 \le v \le 2\pi$. Use the results to describe the effect of a and b on the shape of the torus.

a. $a = 4, b = 1$ **b.** $a = 4, b = 2$
c. $a = 8, b = 1$ **d.** $a = 8, b = 3$

C **20.** Consider the vector-valued function in Exercise 16.
a. Sketch a graph of the function where u is held constant at $u = 1$. Identify the graph.
b. Sketch a graph of the function where v is held constant at $v = 2\pi/3$. Identify the graph.
c. If a surface is represented by the vector-valued function $\mathbf{r} = \mathbf{r}(u, v)$, what generalization can you make about the graph of the function if one of the parameters is held constant?

In Exercises 21–28, find a vector-valued function whose graph is the specified surface.

21. The plane $z = y$

22. The plane $x + y + z = 6$

23. The cylinder $x^2 + y^2 = 16$

24. The cylinder $x^2 + 4y^2 = 16$

25. The cylinder $z = x^2$

26. The ellipsoid $\dfrac{x^2}{9} + \dfrac{y^2}{4} + \dfrac{z^2}{1} = 1$

27. The part of the plane $z = 4$ that lies inside the cylinder $x^2 + y^2 = 9$

28. The part of the paraboloid $z = x^2 + y^2$ that lies inside the cylinder $x^2 + y^2 = 9$

Surface of Revolution **In Exercises 29–32, write a set of parametric equations for the surface of revolution obtained by revolving the graph of the function about the specified axis.**

Function	*Axis of revolution*
29. $y = \dfrac{x}{2}, \quad 0 \le x \le 6$	x-axis
30. $y = \sqrt{x}, \quad 0 \le x \le 4$	x-axis
31. $x = \sin z, \quad 0 \le z \le \pi$	z-axis
32. $z = 4 - y^2, \quad 0 \le y \le 2$	y-axis

Tangent Plane **In Exercises 33–36, find an equation of the tangent plane to the surface given by the vector-valued function at the specified point.**

Function	*Point*
33. $\mathbf{r}(u, v) = (u + v)\mathbf{i} + (u - v)\mathbf{j} + v\mathbf{k}$	$(1, -1, 1)$

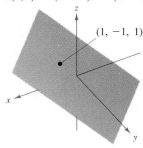

$(1, -1, 1)$

FIGURE FOR 33

34. $\mathbf{r}(u, v) = u\mathbf{i} + v\mathbf{j} + \sqrt{uv}\,\mathbf{k}$ $(1, 1, 1)$

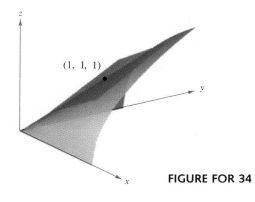

$(1, 1, 1)$

FIGURE FOR 34

Function	*Point*
35. $\mathbf{r}(u, v) = 2u\cos v\,\mathbf{i} + 3u\sin v\,\mathbf{j} + u^2\mathbf{k}$	$(0, 6, 4)$
36. $\mathbf{r}(u, v) = u\cosh v\,\mathbf{i} + u\sinh v\,\mathbf{j} + u^2\mathbf{k}$	$(-2, 0, 4)$

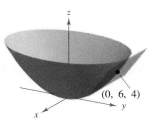 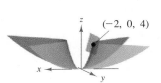

$(0, 6, 4)$ $(-2, 0, 4)$

FIGURE FOR 35   **FIGURE FOR 36**

Area **In Exercises 37–44, find the area of the surface over the specified region.**

37. The part of the plane

$$\mathbf{r}(u, v) = 2u\mathbf{i} - \frac{v}{2}\mathbf{j} + \frac{v}{2}\mathbf{k}$$

where $0 \le u \le 2$ and $0 \le v \le 1$

38. The part of the paraboloid

$$\mathbf{r}(u, v) = 2u\cos v\,\mathbf{i} + 2u\sin v\,\mathbf{j} + u^2\mathbf{k}$$

where $0 \le u \le 2$ and $0 \le v \le 2\pi$

39. The part of the cylinder

$$\mathbf{r}(u, v) = a\cos u\,\mathbf{i} + a\sin u\,\mathbf{j} + v\mathbf{k}$$

where $0 \le u \le 2\pi$ and $0 \le v \le b$

40. The sphere

$$\mathbf{r}(u, v) = a\sin u\cos v\,\mathbf{i} + a\sin u\sin v\,\mathbf{j} + a\cos u\,\mathbf{k}$$

where $0 \le u \le \pi$ and $0 \le v \le 2\pi$

41. The part of the cone

$$\mathbf{r}(u, v) = au\cos v\,\mathbf{i} + au\sin v\,\mathbf{j} + u\mathbf{k}$$

where $0 \le u \le b$ and $0 \le v \le 2\pi$

42. The torus

$$\mathbf{r}(u, v) = (a + b\cos v)\cos u\,\mathbf{i} + (a + b\cos v)\sin u\,\mathbf{j} + b\sin v\,\mathbf{k}$$

where $a > b$, $0 \le u \le 2\pi$, and $0 \le v \le 2\pi$

43. The surface of revolution

$$\mathbf{r}(u, v) = \sqrt{u}\cos v\,\mathbf{i} + \sqrt{u}\sin v\,\mathbf{j} + u\mathbf{k}$$

where $0 \le u \le 4$ and $0 \le v \le 2\pi$

44. The surface of revolution

$$\mathbf{r}(u, v) = u\mathbf{i} + \sin u\cos v\,\mathbf{j} + \sin u\sin v\,\mathbf{k}$$

where $0 \le u \le \pi$ and $0 \le v \le 2\pi$

45. Graph and find the area of one turn of the spiral ramp $\mathbf{r}(u, v) = u\cos v\,\mathbf{i} + u\sin v\,\mathbf{j} + 2v\mathbf{k}$, $\quad 0 \le u \le 3$, $\quad 0 \le v \le 2\pi$.

46. Find a set of parametric equations for the hyperboloid $x^2 + y^2 - z^2 = 1$, and determine the tangent plane at $(1, 0, 0)$.

47. Let f be a nonnegative function such that f' is continuous over the interval $[a, b]$. Let S be the surface of revolution formed by revolving the graph of f, where $a \leq x \leq b$, about the x-axis. Let $x = u$, $y = f(u) \cos v$, and $z = f(u) \sin v$, where $a \leq u \leq b$ and $0 \leq v \leq 2\pi$. Then, S is represented parametrically by

$$\mathbf{r}(u, v) = u\,\mathbf{i} + f(u)\cos v\,\mathbf{j} + f(u)\sin v\,\mathbf{k}.$$

Show that the following formulas are equivalent.

$$\text{Surface area} = \int_a^b f(x)\sqrt{1 + [f'(x)]^2}\,dx$$

$$\text{Surface area} = \int_D \int \|\mathbf{r}_u \times \mathbf{r}_v\|\,dA$$

48. Show that the cone in Example 3 can be represented parametrically by

$$\mathbf{s}(u, v) = u\cos v\,\mathbf{i} + u\sin v\,\mathbf{j} + u\,\mathbf{k}$$

where $0 \leq v \leq 2\pi$ and $0 \leq u$.

Surface Integrals

Surface Integrals • Parametric Surfaces and Surface Integrals • Orientation of a Surface • Flux Integrals

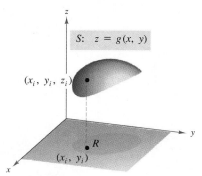

FIGURE 15.44
Scalar function f assigns a number to each point of S.

Surface Integrals

The remainder of this chapter deals primarily with **surface integrals.** We begin by considering surfaces given by $z = g(x, y)$. Later in the section we will consider more general surfaces given in parametric form.

Let S be a surface given by $z = g(x, y)$ and R its projection on the xy-plane, as shown in Figure 15.44. Suppose g, g_x, and g_y are continuous at all points in R, and f is defined on S. Employing the procedure used to find surface area in Section 14.5, evaluate f at (x_i, y_i, z_i) and form the sum

$$\sum_{i=1}^{n} f(x_i, y_i, z_i)\, \Delta S_i$$

where $\Delta S_i \approx \sqrt{1 + [g_x(x_i, y_i)]^2 + [g_y(x_i, y_i)]^2}\, \Delta A_i$. Provided the limit as $\|\Delta\|$ approaches 0 exists, the **surface integral of f over S** is defined as

$$\iint_S f(x, y, z)\, dS = \lim_{\|\Delta\| \to 0} \sum_{i=1}^{n} f(x_i, y_i, z_i)\, \Delta S_i.$$

This integral can be evaluated by a double integral.

THEOREM 15.10   Evaluating a Surface Integral

Let S be a surface with equation $z = g(x, y)$ and R its projection on the xy-plane. If g, g_x, and g_y are continuous on R and f is continuous on S, then the surface integral of f over S is

$$\iint_S f(x, y, z)\, dS = \iint_R f(x, y, g(x, y)) \sqrt{1 + [g_x(x, y)]^2 + [g_y(x, y)]^2}\, dA.$$

For surfaces described by functions of x and z (or y and z), you can make the following adjustments to Theorem 15.10. If S is the graph of $y = g(x, z)$ and R is its projection on the xz-plane, then

$$\iint_S f(x, y, z)\, dS = \iint_R f(x, g(x, z), z) \sqrt{1 + [g_x(x, z)]^2 + [g_z(x, z)]^2}\, dA.$$

If S is the graph of $x = g(y, z)$ and R is its projection on the yz-plane, then

$$\iint_S f(x, y, z)\, dS = \iint_R f(g(y, z), y, z) \sqrt{1 + [g_y(y, z)]^2 + [g_z(y, z)]^2}\, dA.$$

EXAMPLE 1 Evaluating a Surface Integral

Evaluate the surface integral

$$\iint_S (y^2 + 2yz)\, dS$$

where S is the first-octant portion of the plane $2x + y + 2z = 6$.

Solution Begin by writing S as

$$z = \frac{1}{2}(6 - 2x - y)$$

$$g(x, y) = \frac{1}{2}(6 - 2x - y).$$

Using the partial derivatives $g_x(x, y) = -1$ and $g_y(x, y) = -\frac{1}{2}$, you can write

$$\sqrt{1 + [g_x(x, y)]^2 + [g_y(x, y)]^2} = \sqrt{1 + 1 + \frac{1}{4}} = \frac{3}{2}.$$

Using Figure 15.45 and Theorem 15.10, we obtain

$$\begin{aligned}
\iint_S (y^2 + 2yz)\, dS &= \iint_R f(x, y, g(x, y))\sqrt{1 + [g_x(x, y)]^2 + [g_y(x, y)]^2}\, dA \\
&= \iint_R \left[y^2 + 2y\left(\frac{1}{2}\right)(6 - 2x - y) \right]\left(\frac{3}{2}\right) dA \\
&= 3 \int_0^3 \int_0^{2(3-x)} y(3 - x)\, dy\, dx \\
&= 6 \int_0^3 (3 - x)^3\, dx \\
&= -\frac{3}{2}(3 - x)^4 \Big]_0^3 \\
&= \frac{243}{2}.
\end{aligned}$$

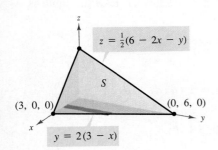

$z = \frac{1}{2}(6 - 2x - y)$

S

$(3, 0, 0)$ $(0, 6, 0)$

$y = 2(3 - x)$

FIGURE 15.45

An alternative solution to Example 1 would be to project S onto the yz-plane, as shown in Figure 15.46. Then, $x = \frac{1}{2}(6 - y - 2z)$, and

$$\sqrt{1 + [g_y(y, z)]^2 + [g_z(y, z)]^2} = \sqrt{1 + \frac{1}{4} + 1} = \frac{3}{2}.$$

Thus, the surface integral is

$$\begin{aligned}
\iint_S (y^2 + 2yz)\, dS &= \iint_R f(g(y, z), y, z)\sqrt{1 + [g_y(y, z)]^2 + [g_z(y, z)]^2}\, dA \\
&= \int_0^6 \int_0^{(6-y)/2} (y^2 + 2yz)\left(\frac{3}{2}\right) dz\, dy \\
&= \frac{3}{8} \int_0^6 (36y - y^3)\, dy \\
&= \frac{243}{2}.
\end{aligned}$$

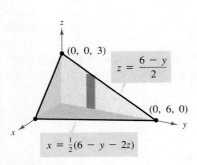

$(0, 0, 3)$

$z = \dfrac{6 - y}{2}$

$(0, 6, 0)$

$x = \frac{1}{2}(6 - y - 2z)$

FIGURE 15.46

Try reworking Example 2 by projecting S onto the xz-plane.

In Example 1, you could have projected the surface S onto any one of the three coordinate planes. In the next example, the surface is a portion of a cylinder centered about the z-axis, and you have the option of projecting S onto either the xz-plane or the xy-plane.

EXAMPLE 2   Evaluating a Surface Integral

Evaluate the surface integral

$$\iint_S (x + z)\, dS$$

where S is the first-octant portion of the cylinder $y^2 + z^2 = 9$ between $x = 0$ and $x = 4$, as shown in Figure 15.47.

Solution   Begin by projecting onto the xy-plane, so that $z = g(x, y) = \sqrt{9 - y^2}$, and obtain

$$\sqrt{1 + [g_x(x, y)]^2 + [g_y(x, y)]^2} = \sqrt{1 + \left(\frac{-y}{\sqrt{9 - y^2}}\right)^2}$$

$$= \frac{3}{\sqrt{9 - y^2}}.$$

Theorem 15.10 does not apply directly, because g_y is not continuous when $y = 3$. However, you can apply the theorem for $0 \le b < 3$ and then take the limit as b approaches 3, as follows.

$$\iint_S (x + z)\, dS = \lim_{b \to 3^-} \int_0^b \int_0^4 (x + \sqrt{9 - y^2})\frac{3}{\sqrt{9 - y^2}}\, dx\, dy$$

$$= \lim_{b \to 3^-} 3\int_0^b \int_0^4 \left(\frac{x}{\sqrt{9 - y^2}} + 1\right) dx\, dy$$

$$= \lim_{b \to 3^-} 3\int_0^b \left[\frac{x^2}{2\sqrt{9 - y^2}} + x\right]_0^4 dy$$

$$= \lim_{b \to 3^-} 3\int_0^b \left(\frac{8}{\sqrt{9 - y^2}} + 4\right) dy$$

$$= \lim_{b \to 3^-} 3\left[4y + 8\arcsin\frac{y}{3}\right]_0^b$$

$$= \lim_{b \to 3^-} 3\left(4b + 8\arcsin\frac{b}{3}\right)$$

$$= 36 + 24\left(\frac{\pi}{2}\right)$$

$$= 36 + 12\pi$$

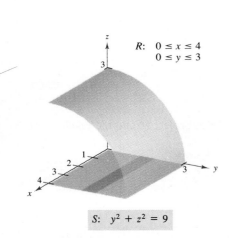

R: $0 \le x \le 4$
       $0 \le y \le 3$

S: $y^2 + z^2 = 9$

FIGURE 15.47

TECHNOLOGY   Some symbolic integration utilities are capable of evaluating improper integrals. If you have access to such computer software, try using it to evaluate the improper integral

$$\int_0^3 \int_0^4 (x + \sqrt{9 - y^2})\frac{3}{\sqrt{9 - y^2}}\, dx\, dy.$$

Do you obtain the same result that was obtained in Example 2?

If the function f defined on the surface S is simply $f(x, y, z) = 1$, then the surface integral yields the *surface area* of S.

$$\text{Area of surface} = \iint_S 1\, dS$$

On the other hand, if S is a lamina of variable density and $\rho(x, y, z)$ is the density at the point (x, y, z), then the *mass* of the lamina is given by

$$\text{Mass of lamina} = \iint_S \rho(x, y, z)\, dS.$$

EXAMPLE 3   Finding the Mass of a Surface Lamina

A cone-shaped surface lamina S is given by

$$z = 4 - 2\sqrt{x^2 + y^2}, \qquad 0 \le z \le 4$$

as shown in Figure 15.48. At each point on S, the density is proportional to the distance between the point and the z-axis. Find the mass m of the lamina.

Solution   Projecting S onto the xy-plane produces the following.

$$S: z = 4 - 2\sqrt{x^2 + y^2} = g(x, y), \qquad 0 \le z \le 4$$
$$R: x^2 + y^2 \le 4$$

Density: $\rho(x, y, z) = k\sqrt{x^2 + y^2}$

Using a surface integral, you can find the mass to be

$$\begin{aligned}
m &= \iint_S \rho(x, y, z)\, dS \\
&= \iint_R k\sqrt{x^2 + y^2}\sqrt{1 + [g_x(x, y)]^2 + [g_y(x, y)]^2}\, dA \\
&= k\iint_R \sqrt{x^2 + y^2}\sqrt{1 + \frac{4x^2}{x^2 + y^2} + \frac{4y^2}{x^2 + y^2}}\, dA \\
&= k\iint_R \sqrt{5}\sqrt{x^2 + y^2}\, dA \\
&= k\int_0^{2\pi}\int_0^2 (\sqrt{5}r)r\, dr\, d\theta \\
&= \frac{\sqrt{5}k}{3}\int_0^{2\pi} r^3\Big]_0^2 d\theta \\
&= \frac{8\sqrt{5}k}{3}\int_0^{2\pi} d\theta \\
&= \frac{8\sqrt{5}k}{3}\Big[\theta\Big]_0^{2\pi} \\
&= \frac{16\sqrt{5}k\pi}{3}.
\end{aligned}$$

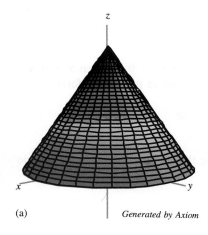

(a)   *Generated by Axiom*

Cone:
$z = 4 - 2\sqrt{x^2 + y^2}$

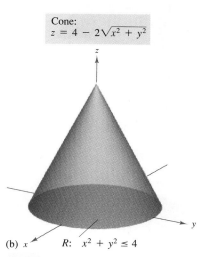

(b) x $R: \ x^2 + y^2 \le 4$

FIGURE 15.48
Density: $\rho(x, y, z) = k\sqrt{x^2 + y^2}$

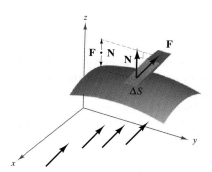

FIGURE 15.51
Velocity field **F** has direction of fluid flow.

Flux Integrals

One of the principal applications involving the vector form of a surface integral relates to the flow of a fluid through a surface S. Suppose an oriented surface S is submerged in a fluid having a continuous velocity field **F**. Let ΔS be the area of a small patch of the surface S over which **F** is nearly constant. Then the amount of fluid crossing this region per unit of time is approximated by the volume of the column of height $\mathbf{F} \cdot \mathbf{N}$, as shown in Figure 15.51. That is,

$$\Delta V = (\text{height})(\text{area of base}) = (\mathbf{F} \cdot \mathbf{N})\,\Delta S.$$

Consequently, the volume of fluid crossing the surface S per unit of time (called the **flux of F across S**) is given by the surface integral in the following definition.

Definition of Flux Integral

Let $\mathbf{F}(x, y, z) = M\mathbf{i} + N\mathbf{j} + P\mathbf{k}$, where M, N, and P have continuous first partial derivatives on the surface S oriented by a unit normal vector **N.** The **flux integral of F across S** is given by

$$\iint_S \mathbf{F} \cdot \mathbf{N}\,dS.$$

Geometrically, a flux integral is the surface integral over S of the *normal component* of **F**. If $\rho(x, y, z)$ is the density of the fluid at (x, y, z), then the flux integral

$$\iint_S \rho\,\mathbf{F} \cdot \mathbf{N}\,dS$$

represents the *mass* of the fluid flowing across S per unit of time.

To evaluate a flux integral for a surface given by $z = g(x, y)$, let $G(x, y, z) = z - g(x, y)$. Then, $\mathbf{N}\,dS$ can be written as follows.

$$\mathbf{N}\,dS = \frac{\nabla G(x, y, z)}{\|\nabla G(x, y, z)\|}\,dS = \frac{\nabla G(x, y, z)}{\sqrt{[g_x]^2 + [g_y]^2 + 1}}\sqrt{(g_x)^2 + (g_y)^2 + 1}\,dA$$
$$= \nabla G(x, y, z)\,dA$$

THEOREM 15.11   Evaluating a Flux Integral

Let S be an oriented surface given by $z = g(x, y)$ and let R be its projection on the xy-plane.

$$\iint_S \mathbf{F} \cdot \mathbf{N}\,dS = \iint_R \mathbf{F} \cdot (-g_x(x, y)\mathbf{i} - g_y(x, y)\mathbf{j} + \mathbf{k})\,dA$$

$$\iint_S \mathbf{F} \cdot \mathbf{N}\,dS = \iint_R \mathbf{F} \cdot (g_x(x, y)\mathbf{i} + g_y(x, y)\mathbf{j} - \mathbf{k})\,dA$$

For the first integral, the surface is oriented upward, and for the second integral, the surface is oriented downward.

EXAMPLE 5   Using a Flux Integral to Find the Rate of Mass Flow

Let S be that portion of the paraboloid

$$z = g(x, y) = 4 - x^2 - y^2$$

lying above the xy-plane, oriented by an upward unit normal vector, as shown in Figure 15.52. A fluid of constant density ρ is flowing through the surface S according to the velocity field

$$\mathbf{F}(x, y, z) = x\mathbf{i} + y\mathbf{j} + z\mathbf{k}.$$

Find the rate of mass flow through S.

Solution   Begin by computing the partial derivatives of g.

$$g_x(x, y) = -2x \quad \text{and} \quad g_y(x, y) = -2y$$

The rate of mass flow through the surface S is

$$\iint_S \rho \mathbf{F} \cdot \mathbf{N} \, dS = \rho \iint_R \mathbf{F} \cdot (-g_x(x, y)\mathbf{i} - g_y(x, y)\mathbf{j} + \mathbf{k}) \, dS$$

$$= \rho \iint_R (x\mathbf{i} + y\mathbf{j} + (4 - x^2 - y^2)\mathbf{k}) \cdot (2x\mathbf{i} + 2y\mathbf{j} + \mathbf{k}) \, dS$$

$$= \rho \iint_R [2x^2 + 2y^2 + (4 - x^2 - y^2)] \, dA$$

$$= \rho \iint_R [4 + x^2 + y^2] \, dA$$

$$= \rho \int_0^{2\pi} \int_0^2 [4 + r^2] r \, dr \, d\theta \qquad \text{Polar coordinates}$$

$$= \rho \int_0^{2\pi} 12 \, d\theta$$

$$= 24\pi\rho.$$

$z = 4 - x^2 - y^2$

FIGURE 15.52

For an oriented surface S given by the vector-valued function

$$\mathbf{r}(u, v) = x(u, v)\mathbf{i} + y(u, v)\mathbf{j} + z(u, v)\mathbf{k} \qquad \text{Parametric surface}$$

defined over a region D in the uv-plane, you can define the flux integral of $\mathbf{F}$ across S as

$$\iint_S \mathbf{F} \cdot \mathbf{N} \, dS = \iint_D \mathbf{F} \cdot \left(\frac{\mathbf{r}_u \times \mathbf{r}_v}{\| \mathbf{r}_u \times \mathbf{r}_v \|} \right) \| \mathbf{r}_u \times \mathbf{r}_v \| \, dA$$

$$= \iint_D \mathbf{F} \cdot (\mathbf{r}_u \times \mathbf{r}_v) \, dA.$$

Note the similarity of this integral to the line integral

$$\int_C \mathbf{F} \cdot d\mathbf{r} = \int_C \mathbf{F} \cdot \mathbf{T} \, ds.$$

A summary of formulas for line integrals and surface integrals is listed at the end of this section.

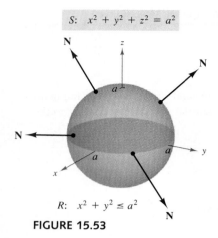

$S: \ x^2 + y^2 + z^2 = a^2$

$R: \ x^2 + y^2 \le a^2$

FIGURE 15.53

EXAMPLE 6   Finding the Flux of an Inverse Square Field

Find the flux over the sphere S given by $x^2 + y^2 + z^2 = a^2$, where $\mathbf{F}$ is an inverse square field given by

$$\mathbf{F}(x, y, z) = \frac{q}{\|\mathbf{r}\|^2} \frac{\mathbf{r}}{\|\mathbf{r}\|} = \frac{q\,\mathbf{r}}{\|\mathbf{r}\|^3}$$

where $\mathbf{r} = x\mathbf{i} + y\mathbf{j} + z\mathbf{k}$. Assume S is oriented outward, as shown in Figure 15.53.

Solution   The sphere is given by

$$\begin{aligned}
\mathbf{r}(u, v) &= x(u, v)\mathbf{i} + y(u, v)\mathbf{j} + z(u, v)\mathbf{k} \\
&= a \sin u \cos v\,\mathbf{i} + a \sin u \sin v\,\mathbf{j} + a \cos u\,\mathbf{k}
\end{aligned}$$

where $0 \le u \le \pi$ and $0 \le v \le 2\pi$. The partial derivatives of $\mathbf{r}$ are

$$\mathbf{r}_u(u, v) = a \cos u \cos v\,\mathbf{i} + a \cos u \sin v\,\mathbf{j} - a \sin u\,\mathbf{k}$$

and

$$\mathbf{r}_v(u, v) = -a \sin u \sin v\,\mathbf{i} + a \sin u \cos v\,\mathbf{j}$$

which implies that the normal vector $\mathbf{r}_u \times \mathbf{r}_v$ is

$$\begin{aligned}
\mathbf{r}_u \times \mathbf{r}_v &= \begin{vmatrix} \mathbf{i} & \mathbf{j} & \mathbf{k} \\ a \cos u \cos v & a \cos u \sin v & -a \sin u \\ -a \sin u \sin v & a \sin u \cos v & 0 \end{vmatrix} \\
&= a^2(\sin^2 u \cos v\,\mathbf{i} + \sin^2 u \sin v\,\mathbf{j} + \sin u \cos u\,\mathbf{k}).
\end{aligned}$$

Now, using

$$\begin{aligned}
\mathbf{F}(x, y, z) &= \frac{q\,\mathbf{r}}{\|\mathbf{r}\|^3} \\
&= q \frac{x\mathbf{i} + y\mathbf{j} + z\mathbf{k}}{\|x\mathbf{i} + y\mathbf{j} + z\mathbf{k}\|^3} \\
&= \frac{q}{a^3}(a \sin u \cos v\,\mathbf{i} + a \sin u \sin v\,\mathbf{j} + a \cos u\,\mathbf{k})
\end{aligned}$$

it follows that

$$\begin{aligned}
\mathbf{F} \cdot (\mathbf{r}_u \times \mathbf{r}_v) &= \frac{q}{a^3}[(a \sin u \cos v\,\mathbf{i} + a \sin u \sin v\,\mathbf{j} + a \cos u\,\mathbf{k}) \cdot \\
&\quad\quad a^2(\sin^2 u \cos v\,\mathbf{i} + \sin^2 u \sin v\,\mathbf{j} + \sin u \cos u\,\mathbf{k}) \\
&= q(\sin^3 \cos^2 v + \sin^3 u \sin^2 v + \sin u \cos^2 u) \\
&= q \sin u.
\end{aligned}$$

Finally, the flux over the sphere S is given by

$$\begin{aligned}
\iint_S \mathbf{F} \cdot \mathbf{N}\,dS &= \iint_D (q \sin u)\,dA \\
&= \int_0^{2\pi} \int_0^{\pi} q \sin u\,du\,dv \\
&= 4\pi q.
\end{aligned}$$

The result in Example 6 shows that the flux across a sphere S in an inverse square field is independent of the radius of S. In particular, if $\mathbf{E}$ is an electric field, then the result in Example 6, along with Coulomb's Law, yields one of the basic laws of electrostatics, known as **Gauss's Law:**

$$\iint_S \mathbf{E} \cdot \mathbf{N} \, dS = 4\pi q \qquad \text{Gauss's Law}$$

where q is a point charge located at the center of the sphere. Gauss's Law is valid for more general closed surfaces that enclose the origin, and relates the flux out of the surface to the total charge q inside the surface.

We conclude this section with a summary of different forms of line integrals and surface integrals.

Summary of Line and Surface Integrals

Line Integrals

$$ds = \| \mathbf{r}'(t) \| \, dt = \sqrt{[x'(t)]^2 + [y'(t)]^2 + [z'(t)]^2} \, dt$$

$$\int_C f(x, y, z) \, ds = \int_a^b f(x(t), y(t), z(t)) \, ds \qquad \text{Scalar form}$$

$$\int_C \mathbf{F} \cdot d\mathbf{r} = \int_C \mathbf{F} \cdot \mathbf{T} \, ds = \int_a^b \mathbf{F}(x(t), y(t), z(t)) \cdot \mathbf{r}'(t) \, dt \qquad \text{Vector form}$$

Surface Integrals $(z = g(x, y))$

$$dS = \sqrt{1 + [g_x(x, y)]^2 + [g_y(x, y)]^2} \, dA$$

$$\iint_S f(x, y, z) \, dS = \iint_R f(x, y, g(x, y)) \sqrt{1 + [g_x(x, y)]^2 + [g_y(x, y)]^2} \, dA \qquad \text{Scalar form}$$

$$\iint_S \mathbf{F} \cdot \mathbf{N} \, dS = \iint_R \mathbf{F} \cdot (-g_x(x, y)\mathbf{i} - g_y(x, y)\mathbf{j} + \mathbf{k}) \, dA \qquad \text{Vector form (upward normal)}$$

Surface Integrals *(parametric form)*

$$dS = \| \mathbf{r}_u(u, v) \times \mathbf{r}_v(u, v) \| \, dA$$

$$\iint_S f(x, y, z) \, dS = \iint_D f(x(u, v), y(u, v), z(u, v)) \, dS \qquad \text{Scalar form}$$

$$\iint_S \mathbf{F} \cdot \mathbf{N} \, dS = \iint_D \mathbf{F} \cdot (\mathbf{r}_u \times \mathbf{r}_v) \, dA \qquad \text{Vector form}$$

TECHNOLOGY
Laboratory Guide
Lab 15.6

EXERCISES for Section 15.6

In Exercises 1–4, evaluate

$$\iint_S (x - 2y + z) \, dS.$$

1. S: $z = 4 - x, \ 0 \le x \le 4, \ 0 \le y \le 4$

2. S: $z = 10 - 2x + 2y, \ 0 \le x \le 2, \ 0 \le y \le 4$

3. S: $z = 10, \ x^2 + y^2 \le 1$

4. S: $z = \frac{2}{3}x^{3/2}, \ 0 \le x \le 1, \ 0 \le y \le x$

In Exercises 5 and 6, evaluate

$$\iint_S xy \, dS.$$

5. S: $z = 6 - x - 2y$ (first octant)

6. S: $z = h, \ 0 \le x \le 2, \ 0 \le y \le \sqrt{4 - x^2}$

C In Exercises 7 and 8, use a symbolic integration utility to evaluate

$$\iint_S xy\, dS.$$

7. $S: z = 9 - x^2, 0 \le x \le 2, 0 \le y \le x$

8. $S: z = xy, 0 \le x \le 2, 0 \le y \le 2$

C In Exercises 9 and 10, use a symbolic integration utility to evaluate

$$\iint_S (x^2 - 2xy)\, dS$$

over the specified surface S.

9. $S: z = 10 - x^2 - y^2, 0 \le x \le 2, 0 \le y \le 2$

10. $S: z = \cos x, 0 \le x \le \dfrac{\pi}{2}, 0 \le y \le \dfrac{1}{2}x$

In Exercises 11–14, evaluate

$$\iint_S f(x, y)\, dS$$

over the specified surface S.

11. $f(x, y) = y + 5$

$S: \mathbf{r}(u, v) = u\mathbf{i} + v\mathbf{j} + \dfrac{v}{2}\mathbf{k}$

$0 \le u \le 1, 0 \le v \le 2$

12. $f(x, y) = x + y$

$S: \mathbf{r}(u, v) = 2\cos u\,\mathbf{i} + 2\sin u\,\mathbf{j} + v\mathbf{k}$

$0 \le u \le \dfrac{\pi}{2}, 0 \le v \le 2$

13. $f(x, y) = xy$

$S: \mathbf{r}(u, v) = 2\cos u\,\mathbf{i} + 2\sin u\,\mathbf{j} + v\mathbf{k}$

$0 \le u \le \dfrac{\pi}{2}, 0 \le v \le 2$

14. $f(x, y) = x + y$

$S: \mathbf{r}(u, v) = 2u\cos v\,\mathbf{i} + 2u\sin v\,\mathbf{j} + u\mathbf{k}$

$0 \le u \le 4, 0 \le v \le \pi$

In Exercises 15–20, evaluate

$$\iint_S f(x, y, z)\, dS.$$

15. $f(x, y, z) = x^2 + y^2 + z^2$

$S: z = x + 2, x^2 + y^2 \le 1$

16. $f(x, y, z) = \dfrac{xy}{z}$

$S: z = x^2 + y^2, 4 \le x^2 + y^2 \le 16$

17. $f(x, y, z) = \sqrt{x^2 + y^2 + z^2}$

$S: z = \sqrt{x^2 + y^2}, x^2 + y^2 \le 4$

18. $f(x, y, z) = \sqrt{x^2 + y^2 + z^2}$

$S: z = \sqrt{x^2 + y^2}, (x - 1)^2 + y^2 \le 1$

19. $f(x, y, z) = x^2 + y^2 + z^2$

$S: x^2 + y^2 = 9, 0 \le x \le 3, 0 \le y \le 3, 0 \le z \le 9$

20. $f(x, y, z) = x^2 + y^2 + z^2$

$S: x^2 + y^2 = 9, 0 \le x \le 3, 0 \le z \le x$

In Exercises 21–26, find the flux of F through S,

$$\iint_S \mathbf{F} \cdot \mathbf{N}\, dS$$

where N is the upper unit normal vector to S.

21. $\mathbf{F}(x, y, z) = 3z\mathbf{i} - 4\mathbf{j} + y\mathbf{k}$

$S: x + y + z = 1$ (first octant)

22. $\mathbf{F}(x, y, z) = x\mathbf{i} + y\mathbf{j}$

$S: 2x + 3y + z = 6$ (first octant)

23. $\mathbf{F}(x, y, z) = x\mathbf{i} + y\mathbf{j} + z\mathbf{k}$

$S: z = 9 - x^2 - y^2, 0 \le z$

24. $\mathbf{F}(x, y, z) = x\mathbf{i} + y\mathbf{j} + z\mathbf{k}$

$S: x^2 + y^2 + z^2 = 16$ (first octant)

25. $\mathbf{F}(x, y, z) = 4\mathbf{i} - 3\mathbf{j} + 5\mathbf{k}$

$S: z = x^2 + y^2, x^2 + y^2 \le 4$

26. $\mathbf{F}(x, y, z) = x\mathbf{i} + y\mathbf{j} - 2z\mathbf{k}$

$S: z = \sqrt{a^2 - x^2 - y^2}$

In Exercises 27 and 28, find the flux of F over the closed surface. (Let N be the outward unit normal vector of each surface.)

27. $\mathbf{F}(x, y, z) = 4xy\mathbf{i} + z^2\mathbf{j} + yz\mathbf{k}$

$S:$ unit cube bounded by $x = 0, x = 1, y = 0, y = 1,$ $z = 0, z = 1$

28. $\mathbf{F}(x, y, z) = (x + y)\mathbf{i} + y\mathbf{j} + z\mathbf{k}$

$S: z = 1 - x^2 - y^2, z \ge 0$

Mass **In Exercises 29 and 30, find the mass of the surface lamina S of density ρ.**

29. $S: 2x + 3y + 6z = 12$ (first octant), $\rho(x, y, z) = x^2 + y^2$

30. $S: z = \sqrt{a^2 - x^2 - y^2}, \rho(x, y, z) = kz$

Moment of Inertia **In Exercises 31 and 32, use the following formulas for the moments of inertia about the coordinate axes of a surface lamina of density ρ.**

$$I_x = \iint_S (y^2 + z^2)\rho(x, y, z)\, dS$$

$$I_y = \iint_S (x^2 + z^2)\rho(x, y, z)\, dS$$

$$I_z = \iint_S (x^2 + y^2)\rho(x, y, z)\, dS$$

31. Show that the moment of inertia of a conical shell about its axis is $\dfrac{1}{2}ma^2$, where m is the mass and a is the radius.

32. Show that the moment of inertia of a spherical shell of uniform density about its diameter is $\dfrac{2}{3}ma^2$, where m is the mass and a is the radius.

Moment of Inertia **In Exercises 33 and 34, find I_z for the given lamina with uniform density of 1.**

33. $x^2 + y^2 = a^2, 0 \le z \le h$ 34. $z = x^2 + y^2, 0 \le z \le h$

Flow Rate   In Exercises 35 and 36, find the rate of mass flow of a fluid of density ρ through the surface S oriented upwards if the velocity field is given by $F(x,y,z) = 0.5z\,\mathbf{k}$.

35. $S: z = 16 - x^2 - y^2, z \geq 0$

36. $S: z = \sqrt{16 - x^2 - y^2}$

37. The surface shown in the figure is called a Möbius strip. Explain why this surface is not orientable. (To create a Möbius strip, cut a strip of paper, make a single twist, and paste the ends together.)

38. Is the surface shown in the figure orientable?

Single twist   Double twist

FIGURE FOR 37   **FIGURE FOR 38**

39. *Electrical Charge*   Let $\mathbf{E} = yz\,\mathbf{i} + xz\,\mathbf{j} + xy\,\mathbf{k}$ be an electrostatic field. Use Gauss's Law to find the total charge enclosed by the closed surface consisting of the hemisphere $z = \sqrt{1 - x^2 - y^2}$ and its circular base in the xy-plane.

Divergence Theorem

Recall from Section 15.4 that an alternative form of Green's Theorem is

$$\int_C \mathbf{F} \cdot \mathbf{N} \, ds = \iint_R \left(\frac{\partial M}{\partial x} + \frac{\partial N}{\partial y} \right) dA$$

$$= \iint_R \operatorname{div} \mathbf{F} \, dA.$$

In an analogous way, the **Divergence Theorem** gives the relationship between a triple integral over a solid region Q and a surface integral over the surface of Q. In the statement of the theorem, the surface S is **closed** in the sense that it forms the complete boundary of the solid Q. Regions bounded by spheres, ellipsoids, cubes, tetrahedrons, or some combination of these surfaces are typical examples of closed surfaces. Assume that Q is a solid region on which a triple integral can be evaluated, and that the closed surface S is oriented by *outward* unit normal vectors, as shown in Figure 15.54. With these restrictions on S and Q, we state the following theorem.

CARL FRIEDRICH GAUSS

The Divergence Theorem is also called Gauss's Theorem, after the famous German mathematician Carl Friedrich Gauss (1777–1855). Gauss is recognized, with Newton and Archimedes, as one of the three greatest mathematicians in history. One of his many contributions to mathematics was made at the age of 22, when, as part of his doctoral dissertation, he proved the *Fundamental Theorem of Algebra*.

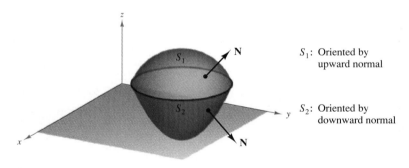

S_1: Oriented by upward normal

S_2: Oriented by downward normal

FIGURE 15.54

THEOREM 15.12   The Divergence Theorem

Let Q be a solid region bounded by a closed surface S oriented by a unit normal vector directed outward from Q. If $\mathbf{F}$ is a vector field whose component functions have continuous partial derivatives in Q, then

$$\iint_S \mathbf{F} \cdot \mathbf{N} \, dS = \iiint_Q \operatorname{div} \mathbf{F} \, dV.$$

Proof By letting $\mathbf{F}(x, y, z) = M\mathbf{i} + N\mathbf{j} + P\mathbf{k}$, the theorem takes the form

$$\iint_S \mathbf{F} \cdot \mathbf{N}\, dS = \iint_S (M\mathbf{i} \cdot \mathbf{N} + N\mathbf{j} \cdot \mathbf{N} + P\mathbf{k} \cdot \mathbf{N})\, dS$$

$$= \iiint_Q \left(\frac{\partial M}{\partial x} + \frac{\partial N}{\partial y} + \frac{\partial P}{\partial z} \right) dV.$$

You can prove this by verifying the following three equations.

$$\iint_S M\mathbf{i} \cdot \mathbf{N}\, dS = \iiint_Q \frac{\partial M}{\partial x}\, dV$$

$$\iint_S N\mathbf{j} \cdot \mathbf{N}\, dS = \iiint_Q \frac{\partial N}{\partial y}\, dV$$

$$\iint_S P\mathbf{k} \cdot \mathbf{N}\, dS = \iiint_Q \frac{\partial P}{\partial z}\, dV$$

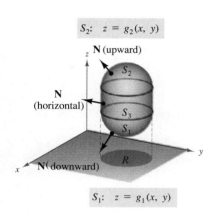

S_2: $z = g_2(x, y)$

$\mathbf{N}$ (upward)

$\mathbf{N}$ (horizontal)

$\mathbf{N}$ (downward)

S_1: $z = g_1(x, y)$

FIGURE 15.55

Because the verifications of the three equations are similar, we will discuss only the third. We restrict the proof to a **simple solid** region with upper surface $z = g_2(x, y)$ and lower surface $z = g_1(x, y)$, whose projections on the xy-plane coincide and form region R. If Q has a lateral surface such as S_3 in Figure 15.55, then a normal vector is horizontal, which implies that $P\mathbf{k} \cdot \mathbf{N} = 0$. Consequently, you have

$$\iint_S P\mathbf{k} \cdot \mathbf{N}\, dS = \iint_{S_1} P\mathbf{k} \cdot \mathbf{N}\, dS + \iint_{S_2} P\mathbf{k} \cdot \mathbf{N}\, dS + 0.$$

On the upper surface S_2, the outward normal vector is upward, whereas on the lower surface S_1, the outward normal vector is downward. Therefore, by Theorem 15.11, you have the following.

$$\iint_{S_1} P\mathbf{k} \cdot \mathbf{N}\, dS = \iint_R P(x, y, g_1(x, y))\mathbf{k} \cdot \left(\frac{\partial g_1}{\partial x}\mathbf{i} + \frac{\partial g_1}{\partial y}\mathbf{j} - \mathbf{k} \right) dA$$

$$= -\iint_R P(x, y, g_1(x, y))\, dA$$

$$\iint_{S_2} P\mathbf{k} \cdot \mathbf{N}\, dS = \iint_R P(x, y, g_2(x, y))\mathbf{k} \cdot \left(-\frac{\partial g_2}{\partial x}\mathbf{i} - \frac{\partial g_2}{\partial y}\mathbf{j} + \mathbf{k} \right) dA$$

$$= \iint_R P(x, y, g_2(x, y))\, dA$$

Adding these results, you obtain

$$\iint_S P\mathbf{k} \cdot \mathbf{N}\, dS = \iint_R [P(x, y, g_2(x, y)) - P(x, y, g_1(x, y))]\, dA$$

$$= \iint_R \left[\int_{g_1(x,y)}^{g_2(x,y)} \frac{\partial P}{\partial z}\, dz \right] dA$$

$$= \iiint_Q \frac{\partial P}{\partial z}\, dV.$$

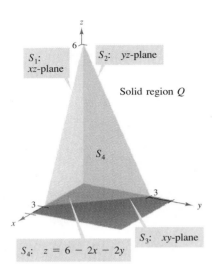

S_1: xz-plane

S_2: yz-plane

Solid region Q

S_4

S_3: xy-plane

S_4:　$z = 6 - 2x - 2y$

FIGURE 15.56

EXAMPLE 1　Using the Divergence Theorem

Let Q be the solid region bounded by the coordinate planes and the plane $2x + 2y + z = 6$, and let $\mathbf{F} = x\mathbf{i} + y^2\mathbf{j} + z\mathbf{k}$. Find

$$\iint_S \mathbf{F} \cdot \mathbf{N}\, dS$$

where S is the surface of Q.

Solution　In Figure 15.56, you can see that Q is bounded by four subsurfaces. Thus, you would need four *surface integrals* to evaluate

$$\iint_S \mathbf{F} \cdot \mathbf{N}\, dS.$$

However, by the Divergence Theorem, you need only one triple integral. Because

$$\text{div }\mathbf{F} = \frac{\partial M}{\partial x} + \frac{\partial N}{\partial y} + \frac{\partial P}{\partial z} = 1 + 2y + 1 = 2 + 2y$$

you have

$$\iint_S \mathbf{F} \cdot \mathbf{N}\, dS = \iiint_Q \text{div }\mathbf{F}\, dV$$

$$= \int_0^3 \int_0^{3-y} \int_0^{6-2x-2y} (2 + 2y)\, dz\, dx\, dy$$

$$= \int_0^3 \int_0^{3-y} (2z + 2yz) \Big]_0^{6-2x-2y} dx\, dy$$

$$= \int_0^3 \int_0^{3-y} (12 - 4x + 8y - 4xy - 4y^2)\, dx\, dy$$

$$= \int_0^3 \left[12x - 2x^2 + 8xy - 2x^2y - 4xy^2 \right]_0^{3-y} dy$$

$$= \int_0^3 (18 + 6y - 10y^2 + 2y^3)\, dy$$

$$= \left[18y + 3y^2 - \frac{10y^3}{3} + \frac{y^4}{2} \right]_0^3$$

$$= \frac{63}{2}.$$

TECHNOLOGY　In you have access to a symbolic integration utility that can evaluate triple-iterated integrals, try using it to verify the result of Example 1. When you are using such a utility, note that the first step is to convert the triple integral to an iterated integral—this step must be done by hand. To give yourself some practice with this important step, try finding the limits of integration for the following iterated integrals. Then use a computer to verify that the value is the same as that obtained in Example 1.

$$\int_?^? \int_?^? \int_?^? (2 + 2y)\, dy\, dz\, dx, \qquad \int_?^? \int_?^? \int_?^? (2 + 2y)\, dx\, dy\, dz$$

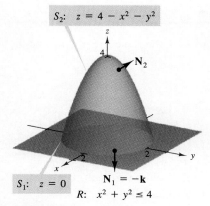

S_2: $z = 4 - x^2 - y^2$

N_2

S_1: $z = 0$

$N_1 = -k$

R: $x^2 + y^2 \le 4$

FIGURE 15.57

EXAMPLE 2 **Verifying the Divergence Theorem**

Let Q be the solid region between the paraboloid

$$z = 4 - x^2 - y^2$$

and the xy-plane. Verify the Divergence Theorem for

$$\mathbf{F}(x, y, z) = 2z\mathbf{i} + x\mathbf{j} + y^2\mathbf{k}.$$

Solution In Figure 15.57, you can see that the outward normal vector for the surface S_1 is $\mathbf{N}_1 = -\mathbf{k}$, whereas the outward normal vector for the surface S_2 is

$$\mathbf{N}_2 = \frac{2x\mathbf{i} + 2y\mathbf{j} + \mathbf{k}}{\sqrt{4x^2 + 4y^2 + 1}}.$$

Thus, by Theorem 15.11, you have

$$\iint_S \mathbf{F} \cdot \mathbf{N}\, dS$$

$$= \iint_{S_1} \mathbf{F} \cdot \mathbf{N}_1\, dS + \iint_{S_2} \mathbf{F} \cdot \mathbf{N}_2\, dS$$

$$= \iint_{S_1} \mathbf{F} \cdot (-\mathbf{k})\, dS + \iint_{S_2} \mathbf{F} \cdot (2x\mathbf{i} + 2y\mathbf{j} + \mathbf{k})\, dA$$

$$= \iint_R -y^2\, dA + \iint_R (4xz + 2xy + y^2)\, dA$$

$$= -\int_{-2}^{2} \int_{-\sqrt{4-y^2}}^{\sqrt{4-y^2}} y^2\, dx\, dy + \int_{-2}^{2} \int_{-\sqrt{4-y^2}}^{\sqrt{4-y^2}} (4xz + 2xy + y^2)\, dx\, dy$$

$$= \int_{-2}^{2} \int_{-\sqrt{4-y^2}}^{\sqrt{4-y^2}} (4xz + 2xy)\, dx\, dy$$

$$= \int_{-2}^{2} \int_{-\sqrt{4-y^2}}^{\sqrt{4-y^2}} [4x(4 - x^2 - y^2) + 2xy]\, dx\, dy$$

$$= \int_{-2}^{2} \int_{-\sqrt{4-y^2}}^{\sqrt{4-y^2}} (16x - 4x^3 - 4xy^2 + 2xy)\, dx\, dy$$

$$= \int_{-2}^{2} \left[8x^2 - x^4 - 2x^2y^2 + x^2y \right]_{-\sqrt{4-y^2}}^{\sqrt{4-y^2}} dy$$

$$= \int_{-2}^{2} 0\, dy$$

$$= 0.$$

On the other hand, because

$$\text{div } \mathbf{F} = \frac{\partial}{\partial x}[2z] + \frac{\partial}{\partial y}[x] + \frac{\partial}{\partial z}[y^2] = 0 + 0 + 0 = 0$$

you can apply the Divergence Theorem to obtain the equivalent result

$$\iint_S \mathbf{F} \cdot \mathbf{N}\, dS = \iiint_Q \text{div } \mathbf{F}\, dV = \iiint_Q 0\, dV = 0.$$

EXAMPLE 3   Using the Divergence Theorem

Let Q be the solid bounded by the cylinder $x^2 + y^2 = 4$, the plane $x + z = 6$, and the xy-plane, as shown in Figure 15.58. Find

$$\iint_S \mathbf{F} \cdot \mathbf{N} \, dS$$

where S is the surface of Q and

$$\mathbf{F}(x, y, z) = (x^2 + \sin z)\mathbf{i} + (xy + \cos z)\mathbf{j} + e^y \mathbf{k}.$$

Solution   Direct evaluation of this surface integral would be difficult. However, by the Divergence Theorem, you can evaluate the integral as follows.

$$\iint_S \mathbf{F} \cdot \mathbf{N} \, dS = \iiint_Q \operatorname{div} \mathbf{F} \, dV$$

$$= \iiint_Q (2x + x + 0) \, dV$$

$$= \iiint_Q 3x \, dV$$

$$= \int_0^{2\pi} \int_0^2 \int_0^{6 - r\cos\theta} (3r\cos\theta)r \, dz \, dr \, d\theta$$

$$= \int_0^{2\pi} \int_0^2 (18r^2 \cos\theta - 3r^3 \cos^2\theta) \, dr \, d\theta$$

$$= \int_0^{2\pi} (48\cos\theta - 12\cos^2\theta) \, d\theta$$

$$= \left[48\sin\theta - 6\left(\theta + \frac{1}{2}\sin 2\theta\right) \right]_0^{2\pi}$$

$$= -12\pi$$

Notice that cylindrical coordinates with $x = r\cos\theta$ and $dV = r \, dz \, dr \, d\theta$ were used to evaluate the triple integral.

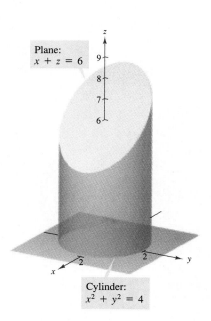

Plane:
$x + z = 6$

Cylinder:
$x^2 + y^2 = 4$

FIGURE 15.58

Even though we stated the Divergence Theorem for a simple solid region Q bounded by a closed surface, the theorem is also valid for regions that are the finite unions of simple solid regions. For example, let Q be the solid bounded by the closed surfaces S_1 and S_2, as shown in Figure 15.59. To apply the Divergence Theorem to this solid, let $S = S_1 \cup S_2$. The normal vector $\mathbf{N}$ to S is given by $-\mathbf{N}_1$ on S_1 and by $\mathbf{N}_2$ on S_2. Thus, you can write

$$\iiint_Q \operatorname{div} \mathbf{F} \, dV = \iint_S \mathbf{F} \cdot \mathbf{N} \, dS$$

$$= \iint_S \mathbf{F} \cdot (-\mathbf{N}_1) \, dS + \iint_S \mathbf{F} \cdot \mathbf{N}_2 \, dS$$

$$= -\iint_S \mathbf{F} \cdot \mathbf{N}_1 \, dS + \iint_S \mathbf{F} \cdot \mathbf{N}_2 \, dS.$$

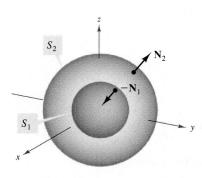

FIGURE 15.59

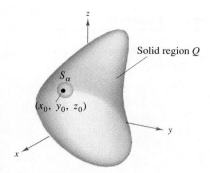

S_α

(x_0, y_0, z_0)

Solid region Q

FIGURE 15.60

(a) Source: div **F** > 0

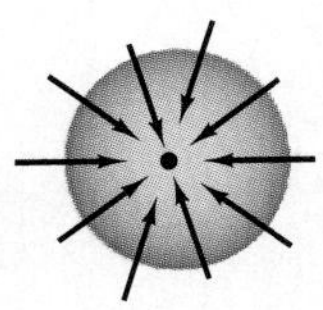

(b) Sink: div **F** < 0

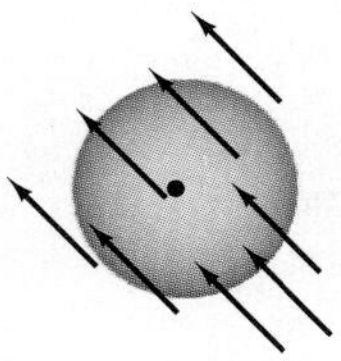

(c) Incompressible: div **F** = 0

FIGURE 15.61

Flux and the Divergence Theorem

To help understand the Divergence Theorem, consider the two sides of the equation

$$\int_S \int \mathbf{F} \cdot \mathbf{N}\, dS = \iiint_Q \operatorname{div} \mathbf{F}\, dV.$$

You know from Section 15.6 that the flux integral on the left determines the total fluid flow across the surface S per unit of time. This can be approximated by summing the fluid flow across small patches of the surface. The triple integral on the right measures this same fluid flow across S, but from a very different perspective—namely, by calculating the flow of fluid into (or out of) small *cubes* of volume ΔV_i. The flux of the ith cube is approximately

$$\text{Flux of } i\text{th cube} \approx \operatorname{div} \mathbf{F}(x_i, y_i, z_i)\, \Delta V_i$$

for some point (x_i, y_i, z_i) in the ith cube. Note that for a cube in the interior of Q, the gain (or loss) of fluid through any one of its six sides is offset by a corresponding loss (or gain) through one of the sides of an adjacent cube. After summing over all the cubes in Q, the only fluid flow that is not canceled by adjoining cubes is that on the outside edges of the cubes on the boundary. Thus, the sum

$$\sum_{i=1}^{n} \operatorname{div} \mathbf{F}(x_i, y_i, z_i)\, \Delta V_i$$

approximates the total flux into (or out of) Q, and therefore through the surface S.

To see what is meant by the divergence of **F** at a point, we consider ΔV_α to be the volume of a small sphere S_α of radius α and center (x_0, y_0, z_0), contained in region Q, as shown in Figure 15.60. Applying the Divergence Theorem to S_α produces

$$\text{Flux of } \mathbf{F} \text{ across } S_\alpha = \iiint_{Q_\alpha} \operatorname{div} \mathbf{F}\, dV \approx \operatorname{div} \mathbf{F}(x_0, y_0, z_0)\, \Delta V_\alpha$$

where Q_α is the interior of S_α. Consequently, you have

$$\operatorname{div} \mathbf{F}(x_0, y_0, z_0) \approx \frac{\text{flux of } \mathbf{F} \text{ across } S_\alpha}{\Delta V_\alpha}$$

and, by taking the limit as $\alpha \to 0$, you obtain the divergence of **F** at the point (x_0, y_0, z_0).

$$\operatorname{div} \mathbf{F}(x_0, y_0, z_0) = \lim_{\alpha \to 0} \frac{\text{flux of } \mathbf{F} \text{ across } S_\alpha}{\Delta V_\alpha}$$
$$= \text{flux per unit volume at } (x_0, y_0, z_0).$$

The point (x_0, y_0, z_0) in a vector field is classified as a source, a sink, or incompressible, as follows.

1. **Source,** if div **F** > 0 (see Figure 15.61a).
2. **Sink,** if div **F** < 0 (see Figure 15.61b).
3. **Incompressible,** if div **F** = 0 (see Figure 15.61c).

EXAMPLE 4 Calculating Flux by the Divergence Theorem

Let Q be the region bounded by the sphere $x^2 + y^2 + z^2 = 4$. Find the outward flux of the vector field $\mathbf{F}(x, y, z) = 2x^3\mathbf{i} + 2y^3\mathbf{j} + 2z^3\mathbf{k}$ through the sphere.

Solution By the Divergence Theorem, you have

$$
\begin{aligned}
\text{Flux across } S &= \iint_S \mathbf{F} \cdot \mathbf{N}\, dS \\
&= \iiint_Q \operatorname{div} \mathbf{F}\, dV \\
&= \iiint_Q 6(x^2 + y^2 + z^2)\, dV \\
&= 6 \int_0^2 \int_0^\pi \int_0^{2\pi} \rho^4 \sin\phi\, d\theta\, d\phi\, d\rho \qquad \text{Spherical coordinates} \\
&= 6 \int_0^2 \int_0^\pi 2\pi\rho^4 \sin\phi\, d\phi\, d\rho \\
&= 12\pi \int_0^2 2\rho^4\, d\rho \\
&= 24\pi\left(\frac{32}{5}\right) \\
&= \frac{768\pi}{5}.
\end{aligned}
$$

TECHNOLOGY
Laboratory Guide
Labs 15.7–15.8

In Exercises 1–4, verify the Divergence Theorem by evaluating

$$\iint_S \mathbf{F} \cdot \mathbf{N}\, dS$$

as a surface integral and as a triple integral.

1. $\mathbf{F}(x, y, z) = 2x\mathbf{i} - 2y\mathbf{j} + z^2\mathbf{k}$
   S: cube bounded by the planes $x = 0$, $x = a$, $y = 0$, $y = a$, $z = 0$, and $z = a$

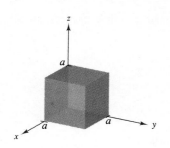

2. $\mathbf{F}(x, y, z) = 2x\mathbf{i} - 2y\mathbf{j} + z^2\mathbf{k}$
   S: cylinder $x^2 + y^2 = 1$, $0 \le z \le h$

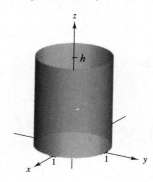

3. $\mathbf{F}(x, y, z) = (2x - y)\mathbf{i} - (2y - z)\mathbf{j} + z\mathbf{k}$

   S: surface bounded by the plane $2x + 4y + 2z = 12$ and the coordinate planes

4. $\mathbf{F}(x, y, z) = xy\mathbf{i} + z\mathbf{j} + (x + y)\mathbf{k}$

   S: surface bounded by the planes $y = 4$ and $z = 4 - x$, and the coordinate planes

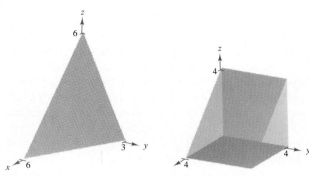

FIGURE FOR 3   **FIGURE FOR 4**

In Exercises 5–14, use the Divergence Theorem to evaluate

$$\iint_S \mathbf{F} \cdot \mathbf{N} \, dS$$

and find the outward flux of F through the surface of the solid bounded by the graphs of the equations.

5. $\mathbf{F}(x, y, z) = x^2\mathbf{i} + y^2\mathbf{j} + z^2\mathbf{k}$

   S: $x = 0, x = a, y = 0, y = a, z = 0, z = a$

6. $\mathbf{F}(x, y, z) = x^2 z\mathbf{i} - y\mathbf{j} + xyz\mathbf{k}$

   S: $x = 0, x = a, y = 0, y = a, z = 0, z = a$

7. $\mathbf{F}(x, y, z) = x^2\mathbf{i} - 2xy\mathbf{j} + xyz^2\mathbf{k}$

   S: $z = \sqrt{a^2 - x^2 - y^2}, z = 0$

8. $\mathbf{F}(x, y, z) = xy\mathbf{i} + yz\mathbf{j} - yz\mathbf{k}$

   S: $z = \sqrt{a^2 - x^2 - y^2}, z = 0$

9. $\mathbf{F}(x, y, z) = x\mathbf{i} + y\mathbf{j} + z\mathbf{k}$

   S: $x^2 + y^2 + z^2 = 4$

10. $\mathbf{F}(x, y, z) = xyz\mathbf{j}$

   S: $x^2 + y^2 = 9, z = 0, z = 4$

11. $\mathbf{F}(x, y, z) = x\mathbf{i} + y^2\mathbf{j} - z\mathbf{k}$

   S: $x^2 + y^2 = 9, z = 0, z = 4$

12. $\mathbf{F}(x, y, z) = (xy^2 + \cos z)\mathbf{i} + (x^2 y + \sin z)\mathbf{j} + e^z\mathbf{k}$

   S: $z = \sqrt{x^2 + y^2}, z = 4$

13. $\mathbf{F}(x, y, z) = x^3\mathbf{i} + x^2 y\mathbf{j} + x^2 e^y\mathbf{k}$

   S: $z = 4 - y, z = 0, x = 0, x = 6, y = 0$

14. $\mathbf{F}(x, y, z) = xe^z\mathbf{i} + ye^z\mathbf{j} + e^z\mathbf{k}$

   S: $z = 4 - y, z = 0, x = 0, x = 6, y = 0$

15. Use the Divergence Theorem to show that the volume of the solid bounded by a surface S is

$$\iint_S x \, dy \, dz = \iint_S y \, dz \, dx = \iint_S z \, dx \, dy.$$

16. Verify the result of Exercise 15 for the cube bounded by $x = 0, x = a, y = 0, y = a, z = 0$, and $z = a$.

In Exercises 17 and 18, evaluate

$$\iint_S \text{curl } \mathbf{F} \cdot \mathbf{N} \, dS$$

where S is the closed surface of the solid bounded by the graphs of $x = 4$ and $z = 9 - y^2$, and the coordinate planes.

17. $\mathbf{F}(x, y, z) = (4xy + z^2)\mathbf{i} + (2x^2 + 6yz)\mathbf{j} + 2xz\mathbf{k}$

18. $\mathbf{F}(x, y, z) = xy \cos z\mathbf{i} + yz \sin x\mathbf{j} + xyz\mathbf{k}$

19. Show that

$$\iint_S \text{curl } \mathbf{F} \cdot \mathbf{N} \, dS = 0$$

for any closed surface S.

20. For the constant vector field given by

   $\mathbf{F}(x, y, z) = a_1\mathbf{i} + a_2\mathbf{j} + a_3\mathbf{k}$

show that

$$\iint_S \mathbf{F} \cdot \mathbf{N} \, dS = 0$$

where V is the volume of the solid bounded by the closed surface S.

21. Given the vector field

   $\mathbf{F}(x, y, z) = x\mathbf{i} + y\mathbf{j} + z\mathbf{k}$

show that

$$\iint_S \mathbf{F} \cdot \mathbf{N} \, dS = 3V$$

where V is the volume of the solid bounded by the closed surface S.

22. Given the vector field

   $\mathbf{F}(x, y, z) = x\mathbf{i} + y\mathbf{j} + z\mathbf{k}$

show that

$$\frac{1}{\|\mathbf{F}\|} \iint_S \mathbf{F} \cdot \mathbf{N} \, dS = \frac{3}{\|\mathbf{F}\|} \iiint_Q dV.$$

In Exercises 23 and 24, prove the identity, assuming that Q, S, and N meet the conditions of the Divergence Theorem and that the required partial derivatives of the scalar functions f and g are continuous. The expressions $D_{\mathbf{N}} f$ and $D_{\mathbf{N}} g$ are the derivatives in the direction of the vector N and are defined by

$$D_{\mathbf{N}} f = \nabla f \cdot \mathbf{N}, \qquad D_{\mathbf{N}} g = \nabla g \cdot \mathbf{N}.$$

23. $\iiint_Q (f \nabla^2 g + \nabla f \cdot \nabla g) \, dV = \iint_S f D_{\mathbf{N}} g \, dS$

   (*Hint*: Use div $(f \mathbf{G}) = f$ div $\mathbf{G} + \nabla f \cdot \mathbf{G}$.)

24. $\iiint_Q (f \nabla^2 g - g \nabla^2 f) \, dV = \iint_S (f D_{\mathbf{N}} g - g D_{\mathbf{N}} f) \, dS$

   (*Hint*: Use Exercise 23 twice.)

SECTION
15.8 Stokes's Theorem
Stokes's Theorem • Physical Interpretation of Curl

GEORGE GABRIEL STOKES

Stokes's Theorem

A second higher-dimension analog of Green's Theorem is called **Stokes's Theorem,** after the English mathematical physicist George Gabriel Stokes (1819–1903). Stokes was part of a group of English mathematical physicists referred to as the Cambridge School, which included William Thompson (Lord Kelvin) and James Clerk Maxwell. In addition to making contributions to physics, Stokes worked with infinite series and differential equations, as well as with the integration results presented in this section.

Stokes's Theorem gives the relationship between a surface integral over an oriented surface S and a line integral along a closed space curve C forming the boundary of S, as shown in Figure 15.62. The positive direction along C is counterclockwise relative to the normal vector **N**. That is, if you imagine grasping the normal vector **N** with your right hand, with your thumb pointing in the direction of **N**, then your fingers will point toward the positive direction C, as shown in Figure 15.63.

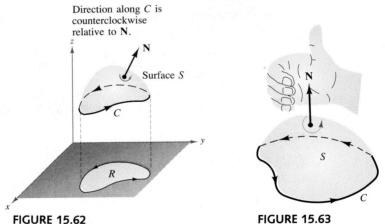

FIGURE 15.62   **FIGURE 15.63**

THEOREM 15.13   Stokes's Theorem

Let S be an oriented surface with unit normal vector **N**, bounded by a piecewise smooth, simple closed curve C. If **F** is a vector field whose component functions have continuous partial derivatives on an open region containing S and C, then

$$\int_C \mathbf{F} \cdot d\mathbf{r} = \int\int_S (\mathbf{curl\ F}) \cdot \mathbf{N}\, dS.$$

REMARK   The line integral may be expressed in the differential form $\int_C M\,dx + N\,dy + P\,dz$ or in the vector form $\int_C \mathbf{F} \cdot \mathbf{T}\, ds$.

EXAMPLE 1   Using Stokes's Theorem

Let C be the oriented triangle lying in the plane $2x + 2y + z = 6$, as shown in Figure 15.64. Evaluate

$$\int_C \mathbf{F} \cdot d\mathbf{r}$$

where $\mathbf{F}(x, y, z) = -y^2 \mathbf{i} + z \mathbf{j} + x \mathbf{k}$.

Solution   Using Stokes's Theorem, you can begin by finding the curl of $\mathbf{F}$.

$$\mathbf{curl\ F} = \begin{vmatrix} \mathbf{i} & \mathbf{j} & \mathbf{k} \\ \dfrac{\partial}{\partial x} & \dfrac{\partial}{\partial y} & \dfrac{\partial}{\partial z} \\ -y^2 & z & x \end{vmatrix} = -\mathbf{i} - \mathbf{j} + 2y\,\mathbf{k}$$

Considering $z = 6 - 2x - 2y = g(x, y)$, you can use Theorem 15.11 for an upward normal vector to obtain

$$\begin{aligned}
\int_C \mathbf{F} \cdot d\mathbf{r} &= \iint_S (\mathbf{curl\ F}) \cdot \mathbf{N}\, dS \\
&= \iint_R (-\mathbf{i} - \mathbf{j} + 2y\,\mathbf{k}) \cdot [-g_x(x, y)\mathbf{i} - g_y(x, y)\mathbf{j} + \mathbf{k}]\, dA \\
&= \iint_R (-\mathbf{i} - \mathbf{j} + 2y\,\mathbf{k}) \cdot (2\mathbf{i} + 2\mathbf{j} + \mathbf{k})\, dA \\
&= \int_0^3 \int_0^{3-y} (2y - 4)\, dx\, dy \\
&= \int_0^3 (-2y^2 + 10y - 12)\, dy \\
&= \left[-\frac{2y^3}{3} + 5y^2 - 12y \right]_0^3 \\
&= -9.
\end{aligned}$$

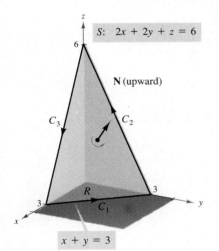

FIGURE 15.64

Try evaluating the line integral in Example 1 directly, *without* using Stokes's Theorem. One way to do this would be to consider C as the union of C_1, C_2, and C_3, as follows.

$$\begin{aligned}
C_1&: \mathbf{r}_1(t) = (3 - t)\mathbf{i} + t\mathbf{j}, & 0 \le t \le 3 \\
C_2&: \mathbf{r}_2(t) = (6 - t)\mathbf{j} + (2t - 6)\mathbf{k}, & 3 \le t \le 6 \\
C_3&: \mathbf{r}_3(t) = (t - 6)\mathbf{i} + (18 - 2t)\mathbf{k}, & 6 \le t \le 9
\end{aligned}$$

The value of the line integral is

$$\begin{aligned}
\int_C \mathbf{F} \cdot d\mathbf{r} &= \int_{C_1} \mathbf{F} \cdot \mathbf{r}_1{}'(t)\, dt + \int_{C_2} \mathbf{F} \cdot \mathbf{r}_2{}'(t)\, dt + \int_{C_3} \mathbf{F} \cdot \mathbf{r}_3{}'(t)\, dt \\
&= \int_0^3 t^2\, dt + \int_3^6 (-2t + 6)\, dt + \int_6^9 (-2t + 12)\, dt \\
&= 9 - 9 - 9 \\
&= -9.
\end{aligned}$$

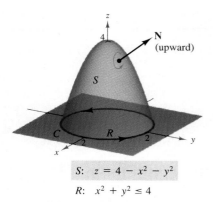

S: $z = 4 - x^2 - y^2$

R: $x^2 + y^2 \le 4$

FIGURE 15.65

EXAMPLE 2   Verifying Stokes's Theorem

Verify Stokes's Theorem for $\mathbf{F}(x, y, z) = 2z\mathbf{i} + x\mathbf{j} + y^2\mathbf{k}$, where S is the surface of the paraboloid $z = 4 - x^2 - y^2$ and C is the trace of S in the xy-plane, as shown in Figure 15.65.

Solution   As a *surface integral,* you have $z = g(x, y) = 4 - x^2 - y^2$ and

$$\mathbf{curl\ F} = \begin{vmatrix} \mathbf{i} & \mathbf{j} & \mathbf{k} \\ \dfrac{\partial}{\partial x} & \dfrac{\partial}{\partial y} & \dfrac{\partial}{\partial z} \\ 2z & x & y^2 \end{vmatrix} = 2y\mathbf{i} + 2\mathbf{j} + \mathbf{k}.$$

By Theorem 15.11 for an upward normal vector $\mathbf{N}$, you obtain

$$\iint_S (\mathbf{curl\ F}) \cdot \mathbf{N}\, dS = \iint_R (2y\mathbf{i} + 2\mathbf{j} + \mathbf{k}) \cdot (2x\mathbf{i} + 2y\mathbf{j} + \mathbf{k})\, dA$$

$$= \int_{-2}^{2} \int_{-\sqrt{4-y^2}}^{\sqrt{4-y^2}} (4xy + 4y + 1)\, dx\, dy$$

$$= \int_{-2}^{2} \left[2x^2y + (4y + 1)x \right]_{-\sqrt{4-y^2}}^{\sqrt{4-y^2}} dy$$

$$= \int_{-2}^{2} 2(4y + 1)\sqrt{4 - y^2}\, dy$$

$$= \int_{-2}^{2} (8y\sqrt{4 - y^2} + 2\sqrt{4 - y^2})\, dy$$

$$= \left[-\frac{8}{3}(4 - y^2)^{3/2} + y\sqrt{4 - y^2} + 4\arcsin\frac{y}{2} \right]_{-2}^{2}$$

$$= 4\pi.$$

As a *line integral,* you can parametrize C by

$$\mathbf{r}(t) = 2\cos t\,\mathbf{i} + 2\sin t\,\mathbf{j} + 0\mathbf{k}, \qquad 0 \le t \le 2\pi.$$

For $\mathbf{F}(x, y, z) = 2z\mathbf{i} + x\mathbf{j} + y^2\mathbf{k}$, you obtain

$$\int_C \mathbf{F} \cdot d\mathbf{r} = \int_C M\, dx + N\, dy + P\, dz$$

$$= \int_C 2z\, dx + x\, dy + y^2\, dz$$

$$= \int_0^{2\pi} [0 + 2\cos t(2\cos t) + 0]\, dt$$

$$= \int_0^{2\pi} 4\cos^2 t\, dt$$

$$= 2\int_0^{2\pi} (1 + \cos 2t)\, dt$$

$$= 2\left[t + \frac{1}{2}\sin 2t \right]_0^{2\pi}$$

$$= 4\pi.$$

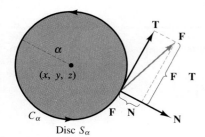

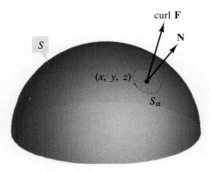

FIGURE 15.66

FIGURE 15.67

Physical Interpretation of Curl

Stokes's Theorem provides insight into a physical interpretation of curl. In a vector field **F**, let S_α be a *small* circular disc of radius α, centered at (x, y, z) and with boundary C_α, as shown in Figure 15.66. At each point on the circle C_α, **F** has a normal component $\mathbf{F} \cdot \mathbf{N}$ and a tangential component $\mathbf{F} \cdot \mathbf{T}$. The more closely **F** and **T** are aligned, the greater the value of $\mathbf{F} \cdot \mathbf{T}$. Thus, a fluid tends to move along the circle rather than across it. Consequently, we say that the line integral around C_α measures the **circulation of F around C_α.** That is,

$$\int_{C_\alpha} \mathbf{F} \cdot \mathbf{T} \, ds = \text{circulation of } \mathbf{F} \text{ around } C_\alpha.$$

Now consider a small disc S_α to be centered at some point (x, y, z) on the surface S, as shown in Figure 15.67. On such a small disc, **curl F** is nearly constant, because it varies little from its value at (x, y, z). Moreover, **curl F** $\cdot$ **N** is also nearly constant on S_α, because all unit normals to S_α are about the same. Consequently, Stokes's Theorem yields

$$\int_{C_\alpha} \mathbf{F} \cdot \mathbf{T} \, ds = \iint_{S_\alpha} (\mathbf{curl}\ \mathbf{F}) \cdot \mathbf{N} \, ds$$

$$\approx (\mathbf{curl}\ \mathbf{F}) \cdot \mathbf{N} \iint_{S_\alpha} dS$$

$$\approx (\mathbf{curl}\ \mathbf{F}) \cdot \mathbf{N}(\pi\alpha^2).$$

Therefore,

$$(\mathbf{curl}\ \mathbf{F}) \cdot \mathbf{N} \approx \frac{\displaystyle\int_{C_\alpha} \mathbf{F} \cdot \mathbf{T} \, ds}{\pi\alpha^2}$$

$$= \frac{\text{circulation of } \mathbf{F} \text{ around } C_\alpha}{\text{area of disc } S_\alpha}$$

$$= \text{rate of circulation.}$$

Assuming conditions are such that the approximation improves for smaller and smaller discs $(\alpha \to 0)$, it follows that

$$(\mathbf{curl}\ \mathbf{F}) \cdot \mathbf{N} = \lim_{\alpha \to 0} \frac{1}{\pi\alpha^2} \int_{C_\alpha} \mathbf{F} \cdot \mathbf{T} \, ds$$

which is referred to as the **rotation of F about N.** That is,

$$\mathbf{curl}\ \mathbf{F}(x, y, z) \cdot \mathbf{N} = \text{rotation of } \mathbf{F} \text{ about } \mathbf{N} \text{ at } (x, y, z).$$

In this case, the rotation of **F** is maximum when **curl F** and **N** have the same direction. Normally, this tendency to rotate will vary from point to point on the surface S, and Stokes's Theorem

$$\underbrace{\iint_S (\mathbf{curl}\ \mathbf{F}) \cdot \mathbf{N} \, dS}_{\text{Surface integral}} = \underbrace{\int_C \mathbf{F} \cdot d\mathbf{r}}_{\text{Line integral}}$$

says that the collective measure of this *rotational* tendency taken over the entire surface S (surface integral) is equal to the tendency of a fluid to *circulate* around the boundary C (line integral).

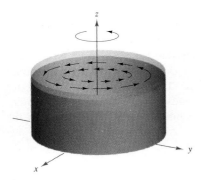

FIGURE 15.68

REMARK   If **curl F** = **0** throughout region Q, then the rotation of **F** about each unit normal **N** is zero. That is, **F** is irrotational. From earlier work, you know that this is a characteristic of conservative vector fields.

EXAMPLE 3   Motion of a Swirling Liquid

A liquid is swirling around in a cylindrical container of radius 2 such that its motion is described by the velocity field

$$\mathbf{F}(x, y, z) = -y\sqrt{x^2 + y^2}\,\mathbf{i} + x\sqrt{x^2 + y^2}\,\mathbf{j}$$

as shown in Figure 15.68. Find

$$\iint_S (\operatorname{curl} \mathbf{F}) \cdot \mathbf{N}\, dS$$

where S is the upper surface of the cylindrical tank.

Solution   The curl of **F** is given by

$$\operatorname{curl} \mathbf{F} = \begin{vmatrix} \mathbf{i} & \mathbf{j} & \mathbf{k} \\ \dfrac{\partial}{\partial x} & \dfrac{\partial}{\partial y} & \dfrac{\partial}{\partial z} \\ -y\sqrt{x^2 + y^2} & x\sqrt{x^2 + y^2} & 0 \end{vmatrix}$$

$$= 3\sqrt{x^2 + y^2}\,\mathbf{k}.$$

Letting $\mathbf{N} = \mathbf{k}$, you have

$$\iint_S (\operatorname{curl} \mathbf{F}) \cdot \mathbf{N}\, dS = \iint_R 3\sqrt{x^2 + y^2}\, dA$$

$$= \int_0^{2\pi} \int_0^2 (3r) r\, dr\, d\theta$$

$$= \int_0^{2\pi} r^3 \Big]_0^2 d\theta$$

$$= \int_0^{2\pi} 8\, d\theta$$

$$= 16\pi.$$

Summary of Integration Formulas

Fundamental Theorem of Calculus

$$\int_a^b F'(x)\, dx = F(b) - F(a)$$

Fundamental Theorem of Line Integrals

$$\int_C \mathbf{F} \cdot d\mathbf{r} = \int_C \nabla f \cdot d\mathbf{r} = f(x(b), y(b)) - f(x(a), y(a))$$

Green's Theorem

$$\int_C M\, dx + N\, dy = \iint_R \left(\frac{\partial N}{\partial x} - \frac{\partial M}{\partial y}\right) dA = \int_C \mathbf{F} \cdot \mathbf{T}\, ds = \int_C \mathbf{F} \cdot d\mathbf{r} = \iint_R (\operatorname{curl} \mathbf{F}) \cdot \mathbf{k}\, dA$$

$$\int_C \mathbf{F} \cdot \mathbf{N}\, ds = \iint_R \operatorname{div} \mathbf{F}\, dA$$

Divergence Theorem

$$\iint_S \mathbf{F} \cdot \mathbf{N}\, dS = \iiint_Q \operatorname{div} \mathbf{F}\, dV$$

Stokes's Theorem

$$\int_C \mathbf{F} \cdot d\mathbf{r} = \iint_S (\operatorname{curl} \mathbf{F}) \cdot \mathbf{N}\, dS$$

EXERCISES for Section 15.8

TECHNOLOGY
Laboratory Guide
Labs 15.7–15.8

In Exercises 1–6, find the curl of the vector field F.

1. $\mathbf{F}(x, y, z) = (2y - z)\mathbf{i} + xyz\mathbf{j} + e^z\mathbf{k}$

2. $\mathbf{F}(x, y, z) = x^2\mathbf{i} + y^2\mathbf{j} + x^2\mathbf{k}$

3. $\mathbf{F}(x, y, z) = 2z\mathbf{i} - 4x^2\mathbf{j} + \arctan x\,\mathbf{k}$

4. $\mathbf{F}(x, y, z) = x\sin y\,\mathbf{i} - y\cos x\,\mathbf{j} + yz^2\mathbf{k}$

5. $\mathbf{F}(x, y, z) = e^{x^2+y^2}\mathbf{i} + e^{y^2+z^2}\mathbf{j} + xyz\mathbf{k}$

6. $\mathbf{F}(x, y, z) = \arcsin y\,\mathbf{i} + \sqrt{1 - x^2}\,\mathbf{j} + y^2\mathbf{k}$

In Exercises 7–10, verify Stokes's Theorem by evaluating

$$\int_C \mathbf{F} \cdot \mathbf{T}\,ds$$

as a line integral and as a double integral.

7. $\mathbf{F}(x, y, z) = (-y + z)\mathbf{i} + (x - z)\mathbf{j} + (x - y)\mathbf{k}$
   $S: z = \sqrt{1 - x^2 - y^2}$

8. $\mathbf{F}(x, y, z) = (-y + z)\mathbf{i} + (x - z)\mathbf{j} + (x - y)\mathbf{k}$
   $S: z = 4 - x^2 - y^2, \ 0 \le z$

9. $\mathbf{F}(x, y, z) = xyz\mathbf{i} + y\mathbf{j} + z\mathbf{k}$
   $S: 3x + 4y + 2z = 12$ (first octant)

10. $\mathbf{F}(x, y, z) = z^2\mathbf{i} + x^2\mathbf{j} + y^2\mathbf{k}$
    $S: z = x^2, \ 0 \le x \le a, \ 0 \le y \le a$

In Exercises 11–20, use Stokes's Theorem to evaluate

$$\int_C \mathbf{F} \cdot d\mathbf{r}.$$

11. $\mathbf{F}(x, y, z) = 2y\mathbf{i} + 3z\mathbf{j} + x\mathbf{k}$
    $C:$ triangle with vertices $(0, 0, 0)$, $(0, 2, 0)$, and $(1, 1, 1)$

12. $\mathbf{F}(x, y, z) = \arctan \dfrac{x}{y}\mathbf{i} + \ln\sqrt{x^2 + y^2}\,\mathbf{j} + \mathbf{k}$
    $C:$ triangle with vertices $(0, 0, 0)$, $(1, 1, 1)$, and $(0, 0, 2)$

13. $\mathbf{F}(x, y, z) = z^2\mathbf{i} + x^2\mathbf{j} + y^2\mathbf{k}$
    $S: z = 4 - x^2 - y^2, \ 0 \le z$

14. $\mathbf{F}(x, y, z) = 4xz\mathbf{i} + y\mathbf{j} + 4xy\mathbf{k}$
    $S: z = 4 - x^2 - y^2, \ 0 \le z$

15. $\mathbf{F}(x, y, z) = z^2\mathbf{i} + y\mathbf{j} + xz\mathbf{k}$
    $S: z = \sqrt{4 - x^2 - y^2}$

16. $\mathbf{F}(x, y, z) = x^2\mathbf{i} + z^2\mathbf{j} - xyz\mathbf{k}$
    $S: z = \sqrt{4 - x^2 - y^2}$

17. $\mathbf{F}(x, y, z) = -\ln\sqrt{x^2 + y^2}\,\mathbf{i} + \arctan\dfrac{x}{y}\mathbf{j} + \mathbf{k}$
    $S: z = 9 - 2x - 3y$ over one petal of $r = 2\sin 2\theta$ in the first octant

18. $\mathbf{F}(x, y, z) = yz\mathbf{i} + (2 - 3y)\mathbf{j} + (x^2 + y^2)\mathbf{k}$
    $S:$ the first-octant portion of $x^2 + z^2 = 16$ over $x^2 + y^2 = 16$

19. $\mathbf{F}(x, y, z) = xyz\mathbf{i} + y\mathbf{j} + z\mathbf{k}$
    $S: z = x^2, \ 0 \le x \le a, \ 0 \le y \le a$

20. $\mathbf{F}(x, y, z) = xyz\mathbf{i} + y\mathbf{j} + z\mathbf{k}$
    $S:$ the first-octant portion of $z = x^2$ over $x^2 + y^2 = a^2$

Motion of a Liquid   **In Exercises 21 and 22, the motion of a liquid in a cylindrical container of radius 1 is described by the velocity field $\mathbf{F}(x, y, z)$. Find**

$$\int_S \int (\text{curl } \mathbf{F}) \cdot \mathbf{N}\,dS$$

where S is the upper surface of the cylindrical tank.

21. $\mathbf{F}(x, y, z) = \mathbf{i} + \mathbf{j} - 2\mathbf{k}$

22. $\mathbf{F}(x, y, z) = -y\mathbf{i} + x\mathbf{j}$

23. Let f and g be scalar functions with continuous partial derivatives, and let C and S satisfy the conditions of Stokes's Theorem. Verify each of the following identities.

    a. $\displaystyle\int_C (f\nabla g) \cdot d\mathbf{r} = \int_S \int (\nabla f \times \nabla g) \cdot \mathbf{N}\,dS$

    b. $\displaystyle\int_C (f\nabla f) \cdot d\mathbf{r} = 0$

    c. $\displaystyle\int_C (f\nabla g + g\nabla f) \cdot d\mathbf{r} = 0$

24. Demonstrate the result of Exercise 23 for the functions $f(x, y, z) = xyz$ and $g(x, y, z) = z$. Let S be the hemisphere $z = \sqrt{4 - x^2 - y^2}$.

25. Let $\mathbf{C}$ be a constant vector. Let S be an oriented surface with a unit normal vector $\mathbf{N}$, bounded by a smooth curve C. Prove that

    $$\int_S \int \mathbf{C} \cdot \mathbf{N}\,dS = \frac{1}{2}\int_C (\mathbf{C} \times \mathbf{r})\,d\mathbf{r}.$$

REVIEW EXERCISES for Chapter 15

In Exercises 1 and 2, sketch several representative vectors in the given vector field.

1. $\mathbf{F}(x, y, z) = x\mathbf{i} + \mathbf{j} + 2\mathbf{k}$

2. $\mathbf{F}(x, y) = \mathbf{i} - 2y\mathbf{j}$

In Exercises 3 and 4, find a three-dimensional vector field that has the potential function f.

3. $f(x, y, z) = 8x^2 + xy + z^2$

4. $f(x, y, z) = x^2 e^{yz}$

In Exercises 5–12, determine whether F is conservative. If it is, find the potential function _f_.

5. $F(x, y) = \dfrac{1}{y}i - \dfrac{y}{x^2}j$

6. $F(x, y) = -\dfrac{y}{x^2}i + \dfrac{1}{x}j$

7. $F(x, y) = (6xy^2 - 3x^2)i + (6x^2y + 3y^2 - 7)j$

8. $F(x, y) = (-2y^3 \sin 2x)i + 3y^2(1 + \cos 2x)j$

9. $F(x, y, z) = (4xy + z)i + (2x^2 + 6y)j + 2z\,k$

10. $F(x, y, z) = (4xy + z^2)i + (2x^2 + 6yz)j + 2xz\,k$

11. $F(x, y, z) = \dfrac{yz\,i - xz\,j - xy\,k}{y^2z^2}$

12. $F(x, y, z) = \sin z(y\,i + x\,j + k)$

In Exercises 13–20, find (a) the divergence of the vector field F, and (b) the curl of the vector field F.

13. $F(x, y, z) = x^2i + y^2j + z^2k$

14. $F(x, y, z) = xy^2j - zx^2k$

15. $F(x, y, z) = (\cos y + y \cos x)i + (\sin x - x \sin y)j + xyz\,k$

16. $F(x, y, z) = (3x - y)i + (y - 2z)j + (z - 3x)k$

17. $F(x, y, z) = \arcsin x\,i + xy^2j + yz^2k$

18. $F(x, y, z) = (x^2 - y)i - (x + \sin^2 y)j$

19. $F(x, y, z) = \ln(x^2 + y^2)i + \ln(x^2 + y^2)j + z\,k$

20. $F(x, y, z) = \dfrac{z}{x}i + \dfrac{z}{y}j + z^2k$

In Exercises 21–26, evaluate the line over the specified path(s).

21. $\displaystyle\int_C (x^2 + y^2)\,ds$
 a. _C_: line segment from $(-1, -1)$ to $(2, 2)$
 b. _C_: $x^2 + y^2 = 16$, one revolution counterclockwise, starting at $(4, 0)$

22. $\displaystyle\int_C xy\,ds$
 a. _C_: line segment from $(0, 0)$ to $(5, 4)$
 b. _C_: counterclockwise around the triangle with vertices $(0, 0)$, $(4, 0)$, and $(0, 2)$

23. $\displaystyle\int_C (x^2 + y^2)\,ds$
 _C_: $r(t) = (\cos t + t \sin t)i + (\sin t - t \cos t)j$,
  $0 \le t \le 2\pi$

24. $\displaystyle\int_C x\,ds$
 _C_: $r(t) = (t - \sin t)i + (1 - \cos t)j, \ 0 \le t \le 2\pi$

25. $\displaystyle\int_C (2x - y)\,dx + (x + 3y)\,dy$
 a. _C_: line segment from $(0, 0)$ to $(2, -3)$
 b. _C_: counterclockwise around the circle $x = 3 \cos t$, $y = 3 \sin t$

26. $\displaystyle\int_C (2x - y)\,dx + (x + 3y)\,dy$
 _C_: $r(t) = (\cos t + t \sin t)i + (\sin t - t \sin t)j, \ 0 \le t \le \pi/2$

**Lateral Surface Area**   **In Exercises 27 and 28, find the lateral surface area over the curve _C_ in the _xy_-plane and under the surface $z = f(x, y)$.**

27. $f(x, y) = 5 + \sin(x + y)$
 _C_: $y = 3x$ from $(0, 0)$ to $(2, 6)$

28. $f(x, y) = 12 - x - y$
 _C_: $y = x^2$ from $(0, 0)$ to $(2, 4)$

In Exercises 29–34, evaluate

$$\int_C F \cdot d\,r.$$

29. $F(x, y) = xy\,i + x^2j$
 _C_: $r(t) = t^2i + t^3j, \ 0 \le t \le 1$

30. $F(x, y) = (x - y)i + (x + y)j$
 _C_: $r(t) = 4\cos t\,i + 3 \sin t\,j, \ 0 \le t \le 2\pi$

31. $F(x, y, z) = x\,i + y\,j + z\,k$
 _C_: $r(t) = 2\cos t\,i + 2 \sin t\,j + t\,k, \ 0 \le t \le 2\pi$

32. $F(x, y, z) = (2y - z)i + (z - x)j + (x - y)k$
 _C_: curve of intersection of $x^2 + z^2 = 4$ and $y^2 + z^2 = 4$
  from $(2, 2, 0)$ to $(0, 0, 2)$

33. $F(x, y, z) = (y - z)i + (z - x)j + (x - y)k$
 _C_: curve of intersection of $z = x^2 + y^2$ and $x + y = 0$
  from $(-2, 2, 8)$ to $(2, -2, 8)$

34. $F(x, y, z) = (x^2 - z)i + (y^2 + z)j + x\,k$
 _C_: curve of intersection of $z = x^2$ and $x^2 + y^2 = 4$ from
  $(0, -2, 0)$ to $(0, 2, 0)$

35. _Work_   Find the work done by the force field $F = x\,i - \sqrt{y}\,j$ along the path $y = x^{3/2}$ from $(0, 0)$ to $(4, 8)$.

36. _Work_   Find the work done by the engines on a 20-ton aircraft if it climbs 2000 feet while making a 90° turn in a circular arc of radius 10 miles.

In Exercises 37 and 38, use the Fundamental Theorem of Line Integrals to evaluate the given integral.

37. $\displaystyle\int_C 2xyz\,dx + x^2z\,dy + x^2y\,dz$
 _C_: smooth curve from $(0, 0, 0)$ to $(1, 4, 3)$

38. $\displaystyle\int_C y\,dx + x\,dy + \dfrac{1}{z}dz$
 _C_: smooth curve from $(0, 0, 1)$ to $(4, 4, 4)$

In Exercises 39–44, use Green's Theorem to evaluate the line integral.

39. $\displaystyle\int_C y\,dx + 2x\,dy$
 _C_: boundary of the square with vertices $(0, 0)$, $(0, 2)$, $(2, 0)$, and $(2, 2)$

40. $\displaystyle\int_C xy\,dx + (x^2 + y^2)\,dy$

C: boundary of the square with vertices $(0, 0)$, $(0, 2)$, $(2, 0)$, and $(2, 2)$

41. $\displaystyle\int_C xy^2\,dx + x^2y\,dy$

C: $x = 4\cos t$, $y = 2\sin t$

42. $\displaystyle\int_C (x^2 - y^2)\,dx + 2xy\,dy$

C: $x^2 + y^2 = a^2$

43. $\displaystyle\int_C xy\,dx + x^2\,dy$

C: boundary of the region between the graphs of $y = x^2$ and $y = x$

44. $\displaystyle\int_C y^2\,dx + x^{2/3}\,dy$

C: $x^{2/3} + y^{2/3} = 1$

[C] **In Exercises 45 and 46, use a graphing utility to graph the surface represented by the vector-valued function.**

45. $\mathbf{r}(u, v) = \sec u\cos v\,\mathbf{i} + (1 + 2\tan u)\sin v\,\mathbf{j} + 2u\,\mathbf{k}$

$0 \le u \le \dfrac{\pi}{3}$, $0 \le v \le 2\pi$

46. $\mathbf{r}(u, v) = e^{-u/4}\cos v\,\mathbf{i} + e^{-u/4}\sin v\,\mathbf{j} + \dfrac{u}{6}\mathbf{k}$

$0 \le u \le 4$, $0 \le v \le 2\pi$

47. Evaluate the surface integral

$$\iint_S z\,dS$$

over the surface

S: $\mathbf{r}(u, v) = (u + v)\mathbf{i} + (u - v)\mathbf{j} + \sin v\,\mathbf{k}$

where $0 \le u \le 2$ and $0 \le v \le \pi$.

[C] **48.** Use a computer to graph the surface S and to approximate the surface integral

$$\iint_S (x + y)\,dS$$

where S is the surface

S: $\mathbf{r}(u, v,) = u\cos v\,\mathbf{i} + u\sin v\,\mathbf{j} + (u - 1)(2 - u)\mathbf{k}$ over $0 \le u \le 2$ and $0 \le v \le 2\pi$.

In Exercises 49 and 50, verify the Divergence Theorem by evaluating

$$\iint_S \mathbf{F}\cdot\mathbf{N}\,dS$$

as a surface integral and as a triple integral.

49. $\mathbf{F}(x, y, z) = x^2\mathbf{i} + xy\mathbf{j} + z\mathbf{k}$

Q: solid region bounded by the coordinate planes and the plane $2x + 3y + 4z = 12$

50. $\mathbf{F}(x, y, z) = x\mathbf{i} + y\mathbf{j} + z\mathbf{k}$

Q: solid region bounded by the coordinate planes and the plane $2x + 3y + 4z = 12$

In Exercises 51 and 52, verify Stokes's Theorem by evaluating

$$\int_C \mathbf{F}\cdot d\mathbf{r}$$

as a line integral and as a double integral.

51. $\mathbf{F}(x, y, z) = (\cos y + y\cos x)\mathbf{i} + (\sin x - x\sin y)\mathbf{j} + xyz\,\mathbf{k}$

S: portion of $z = y^2$ over the square in the xy-plane with vertices $(0, 0)$, $(a, 0)$, (a, a), and $(0, a)$

52. $\mathbf{F}(x, y, z) = (x - z)\mathbf{i} + (y - z)\mathbf{j} + x^2\mathbf{k}$

S: first-octant portion of the plane $3x + y + 2z = 12$

53. Consider the integral

$$\int_C \mathbf{F}\cdot d\mathbf{r}$$

where

$$\mathbf{F}(x, y) = \dfrac{-y}{x^2 + y^2}\mathbf{i} + \dfrac{x}{x^2 + y^2}\mathbf{j}$$

and

$$\mathbf{r}(t) = \cos t\,\mathbf{i} + \sin t\,\mathbf{j}.$$

Because $N_x = M_y$ and C is a circle, it is expected that the line integral will have a value of 0. However, upon direct integration we obtain

$$\int_C \mathbf{F}\cdot d\mathbf{r} = 2\pi.$$

Which is correct, and why?

Chapter 16

Differential Equations

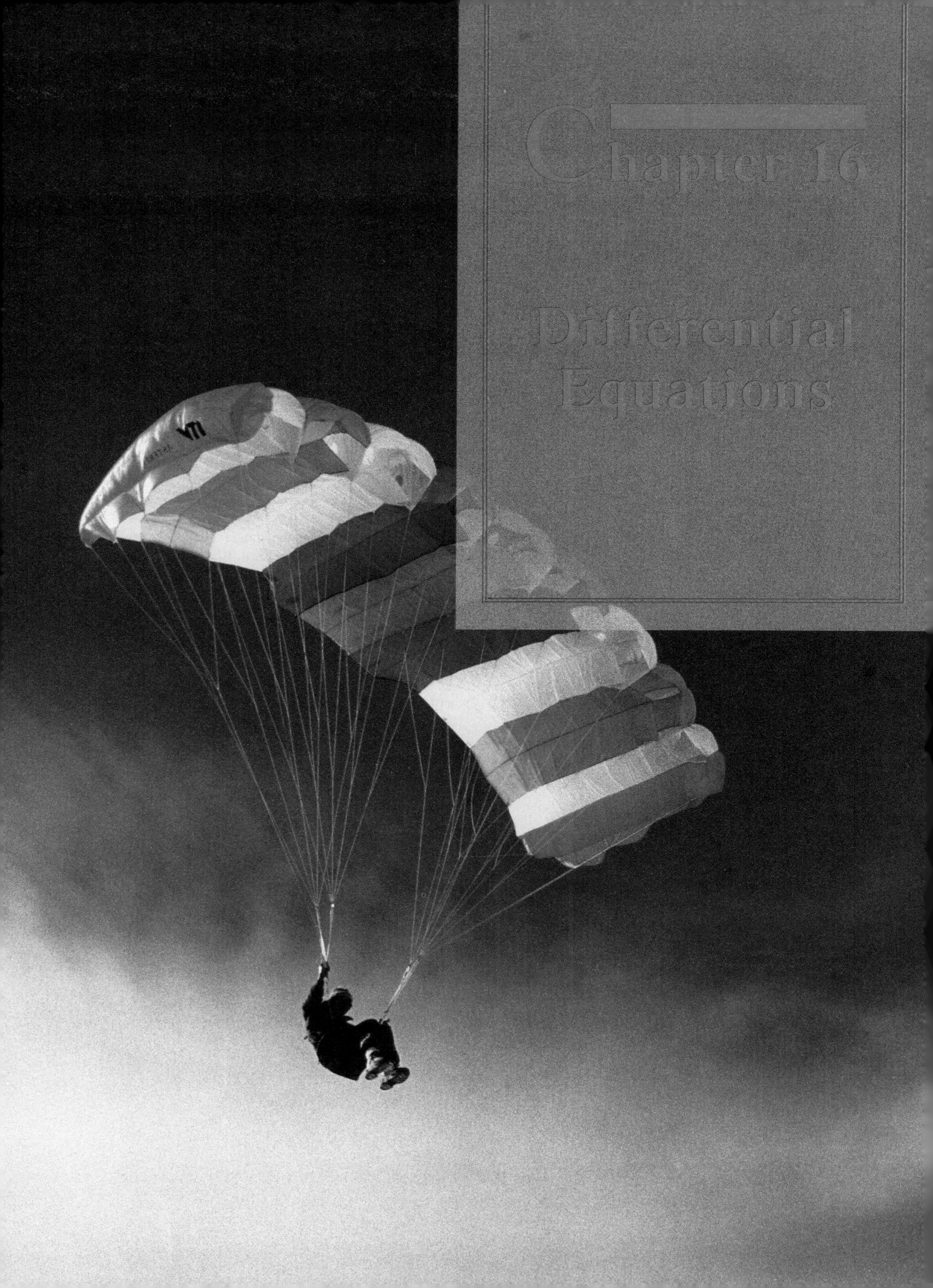

Definitions and Basic Concepts

Type and Order • General and Particular Solutions

Type and Order

Several times in the text, we have identified physical phenomena that can be described by differential equations. For example, we saw that problems involving radioactive decay, population growth, chemical reactions, Newton's Law of Cooling, and gravitational force can be formulated in terms of differential equations. In this chapter, we review the terminology and techniques of differential equations discussed earlier in the text and introduce new terminology and techniques.

A **differential equation** is an equation involving a function and one or more of its derivatives. If the function has only one independent variable, the equation is called an **ordinary differential equation.** For instance,

$$\frac{d^2y}{dx^2} + 3\frac{dy}{dx} - 2y = 0$$

is an ordinary differential equation in which the dependent variable $y = f(x)$ is a twice-differentiable function of x. A differential equation involving a function of several variables and its partial derivatives is called a **partial differential equation.** In this chapter, the discussion is restricted to ordinary differential equations.

In addition to **type** (ordinary or partial), differential equations are classified by order. The **order** of a differential equation is determined by the highest-order derivative in the equation. For instance,

$$y' = y \qquad \text{First-order differential equation}$$

is a first-order differential equation and

$$\frac{d^2y}{dx^2} = 4y \qquad \text{Second-order differential equation}$$

is a second-order differential equation.

EXAMPLE 1   Classifying Differential Equations

Equation	Type	Order
a. $y''' + 4y = 2$	Ordinary	3
b. $\dfrac{d^2s}{dt^2} = -32$	Ordinary	2
c. $(y')^2 - 3y = e^x$	Ordinary	1
d. $\dfrac{\partial^2 u}{\partial x^2} + \dfrac{\partial^2 u}{\partial y^2} = 0$	Partial	2
e. $y - \sin y' = 0$	Ordinary	1

◄ *The fall of a parachutist can be modeled by a differential equation, as discussed in Section 16.6, Exercise 35.*

General and Particular Solutions

A function $y = f(x)$ is called a **solution** of a differential equation if the equation is satisfied when y and its derivatives are replaced by $f(x)$ and its derivatives, respectively. For example, differentiation and substitution would show that $y = e^{-2x}$ is a solution of the differential equation

$$y' + 2y = 0.$$

It can be shown that every solution of this differential equation is of the form $y = Ce^{-2x}$, where C is any real number, and we call $y = Ce^{-2x}$ the **general solution.** (Some differential equations have **singular solutions** that cannot be written as special cases of the general solution. However, we will not consider such solutions in this text.)

In Section 4.1, Example 8, you saw that the second-order differential equation $s''(t) = -32$ has the general solution

$$s(t) = -16t^2 + C_1 t + C_2$$

which contains two arbitrary constants. It can be shown that a differential equation of order n has a general solution with n arbitrary constants.

EXAMPLE 2   Verifying Solutions

Determine whether or not the given functions are solutions of the differential equation $y'' - y = 0$.

a. $y = \sin x$ **b.** $y = e^{2x}$ **c.** $y = 4e^{-x}$ **d.** $y = Ce^x$

Solution

a. Because $y = \sin x$, $y' = \cos x$, and $y'' = -\sin x$, it follows that

$$y'' - y = -\sin x - \sin x = -2\sin x \neq 0.$$

Hence, $y = \sin x$ *is not* a solution.

b. Because $y = e^{2x}$, $y' = 2e^{2x}$, and $y'' = 4e^{2x}$, it follows that

$$y'' - y = 4e^{2x} - e^{2x} = 3e^{2x} \neq 0.$$

Hence, $y = e^{2x}$ *is not* a solution.

c. Because $y = 4e^{-x}$, $y' = -4e^{-x}$, and $y'' = 4e^{-x}$, it follows that

$$y'' - y = 4e^{-x} - 4e^{-x} = 0.$$

Hence, $y = 4e^{-x}$ *is* a solution.

d. Because $y = Ce^x$, $y' = Ce^x$, and $y'' = Ce^x$, it follows that

$$y'' - y = Ce^x - Ce^x = 0.$$

Hence, $y = Ce^x$ *is* a solution for any value of C. ▬

Later in this chapter, you will see that the general solution of the differential equation in Example 2 is $y = C_1 e^x + C_2 e^{-x}$. A **particular solution** of a differential equation is any solution that is obtained by assigning specific values to the constants in the general solution.

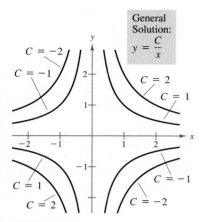

FIGURE 16.1

Solution curves for $xy' + y = 0$.

Geometrically, the general solution of a first-order differential equation represents a family of curves known as **solution curves,** one for each value assigned to the arbitrary constant. For instance, you can easily verify that every function of the form $y = C/x$ is a solution of the differential equation $xy' + y = 0$. Figure 16.1 shows some of the solution curves corresponding to different values of C.

Particular solutions of a differential equation are obtained from **initial conditions** that give the value of the dependent variable or one of its derivatives for a particular value of the independent variable. The term "initial condition" stems from the fact that, often in problems involving time, the value of the dependent variable or one of its derivatives is known at the *initial* time $t = 0$. For instance, the second-order differential equation $s''(t) = -32$, which has the general solution

$$s(t) = -16t^2 + C_1 t + C_2 \qquad \text{General solution}$$

might have the following initial conditions.

$$s(0) = 80, \qquad s'(0) = 64 \qquad \text{Initial conditions}$$

In this case, the initial conditions yield the particular solution

$$s(t) = -16t^2 + 64t + 80. \qquad \text{Particular solution}$$

EXAMPLE 3   Finding a Particular Solution

For the differential equation

$$xy' - 3y = 0$$

verify that $y = Cx^3$ is a solution and find the particular solution determined by the initial condition $y = 2$ when $x = -3$.

Solution   You know that $y = Cx^3$ is a solution because $y' = 3Cx^2$ and

$$xy' - 3y = x(3Cx^2) - 3(Cx^3) = 0.$$

Furthermore, the initial condition $y = 2$ when $x = -3$ yields

$$y = Cx^3 \quad \rightarrow \quad 2 = C(-3)^3 \quad \rightarrow \quad C = -\frac{2}{27}$$

and you can conclude that the particular solution is $y = -2x^3/27$. ∎

REMARK   To determine a particular solution, the number of initial conditions must match the number of constants in the general solution.

In the remainder of this chapter, you will study procedures for finding the general solutions of several classes of differential equations. Each section will include practical applications of that particular type of differential equation. The discussion focuses mainly on first- and second-order equations and linear equations with constant coefficients. By a **linear differential equation with constant coefficients** $a_0, a_1, a_2, \ldots, a_n$, we mean an equation of the form

$$a_n y^{(n)} + a_{n-1} y^{(n-1)} + \cdots + a_2 y'' + a_1 y' + a_0 y = F(x)$$

which is linear in y and its derivatives.

EXERCISES for Section 16.1

In Exercises 1–12, classify the differential equation according to type and order.

1. $\dfrac{dy}{dx} + 3xy = x^2$

2. $y'' + 2y' + y = 1$

3. $\dfrac{d^2x}{dt^2} + 2\dfrac{dx}{dt} - 4x = e^t$

4. $\dfrac{d^2u}{dt^2} + \dfrac{du}{dt} = \sec t$

5. $y^{(4)} + 3(y')^2 - 4y = 0$

6. $x^2y'' + 3xy' = 0$

7. $(y'')^2 + 3y' - 4y = 0$

8. $\dfrac{\partial u}{\partial t} = C^2\dfrac{\partial^2 u}{\partial x^2}$

9. $\dfrac{\partial u}{\partial t} + \dfrac{\partial u}{\partial y} = 2u$

10. $\dfrac{\partial^2 u}{\partial x\,\partial y} = \dfrac{\partial u}{\partial y}$

11. $\dfrac{d^2y}{dx^2} = \sqrt{1 + \left(\dfrac{dy}{dx}\right)^2}$

12. $\sqrt{\dfrac{d^2y}{dx^2}} = \dfrac{dy}{dx}$

In Exercises 13–18, verify the given solution of the differential equation.

Solution	Differential equation
13. $y = Ce^{4x}$	$\dfrac{dy}{dx} = 4y$
14. $x^2 + y^2 = Cy$	$y' = \dfrac{2xy}{x^2 - y^2}$
15. $y = C_1\cos x + C_2\sin x$	$y'' + y = 0$
16. $y = C_1e^{-x}\cos x + C_2e^{-x}\sin x$	$y'' + 2y' + 2y = 0$
17. $u = e^{-t}\sin bx$	$b^2\dfrac{\partial u}{\partial t} = \dfrac{\partial^2 u}{\partial x^2}$
18. $u = \dfrac{y}{x^2 + y^2}$	$\dfrac{\partial^2 u}{\partial x^2} + \dfrac{\partial^2 u}{\partial y^2} = 0$

In Exercises 19–24, determine whether the function is a solution of the differential equation

$$y^{(4)} - 16y = 0.$$

19. $y = 3\cos x$ **20.** $y = 3\cos 2x$

21. $y = e^{-2x}$ **22.** $y = 5\ln x$

23. $y = C_1e^{2x} + C_2e^{-2x} + C_3\sin 2x + C_4\cos 2x$

24. $y = 5e^{-2x} + 3\cos 2x$

In Exercises 25–30, determine whether the function is a solution of the differential equation

$$x\dfrac{\partial u}{\partial x} - y\dfrac{\partial u}{\partial y} = 0.$$

25. $u = e^{x+y}$ **26.** $u = 5$

27. $u = x^2y^2$ **28.** $u = \sin xy$

29. $u = (xy)^n$ **30.** $u = x^2 + y^2$

31. It is known that $y = Ce^{kx}$ is a solution of the differential equation

$$\dfrac{dy}{dx} = 0.07y.$$

Is it possible to determine C or k from the information given? If so, find its value.

32. It is known that $y = A\sin\omega t$ is a solution of the differential equation

$$\dfrac{d^2y}{dt^2} + 16y = 0.$$

Find the value of ω.

In Exercises 33 and 34, some of the curves corresponding to different values of C in the general solution of the differential equation are given. Find the particular solution that passes through the point indicated on each graph.

Solution	Differential equation
33. $y^2 = Cx^3$	$2xy' - 3y = 0$
34. $2x^2 - y^2 = C$	$yy' - 2x = 0$

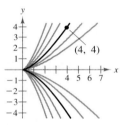

FIGURE FOR 33

FIGURE FOR 34

In Exercises 35 and 36, the general solution of the differential equation is given. Sketch the graph of the particular solutions for the given values of C.

35. $4yy' - x = 0$
$2y^2 - x^2 = C$
$C = 0,\ C = \pm 1,\ C = \pm 4$

36. $yy' + x = 0$
$x^2 + y^2 = C$
$C = 0,\ C = 1,\ C = 4$

In Exercises 37–42, verify that the general solutions satisfy the differential equation. Then find the particular solution that satisfies the given initial condition.

37. $y = Ce^{-2x}$
$y' + 2y = 0$
$y = 3$ when $x = 0$

38. $2x^2 + 3y^2 = C$
$2x + 3yy' = 0$
$y = 2$ when $x = 1$

39. $y = C_1 \sin 3x + C_2 \cos 3x$
$y'' + 9y = 0$

$y = 2$ and $y' = 1$ when $x = \dfrac{\pi}{6}$

40. $y = C_1 + C_2 \ln x$
$xy'' + y' = 0$
$y = 0$ and $y' = \frac{1}{2}$ when $x = 2$

41. $y = C_1 x + C_2 x^3$
$x^2 y'' - 3xy' + 3y = 0$
$y = 0$ and $y' = 4$ when $x = 2$

42. $y = e^{2x/3}(C_1 + C_2 x)$
$9y'' - 12y' + 4y = 0$
$y = 4$ when $x = 0$, and $y = 0$ when $x = 3$

In Exercises 43–50, use integration to find a general solution of the differential equation.

43. $\dfrac{dy}{dx} = 3x^2$
44. $\dfrac{dy}{dx} = \dfrac{1}{1 + x^2}$

45. $\dfrac{dy}{dx} = \dfrac{x - 2}{x}$
46. $\dfrac{dy}{dx} = x \cos x$

47. $\dfrac{dy}{dx} = e^x \sin 2x$
48. $\dfrac{dy}{dx} = \tan^2 x$

49. $\dfrac{dy}{dx} = x\sqrt{x - 3}$
50. $\dfrac{dy}{dx} = xe^x$

51. *Population Growth* The limiting capacity of the habitat for a particular wildlife herd is L. The growth rate dN/dt of the herd is proportional to the unused opportunities for growth, as described by the differential equation

$$\frac{dN}{dt} = k(L - N).$$

The general solution of this differential equation is

$N = L - Ce^{-kt}$.

Suppose 100 animals are released into a tract of land that can support 750 of these animals. After 2 years, the herd has grown to 160 animals.

a. Find the population function in terms of the time t in years.

b. Verify that the function from part a is a solution of the differential equation.

c. Sketch the graph of this population function.

52. *Investment* The rate of growth of an investment is proportional to the amount of the investment at any time t. That is,

$$\frac{dA}{dt} = kA.$$

a. Show that $A = Ce^{kt}$ is a solution of this differential equation.

b. Find the particular solution of this differential equation if the initial investment is \$1000, and 10 years later the balance is \$3320.12.

Direction Fields **Consider the first-order differential equation**

$$\frac{dy}{dx} = F(x, y).$$

The function F assigns to each point (x_0, y_0) in its domain a direction (slope) of the solution to the differential equation. To visualize this, draw a short mark at each of several points to indicate the direction associated with each point and obtain a direction field. This field can be used to approximate graphically the solutions of the differential equation. In Exercises 53–56, use the given differential equation and direction field to answer questions about the solutions of the differential equation.

53. $\dfrac{dy}{dx} = x$

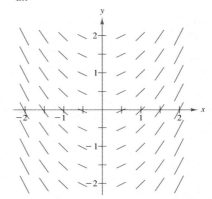

a. Sketch several solution curves for the differential equation on the direction field.

b. Use integration to find the solution of the differential equation. Compare the result with the sketches from part a.

54. $\dfrac{dy}{dx} = -\dfrac{x}{y}$

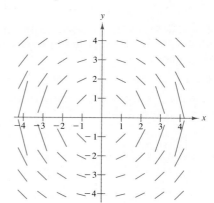

a. Sketch several solution curves for the differential equation on the direction field.

b. If possible, identify the solutions. Then verify your guesses by differentiation.

55. $\dfrac{dy}{dx} = 4 - y$

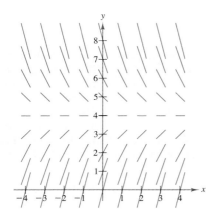

a. Sketch several solution curves for the differential equation on the direction field.

b. What information (if any) can you determine about the solution as $x \to \infty$?

56. $\dfrac{dy}{dx} = 0.25y(4 - y)$

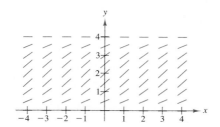

a. Sketch several solution curves for the differential equation on the direction field.

b. What information (if any) can you determine about the solution as $x \to \infty$?

c. What information (if any) can you determine about the solution as $x \to -\infty$?

True or False In Exercises 57 and 58, determine whether the statement is true or false. If it is false, explain why or give an example that shows it is false.

57. For any value of C, $y = (x - C)^3$ is a solution of $y' = 3y^{2/3}$.

58. If $y = f(x)$ is a solution of a first-order differential equation, then $y = f(x) + C$ is also a solution.

CAREER INTERVIEW

George M. Drakeley, III
Electrical Systems Branch Head
Submarine Program Office
Naval Sea Systems Command
Arlington, VA 05250

My organization helps the navy buy, maintain, and improve its ships. Among our responsibilities is the problem of noise generation; we devise ways of minimizing the possibility of detection by other vessels underwater.

It is central to the analysis of acoustics to understand the vibration patterns of different machinery and the amount of time a machine can operate before its vibrations begin to increase. (A new car may run smoothly, but over time the parts will wear, resulting in larger vibrations and more noise.)

Using second order differential equations to model equipment behavior, we analyze the generation of acoustic energy and its transmission into the water outside. At present, we are evaluating an improved, quieter system of magnetic bearings for various rotating machinery.

Separation of Variables in First-Order Equations

16.2 Separation of Variables • Homogeneous Differential Equations • Applications

Separation of Variables

In this section, you will study techniques for solving differential equations that can be written in the form

$$M(x) + N(y)\frac{dy}{dx} = 0$$

where M is a continuous function of x alone and N is a continuous function of y alone. For this type of equation, all x terms can be collected with dx and all y terms with dy, and a solution can be obtained by integration. Such equations are said to be **separable,** and the solution procedure is called **separation of variables.**

EXAMPLE 1 Separation of Variables

Find the general solution of

$$(x^2 + 4)\frac{dy}{dx} = xy.$$

Solution To begin, note that $y = 0$ is a solution. To find other solutions, assume $y \neq 0$ and separate variables as follows.

$$(x^2 + 4)\,dy = xy\,dx \qquad \text{Differential form}$$

$$\frac{dy}{y} = \frac{x}{x^2 + 4}\,dx \qquad \text{Separate variables}$$

Now, integrate to obtain

$$\int \frac{dy}{y} = \int \frac{x}{x^2 + 4}\,dx \qquad \text{Integrate}$$

$$\ln |y| = \frac{1}{2}\ln(x^2 + 4) + C_1$$

$$= \ln \sqrt{x^2 + 4} + C_1$$

$$|y| = e^{C_1}\sqrt{x^2 + 4}$$

$$y = \pm e^{C_1}\sqrt{x^2 + 4}.$$

Because $y = 0$ is also a solution, you can write the general solution as

$$y = C\sqrt{x^2 + 4}. \qquad \text{General solution}$$

REMARK We encourage you to *check your solutions* throughout this chapter. For instance, in Example 1 you can check the solution $y = C\sqrt{x^2 + 4}$ by differentiating and substituting into the original equation.

In some cases, it is not feasible to write the general solution in the explicit form $y = f(x)$. The next example is a case in point; implicit differentiation can be used to verify this solution.

EXAMPLE 2   Finding a Particular Solution

Given the initial condition $y(0) = 1$, find the particular solution of the equation

$$xy\,dx + e^{-x^2}(y^2 - 1)\,dy = 0.$$

Solution   Note that $y = 0$ is a solution of the differential equation—but this solution does not satisfy the initial condition. Hence, you can assume $y \neq 0$. To separate variables, you must rid the first term of y and the second of e^{-x^2}. Thus, you should multiply by e^{x^2}/y and obtain the following.

$$\left(\frac{e^{x^2}}{y}\right)xy\,dx + \left(\frac{e^{x^2}}{y}\right)e^{-x^2}(y^2 - 1)\,dy = 0, \qquad y \neq 0$$

$$xe^{x^2}\,dx + \left(y - \frac{1}{y}\right)dy = 0$$

$$\int xe^{x^2}\,dx + \int \left(y - \frac{1}{y}\right)dy = 0$$

$$\frac{1}{2}e^{x^2} + \frac{y^2}{2} - \ln|y| = C_1$$

$$e^{x^2} + y^2 - \ln y^2 = 2C_1 = C$$

From the given initial condition, use the fact that $y = 1$ when $x = 0$ to obtain $1 + 1 + 0 = 2 = C$. Thus, the particular solution has the implicit form $e^{x^2} + y^2 - \ln y^2 = 2$.

EXAMPLE 3   Finding a Particular Solution Curve

Find the equation of the curve that passes through the point $(1, 3)$ and has a slope of y/x^2 at the point (x, y), as shown in Figure 16.2.

Solution   Because the slope of the curve is given by y/x^2, you have

$$\frac{dy}{dx} = \frac{y}{x^2}$$

with the initial condition $y(1) = 3$. Separating variables and integrating produces

$$\int \frac{dy}{y} = \int \frac{dx}{x^2}, \qquad y \neq 0$$

$$\ln|y| = -\frac{1}{x} + C_1$$

$$y = e^{-(1/x)+C_1} = Ce^{-1/x}.$$

Because $y = 3$ when $x = 1$, it follows that $3 = Ce^{-1}$ and $C = 3e$. Therefore, the equation of the specified curve is

$$y = (3e)e^{-1/x} = 3e^{(x-1)/x}, \qquad x > 0.$$

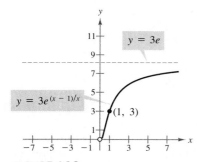

FIGURE 16.2

Homogeneous Differential Equations

Some differential equations that are not separable in x and y can be made separable by a change of variables. This is true for differential equations of the form $y' = f(x, y)$, where f is a **homogeneous function.**

The function given by $z = f(x, y)$ is said to be **homogeneous of degree n** if

$$f(tx, ty) = t^n f(x, y)$$

where n is a real number.

EXAMPLE 4   Verifying Homogeneous Functions

a. $f(x, y) = x^2y - 4x^3 + 3xy^2$ is a homogeneous function of degree 3 because

$$
\begin{aligned}
f(tx, ty) &= (tx)^2(ty) - 4(tx)^3 + 3(tx)(ty)^2 \\
&= t^3(x^2y) - t^3(4x^3) + t^3(3xy^2) \\
&= t^3(x^2y - 4x^3 + 3xy^2) \\
&= t^3 f(x, y).
\end{aligned}
$$

b. $f(x, y) = xe^{x/y} + y\sin(y/x)$ is a homogeneous function of degree 1 because

$$f(tx, ty) = txe^{tx/ty} + ty\sin\frac{ty}{tx} = t\left(xe^{x/y} + y\sin\frac{y}{x}\right) = tf(x, y).$$

c. $f(x, y) = x + y^2$ is not a homogeneous function because

$$f(tx, ty) = tx + t^2y^2 = t(x + ty^2) \neq t^n(x + y^2).$$

d. $f(x, y) = x/y$ is a homogeneous function of degree 0 because

$$f(tx, ty) = \frac{tx}{ty} = t^0\frac{x}{y}.$$

Definition of Homogeneous Differential Equation

A **homogeneous differential equation** is an equation of the form

$$M(x, y)\, dx + N(x, y)\, dy = 0$$

where M and N are homogeneous functions of the same degree.

EXAMPLE 5   Homogeneous Differential Equations

a. $(x^2 + xy)\, dx + y^2\, dy = 0$ is homogeneous of degree 2.
b. $(x^2 + 1)\, dx + y^2\, dy = 0$ is *not* a homogeneous differential equation.

To solve a homogeneous differential equation by the method of separation of variables, we use the following change of variables theorem.

THEOREM 16.1   Change of Variables for Homogeneous Equations

If $M(x, y)\,dx + N(x, y)\,dy = 0$ is homogeneous, then it can be transformed into a differential equation whose variables are separable by the substitution

$$y = vx$$

where v is a differentiable function of x.

EXAMPLE 6   Solving a Homogeneous Differential Equation

Find the general solution of $(x^2 - y^2)\,dx + 3xy\,dy = 0$.

Solution   Because $(x^2 - y^2)$ and $3xy$ are both homogeneous of degree 2, let $y = vx$ to obtain $dy = x\,dv + v\,dx$. Then, by substitution, you have

$$(x^2 - v^2 x^2)\,dx + 3x(vx)\overbrace{(x\,dv + v\,dx)}^{dy} = 0$$
$$(x^2 + 2v^2 x^2)\,dx + 3x^3 v\,dv = 0$$
$$x^2(1 + 2v^2)\,dx + x^2(3vx)\,dv = 0.$$

Dividing by x^2 and separating variables produces

$$(1 + 2v^2)\,dx = -3vx\,dv$$
$$\int \frac{dx}{x} = \int \frac{-3v}{1 + 2v^2}\,dv$$
$$\ln|x| = -\frac{3}{4}\ln(1 + 2v^2) + C_1$$
$$4\ln|x| = -3\ln(1 + 2v^2) + \ln|C|$$
$$\ln x^4 = \ln\left|C(1 + 2v^2)^{-3}\right|$$
$$x^4 = C(1 + 2v^2)^{-3}.$$

Substituting for v produces the following general solution.

$$x^4 = C\left[1 + 2\left(\frac{y}{x}\right)^2\right]^{-3}$$
$$\left(1 + 2\frac{y^2}{x^2}\right)^3 x^4 = C$$
$$(x^2 + 2y^2)^3 = Cx^2 \qquad \text{General solution}$$

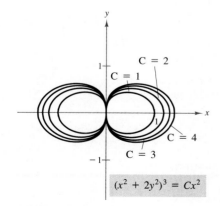

C = 2
C = 1
C = 4
C = 3

$(x^2 + 2y^2)^3 = Cx^2$

FIGURE 16.3

TECHNOLOGY   If you have access to a graphing utility, try using it to graph several of the solutions in Example 6. For instance, Figure 16.3 shows the graphs of $(x^2 + 2y^2)^3 = Cx^2$ for $C = 1, 2, 3,$ and 4.

Applications

EXAMPLE 7   Application to Food Preservation

In the preservation of food, cane sugar is broken down (inverted) into two simpler sugars: glucose and fructose. In dilute solutions, the inversion rate is proportional to the concentration $y(t)$ of unaltered sugar. If the concentration is $\frac{1}{50}$ when $t = 0$ and $\frac{1}{200}$ after 3 hours, find the concentrations of unaltered sugar after 6 hours and after 12 hours.

Solution   Because the rate of inversion is proportional to $y(t)$, you can write the following differential equation.

$$\frac{dy}{dt} = ky$$

Separating the variables and integrating produces

$$\int \frac{1}{y}\,dy = \int k\,dt$$
$$\ln|y| = kt + C_1$$
$$y = Ce^{kt}.$$

From the given conditions, you can obtain the following.

$$y(0) = \frac{1}{50} \quad \rightarrow \quad C = \frac{1}{50}$$

$$y(3) = \frac{1}{200} \quad \rightarrow \quad \frac{1}{200} = \left(\frac{1}{50}\right)e^{3k} \quad \rightarrow \quad k = -\frac{\ln 4}{3}$$

Therefore, the concentration of unaltered sugar is given by

$$y(t) = \frac{1}{50}e^{-(\ln 4)t/3} = \frac{1}{50}(4^{-t/3}).$$

When $t = 6$ and $t = 12$, you have the following concentrations of unaltered sugar.

$$y(6) = \frac{1}{50}(4^{-2}) = \frac{1}{800} \qquad \text{After 6 hours}$$

$$y(12) = \frac{1}{50}(4^{-4}) = \frac{1}{12,800} \qquad \text{After 12 hours}$$

(See Figure 16.4)

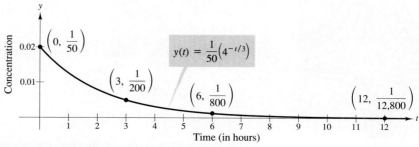

FIGURE 16.4

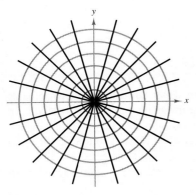

FIGURE 16.5

Each line $y = Kx$ is an orthogonal trajectory to the family of circles.

A common problem in electrostatics, thermodynamics, and hydrodynamics involves finding a family of curves, each of which is orthogonal to all members of a given family of curves. For example, Figure 16.5 shows a family of circles

$$x^2 + y^2 = C \qquad \text{Family of circles}$$

each of which intersects the lines in the family

$$y = Kx \qquad \text{Family of lines}$$

at right angles. Two such families of curves are said to be **mutually orthogonal,** and each curve in one of the families is called an **orthogonal trajectory** of the other family. In electrostatics, lines of force are orthogonal to the *equipotential curves.* In thermodynamics, the flow of heat across a plane surface is orthogonal to the *isothermal curves.* In hydrodynamics, the flow (stream) lines are orthogonal trajectories of the *velocity potential curves.*

EXAMPLE 8   Finding Orthogonal Trajectories

Describe the orthogonal trajectories for the family of curves given by $y = C/x$ for $C \neq 0$. Sketch several members of each family.

Solution   First, solve the given equation for C and write $xy = C$. Then, by differentiating implicitly with respect to x, you obtain the differential equation

$$xy' + y = 0 \qquad \text{Differential equation}$$

$$x\frac{dy}{dx} = -y$$

$$\frac{dy}{dx} = -\frac{y}{x}. \qquad \text{Slope of given family}$$

Because y' represents the slope of the given family of curves at (x, y), it follows that the orthogonal family has the negative reciprocal slope x/y, and we write

$$\frac{dy}{dx} = \frac{x}{y}. \qquad \text{Slope of orthogonal family}$$

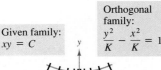

Now you can find the orthogonal family by separating variables and integrating.

$$\int y\,dy = \int x\,dx$$

$$\frac{y^2}{2} = \frac{x^2}{2} + C_1$$

Therefore, each orthogonal trajectory is a hyperbola given by

$$\frac{y^2}{K} - \frac{x^2}{K} = 1$$

$$2C_1 = K \neq 0.$$

The centers are at the origin, and the transverse axes are vertical for $K > 0$ and horizontal for $K < 0$. Several trajectories are shown in Figure 16.6.

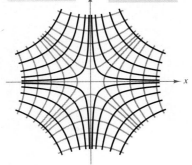

FIGURE 16.6

EXERCISES for Section 16.2

In Exercises 1–10, find the general solution of the differential equation.

1. $\dfrac{dy}{dx} = \dfrac{x}{y}$

2. $\dfrac{dy}{dx} = \dfrac{x^2 + 2}{3y^2}$

3. $\dfrac{dr}{ds} = 0.05r$

4. $\dfrac{dr}{ds} = 0.05s$

5. $(2 + x)y' = 3y$

6. $xy' = y$

7. $yy' = \sin x$

8. $\sqrt{1 - 4x^2}\, y' = 1$

9. $y \ln x - xy' = 0$

10. $yy' - 2xe^x = 0$

In Exercises 11–20, find the particular solution of the differential equation that satisfies the initial condition.

Differential equation	Initial condition
11. $yy' - e^x = 0$	$y(0) = 4$
12. $\sqrt{x} + \sqrt{y}\, y' = 0$	$y(1) = 4$
13. $y(x + 1) + y' = 0$	$y(-2) = 1$
14. $xyy' - \ln x = 0$	$y(1) = 0$
15. $(1 + x^2)y' - (1 + y^2) = 0$	$y(0) = \sqrt{3}$
16. $\sqrt{1 - x^2}\, y' - \sqrt{1 - y^2} = 0$	$y(0) = 1$
17. $\dfrac{du}{dv} = uv \sin v^2$	$u(0) = 1$
18. $\dfrac{dr}{ds} = e^{r+s}$	$r(1) = 0$
19. $dP - kP\, dt = 0$	$P(0) = P_0$
20. $dT + k(T - 70)\, dt = 0$	$T(0) = 140$

In Exercises 21 and 22, find an equation for the curve that passes through the given point and has the specified slope.

Point	Slope
21. $(1, 1)$	$y' = -\dfrac{9x}{16y}$
22. $(8, 2)$	$y' = \dfrac{2y}{3x}$

In Exercises 23 and 24, find all functions f having the specified property.

23. The tangent to the graph of f at the point (x, y) intersects the x-axis at $(x + 2, 0)$.

24. All tangents to the graph of f pass through the origin.

In Exercises 25 and 26, sketch a few solutions of the differential equation on the given direction field and then find the general solution analytically.

25. $\dfrac{dy}{dx} = 0.5y$

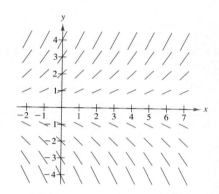

26. $\dfrac{dy}{dx} = 1 + y^2$

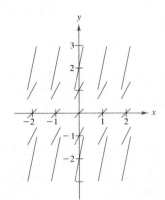

In Exercises 27–32, determine whether the function is homogeneous, and if so, determine its degree.

27. $f(x, y) = x^3 - 4xy^2 + y^3$

28. $f(x, y) = \dfrac{xy}{\sqrt{x^2 + y^2}}$

29. $f(x, y) = 2 \ln xy$

30. $f(x, y) = \tan(x + y)$

31. $f(x, y) = 2 \ln \dfrac{x}{y}$

32. $f(x, y) = \tan \dfrac{y}{x}$

In Exercises 33–38, solve the homogeneous differential equation.

33. $y' = \dfrac{x + y}{2x}$

34. $y' = \dfrac{2x + y}{y}$

35. $y' = \dfrac{x - y}{x + y}$

36. $y' = \dfrac{x^2 + y^2}{2xy}$

37. $y' = \dfrac{xy}{x^2 - y^2}$

38. $y' = \dfrac{3x + 2y}{x}$

In Exercises 39–42, find the particular solution that satisfies the given initial condition.

Differential equation	Initial condition
39. $x\,dy - (2xe^{-y/x} + y)\,dx = 0$	$y(1) = 0$
40. $-y^2\,dx + x(x + y)\,dy = 0$	$y(1) = 1$
41. $\left(x\sec\dfrac{y}{x} + y\right)dx - x\,dy = 0$	$y(1) = 0$
42. $\left(y - \sqrt{x^2 - y^2}\right)dx - x\,dy = 0$	$y(1) = 0$

43. *Investment Growth* The amount A of an investment P increases at a rate proportional to A at any instant of time t.
  a. Find an equation for A as a function of t.
  b. The initial investment is \$1000 and the rate is 11 percent. Find the balance after 10 years.
  c. Find the time necessary to double the investment if the rate is 11 percent.

44. *Population Growth* The rate of growth of a population of fruit flies is proportional to the size of the population at any instant. If there were 180 flies after the second day of the experiment and 300 after the fourth day, how many flies were there in the original population?

45. *Radioactive Decay* The rate of decomposition of radioactive radium is proportional to the amount present at a given instant. Find the percentage of a present amount that remains after 25 years, if the half-life of radioactive radium is 1600 years.

46. *Chemical Reaction* In a chemical reaction, a certain compound changes into another compound at a rate proportional to the unchanged amount. If initially there is 20 grams of the original compound, and there is 16 grams after 1 hour, when will 75 percent of the compound be changed?

47. *Newton's Law of Cooling* Newton's Law of Cooling states that the rate of change in the temperature of an object is proportional to the difference between its temperature and the temperature of the surrounding air. Suppose a room is kept at a constant temperature of 70°, and an object cools from 350° to 150° in 45 minutes. How long will it take for the object to cool to a temperature of 80°?

REMARK To see how Newton's Law of Cooling is applied to the question "How long should I leave a thermometer in my mouth to take my body temperature accurately?", read the article "Fever" by Elmo Moore and Charles M. Biles in the *UMAP Journal*, Volume 4, Number 3, 1983.

*$\boxed{\text{C}}$ **48.** *Radio Reception* In hilly areas, radio reception may be poor. Consider a situation where an FM transmitter is located at the point $(-1, 1)$ behind a hill modeled by the graph of $y = x - x^2$, and a radio receiver is on the opposite side of the hill. (Assume the x-axis is ground level at the base of the hill.)
  a. What is the closest the radio can be to the hill so that reception is unobstructed?
  b. Write the closest position x of the radio as a function of h if the transmitter is located at $(-1, h)$.
  c. Use a graphing utility to graph the function from part b. Determine the vertical asymptote of the function and interpret the result.

$\boxed{\text{C}}$ **49.** *Sales Increase* Let S (in thousands of units) represent the sales of a new product, let L (in thousands of units) represent the maximum level of sales, and let t represent the time (in months). The rate of change of S with respect to t varies jointly as the product of S and $L - S$.
  a. Write and solve the differential equation for this sales model if $L = 100$, $S = 10$ when $t = 0$, and $S = 20$ when $t = 1$.
  b. At what time is the growth in sales increasing most rapidly?
  c. Use a graphing utility to graph the sales function.
  d. The figure shows the direction field for the differential equation. Sketch the solution of part a on the direction field.
  e. If the estimated maximum level of sales is correct, use the direction field to describe the shape of the solution curves for sales if at some period of time sales exceed L.

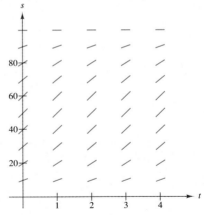

FIGURE FOR 49

$\boxed{\text{C}}$ **50.** *Learning Theory* The rate of change in the proportion P of correct responses after n trials varies jointly as P and $L - P$, where L is the limiting proportion of correct responses.
  a. Write and solve the differential equation for this learning theory model.
  b. Write P as a function of n if $L = 1.00$, $P = 0.25$ when $n = 0$, and $P = 0.60$ when $n = 10$. Use a graphing utility to graph the solution.
  c. Are there any inflection points on the graph from part b? What (if any exist) do they mean in the context of this model?

*A $\boxed{\text{C}}$ indicates an exercise in which you are instructed to use graphing technology or a symbolic computer algebra system. The solutions of other exercises may also be facilitated by appropriate technology.

51. *Sailing*   Ignoring resistance, a sailboat starting from rest accelerates (dv/dt) at a rate proportional to the difference between the velocities of the wind and the boat.

   a. Write the velocity as a function of time if the wind is blowing at 20 knots, and after 1 minute the boat is moving at 5 knots.

   b. Use the result of part a to write the distance traveled by the boat as a function of time.

52. *Boating*   If s gives the position of an object moving in a straight line, the velocity and acceleration are given by

$$v = \frac{ds}{dt}, \qquad a = \frac{dv}{dt} = \frac{ds}{dt}\frac{dv}{ds} = v\frac{dv}{ds}.$$

Suppose that a boat weighing 640 pounds has a motor that exerts a force of 60 pounds. If the resistance (in pounds) to the motion of the boat is 3 times the velocity (in feet per second) and if the boat starts from rest, find its maximum speed. Use the equation

$$\text{Force} = F = ma = mv\frac{dv}{ds} = \frac{w}{32}v\frac{dv}{ds}$$

where w is the weight of the boat.

In Exercises 53–58, find the orthogonal trajectories of the given family and sketch several members of each family.

53. $x^2 + y^2 = C$ **54.** $2x^2 - y^2 = C$

55. $x^2 = Cy$ **56.** $y^2 = 2Cx$

57. $y^2 = Cx^3$ **58.** $y = Ce^x$

True or False   **In Exercises 59–62, determine whether the statement is true or false. If it is false, explain why or give an example that shows it is false.**

59. The differential equation $y' = xy - 2y + x - 2$ can be written in separated variables form.

60. The differential equation $y' = \sin(x + y) + \sin(x - y)$ can be written in separated variables form.

61. The function $f(x, y) = x^2 + xy + 2$ is homogeneous.

62. The families $x^2 + y^2 = 2Cy$ and $x^2 + y^2 = 2Kx$ are mutually orthogonal.

63. *Weight Loss*   A person's weight depends on both the amount of calories consumed and the energy used. Moreover, the amount of energy used depends on a person's weight—the average amount of energy used by a person is 17.5 calories per pound per day. Thus, the more weight a person loses, the less energy the person uses (assuming that the person maintains a constant level of activity). An equation that can be used to model weight loss is

$$3500\left(\frac{dw}{dt}\right) = C - 17.5w$$

where w is the person's weight (in pounds), t is the time in days, and C is the constant daily calorie consumption.

a. Find the general solution of the differential equation.

b. Consider a person who weighs 180 pounds and begins a diet of 2500 calories per day. How long will it take the person to lose 10 pounds? How long will it take the person to lose 35 pounds?

c. The graph shows the person's weight as a function of time. What is the "limiting" weight of the person?

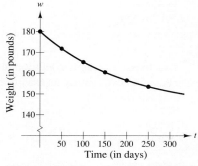

This exercise is based on the article "A Linear Diet Model" by Arthur C. Segal in the January, 1987 issue of the *College Mathematics Journal*.

Exact Differential Equations

In this section, you will study a method for solving the first-order differential equation

$$M(x, y)\,dx + N(x, y)\,dy = 0$$

for the special case in which this equation represents the exact differential of a function $z = f(x, y)$.

Definition of an Exact Differential Equation

The equation $M(x, y)\,dx + N(x, y)\,dy = 0$ is an **exact differential equation** if there exists a function f of two variables x and y having continuous partial derivatives such that

$$f_x(x, y) = M(x, y) \quad \text{and} \quad f_y(x, y) = N(x, y).$$

The general solution of the equation is $f(x, y) = C$.

From Section 14.3, you know that if f has continuous second partials, then

$$\frac{\partial M}{\partial y} = \frac{\partial^2 f}{\partial y\,\partial x} = \frac{\partial^2 f}{\partial x\,\partial y} = \frac{\partial N}{\partial x}.$$

This suggests the following test for exactness.

THEOREM 16.2   Test for Exactness

Let M and N have continuous partial derivatives on an open disc R. The differential equation $M(x, y)\,dx + N(x, y)\,dy = 0$ is exact if and only if

$$\frac{\partial M}{\partial y} = \frac{\partial N}{\partial x}.$$

Exactness is a fragile condition in the sense that seemingly minor alterations in an exact equation can destroy its exactness. This is demonstrated in the following example.

EXAMPLE 1   Testing for Exactness

a. The differential equation $(xy^2 + x)\,dx + yx^2\,dy = 0$ is exact because

$$\frac{\partial M}{\partial y} = \frac{\partial}{\partial y}[xy^2 + x] = 2xy \quad \text{and} \quad \frac{\partial N}{\partial x} = \frac{\partial}{\partial x}[yx^2] = 2xy.$$

But the equation $(y^2 + 1)\,dx + xy\,dy = 0$ is not exact, even though it is obtained by dividing both sides of the first equation by x.

b. The differential equation $\cos y\,dx + (y^2 - x\sin y)\,dy = 0$ is exact because

$$\frac{\partial M}{\partial y} = \frac{\partial}{\partial y}[\cos y] = -\sin y \quad \text{and} \quad \frac{\partial N}{\partial x} = \frac{\partial}{\partial x}[y^2 - x\sin y] = -\sin y.$$

But the equation $\cos y\,dx + (y^2 + x\sin y)\,dy = 0$ is not exact, even though it differs from the first equation only by a single sign.

REMARK Every differential equation of the form

$$M(x)\,dx + N(y)\,dy = 0$$

is exact. In other words, a separable variables equation is actually a special type of an exact equation.

Note that the test for exactness of $M(x, y)\,dx + N(x, y)\,dy = 0$ is the same as the test for determining whether $\mathbf{F}(x, y) = M(x, y)\mathbf{i} + N(x, y)\mathbf{j}$ is the gradient of a potential function (Theorem 15.1). This means that a general solution $f(x, y) = C$ to an exact differential equation can be found by the method used to find a potential function for a conservative vector field.

EXAMPLE 2   Solving an Exact Differential Equation

Solve the differential equation $(2xy - 3x^2)\,dx + (x^2 - 2y)\,dy = 0$.

Solution   The given differential equation is exact because

$$\frac{\partial M}{\partial y} = \frac{\partial}{\partial y}[2xy - 3x^2] = 2x = \frac{\partial N}{\partial x} = \frac{\partial}{\partial x}[x^2 - 2y].$$

The general solution, $f(x, y) = C$, is given by

$$f(x, y) = \int M(x, y)\,dx$$

$$= \int (2xy - 3x^2)\,dx = x^2y - x^3 + g(y).$$

In Section 15.1, you determined $g(y)$ by integrating $N(x, y)$ with respect to y and reconciling the two expressions for $f(x, y)$. An alternative method is to partially differentiate this version of $f(x, y)$ with respect to y and compare the result with $N(x, y)$. In other words,

$$f_y(x, y) = \frac{\partial}{\partial y}[x^2y - x^3 + g(y)] = x^2 + g'(y) = \overset{\overset{\textstyle N(x,\,y)}{}}{x^2 - 2y}.$$

$$\boxed{g'(y) = -2y}$$

Thus, $g'(y) = -2y$, and it follows that $g(y) = -y^2 + C_1$. Therefore,

$$f(x, y) = x^2y - x^3 - y^2 + C_1$$

and the general solution is $x^2y - x^3 - y^2 = C$. Figure 16.7 shows the solution curves that correspond to $C = 1, 10, 100,$ and 1000.

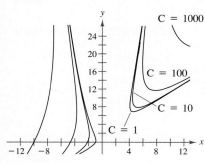

$C = 1000$

$C = 100$

$C = 10$

$C = 1$

FIGURE 16.7

EXAMPLE 3   Solving an Exact Differential Equation

Find the particular solution of

$$(\cos x - x\sin x + y^2)\,dx + 2xy\,dy = 0$$

that satisfies the initial condition $y = 1$ when $x = \pi$.

Solution   The differential equation is exact because

$$\overbrace{\frac{\partial}{\partial y}[\cos x - x\sin x + y^2]}^{\frac{\partial M}{\partial y}} = 2y = \overbrace{\frac{\partial}{\partial x}[2xy]}^{\frac{\partial N}{\partial x}}.$$

Because $N(x, y)$ is simpler than $M(x, y)$, it is better to begin by integrating $N(x, y)$.

$$f(x, y) = \int N(x, y)\,dy = \int 2xy\,dy = xy^2 + g(x)$$

$$f_x(x, y) = \frac{\partial}{\partial x}[xy^2 + g(x)] = y^2 + g'(x) = \overbrace{\cos x - x\sin x + y^2}^{M(x, y)}$$

$$\boxed{g'(x) = \cos x - x\sin x}$$

Thus, $g'(x) = \cos x - x\sin x$ and

$$g(x) = \int (\cos x - x\sin x)\,dx$$

$$= x\cos x + C_1$$

which implies $f(x, y) = xy^2 + x\cos x + C_1$, and the general solution is

$$xy^2 + x\cos x = C. \qquad \text{General solution}$$

Applying the given initial condition produces

$$\pi(1)^2 + \pi\cos\pi = C$$

which implies that $C = 0$. Hence, the particular solution is

$$xy^2 + x\cos x = 0. \qquad \text{Particular solution}$$

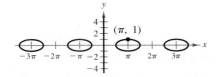

FIGURE 16.8

The graph of the particular solution is shown in Figure 16.8. Notice that the graph consists of two parts: the ovals are given by $y^2 + \cos x = 0$, and the y-axis is given by $x = 0$.

In Example 3, note that if $z = f(x, y) = xy^2 + x\cos x$, then the total differential of z is given by

$$dz = f_x(x, y)\,dx + f_y(x, y)\,dy$$

$$= (\cos x - x\sin x + y^2)\,dx + 2xy\,dy$$

$$= M(x, y)\,dx + N(x, y)\,dy.$$

In other words, $M\,dx + N\,dy = 0$ is called an *exact* differential equation because $M\,dx + N\,dy$ is exactly the differential of $f(x, y)$.

Integrating Factors

If the differential equation $M(x, y)\, dx + N(x, y)\, dy = 0$ is not exact, it may be possible to make it exact by multiplying by an appropriate factor $u(x, y)$, which is called an **integrating factor** for the differential equation.

EXAMPLE 4   Multiplying by an Integrating Factor

a. If the differential equation

$$2y\, dx + x\, dy = 0 \qquad \text{Not an exact equation}$$

is multiplied by the integrating factor $u(x, y) = x$, the resulting equation

$$2xy\, dx + x^2\, dy = 0 \qquad \text{Exact equation}$$

is exact—the left side is the total differential of $x^2 y$.

b. If the equation

$$y\, dx - x\, dy = 0 \qquad \text{Not an exact equation}$$

is multiplied by the integrating factor $u(x, y) = 1/y^2$, the resulting equation

$$\frac{1}{y}\, dx - \frac{x}{y^2}\, dy = 0 \qquad \text{Exact equation}$$

is exact—the left side is the total differential of x/y.

Finding an integrating factor can be difficult. However, there are two classes of differential equations whose integrating factors can be found routinely—namely, those that possess integrating factors that are functions of either x alone or y alone. The following theorem, which we present without proof, outlines a procedure for finding these two special categories of integrating factors.

THEOREM 16.3   Integrating Factors

Consider the differential equation $M(x, y)\, dx + N(x, y)\, dy = 0$.

1. If

$$\frac{1}{N(x, y)}[M_y(x, y) - N_x(x, y)] = h(x)$$

   is a function of x alone, then $e^{\int h(x)\, dx}$ is an integrating factor.

2. If

$$\frac{1}{M(x, y)}[N_x(x, y) - M_y(x, y)] = k(y)$$

   is a function of y alone, then $e^{\int k(y)\, dy}$ is an integrating factor.

REMARK   If either $h(x)$ or $k(y)$ is constant, Theorem 16.3 still applies. As an aid to remembering these formulas, note that the subtracted partial derivative identifies both the denominator and the variable for the integrating factor.

EXAMPLE 5   Finding an Integrating Factor

Solve the differential equation $(y^2 - x)\,dx + 2y\,dy = 0$.

Solution   The given equation is not exact because $M_y(x, y) = 2y$ and $N_x(x, y) = 0$. However, because

$$\frac{M_y(x, y) - N_x(x, y)}{N(x, y)} = \frac{2y - 0}{2y} = 1 = h(x)$$

it follows that $e^{\int h(x)\,dx} = e^{\int dx} = e^x$ is an integrating factor. Multiplying the given differential equation by e^x produces the exact differential equation

$$(y^2 e^x - xe^x)\,dx + 2ye^x\,dy = 0$$

whose solution is obtained as follows.

$$f(x, y) = \int N(x, y)\,dy = \int 2ye^x\,dy = y^2 e^x + g(x)$$

$$f_x(x, y) = y^2 e^x + g'(x) = \overbrace{y^2 e^x - xe^x}^{M(x, y)}$$

$$\boxed{g'(x) = -xe^x}$$

Therefore, $g'(x) = -xe^x$ and $g(x) = -xe^x + e^x + C_1$, which implies that

$$f(x, y) = y^2 e^x - xe^x + e^x + C_1.$$

The general solution is $y^2 e^x - xe^x + e^x = C$, or $y^2 - x + 1 = Ce^{-x}$.   ▬

In the next example, we show how a differential equation can help in sketching a force field given by $\mathbf{F}(x, y) = M(x, y)\mathbf{i} + N(x, y)\mathbf{j}$.

EXAMPLE 6   An Application to Force Fields

Sketch the force field given by

$$\mathbf{F}(x, y) = \frac{2y}{\sqrt{x^2 + y^2}}\mathbf{i} - \frac{y^2 - x}{\sqrt{x^2 - y^2}}\mathbf{j}$$

by finding and sketching the family of curves tangent to $\mathbf{F}$.

Solution   At the point (x, y) in the plane, the vector $\mathbf{F}(x, y)$ has a slope of

$$\frac{dy}{dx} = \frac{-(y^2 - x)/\sqrt{x^2 - y^2}}{2y/\sqrt{x^2 + y^2}} = \frac{-(y^2 - x)}{2y}$$

which, in differential form, is

$$2y\,dy = -(y^2 - x)\,dx$$
$$(y^2 - x)\,dx + 2y\,dy = 0.$$

From Example 5, we know that the general solution of this differential equation is $y^2 - x + 1 = Ce^{-x}$, or $y^2 = x - 1 + Ce^{-x}$. Figure 16.9 shows several representative curves from this family. Note that the force vector at (x, y) is tangent to the curve passing through (x, y).   ▬

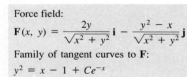

Force field:
$$\mathbf{F}(x, y) = \frac{2y}{\sqrt{x^2 + y^2}}\mathbf{i} - \frac{y^2 - x}{\sqrt{x^2 + y^2}}\mathbf{j}$$
Family of tangent curves to $\mathbf{F}$:
$$y^2 = x - 1 + Ce^{-x}$$

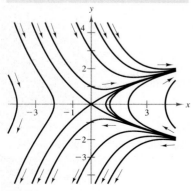

FIGURE 16.9

EXERCISES for Section 16.3

In Exercises 1–10, determine whether the differential equation is exact. If it is, find the general solution.

1. $(2x - 3y)\,dx + (2y - 3x)\,dy = 0$

2. $ye^x\,dx + e^x\,dy = 0$

3. $(3y^2 + 10xy^2)\,dx + (6xy - 2 + 10x^2y)\,dy = 0$

4. $2\cos(2x - y)\,dx - \cos(2x - y)\,dy = 0$

5. $(4x^3 - 6xy^2)\,dx + (4y^3 - 6xy)\,dy = 0$

6. $2y^2e^{xy^2}\,dx + 2xye^{xy^2}\,dy = 0$

7. $\dfrac{1}{x^2 + y^2}(x\,dy - y\,dx) = 0$

8. $e^{-(x^2+y^2)}(x\,dx + y\,dy) = 0$

9. $\dfrac{1}{(x - y)^2}(y^2\,dx + x^2\,dy) = 0$

10. $e^y\cos xy\,[y\,dx + (x + \tan xy)\,dy] = 0$

In Exercises 11–16, find the particular solution that satisfies the initial condition.

Differential equation	Initial condition
11. $\dfrac{y}{x - 1}\,dx + [\ln(x - 1) + 2y]\,dy = 0$	$y(2) = 4$
12. $\dfrac{1}{\sqrt{x^2 + y^2}}(x\,dx + y\,dy) = 0$	$y(4) = 3$
13. $\dfrac{1}{x^2 + y^2}(x\,dx + y\,dy) = 0$	$y(0) = 4$
14. $e^{3x}(\sin 3y\,dx + \cos 3y\,dy) = 0$	$y(0) = \pi$
15. $(2x\tan y + 5)\,dx + (x^2\sec^2 y)\,dy = 0$	$y(0) = 0$
16. $(x^2 + y^2)\,dx + 2xy\,dy = 0$	$y(3) = 1$

In Exercises 17–26, find the integrating factor that is a function of x or y alone and use it to find the general solution of the differential equation.

17. $y\,dx - (x + 6y^2)\,dy = 0$ **18.** $(2x^3 + y)\,dx - x\,dy = 0$

19. $(5x^2 - y)\,dx + x\,dy = 0$

20. $(5x^2 - y^2)\,dx + 2y\,dy = 0$

21. $(x + y)\,dx + \tan x\,dy = 0$

22. $(2x^2y - 1)\,dx + x^3\,dy = 0$

23. $y^2\,dx + (xy - 1)\,dy = 0$

24. $(x^2 + 2x + y)\,dx + 2\,dy = 0$

25. $2y\,dx + (x - \sin\sqrt{y})\,dy = 0$

26. $(-2y^3 + 1)\,dx + (3xy^2 + x^3)\,dy = 0$

In Exercises 27–30, use the integrating factor to find the general solution of the differential equation.

27. $(4x^2y + 2y^2)\,dx + (3x^3 + 4xy)\,dy = 0$
$u(x, y) = xy^2$

28. $(3y^2 + 5x^2y)\,dx + (3xy + 2x^3)\,dy = 0$
$u(x, y) = x^2y$

29. $(-y^5 + x^2y)\,dx + (2xy^4 - 2x^3)\,dy = 0$
$u(x, y) = x^{-2}y^{-3}$

30. $-y^3\,dx + (xy^2 - x^2)\,dy = 0$
$u(x, y) = x^{-2}y^{-2}$

31. Show that each of the following are integrating factors for the differential equation

$$y\,dx - x\,dy = 0.$$

   a. $\dfrac{1}{x^2}$ **b.** $\dfrac{1}{y^2}$ **c.** $\dfrac{1}{xy}$ **d.** $\dfrac{1}{x^2 + y^2}$

32. Show that the differential equation

$$(axy^2 + by)\,dx + (bx^2y + ax)\,dy = 0$$

is exact only if $a = b$. If $a \ne b$, show that x^my^n is an integrating factor, where

$$m = -\frac{2b + a}{a + b}, \qquad n = -\frac{2a + b}{a + b}.$$

C In Exercises 33–36, use a graphing utility to graph the family of tangent curves to the given force field.

33. $\mathbf{F}(x, y) = \dfrac{y}{\sqrt{x^2 + y^2}}\mathbf{i} - \dfrac{x}{\sqrt{x^2 + y^2}}\mathbf{j}$

34. $\mathbf{F}(x, y) = \dfrac{x}{\sqrt{x^2 + y^2}}\mathbf{i} - \dfrac{y}{\sqrt{x^2 + y^2}}\mathbf{j}$

35. $\mathbf{F}(x, y) = 4x^2y\,\mathbf{i} - \left(2xy^2 + \dfrac{x}{y^2}\right)\mathbf{j}$

36. $\mathbf{F}(x, y) = (1 + x^2)\mathbf{i} - 2xy\,\mathbf{j}$

In Exercises 37 and 38, find an equation for the curve passing through the point with the specified slope.

	Point	Slope
37.	$(2, 1)$	$\dfrac{dy}{dx} = \dfrac{y - x}{3y - x}$
38.	$(0, 2)$	$\dfrac{dy}{dx} = \dfrac{-2xy}{x^2 + y^2}$

39. *Cost*   If $y = C(x)$ represents the cost of producing x units in a manufacturing process, then the **elasticity of cost** is defined as

$$E(x) = \frac{\text{marginal cost}}{\text{average cost}} = \frac{C'(x)}{C(x)/x} = \frac{x}{y}\frac{dy}{dx}.$$

Find the cost function if the elasticity function is

$$E(x) = \frac{20x - y}{2y - 10x}$$

where $C(100) = 500$ and $100 \le x$.

40. *Euler Method*   Consider the differential equation $y' = F(x, y)$ with the initial condition $y(x_0) = y_0$. At any point (x_k, y_k) in the domain of F, $F(x_k, y_k)$ yields the slope of the solution at that point. The Euler Method gives a discrete set of estimates of the y values of a solution of the differential equation using the iterative formula

$$y_{k+1} = y_k + F(x_k, y_k) \Delta x$$

where $\Delta x = x_{k+1} - x_k$.

a. Write a short paragraph describing the general idea of how the Euler Method works.

b. How will decreasing the magnitude of Δx affect the accuracy of the Euler Method?

41. *Euler Method*   Use the Euler Method to approximate $y(1)$ for the values of Δx given in the table if $y' = x + \sqrt{y}$ and $y(0) = 2$. (Note that the number of iterations increases as Δx decreases.) Sketch a graph of the approximate solution on the direction field in the figure.

Δx	0.50	0.25	0.10
Estimate of $y(1)$			

The value of $y(1)$, accurate to three decimal places, is 4.213.

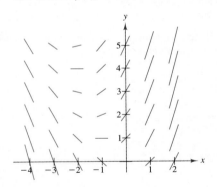

FIGURE FOR 41

42. a. *Euler Method*   Write a computer program or use a spreadsheet to perform the calculations of the Euler Method. The output should be two columns giving x_k and y_k, respectively. Use the program to approximate the solution of the differential equation $y' = x\sqrt[3]{y}$ over the interval $[1, 2]$ if $\Delta x = 0.01$ and $y(1) = 1$.

b. Solve the differential equation analytically, and compare the exact value of $y(2)$ with the estimate found in part a.

True or False   **In Exercises 43–46, determine whether the statement is true or false. If it is false, explain why or give an example that shows it is false.**

43. The differential equation $2xy\,dx + (y^2 - x^2)\,dy = 0$ is exact.

44. If $M\,dx + N\,dy = 0$ is exact, then $xM\,dx + xN\,dy = 0$ is also exact.

45. If $M\,dx + N\,dy = 0$ is exact, then $[f(x) + M]\,dx + [g(y) + N]\,dy = 0$ is also exact.

46. The differential equation $f(x)\,dx + g(y)\,dy = 0$ is exact.

First-Order Linear Differential Equations

First-Order Linear Differential Equations • Bernoulli Equations • Applications

First-Order Linear Differential Equations

In this section, you will see how integrating factors help to solve a very important class of first-order differential equations—first-order *linear* differential equations.

Definition of First-Order Linear Differential Equation

A first-order linear differential equation is an equation of the form

$$\frac{dy}{dx} + P(x)y = Q(x)$$

where P and Q are continuous functions of x. This first-order linear differential equation is said to be in **standard form.**

To solve a first-order linear differential equation, you can use an integrating factor $u(x)$, which converts the left side into the derivative of the product $u(x)y$. That is, you need a factor $u(x)$ such that

$$u(x)\frac{dy}{dx} + u(x)P(x)y = \frac{d[u(x)y]}{dx}$$

$$u(x)y' + u(x)P(x)y = u(x)y' + yu'(x)$$

$$u(x)P(x)y = yu'(x)$$

$$P(x) = \frac{u'(x)}{u(x)}$$

$$\ln|u(x)| = \int P(x)\,dx + C_1$$

$$u(x) = Ce^{\int P(x)\,dx}.$$

Because you don't need the most general integrating factor, let $C = 1$. Multiplying the original equation $y' + P(x)y = Q(x)$ by $u(x) = e^{\int P(x)\,dx}$ produces

$$y'e^{\int P(x)\,dx} + yP(x)e^{\int P(x)\,dx} = Q(x)e^{\int P(x)\,dx}$$

$$\frac{d}{dx}\left[ye^{\int P(x)\,dx}\right] = Q(x)e^{\int P(x)\,dx}.$$

The general solution is given by

$$ye^{\int P(x)\,dx} = \int Q(x)e^{\int P(x)\,dx}\,dx + C.$$

> **THEOREM 16.4   Solution of a First-Order Linear Differential Equation**
>
> An integrating factor for the first-order differential equation
>
> $$y' + P(x)y = Q(x)$$
>
> is $u(x) = e^{\int P(x)\,dx}$. The solution of the differential equation is
>
> $$ye^{\int P(x)\,dx} = \int Q(x)e^{\int P(x)\,dx}\,dx + C.$$

REMARK   Rather than memorizing this formula, just remember that multiplication by the integrating factor $e^{\int P(x)\,dx}$ converts the left side of the differential equation into the derivative of the product $ye^{\int P(x)\,dx}$.

EXAMPLE 1   Solving a First-Order Linear Differential Equation

Find the general solution of

$$xy' - 2y = x^2.$$

Solution   The *standard form* of the given equation is

$$y' + P(x)y = Q(x)$$

$$y' - \left(\frac{2}{x}\right)y = x. \qquad \text{Standard form}$$

Thus, $P(x) = -2/x$, and you have

$$\int P(x)\,dx = -\int \frac{2}{x}\,dx = -\ln x^2$$

$$e^{\int P(x)\,dx} = e^{-\ln x^2} = \frac{1}{x^2}. \qquad \text{Integrating factor}$$

Therefore, multiplying both sides of the standard form by $1/x^2$ yields

$$\frac{y'}{x^2} - \frac{2y}{x^3} = \frac{1}{x}$$

$$\frac{d}{dx}\left[\frac{y}{x^2}\right] = \frac{1}{x}$$

$$\frac{y}{x^2} = \int \frac{1}{x}\,dx$$

$$\frac{y}{x^2} = \ln|x| + C$$

$$y = x^2(\ln|x| + C). \qquad \text{General solution}$$

Several solution curves (for $C = -2, -1, 0, 1, 2, 3,$ and 4) are shown in Figure 16.10.

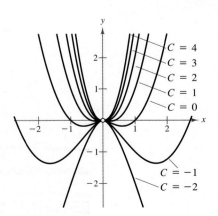

FIGURE 16.10

EXAMPLE 2   Solving a First-Order Linear Differential Equation

Find the general solution

$$y' - y \tan t = 1, \qquad -\frac{\pi}{2} < t < \frac{\pi}{2}.$$

Solution The equation is already in the standard form $y' + P(t)y = Q(t)$. Thus, $P(t) = -\tan t$, and

$$\int P(t)\,dt = -\int \tan t\,dt = \ln|\cos t|$$

which implies that the integrating factor is

$$e^{\int P(t)\,dt} = e^{\ln|\cos t|}$$
$$= |\cos t|. \qquad \text{Integrating factor}$$

A quick check shows that $\cos t$ is also an integrating factor. Thus, multiplying $y' - y \tan t = 1$ by $\cos t$ produces

$$\frac{d}{dt}[y \cos t] = \cos t$$

$$y \cos t = \int \cos t\,dt$$

$$y \cos t = \sin t + C$$

$$y = \tan t + C \sec t. \qquad \text{General solution}$$

Several solution curves are shown in Figure 16.11.

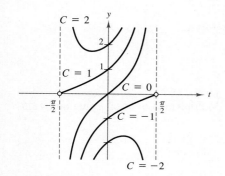

FIGURE 16.11

Bernoulli Equations

A well-known *nonlinear* equation that reduces to a linear one with an appropriate substitution is the **Bernoulli equation,** named after James Bernoulli (1654–1705).

$$y' + P(x)y = Q(x)y^n \qquad \text{Bernoulli equation}$$

This equation is linear if $n = 0$, and has separable variables if $n = 1$. Thus, in the following development, assume that $n \neq 0$ and $n \neq 1$. Begin by multiplying by y^{-n} and $(1 - n)$ to obtain

$$y^{-n}y' + P(x)y^{1-n} = Q(x)$$
$$(1 - n)y^{-n}y' + (1 - n)P(x)y^{1-n} = (1 - n)Q(x)$$
$$\frac{d}{dx}[y^{1-n}] + (1 - n)P(x)y^{1-n} = (1 - n)Q(x)$$

which is a linear equation in the variable y^{1-n}. Letting $z = y^{1-n}$ produces the linear equation

$$\frac{dz}{dx} + (1 - n)P(x)z = (1 - n)Q(x).$$

Finally, by Theorem 16.4, the *general solution of the Bernoulli equation* is

$$y^{1-n}e^{\int (1-n)P(x)\,dx} = \int (1 - n)Q(x)e^{\int (1-n)P(x)\,dx}\,dx + C.$$

EXAMPLE 3   Solving a Bernoulli Equation

Find the general solution of $y' + xy = xe^{-x^2}y^{-3}$.

Solution   For this Bernoulli equation, let $n = -3$, and use the substitution

$$z = y^4$$ Let $z = y^{1-n} = y^{1-(-3)}$

$$z' = 4y^3y'.$$ Differentiate

Multiplying the original equation by $4y^3$ produces

$$y' + xy = xe^{-x^2}y^{-3}$$ Original equation

$$4y^3y' + 4xy^4 = 4xe^{-x^2}$$ Multiply both sides by $4y^3$

$$z' + 4xz = 4xe^{-x^2}.$$ Linear equation: $z' + P(x)z = Q(x)$

This equation is linear in z. Using $P(x) = 4x$ produces

$$\int P(x)\,dx = \int 4x\,dx = 2x^2$$

which implies that e^{2x^2} is an integrating factor. Multiplying the linear equation by this factor produces

$$z' + 4xz = 4xe^{-x^2}$$ Linear equation

$$z'e^{2x^2} + 4xze^{2x^2} = 4xe^{x^2}$$ Exact equation

$$\frac{d}{dx}\left[ze^{2x^2}\right] = 4xe^{x^2}$$ Write left side as total differential

$$ze^{2x^2} = \int 4xe^{x^2}\,dx$$ Integrate both sides

$$ze^{2x^2} = 2e^{x^2} + C$$

$$z = 2e^{-x^2} + Ce^{-2x^2}.$$ Divide both sides by e^{2x^2}

Finally, substituting $z = y^4$, the general solution is

$$y^4 = 2e^{-x^2} + Ce^{-2x^2}.$$ General solution

So far you have studied several types of first-order differential equations. Of these, the separable variables case is usually the simplest, and solution by an integrating factor is usually a last resort.

Summary of First-Order Differential Equations

Method	Form of equation
1. Separable variables:	$M(x)\,dx + N(y)\,dy = 0$
2. Homogeneous:	$M(x, y)\,dx + N(x, y)\,dy = 0$, where M and N are nth-degree homogeneous.
3. Exact:	$M(x, y)\,dx + N(x, y)\,dy = 0$ where $\partial M/\partial y = \partial N/\partial x$.
4. Integrating factor:	$u(x, y)\,M(x, y)\,dx + u(x, y)N(x, y)\,dy = 0$ is exact.
5. Linear:	$y' + P(x)y = Q(x)$
6. Bernoulli equation:	$y' + P(x)y = Q(x)y^n$

Applications

One type of problem that can be described in terms of a differential equation involves chemical mixtures, as illustrated in the next example.

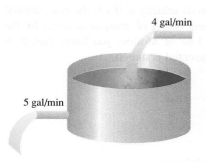

4 gal/min

5 gal/min

FIGURE 16.12

EXAMPLE 4   A Mixture Problem

A tank contains 50 gallons of a solution composed of 90 percent water and 10 percent alcohol. A second solution containing 50 percent water and 50 percent alcohol is added to the tank at the rate of 4 gallons per minute. As the second solution is being added, the tank is being drained at the rate of 5 gallons per minute, as shown in Figure 16.12. Assuming the solution in the tank is stirred constantly, how much alcohol is in the tank after 10 minutes?

Solution   Let y be the number of gallons of alcohol in the tank at any time t. You know that $y = 5$ when $t = 0$. Because the number of gallons of solution in the tank at any time is $50 - t$, and the tank loses 5 gallons of solution per minute, it must lose

$$\left(\frac{5}{50 - t}\right)y$$

gallons of alcohol per minute. Furthermore, because the tank is gaining 2 gallons of alcohol per minute, the rate of change of alcohol in the tank is given by

$$\frac{dy}{dt} = 2 - \left(\frac{5}{50 - t}\right)y \quad \rightarrow \quad \frac{dy}{dt} + \left(\frac{5}{50 - t}\right)y = 2.$$

To solve this linear equation, let $P(t) = 5/(50 - t)$ and obtain

$$\int P(t)\, dt = \int \frac{5}{50 - t}\, dt = -5 \ln|50 - t|.$$

Because $t < 50$, you can drop the absolute value signs and conclude that

$$e^{\int P(t)\, dt} = e^{-5\ln(50-t)} = \frac{1}{(50 - t)^5}.$$

Thus, the general solution is

$$\frac{y}{(50 - t)^5} = \int \frac{2}{(50 - t)^5}\, dt = \frac{1}{2(50 - t)^4} + C$$

$$y = \frac{50 - t}{2} + C(50 - t)^5.$$

Because $y = 5$ when $t = 0$, you have

$$5 = \frac{50}{2} + C(50)^5 \quad \rightarrow \quad -\frac{20}{50^5} = C$$

which means that the particular solution is

$$y = \frac{50 - t}{2} - 20\left(\frac{50 - t}{50}\right)^5.$$

Finally, when $t = 10$, the amount of alcohol in the tank is

$$y = \frac{50 - 10}{2} - 20\left(\frac{50 - 10}{50}\right)^5 = 13.45 \text{ gal}$$

which represents a solution containing 33.6 percent alcohol.

28. Verify that the solution of Exercise 27 can be written in the form

$$I = ce^{-(R/L)t} + \frac{E_0}{\sqrt{R^2 + \omega^2 L^2}} \sin(\omega t + \phi)$$

where ϕ, the phase angle, is given by $\arctan(\omega L/R)$. (Note that the exponential term approaches 0 as $t \to \infty$. This implies that the current approaches a periodic function.

29. *Population Growth*   When predicting population growth, demographers must consider birth and death rates as well as the net change caused by the difference between the rates of immigration and emigration. Let P be the population at time t and N be the net increase per unit time due to the difference between immigration and emigration. Thus, the rate of growth of the population is given by

$$\frac{dP}{dt} = kP + N, \qquad N \text{ is constant.}$$

Solve this differential equation to find P as a function of time if at time $t = 0$ the size of the population is P_0.

30. *Investment Growth*   A large corportion starts at time $t = 0$ to continuously invest part of its receipts at a rate of P dollars per year in a fund for future corporate expansion. Assume that the fund earns r percent interest per year compounded continuously. Thus, the rate of growth of the amount A in the fund is given by

$$\frac{dA}{dt} = rA + P$$

where $A = 0$ when $t = 0$. Solve this differential equation for A as a function of t.

Investment Growth   In Exercises 31 and 32, use the result of Exercise 30.

31. Find A for the following.
 a. $P = \$100,000$, $r = 12\%$, and $t = 5$ years
 b. $P = \$250,000$, $r = 15\%$, and $t = 10$ years

32. Find t if the corporation needs $\$800,000$ and it can invest $\$75,000$ per year in a fund earning 13% interest compounded continuously.

33. *Intravenous Feeding*   Glucose is added intravenously to the bloodstream at the rate of q units per minute, and the body removes glucose from the bloodstream at a rate proportional to the amount present. Assume $Q(t)$ is the amount of glucose in the bloodstream at time t.
 a. Determine the differential equation describing the rate of change with respect to time of glucose in the bloodstream.
 b. Solve the differential equation from part a, letting $Q = Q_0$ when $t = 0$.
 c. Find the limit of $Q(t)$ as $t \to \infty$.

34. *Learning Curve*   The management at a certain factory has found that the maximum number of units a worker can produce in a day is 30. The rate of increase in the number of units N produced with respect to time t in days by a new employee is proportional to $30 - N$.

 a. Determine the differential equation describing the rate of change of performance with respect to time.
 b. Solve the differential equation from part a.
 c. Find the particular solution for a new employee who produced 10 units on the first day at the factory and 19 units on the twentieth day.

Mixture   In Exercises 35–38, consider a tank that at time $t = 0$ contains v_0 gallons of a solution of which, by weight, q_0 pounds is soluble concentrate. Another solution containing q_1 pounds of the concentrate per gallon is running into the tank at the rate of r_1 gallons per minute. The solution in the tank is kept well stirred and is withdrawn at the rate of r_2 gallons per minute.

35. If Q is the amount of concentrate in the solution at any time t, show that

$$\frac{dQ}{dt} + \frac{r_2 Q}{v_0 + (r_1 - r_2)t} = q_1 r_1.$$

36. A 200-gallon tank is full of a solution containing 25 pounds of concentrate. Starting at time $t = 0$, distilled water is admitted to the tank at the rate of 10 gallons per minute, and the well-stirred solution is withdrawn at the same rate.
 a. Find the amount of the concentrate in the solution as a function of t.
 b. Find the time at which the amount of concentrate in the tank reaches 15 pounds.
 c. Find the quantity of the concentrate in the solution as $t \to \infty$.

37. Repeat Exercise 36, assuming that the solution entering the tank contains 0.05 pounds of concentrate per gallon.

38. A 200-gallon tank is half full of distilled water. At time $t = 0$, a solution containing 0.5 pound of concentrate per gallon enters the tank at the rate of 5 gallons per minute, and the well-stirred mixture is withdrawn at the rate of 3 gallons per minute.
 a. At what time will the tank be full?
 b. At the time the tank is full, how many pounds of concentrate will it contain?

In Exercises 39–42, match the differential equation with its solution.

Differential equation	Solution
39. $y' - 2x = 0$	**a.** $y = Ce^{x^2}$
40. $y' - 2y = 0$	**b.** $y = -\frac{1}{2} + Ce^{x^2}$
41. $y' - 2xy = 0$	**c.** $y = x^2 + C$
42. $y' - 2xy = x$	**d.** $y = Ce^{2x}$

In Exercises 43–58, solve the first-order differential equation by any appropriate method.

43. $\dfrac{dy}{dx} = \dfrac{e^{2x+y}}{e^{x-y}}$

44. $\dfrac{dy}{dx} = \dfrac{x+1}{y(y+2)}$

45. $(1 + y^2)\,dx + (2xy + y + 2)\,dy = 0$

46. $(1 + 2e^{2x+y})\,dx + e^{2x+y}\,dy = 0$

47. $y\cos x - \cos x + \dfrac{dy}{dx} = 0$

48. $(x + 1)\dfrac{dy}{dx} = e^x - y$

49. $(x^2 + \cos y)\dfrac{dy}{dx} = -2xy$

50. $y' = 2x\sqrt{1 - y^2}$

51. $(3y^2 + 4xy)\,dx + (2xy + x^2)\,dy = 0$

52. $(x + y)\,dx - x\,dy = 0$

53. $(2y - e^x)\,dx + x\,dy = 0$

54. $(y^2 + xy)\,dx - x^2\,dy = 0$

55. $(x^2y^4 - 1)\,dx + x^3y^3\,dy = 0$

56. $y\,dx + (3x + 4y)\,dy = 0$

57. $3y\,dx - (x^2 + 3x + y^2)\,dy = 0$

58. $x\,dx + (y + e^y)(x^2 + 1)\,dy = 0$

EXAMPLE 2   Characteristic Equation with Distinct Real Roots

Solve the differential equation

$$y'' - 4y = 0.$$

Solution   In this case, the characteristic equation is

$$m^2 - 4 = 0 \qquad \text{Characteristic equation}$$

so $m = \pm 2$. Thus, $y_1 = e^{m_1 x} = e^{2x}$ and $y_2 = e^{m_2 x} = e^{-2x}$ are particular solutions of the given differential equation. Furthermore, because these two solutions are linearly independent, you can apply Theorem 16.5 to conclude that the general solution is

$$y = C_1 e^{2x} + C_2 e^{-2x}. \qquad \text{General solution}$$

The characteristic equation in Example 2 has two distinct real roots. From algebra, you know that this is only one of *three* possibilities for quadratic equations. In general, the quadratic equation $m^2 + am + b = 0$ has roots

$$m_1 = \frac{-a + \sqrt{a^2 - 4b}}{2} \quad \text{and} \quad m_2 = \frac{-a - \sqrt{a^2 - 4b}}{2}$$

which fall into one of three cases.

1. Two distinct real roots, $m_1 \neq m_2$
2. Two equal real roots, $m_1 = m_2$
3. Two complex conjugate roots, $m_1 = \alpha + \beta i$ and $m_2 = \alpha - \beta i$

In terms of the differential equation $y'' + ay' + by = 0$, these three cases correspo. to three different types of general solutions.

THEOREM 16.6   Solutions of $y'' + ay' + by = 0$

The solutions of
$$y'' + ay' + by = 0$$
fall into one of the following three cases, depending on the solutions of the characteristic equation, $m^2 + am + b = 0$.

1. *Distinct Real Roots*   If $m_1 \neq m_2$ are distinct real roots of the characteristic equation, then the general solution is
   $$y = C_1 e^{m_1 x} + C_2 e^{m_2 x}.$$
2. *Equal Real Roots*   If $m_1 = m_2$ are equal real roots of the characteristic equation, then the general solution is
   $$y = C_1 e^{m_1 x} + C_2 x e^{m_1 x} = (C_1 + C_2 x)e^{m_1 x}.$$
3. *Complex Roots*   If $m_1 = \alpha + \beta i$ and $m_2 = \alpha - \beta i$ are complex roots of the characteristic equation, then the general solution is
   $$y = C_1 e^{\alpha x} \cos \beta x + C_2 e^{\alpha x} \sin \beta x.$$

FOR FURTHER INFORMATION
For more information on Theorem 16.6, see "A Note on a Differential Equation" by Russell Euler in the 1989 winter issue of the *Missouri Journal of Mathematical Sciences*.

EXAMPLE 3   Characteristic Equation with Complex Roots

Find the general solution of the differential equation

$$y'' + 6y' + 12y = 0.$$

Solution   The characteristic equation

$$m^2 + 6m + 12 = 0$$

has two complex roots, as follows.

$$\begin{aligned} m &= \frac{-6 \pm \sqrt{36 - 48}}{2} \\ &= \frac{-6 \pm \sqrt{-12}}{2} \\ &= -3 \pm \sqrt{-3} \\ &= -3 \pm \sqrt{3}i \end{aligned}$$

Thus, $\alpha = -3$ and $\beta = \sqrt{3}$, and the general solution is

$$y = C_1 e^{-3x} \cos \sqrt{3}x + C_2 e^{-3x} \sin \sqrt{3}x.$$

REMARK   In Example 3, note that although the characteristic equation has two *complex* roots, the solution of the differential equation is *real*.

EXAMPLE 4   Characteristic Equation with Repeated Roots

Solve the differential equation

$$y'' + 4y' + 4y = 0$$

subject to the initial conditions $y(0) = 2$ and $y'(0) = 1$.

Solution   The characteristic equation

$$m^2 + 4m + 4 = (m + 2)^2 = 0$$

has two equal real roots given by $m = -2$. Thus, the general solution is

$$y = C_1 e^{-2x} + C_2 x e^{-2x}. \qquad \text{\small General solution}$$

Now, because $y = 2$ when $x = 0$, we have

$$2 = C_1(1) + C_2(0)(1) = C_1.$$

Furthermore, because $y' = 1$ when $x = 0$, we have

$$\begin{aligned} y' &= -2C_1 e^{-2x} + C_2(-2xe^{-2x} + e^{-2x}) \\ 1 &= -2(2)(1) + C_2[-2(0)(1) + 1] \\ 5 &= C_2. \end{aligned}$$

Therefore, the solution is

$$y = 2e^{-2x} + 5xe^{-2x}. \qquad \text{\small Particular solution}$$

Try checking this solution in the original differential equation.

FIGURE 16.15
A damped vibration could be caused by friction and movement through a liquid.

Suppose the object in Figure 16.15 undergoes an additional damping or frictional force that is proportional to its velocity. A case in point would be the damping force due to friction and movement through a fluid. Considering this damping force, $-p(dy/dt)$, the differential equation for the oscillation is

$$m\frac{d^2y}{dt^2} = -ky - p\frac{dy}{dt}$$

or, in standard linear form,

$$\frac{d^2y}{dt^2} + \frac{p}{m}\left(\frac{dy}{dt}\right) + \frac{k}{m}y = 0. \qquad \text{Damped motion of a spring}$$

EXERCISES for Section 16.5

TECHNOLOGY
Laboratory Guide
Labs 16.5–16.6

In Exercises 1–4, verify that the equation is a solution of the differential equation.

Solution	Differential equation
1. $y = (C_1 + C_2x)e^{-3x}$	$y'' + 6y' + 9y = 0$
2. $y = C_1e^{2x} + C_2e^{-2x}$	$y'' - 4y = 0$
3. $y = C_1\cos 2x + C_2\sin 2x$	$y'' + 4y = 0$
4. $y = e^{-x}\sin 3x$	$y'' + 2y' + 10y = 0$

In Exercises 5–30, find the general solution of the linear differential equation.

5. $y'' - y' = 0$ 6. $y'' + 2y' = 0$

7. $y'' - y' - 6y = 0$ 8. $y'' + 6y' + 5y = 0$

9. $2y'' + 3y' - 2y = 0$ 10. $16y'' - 16y' + 3y = 0$

11. $y'' + 6y' + 9y = 0$ 12. $y'' - 10y' + 25y = 0$

13. $16y'' - 8y' + y = 0$ 14. $9y'' - 12y' + 4y = 0$

15. $y'' + y = 0$ 16. $y'' + 4y = 0$

17. $y'' - 9y = 0$ 18. $y'' - 2y = 0$

19. $y'' - 2y' + 4y = 0$ 20. $y'' - 4y' + 21y = 0$

21. $y'' - 3y' + y = 0$ 22. $3y'' + 4y' - y = 0$

23. $9y'' - 12y' + 11y = 0$ 24. $2y'' - 6y' + 7y = 0$

25. $y^{(4)} - y = 0$ 26. $y^{(4)} - y'' = 0$

27. $y''' - 6y'' + 11y' - 6y = 0$

28. $y''' - y'' - y' + y = 0$

29. $y''' - 3y'' + 7y' - 5y = 0$

30. $y''' - 3y'' + 3y' - y = 0$

31. Consider the differential equation $y'' + 100y = 0$ and the solution $y = C_1\cos 10x + C_2\sin 10x$. Find the particular solution satisfying each of the following initial conditions.
    a. $y(0) = 2$, $y'(0) = 0$
    b. $y(0) = 0$, $y'(0) = 2$
    c. $y(0) = -1$, $y'(0) = 3$

32. Determine C and ω such that $y = C\sin\sqrt{3}\,t$ is a particular solution of the differential equation $y'' + \omega y = 0$, where $y'(0) = -5$.

In Exercises 33 and 34, find the particular solution of the linear differential equation.

33. $y'' - y' - 30y = 0$ 34. $y'' + 2y' + 3y = 0$
    $y(0) = 1$, $y'(0) = -4$ $y(0) = 2$, $y'(0) = 1$

Vibrating Spring   **In Exercises 35–40, describe the motion of a 32-pound weight suspended on a spring. Assume that the weight stretches the spring $\frac{2}{3}$ foot from its natural position.**

35. The weight is pulled $\frac{1}{2}$ foot below the equilibrium position and released.

36. The weight is raised $\frac{2}{3}$ foot above the equilibrium position and released.

37. The weight is raised $\frac{2}{3}$ foot above the equilibrium position and started off with a downward velocity of $\frac{1}{2}$ foot per second.

38. The weight is pulled $\frac{1}{2}$ foot below the equilibrium position and started off with an upward velocity of $\frac{1}{2}$ foot per second.

39. The weight is pulled $\frac{1}{2}$ foot below the equilibrium position and released. The motion takes place in a medium that furnishes a damping force of magnitude $\frac{1}{8}$ speed at all times.

40. The weight is pulled $\frac{1}{2}$ foot below the equilibrium position and released. The motion takes place in a medium that furnishes a damping force of magnitude $\frac{1}{4}|v|$ at all times.

Vibrating Spring   **In Exercises 41–44, match the differential equation with the graph of a particular solution. [The graphs are labeled (a), (b), (c), and (d).] The correct match can be made by comparing the frequency of the oscillations or the rate at which the oscillations are being damped with the appropriate coefficient in the differential equation.**

41. $y'' + 9y = 0$ 42. $y'' + 25y = 0$

43. $y'' + 2y' + 10y = 0$ **44.** $y'' + y' + \frac{37}{4}y = 0$

(a)

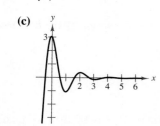

(b)

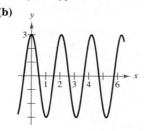

(c)

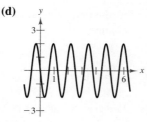

(d)

45. If the characteristic equation of the differential equation

$$y'' + ay' + by = 0$$

has two equal real roots given by $m = r$, show that

$$y = C_1 e^{rx} + C_2 x e^{rx}$$

is a solution.

46. If the characteristic equation of the differential equation

$$y'' + ay' + by = 0$$

has complex roots given by $m_1 = \alpha + \beta i$ and $m_2 = \alpha - \beta i$, show that

$$y = C_1 e^{\alpha x} \cos \beta x + C_2 e^{\alpha x} \sin \beta x$$

is a solution.

True or False **In Exercises 47–50, determine whether the statement is true or false. If it is false, explain why or give an example that shows it is false.**

47. $y = C_1 e^{3x} + C_2 e^{-3x}$ is the general solution of $y'' - 6y' + 9 = 0$.

48. $y = (C_1 + C_2 x)\sin x + (C_3 + C_4 x)\cos x$ is the general solution of $y^{(4)} + 2y' + y = 0$.

49. $y = x$ is a solution of $a_n y^{(n)} + a_{n-1} y^{(n-1)} + \cdots + a_1 y' + a_0 y = 0$ if and only if $a_1 = a_0 = 0$.

50. It is possible to choose a and b so that $y = x^2 e^x$ is a solution of $y'' + ay' + by = 0$.

The *Wronskian* of two differentiable functions f and g, denoted by $W(f,g)$, is defined as the function given by the determinant

$$W(f,g) = \begin{vmatrix} f & g \\ f' & g' \end{vmatrix}.$$

The functions f and g are linearly independent if there exists at least one value of x for which $W(f,g) \neq 0$. In Exercises 51–54, use the Wronskian to verify the linear independence of the two functions.

51. $y_1 = e^{ax}$ **52.** $y_1 = e^{ax}$
    $y_2 = e^{bx}$ $(a \neq b)$ $y_2 = xe^{ax}$

53. $y_1 = e^{ax}\sin bx$ **54.** $y_1 = x$
    $y_2 = e^{ax}\cos bx$, $b \neq 0$ $y_2 = x^2$

55. Euler's differential equation is of the form

$$x^2 y'' + axy' + by = 0, \qquad x > 0$$

where a and b are constants.

   a. Show that this equation can be transformed into a second-order linear equation with constant coefficients by using the substitution $x = e^t$.

   b. Solve $x^2 y'' + 6xy' + 6y = 0$.

56. Solve

$$y'' + Ay = 0$$

where A is constant, subject to the conditions $y(0) = 0$ and $y(\pi) = 0$.

Second-Order Nonhomogeneous Linear Equations

Nonhomogeneous Equations • Method of Undetermined Coefficients • Variation of Parameters

Nonhomogeneous Equations

In the previous section, we represented damped oscillations of a spring by the *homogeneous* second-order linear equation

$$\frac{d^2y}{dt^2} + \frac{p}{m}\left(\frac{dy}{dt}\right) + \frac{k}{m}y = 0. \qquad \text{Free motion}$$

This type of oscillation is called **free** because it is determined solely by the spring and gravity and is free of the action of other external forces. If such a system is also subject to an external periodic force such as $a \sin bt$, caused by vibrations at the opposite end of the spring, then the motion is called **forced,** and it is characterized by the *nonhomogeneous* equation

$$\frac{d^2y}{dt^2} + \frac{p}{m}\left(\frac{dy}{dt}\right) + \frac{k}{m}y = a \sin bt. \qquad \text{Forced motion}$$

In this section, you will study two methods for finding the general solution of a nonhomogeneous linear differential equation. In both methods, the first step is to find the general solution of the corresponding homogeneous equation.

$$y = y_h \qquad\qquad \text{General solution of homogeneous equation}$$

Having done this, you try to find a particular solution of the nonhomogeneous equation.

$$y = y_p \qquad\qquad \text{Particular solution of nonhomogeneous equation}$$

By combining these two results, you can conclude that the general solution of the nonhomogeneous equation is $y = y_h + y_p$, as stated in the following theorem.

SOPHIE GERMAIN

Many of the early contributors to calculus were interested in forming mathematical models for vibrating strings and membranes, oscillating springs, and elasticity. One of these was the French mathematician Sophie Germain (1776–1831), who in 1816 was awarded a prize by the French Academy for a paper entitled "Memoir on the Vibrations of Elastic Plates."

THEOREM 16.7 Solution of Nonhomogeneous Linear Equation

Let

$$y'' + ay' + by = F(x)$$

be a second-order nonhomogeneous linear differential equation. If y_p is a particular solution of this equation and y_h is the general solution of the corresponding homogeneous equation, then

$$y = y_h + y_p$$

is the general solution of the nonhomogeneous equation.

Method of Undetermined Coefficients

You already know how to find the solution y_h of a linear *homogeneous* differential equation. The remainder of this section looks at ways to find the particular solution y_p. If $F(x)$ in

$$y'' + ay' + by = F(x)$$

consists of sums or products of x^n, e^{mx}, $\cos \beta x$, or $\sin \beta x$, then you can find a particular solution y_p by the method of **undetermined coefficients.** The gist of this method is to guess that the solution y_p is a generalized form of $F(x)$. Here are some examples.

a. If $F(x) = 3x^2$, choose $y_p = Ax^2 + Bx + C$.
b. If $F(x) = 4xe^x$, choose $y_p = Axe^x + Be^x$.
c. If $F(x) = x + \sin 2x$, choose $y_p = (Ax + B) + C \sin 2x + D \cos 2x$.

Then, by substitution, determine the coefficients for the generalized solution.

EXAMPLE 1   Method of Undetermined Coefficients

Find the general solution of the equation

$$y'' - 2y' - 3y = 2 \sin x.$$

Solution   To find y_h, solve the characteristic equation.

$$m^2 - 2m - 3 = 0$$
$$(m + 1)(m - 3) = 0$$
$$m = -1 \quad \text{or} \quad m = 3$$

Thus, $y_h = C_1 e^{-x} + C_2 e^{3x}$. Next, let y_p be a generalized form of $2 \sin x$.

$$y_p = A \cos x + B \sin x$$
$$y_p' = -A \sin x + B \cos x$$
$$y_p'' = -A \cos x - B \sin x$$

Substitution into the original differential equation yields

$$y'' - 2y' - 3y = 2 \sin x$$
$$-A \cos x - B \sin x + 2A \sin x - 2B \cos x - 3A \cos x - 3B \sin x = 2 \sin x$$
$$(-4A - 2B) \cos x + (2A - 4B) \sin x = 2 \sin x.$$

By equating coefficients of like terms, you obtain

$$-4A - 2B = 0 \quad \text{and} \quad 2A - 4B = 2$$

with solutions $A = \frac{1}{5}$ and $B = -\frac{2}{5}$. Therefore,

$$y_p = \frac{1}{5} \cos x - \frac{2}{5} \sin x$$

and the general solution is

$$y = y_h + y_p$$
$$= C_1 e^{-x} + C_2 e^{3x} + \frac{1}{5} \cos x - \frac{2}{5} \sin x.$$

In Example 1, the form of the homogeneous solution

$$y_h = C_1 e^{-x} + C_2 e^{3x}$$

has no overlap with the function $F(x)$ in the equation

$$y'' + ay' + by = F(x).$$

However, suppose the given differential equation in Example 1 were of the form

$$y'' - 2y' - 3y = e^{-x}.$$

Now, it would make no sense to guess that the particular solution were $y = Ae^{-x}$, because you know that this solution would yield 0. In such cases, you should alter your guess by multiplying by the lowest power of x that removes the duplication. For this particular problem, you would guess

$$y_p = Axe^{-x}.$$

EXAMPLE 2   Method of Undetermined Coefficients

Find the general solution of

$$y'' - 2y' = x + 2e^x.$$

Solution   The characteristic equation $m^2 - 2m = 0$ has solutions $m = 0$ and $m = 2$. Thus,

$$y_h = C_1 + C_2 e^{2x}.$$

Because $F(x) = x + 2e^x$, your first choice for y_p would be $(A + Bx) + Ce^x$. However, because y_h *already* contains a constant term C_1, you should multiply the *polynomial part* by x and use

$$y_p = Ax + Bx^2 + Ce^x$$
$$y_p{}' = A + 2Bx + Ce^x$$
$$y_p{}'' = 2B + Ce^x.$$

Substitution into the differential equation produces

$$y'' - 2y' = x + 2e^x$$
$$(2B + Ce^x) - 2(A + 2Bx + Ce^x) = x + 2e^x$$
$$(2B - 2A) - 4Bx - Ce^x = x + 2e^x.$$

Equating coefficients of like terms yields the system

$$2B - 2A = 0, \qquad -4B = 1, \qquad -C = 2$$

with solutions $A = B = -\frac{1}{4}$ and $C = -2$. Therefore,

$$y_p = -\frac{1}{4}x - \frac{1}{4}x^2 - 2e^x$$

and the general solution is

$$y = y_h + y_p$$
$$= C_1 + C_2 e^{2x} - \frac{1}{4}x - \frac{1}{4}x^2 - 2e^x.$$

In Example 2, the polynomial part of the initial guess

$$(A + Bx) + Ce^x$$

for y_p overlapped by a constant term with $y_h = C_1 + C_2 e^{2x}$, and it was necessary to multiply the polynomial part by a power of x that removed the overlap. The next example further illustrates some choices for y_p that eliminate overlap with y_h. Remember that in all cases the first guess for y_p should match the types of functions occurring in $F(x)$.

EXAMPLE 3   Choosing the Form of the Particular Solution

Determine a suitable choice for y_p for the following.

$y'' + ay' + by = F(x)$	y_h
a. $y'' = x^2$	$C_1 + C_2 x$
b. $y'' + 2y' + 10y = 4 \sin 3x$	$C_1 e^{-x} \cos 3x + C_2 e^{-x} \sin 3x$
c. $y'' - 4y' + 4 = e^{2x}$	$C_1 e^{2x} + C_2 x e^{2x}$

Solution

a. Because $F(x) = x^2$, the normal choice for y_p would be $A + Bx + Cx^2$. However, because $y_h = C_1 + C_2 x$ already contains a linear term, you should multiply by x^2 to obtain

$$y_p = Ax^2 + Bx^3 + Cx^4.$$

b. Because $F(x) = 4 \sin 3x$ and each term in y_h contains a factor of e^{-x}, you can simply let

$$y_p = A \cos 3x + B \sin 3x.$$

c. Because $F(x) = e^{2x}$, the normal choice for y_p would be Ae^{2x}. However, because $y_h = C_1 e^{2x} + C_2 x e^{2x}$ already contains an xe^{2x} term, you should multiply by x^2 to get

$$y_p = Ax^2 e^{2x}. \qquad \blacksquare$$

EXAMPLE 4   Solving a Third-Order Equation

Find the general solution of

$$y''' + 3y'' + 3y' + y = x.$$

Solution   From Example 6 in the previous section, you know that the homogeneous solution is

$$y_h = C_1 e^{-x} + C_2 x e^{-x} + C_3 x^2 e^{-x}.$$

Because $F(x) = x$, let $y_p = A + Bx$ and obtain $y_p' = B$ and $y_p'' = 0$. Thus, by substitution, you have

$$(0) + 3(0) + 3(B) + (A + Bx) = (3B + A) + Bx = x.$$

Thus, $B = 1$ and $A = -3$, which implies that $y_p = -3 + x$. Therefore, the general solution is

$$\begin{aligned} y &= y_h + y_p \\ &= C_1 e^{-x} + C_2 x e^{-x} + C_3 x^2 e^{-x} - 3 + x. \end{aligned} \qquad \blacksquare$$

EXERCISES for Section 16.6

In Exercises 1–4, verify that the equation is a solution of the differential equation.

Solution	Differential equation
1. $y = 2(e^{2x} - \cos x)$	$y'' + y = 10e^{2x}$
2. $y = (2 + \frac{1}{2}x)\sin x$	$y'' + y = \cos x$
3. $y = 3\sin x - \cos x \ln|\sec x + \tan x|$	$y'' + y = \tan x$
4. $y = \left(5 - \ln|\sin x|\right)\cos x - x\sin x$	$y'' + y = \csc x \cot x$

In Exercises 5–20, solve the differential equation by the method of undetermined coefficients.

5. $y'' - 3y' + 2y = 2x$ **6.** $y'' - 2y' - 3y = x^2 - 1$

7. $y'' + y = x^3$
    $y(0) = 1, y'(0) = 0$

8. $y'' + 4y = 4$
    $y(0) = 1, y'(0) = 6$

9. $y'' + 2y' = 2e^x$ **10.** $y'' - 9y = 5e^{3x}$

11. $y'' - 10y' + 25y = 5 + 6e^x$

12. $16y'' - 8y' + y = 4(x + e^x)$

13. $y'' + y' = 2\sin x$ **14.** $y'' + y' - 2y = 3\cos 2x$
    $y(0) = 0, y'(0) = -3$ $y(0) = -1, y'(0) = 2$

15. $y'' + 9y = \sin 3x$

16. $y'' + 4y' + 5y = \sin x + \cos x$

17. $y''' - 3y' + 2y = 2e^{-2x}$

18. $y''' - y'' = 4x^2$
    $y(0) = 1, y'(0) = 1, y''(0) = 1$

19. $y' - 4y = xe^x - xe^{4x}$ **20.** $y' + 2y = \sin x$
    $y(0) = \dfrac{1}{3}$ $y\left(\dfrac{\pi}{2}\right) = \dfrac{2}{5}$

In Exercises 21–26, solve the differential equation by the method of variation of parameters.

21. $y'' + y = \sec x$ **22.** $y'' + y = \sec x \tan x$

23. $y'' + 4y = \csc 2x$ **24.** $y'' - 4y' + 4y = x^2 e^{2x}$

25. $y'' - 2y' + y = e^x \ln x$

26. $y'' - 4y' + 4y = \dfrac{e^{2x}}{x}$

Electrical Circuits   In Exercises 27 and 28, use the electrical circuit differential equation

$$\frac{d^2q}{dt^2} + \left(\frac{R}{L}\right)\frac{dq}{dt} + \left(\frac{1}{LC}\right)q = \left(\frac{1}{L}\right)E(t)$$

where R is the resistance (in ohms), C is the capacitance (in farads), L is the inductance (in henrys), $E(t)$ is the electromotive force (in volts), and q is the charge on the capacitor (in coulombs). Find the charge q as a function of time for the electrical circuit described. Assume that $q(0) = 0$ and $q'(0) = 0$.

27. $R = 20, C = 0.02, L = 2$
    $E(t) = 12\sin 5t$

28. $R = 20, C = 0.02, L = 1$
    $E(t) = 10\sin 5t$

[C] *Vibrating Spring*   In Exercises 29–32, find the particular solution of the differential equation

$$\frac{w}{g}y''(t) + by'(t) + ky(t) = \frac{w}{g}F(t)$$

for the oscillating motion of an object on the end of a spring. Use a graphing utility to graph the solution. In the equation, y is the displacement from the equilibrium (positive direction is downward) measured in feet, and t is time in seconds (see figure). The constant w is the weight of the object, g is the acceleration due to gravity, b is the magnitude of the resistance to the motion, k is the spring constant from Hooke's Law, and $F(t)$ is the acceleration imposed on the system.

29. $\frac{24}{32}y'' + 48y = \frac{24}{32}(48\sin 4t)$
    $y(0) = \frac{1}{4}, y'(0) = 0$

30. $\frac{2}{32}y'' + 4y = \frac{2}{32}(4\sin 8t)$
    $y(0) = \frac{1}{4}, y'(0) = 0$

31. $\frac{2}{32}y'' + y' + 4y = \frac{2}{32}(4\sin 8t)$
    $y(0) = \frac{1}{4}, y'(0) = -3$

32. $\frac{4}{32}y'' + \frac{1}{2}y' + \frac{25}{2}y = 0$
    $y(0) = \frac{1}{2}, y'(0) = -4$

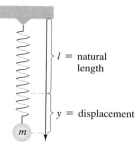

l = natural length

y = displacement

m

Spring displacement

FIGURE FOR 29–32

33. *Vibrating Spring*   Rewrite y_h in the solution for Exercise 29 by using the identity

$$a\cos \omega t + b\sin \omega t = \sqrt{a^2 + b^2}\,\sin(\omega t + \phi)$$

where $\phi = \arctan a/b$.

34. *Vibrating Spring*   The figure shows the particular solution of the differential equation

$$\frac{4}{32}y'' + by' + \frac{25}{2}y = 0$$

$$y(0) = \frac{1}{2}, \; y'(0) = -4$$

for values of the resistance component b in the interval $[0, 1]$. (Note that when $b = \frac{1}{2}$, the problem is identical to that of Exercise 32.)

a. If there is no resistance to the motion ($b = 0$), describe the motion.

b. If $b > 0$, what is the ultimate effect of the retarding force?

c. Is there a real number M such that there will be no oscillations of the spring if $b > M$? Explain your answer.

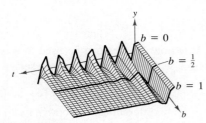

FIGURE FOR 34   *Generated by Mathematica*

35. *Parachute Jump* The fall of a parachutist is described by the second-order linear differential equation

$$\frac{w}{g}\frac{d^2y}{dt^2} - k\frac{dy}{dt} = w$$

where w is the weight of the parachutist, y is the height at time t, g is the acceleration due to gravity, and k is the drag factor of the parachute. If the parachute is opened at 2000 feet, $y(0) = 2000$, and at that time the velocity is $y'(0) = -100$ feet per second, then for a 160-pound parachutist, using $k = 8$, the differential equation is

$$-5y'' - 8y' = 160.$$

Using the given initial conditions, verify that the solution of the differential equation is

$$y = 1950 + 50e^{-1.6t} - 20t.$$

36. *Parachute Jump* Repeat Exercise 35 for a parachutist who weighs 192 pounds and has a parachute with a drag factor of $k = 9$.

37. Solve the differential equation

$$x^2y'' - xy' + y = 4x\ln x$$

given that $y_1 = x$ and $y_2 = x\ln x$ are solutions of the corresponding homogeneous equation.

Power Series Solution of a Differential Equation

We conclude this chapter by showing how power series can be used to solve certain types of differential equations. We begin with the general **power series solution** method.

Recall from Chapter 8 that a power series represents a function f on an interval of convergence, and that you can successively differentiate the power series to obtain a series for f', f'', and so on. These properties are used in the power series solution method demonstrated in the first two examples.

EXAMPLE 1   Power Series Solution

Use a power series to solve the differential equation $y' - 2y = 0$.

Solution   Assume that $y = \sum a_n x^n$ is a solution. Then, $y' = \sum n a_n x^{n-1}$. Substituting for y' and $-2y$, you obtain the following series form of the differential equation. (Note that from the third step to the fourth, the index of summation is changed to ensure that x^n occurs in both sums.)

$$y' - 2y = 0$$

$$\sum_{n=1}^{\infty} n a_n x^{n-1} - 2 \sum_{n=0}^{\infty} a_n x^n = 0$$

$$\sum_{n=1}^{\infty} n a_n x^{n-1} = \sum_{n=0}^{\infty} 2 a_n x^n$$

$$\sum_{n=0}^{\infty} (n + 1) a_{n+1} x^n = \sum_{n=0}^{\infty} 2 a_n x^n$$

Now, by equating coefficients of like terms, you obtain the **recursion formula** $(n + 1)a_{n+1} = 2a_n$, which implies that

$$a_{n+1} = \frac{2a_n}{n + 1}, \qquad n \geq 0.$$

This formula generates the following results.

a_0	a_1	a_2	a_3	a_4	a_5	$\cdots$
a_0	$2a_0$	$\dfrac{2^2 a_0}{2}$	$\dfrac{2^3 a_0}{3!}$	$\dfrac{2^4 a_0}{4!}$	$\dfrac{2^5 a_0}{5!}$	$\cdots$

Using these values as the coefficients for the *solution* series, you have

$$y = \sum_{n=0}^{\infty} \frac{2^n a_0}{n!} x^n = a_0 \sum_{n=0}^{\infty} \frac{(2x)^n}{n!} = a_0 e^{2x}.$$

In Example 1, the differential equation could be solved easily without using a series. The differential equation in Example 2 cannot be solved by any of the methods discussed in previous sections.

EXAMPLE 2 Power Series Solution

Use a power series to solve the differential equation $y'' + xy' + y = 0$.

Solution Assume that $\sum_{n=0}^{\infty} a_n x^n$ is a solution. Then you have

$$y' = \sum_{n=1}^{\infty} n a_n x^{n-1}, \qquad xy' = \sum_{n=1}^{\infty} n a_n x^n, \qquad y'' = \sum_{n=2}^{\infty} n(n-1) a_n x^{n-2}.$$

Substituting for y'', xy', and y in the given differential equation, you obtain the following series.

$$\sum_{n=2}^{\infty} n(n-1) a_n x^{n-2} + \sum_{n=0}^{\infty} n a_n x^n + \sum_{n=0}^{\infty} a_n x^n = 0$$

$$\sum_{n=2}^{\infty} n(n-1) a_n x^{n-2} = -\sum_{n=0}^{\infty} (n+1) a_n x^n$$

To obtain equal powers of x, adjust the summation indices by replacing n by $n + 2$ in the left-hand sum, to obtain

$$\sum_{n=0}^{\infty} (n+2)(n+1) a_{n+2} x^n = -\sum_{n=0}^{\infty} (n+1) a_n x^n.$$

By equating coefficients, you have $(n+2)(n+1) a_{n+2} = -(n+1) a_n$, from which you obtain the recursion formula

$$a_{n+2} = -\frac{(n+1)}{(n+2)(n+1)} a_n = -\frac{a_n}{n+2}, \qquad n \geq 0,$$

and the coefficients of the solution series are as follows.

$$a_2 = -\frac{a_0}{2} \qquad\qquad a_3 = -\frac{a_1}{3}$$

$$a_4 = -\frac{a_2}{4} = \frac{a_0}{2 \cdot 4} \qquad\qquad a_5 = -\frac{a_3}{5} = \frac{a_1}{3 \cdot 5}$$

$$a_6 = -\frac{a_4}{6} = -\frac{a_0}{2 \cdot 4 \cdot 6} \qquad\qquad a_7 = -\frac{a_5}{7} = -\frac{a_1}{3 \cdot 5 \cdot 7}$$

$$\vdots \qquad\qquad\qquad\qquad \vdots$$

$$a_{2k} = \frac{(-1)^k a_0}{2 \cdot 4 \cdot 6 \cdots (2k)} = \frac{(-1)^k a_0}{2^k (k!)} \qquad a_{2k+1} = \frac{(-1)^k a_1}{3 \cdot 5 \cdot 7 \cdots (2k+1)}$$

Thus, you can represent the general solution as the sum of two series—one for the even-powered terms with coefficients in terms of a_0 and one for the odd-powered terms with coefficients in terms of a_1.

$$y = a_0 \left(1 - \frac{x^2}{2} + \frac{x^4}{2 \cdot 4} - \cdots \right) + a_1 \left(x - \frac{x^3}{3} + \frac{x^5}{3 \cdot 5} - \cdots \right)$$

$$= a_0 \sum_{k=0}^{\infty} \frac{(-1)^k x^{2k}}{2^k (k!)} + a_1 \sum_{k=0}^{\infty} \frac{(-1)^k x^{2k+1}}{3 \cdot 5 \cdot 7 \cdots (2k+1)}$$

The solution has two arbitrary constants, a_0 and a_1, as you would expect in the general solution of a second-order differential equation.

Approximation by Taylor Series

A second type of series solution method involves a differential equation *with initial conditions* and makes use of Taylor series, as given in Section 8.10.

EXAMPLE 3   Approximation by Taylor Series

Use a Taylor series to find the series solution of

$$y' = y^2 - x$$

given the initial condition $y = 1$ when $x = 0$. Then, use the first six terms of this series solution to approximate values of y for $0 \le x \le 1$.

Solution   Recall from Section 8.10 that, for $c = 0$,

$$y = y(0) + y'(0)x + \frac{y''(0)}{2!}x^2 + \frac{y'''(0)}{3!}x^3 + \cdots .$$

Because $y(0) = 1$ and $y' = y^2 - x$, you obtain the following.

$$y(0) = 1$$
$$y' = y^2 - x \qquad\qquad y'(0) = 1$$
$$y'' = 2yy' - 1 \qquad\qquad y''(0) = 2 - 1 = 1$$
$$y''' = 2yy'' + 2(y')^2 \qquad\qquad y'''(0) = 2 + 2 = 4$$
$$y^{(4)} = 2yy''' + 6y'y'' \qquad\qquad y^{(4)}(0) = 8 + 6 = 14$$
$$y^{(5)} = 2yy^{(4)} + 8y'y''' + 6(y'')^2 \qquad y^{(5)}(0) = 28 + 32 + 6 = 66$$

Therefore, you can approximate the values of the solution from the series

$$y = y(0) + y'(0)x + \frac{y''(0)}{2!}x^2 + \frac{y'''(0)}{3!}x^3 + \frac{y^{(4)}(0)}{4!}x^4 + \frac{y^{(5)}(0)}{5!}x^5 + \cdots$$

$$= 1 + x + \frac{1}{2}x^2 + \frac{4}{3!}x^3 + \frac{14}{4!}x^4 + \frac{66}{5!}x^5 + \cdots .$$

Using the first six terms of this series, you can compute values for y in the interval $0 \le x \le 1$, as shown in Table 16.1.

TABLE 16.1

x	y
0.0	1.0000
0.1	1.1057
0.2	1.2264
0.3	1.3691
0.4	1.5432
0.5	1.7620
0.6	2.0424
0.7	2.4062
0.8	2.8805
0.9	3.4985
1.0	4.3000

EXERCISES for Section 16.7

In Exercises 1–6, verify that the power series solution of the differential equation is equivalent to the solution found using the techniques in Sections 16.2–16.6.

1. $y' - y = 0$ 2. $y' - ky = 0$

3. $y'' - 9y = 0$ 4. $y'' - k^2y = 0$

5. $y'' + 4y = 0$ 6. $y'' + k^2y = 0$

In Exercises 7–10, use power series to solve the differential equation and find the interval of convergence of the series.

7. $y' + 3xy = 0$ 8. $y' - 2xy = 0$

9. $y'' - xy' = 0$ 10. $y'' - xy' - y = 0$

In Exercises 11 and 12, find the first three terms of each of the power series representing independent solutions of the differential equation.

11. $(x^2 + 4)y'' + y = 0$ 12. $y'' + x^2y = 0$

In Exercises 13 and 14, use Taylor's Theorem to find the series solution of the differential equation under the specified initial conditions. Use n terms of the series to approximate y for the given value of x and compare the result with the approximation given by the Euler Method for $\Delta x = 0.1$.

13. $y' + (2x - 1)y = 0,\ y(0) = 2,\ n = 5,\ x = \frac{1}{2}$

14. $y' - 2xy = 0,\ y(0) = 1,\ n = 4,\ x = 1$

In Exercises 15 and 16, use Taylor's Theorem to find the series solution of the differential equation under the specified initial conditions. Use *n* terms of the series to approximate *y* for the given value of *x*.

15. $y'' - 2xy = 0$, $y(0) = 1$, $y'(0) = -3$, $n = 6$, $x = \frac{1}{4}$

16. $y'' - 2xy' + y = 0$, $y(0) = 1$, $y'(0) = 2$, $n = 8$, $x = \frac{1}{2}$

In Exercises 17–20, verify that the series converges to the given function on the indicated interval. (*Hint:* Use the given differential equation.)

17. $\displaystyle\sum_{n=0}^{\infty} \frac{x^n}{n!} = e^x$, $(-\infty, \infty)$

   Differential equation: $y' - y = 0$

18. $\displaystyle\sum_{n=0}^{\infty} \frac{(-1)^n x^{2n}}{(2n)!} = \cos x$, $(-\infty, \infty)$

   Differential Equation: $y'' + y = 0$

19. $\displaystyle\sum_{n=0}^{\infty} \frac{(-1)^n x^{2n+1}}{2n + 1} = \arctan x$, $(-1, 1)$

   Differential Equation: $(x^2 + 1)y'' + 2xy' = 0$

20. $\displaystyle\sum_{n=0}^{\infty} \frac{(2n)! x^{2n+1}}{(2^n n!)^2 (2n + 1)} = \arcsin x$, $(-1, 1)$

   Differential equation: $(1 - x^2)y'' - xy' = 0$

21. Find the first six terms in the series solution of Airy's equation $y'' - xy = 0$.

REVIEW EXERCISES for Chapter 16

In Exercises 1–4, classify the differential equation according to type and order.

1. $\dfrac{\partial^2 u}{\partial t^2} = c^2 \dfrac{\partial^2 u}{\partial x^2}$

2. $yy'' = x + 1$

3. $y'' + 3y' - 10 = 0$

4. $(y'')^2 + 4y' = 0$

In Exercises 5 and 6, use the given differential equation and its direction field to answer questions about the solutions of the differential equation.

5. $\dfrac{dy}{dx} = \dfrac{y}{x}$

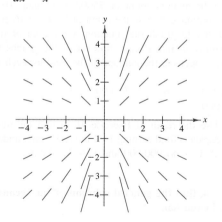

a. Sketch several solution curves for the differential equation on the direction field.
b. Find the general solution of the differential equation. Compare the result with the sketches from part a.

6. $\dfrac{dy}{dx} = \sqrt{1 - y^2}$

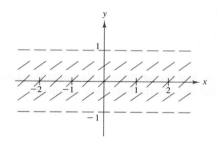

a. Sketch several solution curves for the differential equation on the direction field.
b. When is the rate of change of the solution greatest? When is it least?
c. Find the general solution of the differential equation. Compare the result with the sketches from part a.

In Exercises 7–10, match the differential equation with its solution.

Differential equation	Solution
7. $y' - 4 = 0$	a. $y = C_1 e^{2x} + C_2 e^{-2x}$
8. $y' - 4y = 0$	b. $y = 4x + C$
9. $y'' - 4y = 0$	c. $y = C_1 \cos 2x + C_2 \sin 2x$
10. $y'' + 4y = 0$	d. $y = Ce^{4x}$

$$-\varepsilon < h(x) - L < \varepsilon \qquad \text{and} \qquad -\varepsilon < g(x) - L < \varepsilon$$
$$L - \varepsilon < h(x) \qquad \text{and} \qquad g(x) < L + \varepsilon.$$

Now, because $h(x) \leq f(x) \leq g(x)$, it follows that $L - \varepsilon < f(x) < L + \varepsilon$, which implies that $|f(x) - L| < \varepsilon$. Therefore,

$$\lim_{x \to c} f(x) = L.$$

THEOREM 1.14
VERTICAL ASYMPTOTES
(page 98)

Let f and g be continuous on an open interval containing c. If $f(c) \neq 0$, $g(c) = 0$, and there exists an open interval containing c such that $g(x) \neq 0$ for all $x \neq c$ in the interval, then the graph of the function given by

$$h(x) = \frac{f(x)}{g(x)}$$

has a vertical asymptote at $x = c$.

Proof We consider the case for which $f(c) > 0$, and there exists $b > c$ such that $c < x < b$ implies $g(x) > 0$. Then for $M > 0$, we choose δ_1 such that

$$0 < x - c < \delta_1 \qquad \text{implies that} \qquad \frac{f(c)}{2} < f(x) < \frac{3f(c)}{2}$$

and δ_2 such that

$$0 < x - c < \delta_2 \qquad \text{implies that} \qquad 0 < g(x) < \frac{f(c)}{2M}.$$

Now we let δ be the smaller of δ_1 and δ_2. Then, it follows that

$$0 < x - c < \delta \qquad \text{implies that} \qquad \frac{f(x)}{g(x)} > \frac{f(c)}{2}\left(\frac{2M}{f(c)}\right) = M.$$

Therefore, it follows that

$$\lim_{x \to c^+} \frac{f(x)}{g(x)} = \infty$$

and the line $x = c$ is a vertical asymptote of the graph of h.

ALTERNATE FORM OF THE
DERIVATIVE (page 110)

The derivative of f at c is given by

$$f'(c) = \lim_{x \to c} \frac{f(x) - f(c)}{x - c}$$

provided this limit exists.

Proof The derivative of f at c is given by

$$f'(c) = \lim_{\Delta x \to 0} \frac{f(c + \Delta x) - f(c)}{\Delta x}.$$

Let $x = c + \Delta x$. Then $x \to c$ as $\Delta x \to 0$. Thus, replacing $c + \Delta x$ by x, we have

$$f'(c) = \lim_{\Delta x \to 0} \frac{f(c + \Delta x) - f(c)}{\Delta x} = \lim_{x \to c} \frac{f(x) - f(c)}{x - c}.$$

**THEOREM 2.10
THE CHAIN RULE
(page 138)**

If $y = f(u)$ is a differentiable function of u, and $u = g(x)$ is a differentiable function of x, then $y = f(g(x))$ is a differentiable function of x and

$$\frac{dy}{dx} = \frac{dy}{du} \cdot \frac{du}{dx} \quad \text{or equivalently,} \quad \frac{d}{dx}[f(g(x))] = f'(g(x))g'(x).$$

Proof In Section 2.4, we let $h(x) = f(g(x))$ and used the alternate form of the derivative to show that $h'(c) = f'(g(c))g'(c)$, provided $g(x) \neq g(c)$ for values of x other than c. We now consider a more general proof. We begin by considering the derivative of f.

$$f'(x) = \lim_{\Delta x \to 0} \frac{f(x + \Delta x) - f(x)}{\Delta x} = \lim_{\Delta x \to 0} \frac{\Delta y}{\Delta x}$$

For a fixed value of x, we define a function η such that

$$\eta(\Delta x) = \begin{cases} 0, & \Delta x = 0 \\ \dfrac{\Delta y}{\Delta x} - f'(x), & \Delta x \neq 0. \end{cases}$$

Because the limit of $\eta(\Delta x)$ as $\Delta x \to 0$ doesn't depend upon the value of $\eta(0)$, we have

$$\lim_{\Delta x \to 0} \eta(\Delta x) = \lim_{\Delta x \to 0} \left[\frac{\Delta y}{\Delta x} - f'(x) \right] = 0$$

and we can conclude that η is continuous at 0. Moreover, because $\Delta y = 0$ when $\Delta x = 0$, the equation

$$\Delta y = \Delta x \eta(\Delta x) + \Delta x f'(x)$$

is valid whether Δx is zero or not. Now, by letting $\Delta u = g(x + \Delta x) - g(x)$, we use the continuity of g to conclude that

$$\lim_{\Delta x \to 0} \Delta u = \lim_{\Delta x \to 0} [g(x + \Delta x) - g(x)] = 0,$$

which implies that

$$\lim_{\Delta x \to 0} \eta(\Delta u) = 0.$$

Finally,

$$\Delta y = \Delta u \eta(\Delta u) + \Delta u f'(u) \longrightarrow \frac{\Delta y}{\Delta x} = \frac{\Delta u}{\Delta x} \eta(\Delta u) + \frac{\Delta u}{\Delta x} f'(u), \quad \Delta x \neq 0$$

and taking the limit as $\Delta x \to 0$, we have

$$\frac{dy}{dx} = \frac{du}{dx} \left[\lim_{\Delta x \to 0} \eta(\Delta u) \right] + \frac{du}{dx} f'(u) = \frac{dy}{dx}(0) + \frac{du}{dx} f'(u)$$

$$= \frac{du}{dx} f'(u) = \frac{du}{dx} \cdot \frac{dy}{du}. \qquad \blacksquare$$

**CONCAVITY
INTERPRETATION
(page 189)**

1. Let f be differentiable at c. If the graph of f is concave upward at $(c, f(c))$, then the graph of f lies *above* the tangent line at $(c, f(c))$ on some open interval containing c.
2. Let f be differentiable at c. If the graph of f is concave downward at $(c, f(c))$, then the graph of f lies *below* the tangent line at $(c, f(c))$ on some open interval containing c.

Proof   Assume f is concave upward at c. Then by definition, there exists an interval (a, b) containing c such that f' is increasing on (a, b). The equation of the tangent line to the graph of f at c is given by

$$g(x) = f(c) + f'(c)(x - c).$$

If x is in the open interval (c, b), then the directed distance from the point $(x, f(x))$ (on the graph of f) to the point $(x, g(x))$ (on the tangent line) is given by

$$\begin{aligned} d &= f(x) - [\, f(c) + f'(c)(x - c)] \\ &= f(x) - f(c) - f'(c)(x - c). \end{aligned}$$

Moreover, by the Mean Value Theorem there exists a number z in (c, x) such that

$$f'(z) = \frac{f(x) - f(c)}{x - c}.$$

Thus, we have

$$\begin{aligned} d &= f(x) - f(c) - f'(c)(x - c) \\ &= f'(z)(x - c) - f'(c)(x - c) \\ &= [\, f'(z) - f'(c)](x - c). \end{aligned}$$

The second factor $(x - c)$ is positive because $c < x$. Moreover, because f' is increasing, it follows that the first factor $[\, f'(z) - f'(c)]$ is also positive. Therefore, $d > 0$ and we conclude that the graph of f lies above the tangent line. If x is in the open interval (a, c), a similar argument can be given.   ▬

THEOREM 3.10
LIMITS AT INFINITY
(page 198)

If r is a positive rational number, and c is any real number, then

$$\lim_{x \to \infty} \frac{c}{x^r} = 0.$$

Furthermore, if x^r is defined when $x < 0$, then

$$\lim_{x \to -\infty} \frac{c}{x^r} = 0.$$

Proof   We begin by proving that

$$\lim_{x \to \infty} \frac{1}{x} = 0.$$

For $\varepsilon > 0$, let $M = 1/\varepsilon$. Then, for $x > M$, we have

$$x > M = \frac{1}{\varepsilon} \quad \rightarrow \quad \frac{1}{x} < \varepsilon \quad \rightarrow \quad \left| \frac{1}{x} - 0 \right| < \varepsilon.$$

Therefore, by the definition of a limit at infinity, we conclude that the limit of $1/x$ as $x \to \infty$ is 0. Now, using this result, and letting $r = m/n$, we can write the following.

$$\begin{aligned} \lim_{x \to \infty} \left(\frac{c}{x^r} \right) &= \lim_{x \to \infty} \left(\frac{c}{x^{m/n}} \right) \\ &= c \left[\lim_{x \to \infty} \left(\frac{1}{\sqrt[n]{x}} \right)^m \right] \\ &= c \left[\lim_{x \to \infty} \sqrt[n]{\frac{1}{x}} \right]^m \end{aligned}$$

$$= c \left[\sqrt[n]{\lim_{x \to \infty} \frac{1}{x}} \right]^m$$

$$= c \left[\sqrt[n]{0} \right]^m$$

$$= 0$$

The proof of the second part of the theorem is similar.

THEOREM 4.2
SUMMATION FORMULAS
(page 260)

1. $\displaystyle\sum_{i=1}^{n} c = cn$

2. $\displaystyle\sum_{i=1}^{n} i = \frac{n(n + 1)}{2}$

3. $\displaystyle\sum_{i=1}^{n} i^2 = \frac{n(n + 1)(2n + 1)}{6}$

4. $\displaystyle\sum_{i=1}^{n} i^3 = \frac{n^2(n + 1)^2}{4}$

Proof   The proof of part 1 is straightforward. By adding c to itself n times, we obtain a sum of nc.

To prove part 2, we write the sum in increasing and decreasing order and add corresponding terms as follows.

$$\sum_{i=1}^{n} i = \quad 1 \quad + \quad 2 \quad + \quad 3 \quad + \cdots + (n - 1) + \quad n$$

$$\downarrow \qquad \downarrow \qquad \downarrow \qquad \qquad \downarrow \qquad \downarrow$$

$$\sum_{i=1}^{n} i = \quad n \quad + (n - 1) + (n - 2) + \cdots + \quad 2 \quad + \quad 1$$

$$\downarrow \qquad \downarrow \qquad \downarrow \qquad \qquad \downarrow \qquad \downarrow$$

$$2\sum_{i=1}^{n} i = (n + 1) + (n + 1) + (n + 1) + \cdots + (n + 1) + (n + 1)$$

$$\underbrace{}_{n \text{ terms}}$$

Therefore,

$$\sum_{i=1}^{n} i = \frac{n(n + 1)}{2}.$$

To prove part 3, we use mathematical induction. First, if $n = 1$, the result is true because

$$\sum_{i=1}^{1} i^2 = 1^2 = 1 = \frac{1(1 + 1)(2 + 1)}{6}.$$

Now, assuming the result is true for $n = k$, we show that it is true for $n = k + 1$, as follows.

$$\sum_{i=1}^{k+1} i^2 = \sum_{i=1}^{k} i^2 + (k + 1)^2$$

$$= \frac{k(k + 1)(2k + 1)}{6} + (k + 1)^2$$

$$= \frac{k + 1}{6}(2k^2 + k + 6k + 6)$$

$$= \frac{k + 1}{6}[(2k + 3)(k + 2)]$$

$$= \frac{(k + 1)(k + 2)[2(k + 1) + 1]}{6}$$

Part 4 can be proved using a similar argument with mathematical induction.

▬

**THEOREM 4.8
PRESERVATION OF
INEQUALITY**
(page 277)

1. If f is integrable and nonnegative on the closed interval $[a, b]$, then

$$0 \le \int_a^b f(x)dx.$$

2. If f and g are integrable on the closed interval $[a, b]$, and $f(x) \le g(x)$ for every x in $[a, b]$, then

$$\int_a^b f(x)dx \le \int_a^b g(x)dx.$$

Proof   To prove part 1, we suppose, on the contrary, that

$$\int_a^b f(x)dx = I < 0.$$

Then, let $a = x_0 < x_1 < x_2 < \cdots < x_n = b$ be a partition of $[a, b]$, and let

$$R = \sum_{i=1}^n f(c_i)\Delta x_i$$

be a Riemann sum. Because $f(x) \ge 0$, it follows that $R \ge 0$. Now, for $\|\Delta\|$ sufficiently small, we have $|R - I| < -I/2$, which implies that

$$\sum_{i=1}^n f(c_i)\Delta x_i = R < I - \frac{I}{2} < 0,$$

which is not possible. From this contradiction, we can conclude that

$$0 \le \int_a^b f(x)dx.$$

To prove the second part of the theorem, we note that $f(x) \le g(x)$ implies that $g(x) - f(x) \ge 0$. Hence, we can apply the result of part 1 to conclude that

$$0 \le \int_a^b (g(x) - f(x))dx$$

$$0 \le \int_a^b g(x)dx - \int_a^b f(x)dx$$

$$\int_a^b f(x)dx \le \int_a^b g(x)dx.$$

▬

**PROPERTIES OF THE
NATURAL LOGARITHMIC
FUNCTION** (page 318)

$$\lim_{x \to 0^+} \ln x = -\infty \qquad \text{and} \qquad \lim_{x \to \infty} \ln x = \infty$$

Proof   To begin, we show that $\ln 2 \ge \frac{1}{2}$. From the Mean Value Theorem of Integrals, we can write

$$\ln 2 = \int_1^2 \frac{1}{x}\,dx = (2 - 1)\frac{1}{c} = \frac{1}{c}$$

where c is in $[1, 2]$. This implies that

$$1 \le c \quad \le 2$$

$$1 \ge \frac{1}{c} \quad \ge \frac{1}{2}$$

$$1 \ge \ln 2 \ge \frac{1}{2}.$$

Now, let N be any positive (large) number. Because $\ln x$ is increasing, it follows that if $x > 2^{2N}$, then

$$\ln x > \ln 2^{2N} = 2N \ln 2.$$

However, because $\ln 2 \ge \frac{1}{2}$, it follows that

$$\ln x > 2N \ln 2 \ge 2N\left(\frac{1}{2}\right) = N.$$

This verifies the second limit. To verify the first limit, we let $z = 1/x$. Then, $z \to \infty$ as $x \to 0^+$, and we can write

$$\lim_{x \to 0^+} \ln x = \lim_{x \to 0^+} \left(-\ln \frac{1}{x}\right) = \lim_{z \to \infty} (-\ln z) = -\lim_{z \to \infty} \ln z = -\infty. \qquad \blacksquare$$

THEOREM 5.8
CONTINUITY AND
DIFFERENTIABILITY OF
INVERSE FUNCTIONS
(page 339)

Let f be a function whose domain is an interval I. If f possesses an inverse, then the following statements are true.

1. If f is continuous on its domain, then f^{-1} is continuous on its domain.
2. If f is increasing on its domain, then f^{-1} is increasing on its domain.
3. If f is decreasing on its domain, then f^{-1} is decreasing on its domain.
4. If f is differentiable at c and $f'(c) \ne 0$, then f^{-1} is differentiable at $f(c)$.

Proof To prove part 1, we first show that if f is continuous on I, and has an inverse, then f is strictly monotonic on I. Suppose that f were not strictly monotonic. Then there would exist numbers x_1, x_2, x_3 in I such that $x_1 < x_2 < x_3$ but $f(x_2)$ is not between $f(x_1)$ and $f(x_3)$. Without loss of generality, assume $f(x_1) < f(x_3) < f(x_2)$. By the Intermediate Value Theorem, there exists a number x_0 between x_1 and x_2 such that $f(x_0) = x_3$. Thus, f is not one-to-one, and cannot have an inverse. Hence f must be strictly monotonic.

Because f is continuous, the Intermediate Value Theorem implies that the set of values of f,

$$\{f(x): x \in I\}, \text{ forms an interval } J.$$

Assume that a is an interior point of J. From the previous argument, $f^{-1}(a)$ is an interior point of I. Let $\varepsilon > 0$. There exists $0 < \varepsilon_1 < \varepsilon$ such that

$$I_1 = (f^{-1}(a) - \varepsilon_1, f^{-1}(a) + \varepsilon_1) \subseteq I.$$

Because f is strictly monotonic on I_1, the set of values $\{f(x): x \in I_1\}$ forms an interval $J_1 \subseteq J$. Let $\delta > 0$ such that $(a - \delta, a + \delta) \subseteq J_1$. Finally, if

$$|y - a| < \delta, \text{ then } |f^{-1}(y) - f^{-1}(a)| < \varepsilon_1 < \varepsilon.$$

Hence, f^{-1} is continuous at a. A similar proof can be given if a is an endpoint.

To prove part 2, let y_1 and y_2 be in the domain of f^{-1}, with $y_1 < y_2$. Then, there exist x_1 and x_2 in the domain of f such that

$$f(x_1) = y_1 < y_2 = f(x_2).$$

We can use the Extended Mean Value Theorem to prove L'Hôpital's Rule. Of the several different cases of this rule, we illustrate the proof of only one case and leave the remaining cases for you to prove.

THEOREM 7.4
L'HÔPITAL'S RULE
(page 526)

Let f and g be functions that are differentiable on an open interval (a, b) containing c, except possibly at c itself. Assume that $g'(x) \neq 0$ for all x in (a, b), except possibly at c itself. If the limit of $f(x)/g(x)$ as x approaches c produces the indeterminate form $0/0$, then

$$\lim_{x \to c} \frac{f(x)}{g(x)} = \lim_{x \to c} \frac{f'(x)}{g'(x)}$$

provided the limit on the right exists (or is infinite). This result also applies if the limit of $f(x)/g(x)$ as x approaches c produces the indeterminate forms ∞/∞, $(-\infty)/\infty$, $\infty/(-\infty)$, or $(-\infty)/(-\infty)$.

Proof   We consider the case for which

$$\lim_{x \to c^+} f(x) = 0 \qquad \text{and} \qquad \lim_{x \to c^+} g(x) = 0.$$

Define the following new functions:

$$F(x) = \begin{cases} f(x), & x \neq c \\ 0, & x = c \end{cases} \qquad \text{and} \qquad G(x) = \begin{cases} g(x), & x \neq c \\ 0, & x = c \end{cases}.$$

For any x, $c < x < b$, F and G are differentiable on $(c, x]$ and continuous on $[c, x]$. We can apply the Extended Mean Value Theorem to conclude that there exists a number z in (c, x) such that

$$\frac{F'(z)}{G'(z)} = \frac{F(x) - F(c)}{G(x) - G(c)} = \frac{F(x)}{G(x)} = \frac{f'(z)}{g'(z)} = \frac{f(x)}{g(x)}.$$

Finally, by letting x approach c from the right, $x \to c^+$, we have $z \to c^+$ because $c < z < x$, and

$$\lim_{x \to c^+} \frac{f(x)}{g(x)} = \lim_{x \to c^+} \frac{f'(z)}{g'(z)} = \lim_{z \to c^+} \frac{f'(z)}{g'(z)} = \lim_{x \to c^+} \frac{f'(x)}{g'(x)}$$

The proof for the case where $x \to c^-$ and $x \to c$ are left to the reader.   ∎

THEOREM 8.19
TAYLOR'S THEOREM
(page 602)

If a function f is differentiable through order $n + 1$ in an interval I containing c, then for each x in I, there exists z between x and c such that

$$f(x) = f(c) + f'(c)(x - c) + \frac{f''(c)}{2!}(x - c)^2 + \cdots + \frac{f^{(n)}(c)}{n!}(x - c)^n + R_n(x)$$

where

$$R_n(x) = \frac{f^{(n+1)}(z)}{(n + 1)!}(x - c)^{n+1}.$$

Proof   To find $R_n(x)$ we fix x in I ($x \neq c$) and write

$$R_n(x) = f(x) - P_n(x)$$

where $P_n(x)$ is the nth Taylor polynomial for $f(x)$. Then we let g be a function of t defined by

$$g(t) = f(x) - f(t) - f'(t)(x - t) - \cdots - \frac{f^{(n)}(t)}{n!}(x - t)^n - R_n(x)\frac{(x - t)^{n+1}}{(x - c)^{n+1}}.$$

The reason for defining g this way is that differentiation with respect to t has a telescoping effect. For example, we have

$$\frac{d}{dt}[-f(t) - f'(t)(x - t)] = -f'(t) + f'(t) - f''(t)(x - t)$$

$$= -f''(t)(x - t).$$

The result is that the derivative $g'(t)$ simplifies to

$$g'(t) = -\frac{f^{(n+1)}(t)}{n!}(x - t)^n + (n + 1)R_n(x)\frac{(x - t)^n}{(x - c)^{n+1}}$$

for all t between c and x. Moreover, for a fixed x

$$g(c) = f(x) - [P_n(x) + R_n(x)] = f(x) - f(x) = 0$$

and

$$g(x) = f(x) - f(x) - 0 - \cdots - 0 = f(x) - f(x) = 0.$$

Therefore, g satisfies the conditions of Rolle's Theorem, and it follows that there is a number z between c and x such that $g'(z) = 0$. Substituting z for t in the equation for $g'(t)$ and then solving for $R_n(x)$, we obtain

$$g'(z) = -\frac{f^{(n+1)}(z)}{n!}(x - z)^n + (n + 1)R_n(x)\frac{(x - z)^n}{(x - c)^{n+1}} = 0$$

$$R_n(x) = \frac{f^{(n+1)}(z)}{(n + 1)!}(x - c)^{n+1}.$$

Finally, because $g(c) = 0$, we have

$$0 = f(x) - f(c) - f'(c)(x - c) - \cdots - \frac{f^{(n)}(c)}{n!}(x - c)^n - R_n(x)$$

$$f(x) = f(c) + f'(c)(x - c) + \cdots + \frac{f^{(n)}(c)}{n!}(x - c)^n + R_n(x).$$

THEOREM 9.7
ROTATION OF AXES
(page 660)

$Ax^2 + Bxy + Cy^2 + Dx + Ey + F = 0$ where $B \neq 0$, can be rewritten as

$$A'(x')^2 + C'(y')^2 + D'x' + E'y' + F' = 0$$

by rotating the coordinate axes through an angle θ, where

$$\cot 2\theta = \frac{A - C}{B}.$$

The coefficients of the new equation are obtained by making the substitutions

$$x = x' \cos \theta - y' \sin \theta$$
$$y = x' \sin \theta + y' \cos \theta.$$

Proof   To discover how the coordinates in the xy-system are related to the coordinates in the $x'y'$-system, we choose a point $P = (x, y)$ in the original system and attempt to find its coordinates (x', y') in the rotated system. In either system the distance r between the point P and the origin is the same, thus the equations for x, y, x', and y' are those given in Figure A.1. Using the formulas for the sine and cosine of the difference of two angles, we obtain

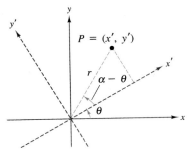

Rotated: $x' = r \cos (\alpha - \theta)$
             $y' = r \sin (\alpha - \theta)$

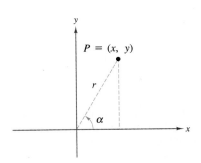

Original: $x = r \cos \alpha$
            $y = r \sin \alpha$

$$x' = r \cos (\alpha - \theta) = r(\cos \alpha \cos \theta + \sin \alpha \sin \theta)$$

$$= r \cos \alpha \cos \theta + r \sin \alpha \sin \theta = x \cos \theta + y \sin \theta$$

$$y' = r \sin (\alpha - \theta) = r(\sin \alpha \cos \theta - \cos \alpha \sin \theta)$$

$$= r \sin \alpha \cos \theta - r \cos \alpha \sin \theta = y \cos \theta - x \sin \theta.$$

Solving this system for x and y yields

$$x = x' \cos \theta - y' \sin \theta \qquad \text{and} \qquad y = x' \sin \theta + y' \cos \theta.$$

Finally, by substituting these values for x and y into the original equation and collecting terms, we obtain the following.

$$A' = A \cos^2 \theta + B \cos \theta \sin \theta + C \sin^2 \theta$$

$$C' = A \sin^2 \theta - B \cos \theta \sin \theta + C \cos^2 \theta$$

$$D' = D \cos \theta + E \sin \theta$$

$$E' = -D \sin \theta + E \cos \theta$$

$$F' = F$$

Now, in order to eliminate the $x'y'$ term, we must select θ so that $B' = 0$ as follows.

$$B' = 2(C - A) \sin \theta \cos \theta + B(\cos^2 \theta - \sin^2 \theta)$$

$$= (C - A) \sin 2\theta + B \cos 2\theta$$

$$= B(\sin 2\theta)\left(\frac{C - A}{B} + \cot 2\theta\right) = 0, \quad \sin 2\theta \neq 0$$

If $B = 0$, no rotation is necessary since the xy term is not present in the original equation. If $B \neq 0$, then the only way to make $B' = 0$ is to let

$$\cot 2\theta = \frac{A - C}{B}, \quad B \neq 0.$$

Thus, we have established the desired results.

THEOREM 10.10 **CLASSIFICATION OF CONICS** **BY ECCENTRICITY** (page 705)	The locus of a point in the plane whose distance from a fixed point (*focus*) has a constant ratio to its distance from a fixed line (*directrix*) is a conic. The constant ratio e is the *eccentricity* of the conic. 1. The conic is an ellipse if $0 < e < 1$. 2. The conic is a parabola if $e = 1$. 3. The conic is a hyperbola if $e > 1$.

Proof If $e = 1$, then by **definition**, the conic must be a parabola. If $e \neq 1$, then we consider the focus F to lie at the origin and the directrix $x = d$ to lie to the right of the origin, as shown in Figure A.2. For the point $P = (r, \theta) = (x, y)$, we have $|PF| = r$ and $|PQ| = d - r\cos\theta$. Given that $e = |PF|/|PQ|$, it follows that

$$|PF| = |PQ|e \rightarrow r = e(d - r\cos\theta).$$

By converting to rectangular coordinates and squaring both sides, we obtain

$$x^2 + y^2 = e^2(d - x)^2 = e^2(d^2 - 2dx + x^2).$$

Completing the square produces

$$\left(x + \frac{e^2 d}{1 - e^2}\right)^2 + \frac{y^2}{1 - e^2} = \frac{e^2 d^2}{(1 - e^2)^2}.$$

If $e < 1$, then this equation represents an ellipse. If $e > 1$, then $1 - e^2 < 0$, and the equation represents a hyperbola. ▮

THEOREM 13.6
CHAIN RULE: ONE
INDEPENDENT VARIABLE
(page 869)

Let $w = f(x, y)$, where f is a differentiable function of x and y. If $x = g(t)$ and $y = h(t)$, where g and h are differentiable functions of t, then w is a differentiable function of t, and

$$\frac{dw}{dt} = \frac{\partial w}{\partial x}\frac{dx}{dt} + \frac{\partial w}{\partial y}\frac{dy}{dt}.$$

Proof Because g and h are differentiable functions of t, we know that both Δx and Δy approach zero as Δt approaches zero. Moreover, because f is a differentiable function of x and y, we know that

$$\Delta w = \frac{\partial w}{\partial x}\Delta x + \frac{\partial w}{\partial y}\Delta y + \varepsilon_1 \Delta x + \varepsilon_2 \Delta y$$

where both ε_1 and $\varepsilon_2 \rightarrow 0$ as $(\Delta x, \Delta y) \rightarrow (0, 0)$. Thus, for $\Delta t \neq 0$, we have

$$\frac{\Delta w}{\Delta t} = \frac{\partial w}{\partial x}\frac{\Delta x}{\Delta t} + \frac{\partial w}{\partial y}\frac{\Delta y}{\Delta t} + \varepsilon_1 \frac{\Delta x}{\Delta t} + \varepsilon_2 \frac{\Delta y}{\Delta t}$$

from which it follows that

$$\frac{dw}{dt} = \lim_{\Delta t \to 0}\frac{\Delta w}{\Delta t} = \frac{\partial w}{\partial x}\frac{dx}{dt} + \frac{\partial w}{\partial y}\frac{dy}{dt} + 0\left(\frac{dx}{dt}\right) + 0\left(\frac{dy}{dt}\right)$$

$$= \frac{\partial w}{\partial x}\frac{dx}{dt} + \frac{\partial w}{\partial y}\frac{dy}{dt}. \quad ▮$$

APPENDIX B

Basic Differentiation Rules for Elementary Functions

1. $\dfrac{d}{dx}[cu] = cu'$

2. $\dfrac{d}{dx}[u \pm v] = u' \pm v'$

3. $\dfrac{d}{dx}[uv] = uv' + vu'$

4. $\dfrac{d}{dx}\left[\dfrac{u}{v}\right] = \dfrac{vu' - uv'}{v^2}$

5. $\dfrac{d}{dx}[c] = 0$

6. $\dfrac{d}{dx}[u^n] = nu^{n-1}u'$

7. $\dfrac{d}{dx}[x] = 1$

8. $\dfrac{d}{dx}[\,|\,u\,|\,] = \dfrac{u}{|u|}(u'),\ u \neq 0$

9. $\dfrac{d}{dx}[\ln u] = \dfrac{u'}{u}$

10. $\dfrac{d}{dx}[e^u] = e^u u'$

11. $\dfrac{d}{dx}[\sin u] = (\cos u)u'$

12. $\dfrac{d}{dx}[\cos u] = -(\sin u)u'$

13. $\dfrac{d}{dx}[\tan u] = (\sec^2 u)u'$

14. $\dfrac{d}{dx}[\cot u] = -(\csc^2 u)u'$

15. $\dfrac{d}{dx}[\sec u] = (\sec u \tan u)u'$

16. $\dfrac{d}{dx}[\csc u] = -(\csc u \cot u)u'$

17. $\dfrac{d}{dx}[\arcsin u] = \dfrac{u'}{\sqrt{1 - u^2}}$

18. $\dfrac{d}{dx}[\arccos u] = \dfrac{-u'}{\sqrt{1 - u^2}}$

19. $\dfrac{d}{dx}[\arctan u] = \dfrac{u'}{1 + u^2}$

20. $\dfrac{d}{dx}[\text{arccot } u] = \dfrac{-u'}{1 + u^2}$

21. $\dfrac{d}{dx}[\text{arcsec } u] = \dfrac{u'}{|u|\sqrt{u^2 - 1}}$

22. $\dfrac{d}{dx}[\text{arccsc } u] = \dfrac{-u'}{|u|\sqrt{u^2 - 1}}$

27. $\int u^2\sqrt{u^2 \pm a^2}\, du = \frac{1}{8}\left[u(2u^2 \pm a^2)\sqrt{u^2 \pm a^2} - a^4 \ln|u + \sqrt{u^2 \pm a^2}|\right] + C$

28. $\int \frac{\sqrt{u^2 + a^2}}{u}\, du = \sqrt{u^2 + a^2} - a \ln\left|\frac{a + \sqrt{u^2 + a^2}}{u}\right| + C$

29. $\int \frac{\sqrt{u^2 - a^2}}{u}\, du = \sqrt{u^2 - a^2} - a \operatorname{arcsec} \frac{|u|}{a} + C$

30. $\int \frac{\sqrt{u^2 \pm a^2}}{u^2}\, du = \frac{-\sqrt{u^2 \pm a^2}}{u} + \ln|u + \sqrt{u^2 \pm a^2}| + C$

31. $\int \frac{1}{\sqrt{u^2 \pm a^2}}\, du = \ln|u + \sqrt{u^2 \pm a^2}| + C$

32. $\int \frac{1}{u\sqrt{u^2 + a^2}}\, du = \frac{-1}{a} \ln\left|\frac{a + \sqrt{u^2 + a^2}}{u}\right| + C$

33. $\int \frac{1}{u\sqrt{u^2 - a^2}}\, du = \frac{1}{a} \operatorname{arcsec} \frac{|u|}{a} + C$

34. $\int \frac{u^2}{\sqrt{u^2 \pm a^2}}\, du = \frac{1}{2}\left(u\sqrt{u^2 \pm a^2} \mp a^2 \ln|u + \sqrt{u^2 \pm a^2}|\right) + C$

35. $\int \frac{1}{u^2\sqrt{u^2 \pm a^2}}\, du = \mp \frac{\sqrt{u^2 \pm a^2}}{a^2 u} + C$

36. $\int \frac{1}{(u^2 \pm a^2)^{3/2}}\, du = \frac{\pm u}{a^2\sqrt{u^2 \pm a^2}} + C$

Forms Involving $\sqrt{a^2 - u^2}$, $0 < a$

37. $\int \sqrt{a^2 - u^2}\, du = \frac{1}{2}\left(u\sqrt{a^2 - u^2} + a^2 \arcsin \frac{u}{a}\right) + C$

38. $\int u^2\sqrt{a^2 - u^2}\, du = \frac{1}{8}\left[u(2u^2 - a^2)\sqrt{a^2 - u^2} + a^4 \arcsin \frac{u}{a}\right] + C$

39. $\int \frac{\sqrt{a^2 - u^2}}{u}\, du = \sqrt{a^2 - u^2} - a \ln\left|\frac{a + \sqrt{a^2 - u^2}}{u}\right| + C$

40. $\int \frac{\sqrt{a^2 - u^2}}{u^2}\, du = \frac{-\sqrt{a^2 - u^2}}{u} - \arcsin \frac{u}{a} + C$

41. $\int \frac{1}{\sqrt{a^2 - u^2}}\, du = \arcsin \frac{u}{a} + C$

42. $\int \frac{1}{u\sqrt{a^2 - u^2}}\, du = \frac{-1}{a} \ln\left|\frac{a + \sqrt{a^2 - u^2}}{u}\right| + C$

43. $\int \frac{u^2}{\sqrt{a^2 - u^2}}\, du = \frac{1}{2}\left(-u\sqrt{a^2 - u^2} + a^2 \arcsin \frac{u}{a}\right) + C$

44. $\int \frac{1}{u^2\sqrt{a^2 - u^2}}\, du = \frac{-\sqrt{a^2 - u^2}}{a^2 u} + C$

45. $\int \frac{1}{(a^2 - u^2)^{3/2}}\, du = \frac{u}{a^2\sqrt{a^2 - u^2}} + C$

Forms Involving $\sin u$ or $\cos u$

46. $\displaystyle\int \sin u \, du = -\cos u + C$

47. $\displaystyle\int \cos u \, du = \sin u + C$

48. $\displaystyle\int \sin^2 u \, du = \frac{1}{2}(u - \sin u \cos u) + C$

49. $\displaystyle\int \cos^2 u \, du = \frac{1}{2}(u + \sin u \cos u) + C$

50. $\displaystyle\int \sin^n u \, du = -\frac{\sin^{n-1} u \cos u}{n} + \frac{n-1}{n}\int \sin^{n-2} u \, du$

51. $\displaystyle\int \cos^n u \, du = \frac{\cos^{n-1} u \sin u}{n} + \frac{n-1}{n}\int \cos^{n-2} u \, du$

52. $\displaystyle\int u \sin u \, du = \sin u - u \cos u + C$

53. $\displaystyle\int u \cos u \, du = \cos u + u \sin u + C$

54. $\displaystyle\int u^n \sin u \, du = -u^n \cos u + n\int u^{n-1} \cos u \, du$

55. $\displaystyle\int u^n \cos u \, du = u^n \sin u - n\int u^{n-1} \sin u \, du$

56. $\displaystyle\int \frac{1}{1 \pm \sin u} \, du = \tan u \mp \sec u + C$

57. $\displaystyle\int \frac{1}{1 \pm \cos u} \, du = -\cot u \pm \csc u + C$

58. $\displaystyle\int \frac{1}{\sin u \cos u} \, du = \ln |\tan u| + C$

Forms Involving $\tan u$, $\cot u$, $\sec u$, $\csc u$

59. $\displaystyle\int \tan u \, du = -\ln |\cos u| + C$

60. $\displaystyle\int \cot u \, du = \ln |\sin u| + C$

61. $\displaystyle\int \sec u \, du = \ln |\sec u + \tan u| + C$

62. $\displaystyle\int \csc u \, du = \ln |\csc u - \cot u| + C$

63. $\displaystyle\int \tan^2 u \, du = -u + \tan u + C$

64. $\displaystyle\int \cot^2 u \, du = -u - \cot u + C$

65. $\displaystyle\int \sec^2 u \, du = \tan u + C$

Answers to Odd-Numbered Exercises

PREREQUISITES CHAPTER

Section P.1 (page 8)

1. Rational   3. Irrational   5. Rational
7. Rational   9. Rational   11. $\frac{4}{11}$ 13. $\frac{11}{37}$
15. a. True   b. False   c. True   d. False
    e. False   f. False
17. $x < -\frac{1}{2}$ 19. $x \geq \frac{1}{2}$

21. $-\frac{1}{2} < x < \frac{7}{2}$ 23. $x < -4$

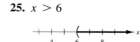

25. $x > 6$ 27. $-1 < x < 1$

29. $x \geq 13,\ x \leq -7$ 31. $a - b < x < a + b$

33. $-3 < x < 2$ 35. $0 < x < 3$

37. $-3 \leq x \leq 1$ 39. $-3 \leq x \leq 2$

41. $4, -4, 4$
43. a. $-51, 51, 51$ b. $51, -51, 51$ 45. 1
47. a. 14   b. 10   49. $|x| \leq 2$ 51. $|x - 2| > 2$
53. a. $|x - 12| \leq 10$ b. $|x - 12| \geq 10$
55. $r > 12.5\%$ 57. $m < 24{,}062.5$ miles
59. $x \leq 41$ or $x \geq 59$
61. a. $\frac{355}{112} > \pi$ b. $\frac{22}{7} > \pi$ 63. b
73. False. The reciprocal of 2 is $\frac{1}{2}$ which is not an integer.
74. True   75. True   76. False, $|0| = 0$.
77. True   78. True
79. $|-3 - 1| > |-3| - |1|$
    $|3 - 1| = |3| - |1|$

Section P.2 (page 15)

1. $d = 2\sqrt{5}$ 3. $d = 2\sqrt{10}$

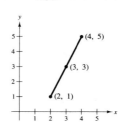

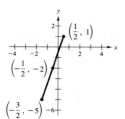

5. $d = \sqrt{8 - 2\sqrt{3}}$ 7. Right triangle
                                        $d_1 = \sqrt{45},\ d_2 = \sqrt{5}$
                                        $d_3 = \sqrt{50}$
                                        $(d_1)^2 + (d_2)^2 = (d_3)^2$

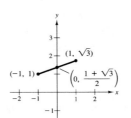

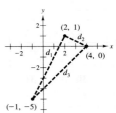

9. Rhombus, the length of each side is $\sqrt{5}$.

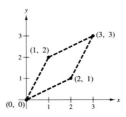

11.

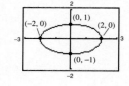

A25

51. $x^2 + 4y^2 = 4$
    Symmetry: origin and both axes

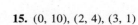

13. $(0, 1), (1, 1), (3, 1)$ 15. $(0, 10), (2, 4), (3, 1)$

13. $d_1 = 2\sqrt{5}, d_2 = \sqrt{5}, d_3 = 3\sqrt{5}$
Collinear, since $d_1 + d_2 = d_3$

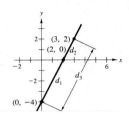

49. $(x + \frac{1}{2})^2 + (y + \frac{5}{4})^2 = \frac{9}{4}$

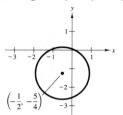

17. a.

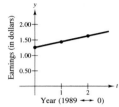

b. 0.185, $1.82
19. $m = -\frac{1}{5}, (0, 4)$ **21.** m is undefined, no y-intercept
23. $2x - y - 3 = 0$ **25.** $3x + y = 0$

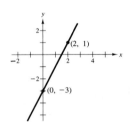   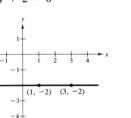

27. $y + 2 = 0$ **29.** $3x - 4y + 12 = 0$

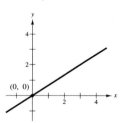   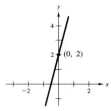

31. $2x - 3y = 0$ **33.** $4x - y + 2 = 0$

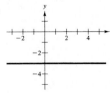   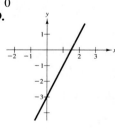

35. $x - 3 = 0$ **37.** $3x + 2y - 6 = 0$
39. $x + y - 3 = 0$
41. a. $2x - y - 3 = 0$ **b.** $x + 2y - 4 = 0$
43. a. $40x + 24y - 53 = 0$ **b.** $24x - 40y + 9 = 0$
45. a. $x - 2 = 0$ **b.** $y - 5 = 0$
47.   **49.**

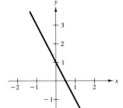   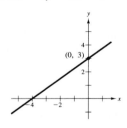

51.

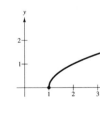

53. $2x - y = 0$ **55.** Not collinear, since $m_1 \neq m_2$
57. $\left(0, \dfrac{-a^2 + b^2 + c^2}{2c}\right)$ **59.** $\left(b, \dfrac{a^2 - b^2}{c}\right)$
61. $5F - 9C - 160 = 0$ **63.** $C = 0.27x + 125$
65. a. $S = 2200t + 28,500$ **b.** $39,500$
67. a. $x = \frac{1}{15}(1130 - p)$ **b.** 45 units   **c.** 49 units
69. 2   **71.** $\dfrac{5\sqrt{2}}{2}$ **73.** $2\sqrt{2}$ **79.** True
80. False, their slopes are negative reciprocals of each other.
81. $y = -\dfrac{\sqrt{2}}{4}x + \sqrt{2}$

$y = \dfrac{\sqrt{2}}{4}x - \sqrt{2}$

Section P.5 (page 42)

1. a. -3 **b.** -9 **c.** $2b - 3$ **d.** $2x - 5$
3. a. 1   **b.** 3   **c.** $\sqrt{c + 3}$ **d.** $\sqrt{x + \Delta x + 3}$
5. a. -1 **b.** 2   **c.** 6   **d.** $2t^2 + 4$
7. $3 + \Delta x, \Delta x \neq 0$ **9.** $3x^2 + 3x\,\Delta x + (\Delta x)^2, \Delta x \neq 0$
11. $\dfrac{-1}{\sqrt{x - 1}\left(1 + \sqrt{x - 1}\right)}$
13. $f(x) = 4 - x$ **15.** $f(x) = \sqrt{x - 1}$
Domain: $(-\infty, \infty)$ Domain: $[1, \infty)$
Range: $(-\infty, \infty)$ Range: $[0, \infty)$

17. $f(x) = \sqrt{9 - x^2}$ **19.** $f(x) = |x - 2|$
Domain: $[-3, 3]$ Domain: $(-\infty, \infty)$
Range: $[0, 3]$ Range: $[0, \infty)$

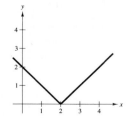

21. Domain: $[-2, 2]$
Range: $\left[-2, 2\sqrt{2}\,\right]$
Intercepts: $\left(-\sqrt{2}, 0\right)$, $(0, 2)$

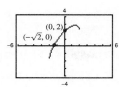

23.

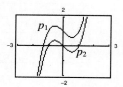

p_1 has one zero and p_2 has three zeros. As x moves away from the origin, the right and left-hand behavior of the graph of a cubic will differ. In the one direction it will rise and in the other direction it will fall. Therefore, a cubic must always have at least one zero.

25. y is not a function of x.   **27.** y is a function of x.
29. y is not a function of x.   **31.** y is a function of x.
33. y is a function of x.   **35.** y is not a function of x.

37. a.

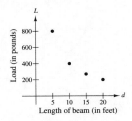

b. L is a function of d with domain and range $(0, \infty)$.
39. a. A vertical translation   **b.** Reflection (about the x-axis)

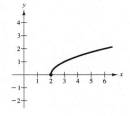

c. A horizontal translation

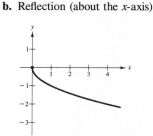

d. Reflection (about the y-axis)

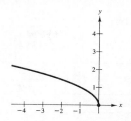

41. a. A reflection in the x-axis followed by a vertical translation.
b. A horizontal translation followed by a vertical translation.
43. a. 0 **b.** 0 **c.** -1 **d.** $\sqrt{15}$
e. $\sqrt{x^2 - 1}$ **f.** $x - 1$

45. $(f \circ g)(x) = x$
Domain: $[0, \infty)$
$(g \circ f)(x) = |x|$
Domain: $(-\infty, \infty)$

47. $(f \circ g)(x) = \dfrac{x + 1}{x}$
Domain: $(-\infty, 0), (0, \infty)$
$(g \circ f)(x) = \dfrac{1}{x + 1}$
Domain: $(-\infty, -1), (-1, \infty)$

49. $(A \circ r)(t) = 0.36\pi t^2$
$A \circ r$ represents the area of the circle at time t.
51. $\frac{10}{7}$ **53.** Even   **55.** Odd
61. a. $f(x) = x^2(4 - x^2)$ **b.** $f(x) = x(4 - x^2)$

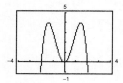   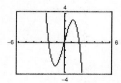

63. $R(x) = 4 - x^2/2$, $r(x) = 2$ **65.** $h(x) = x^2$, $p(x) = x$
67. $A = xy = x\left(\dfrac{100 - 2x}{2}\right) = x(50 - x)$
69. $V = x(12 - 2x)^2 = 4x(6 - x)^2$
71. $V = 108x^2 - 4x^3$
73. $T = \dfrac{\sqrt{x^2 + 4}}{2} + \dfrac{\sqrt{x^2 - 6x + 10}}{4}$
75. False, if $f(x) = x^2$, then $f(-1) = f(1)$.   **76.** True
77. True
78. False, if $f(x) = x^2$, then $f(2x) = 4x^2 \neq 2f(x)$.
79. $f(x) = \frac{1}{2}[f(x) + f(-x)] + \frac{1}{2}[f(x) - f(-x)]$
81. $f(x) = \begin{cases} 1 - x, & x < 3 \\ x - 5, & x \geq 3 \end{cases}$

$g(x) = \begin{cases} 2(1 - x), & x < 0 \\ 2, & 0 \leq x < 2 \\ 2(x - 1), & x \geq 2 \end{cases}$

Section P.6 (*page 53*)

1. a. $396°, -324°$ **b.** $240°, -480°$
3. a. $\dfrac{19\pi}{9}, -\dfrac{17\pi}{9}$ **b.** $\dfrac{10\pi}{3}, -\dfrac{2\pi}{3}$

5. a. $\dfrac{\pi}{6}$, 0.524   **b.** $\dfrac{5\pi}{6}$, 2.618

  c. $\dfrac{7\pi}{4}$, 5.498   **d.** $\dfrac{2\pi}{3}$, 2.094

7. a. 270°   **b.** 210°   **c.** −105°   **d.** −135.6°

9.

r	8 ft	15 in.	85 cm	24 in.	$\dfrac{12{,}963}{\pi}$ mi
s	12 ft	24 in.	63.75π cm	96 in.	8642 mi
θ	1.5	1.6	$\dfrac{3\pi}{4}$	4	$\dfrac{2\pi}{3}$

11. 171.89°

13. a. $\sin\theta = \frac{4}{5}$ $\csc\theta = \frac{5}{4}$ **b.** $\sin\theta = -\frac{15}{17}$ $\csc\theta = -\frac{17}{15}$

  $\cos\theta = \frac{3}{5}$ $\sec\theta = \frac{5}{3}$ $\cos\theta = \frac{8}{17}$ $\sec\theta = \frac{17}{8}$

  $\tan\theta = \frac{4}{3}$ $\cot\theta = \frac{3}{4}$ $\tan\theta = -\frac{15}{8}$ $\cot\theta = -\frac{8}{15}$

15. a. Quadrant III   **b.** Quadrant IV

17. $\dfrac{\sqrt{3}}{2}$ **19.** $\dfrac{4}{3}$ **21.** $\dfrac{17}{15}$

23. a. $\sin 60° = \dfrac{\sqrt{3}}{2}$ **b.** $\sin 120° = \dfrac{\sqrt{3}}{2}$

  $\cos 60° = \dfrac{1}{2}$ $\cos 120° = -\dfrac{1}{2}$

  $\tan 60° = \sqrt{3}$ $\tan 120° = -\sqrt{3}$

  c. $\sin\dfrac{\pi}{4} = \dfrac{\sqrt{2}}{2}$ **d.** $\sin\dfrac{5\pi}{4} = -\dfrac{\sqrt{2}}{2}$

  $\cos\dfrac{\pi}{4} = \dfrac{\sqrt{2}}{2}$ $\cos\dfrac{5\pi}{4} = -\dfrac{\sqrt{2}}{2}$

  $\tan\dfrac{\pi}{4} = 1$ $\tan\dfrac{5\pi}{4} = 1$

25. a. $\sin 225° = -\dfrac{\sqrt{2}}{2}$ **b.** $\sin(-225°) = \dfrac{\sqrt{2}}{2}$

  $\cos 225° = -\dfrac{\sqrt{2}}{2}$ $\cos(-225°) = -\dfrac{\sqrt{2}}{2}$

  $\tan 225° = 1$ $\tan(-225°) = -1$

  c. $\sin\dfrac{5\pi}{3} = -\dfrac{\sqrt{3}}{2}$ **d.** $\sin\dfrac{11\pi}{6} = -\dfrac{1}{2}$

  $\cos\dfrac{5\pi}{3} = \dfrac{1}{2}$ $\cos\dfrac{11\pi}{6} = \dfrac{\sqrt{3}}{2}$

  $\tan\dfrac{5\pi}{3} = -\sqrt{3}$ $\tan\dfrac{11\pi}{6} = -\dfrac{\sqrt{3}}{3}$

27. a. 0.1736   **b.** 5.759   **29. a.** 0.3640   **b.** 0.3640

31. a. $\theta = \dfrac{\pi}{4}, \dfrac{7\pi}{4}$ **b.** $\theta = \dfrac{3\pi}{4}, \dfrac{5\pi}{4}$

33. a. $\theta = \dfrac{\pi}{4}, \dfrac{5\pi}{4}$ **b.** $\theta = \dfrac{5\pi}{6}, \dfrac{11\pi}{6}$

35. $\theta = \dfrac{\pi}{4}, \dfrac{3\pi}{4}, \dfrac{5\pi}{4}, \dfrac{7\pi}{4}$ **37.** $\theta = 0, \dfrac{\pi}{4}, \pi, \dfrac{5\pi}{4}$

39. $\theta = \dfrac{\pi}{3}, \dfrac{5\pi}{3}$ **41.** $\theta = 0, \dfrac{\pi}{2}, \pi$ **43.** $y = \dfrac{100\sqrt{3}}{3}$

45. $x = \dfrac{25\sqrt{3}}{3}$ **47.** 5099 ft   **49.** 2.63 in.

51. a. Period: π **b.** Period: 2   **53.** Period: $\frac{1}{2}$
  Amplitude: 2   Amplitude: $\frac{1}{2}$ Amplitude: 3

55. Period: $\dfrac{\pi}{2}$ **57.** Period: $\dfrac{2\pi}{5}$

59. a. Change in amplitude   **b.** Change in period

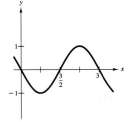   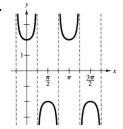

c. Horizontal translation

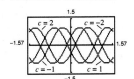

61. 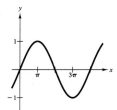   **63.**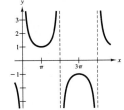

65.   **67.**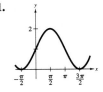

69. 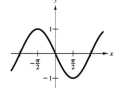   **71.**

73. a. Period of f: 2π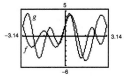
  Period of g: π

  b. $h(x) = A\cos\alpha x + B\sin\beta x$ is periodic. The period of $a\cos\alpha x$ is $2\pi/\alpha$. The period of $B\sin\beta x$ is $2\pi/\beta$. The period of h is the least common multiple of these two periods.

75. $y = 3\cos\left(\dfrac{x}{2} - \dfrac{\pi}{2}\right)$

77. a.

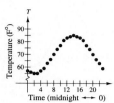

b. $T(t) = 70 + 15 \sin\left(\dfrac{\pi t}{12} - \dfrac{2\pi}{3}\right)$

c.

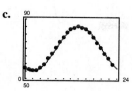

79. a. $\frac{1}{440}$

b. 440   **c.**

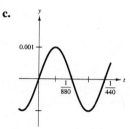

81. $f(x) = \dfrac{4}{\pi}\left(\sin \pi x + \dfrac{1}{3}\sin 3\pi x + \dfrac{1}{5}\sin 5\pi x + \cdots\right)$

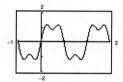

83.

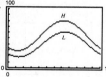

a. Greatest: Summer
Smallest: Winter
b. 15 days

85. If α is the angle the line makes with the positive x-axis, then the slope of the line is $m = \tan \alpha$.

87.

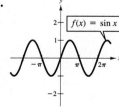

The graph of $|f(x)|$ will reflect any parts of the graph below the x-axis about the x-axis. The graph of $f(|x|)$ will reflect the part of the graph left of the y-axis about the y-axis.

89. a. 0.8845
c. $\frac{1}{262}$
d. 262
e. The sound whose wave is given by p sounds like high C because $30p_2(t)$ has a frequency of 524 and it is the loudest component of the sound.

Review Exercises for the Prerequisites Chapter

1. $-1 \le x \le 5$ **3.** $x < -5, x > -1$

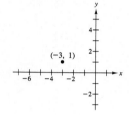

5. $\frac{27}{16}$ **7.** $(-1, 3), (3, 2), (1, 1)$

9. Center: $(-3, 1)$ **11.** Point: $(-3, 1)$
Radius: 3

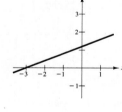

13. $c = -21$
15. $x^2 + y^2 - 2x - 4y - 4 = 0$
a. on the circle
b. inside the circle
c. outside the circle
d. inside the circle
17. $t = \frac{7}{3}$
19.   **21.**

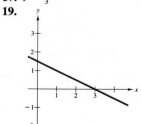

23.   **25.**

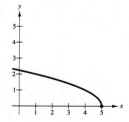

27. a. $7x - 16y + 78 = 0$
b. $5x - 3y + 22 = 0$
c. $y + 2x = 0$
d. $x + 2 = 0$
29. $(-4, 5)$ **31.** $(4, 1)$
33. The speed of the plane is 560 mph.
35. $A = x(12 - x)$
Domain: $\{x: 0 < x < 12\}$

37. $d = 45t$
Domain: $\{t: t \geq 0\}$

39. Not a function   **41.** Function

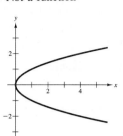

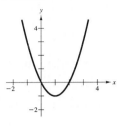

43. a.

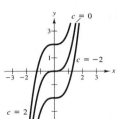

b.

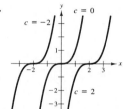

c.

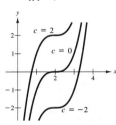

d.

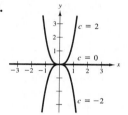

45. a.

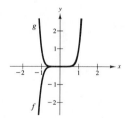

b.

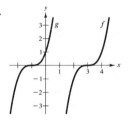

47. a. $f(x) - g(x) = -x^2 - 2x$
    b. $f(x)g(x) = (1 - x^2)(2x + 1)$
    c. $g(f(x)) = 3 - 2x^2$

49. a. 3, Minus   **b.** 2, Plus

51. 47,285 ft $\approx$ 9 mi

53.

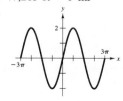

55.

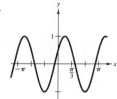

57.

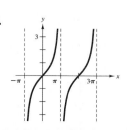

59.

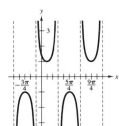

61.

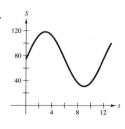

CHAPTER 1

Section 1.1   (*page 68*)

1.

x	1.9	1.99	1.999	2.001	2.01	2.1
$f(x)$	0.3448	0.3344	0.3334	0.3332	0.3322	0.3226

$$\lim_{x \to 2} \frac{x - 2}{x^2 - x - 2} \approx 0.3333 \quad \left(\text{Actual limit is } \frac{1}{3}. \right)$$

3.

x	-0.1	-0.01	-0.001	0.001	0.01	0.1
$f(x)$	0.2911	0.2889	0.2887	0.2887	0.2884	0.2683

$$\lim_{x \to 0} \frac{\sqrt{x + 3} - \sqrt{3}}{x} \approx 0.2887 \quad \left(\text{Actual limit is } \frac{1}{2\sqrt{3}}. \right)$$

5.

x	2.9	2.99	2.999	3.001	3.01	3.1
$f(x)$	-0.0641	-0.0627	-0.0625	-0.0625	-0.0623	-0.0610

$$\lim_{x \to 3} \frac{[1/(x + 1)] - (1/4)}{x - 3} \approx -0.0625 \quad \left(\text{Actual limit is } -\frac{1}{16}. \right)$$

7.

x	-0.1	-0.01	-0.001	0.001	0.01	0.1
$f(x)$	0.9983	0.99998	1.0000	1.0000	0.99998	0.9983

$$\lim_{x \to 0} \frac{\sin x}{x} \approx 1.0000 \quad (\text{Actual limit is } 1.)$$

9. 1   **11.** 2   **13.** Limit does not exist.
15. Limit does not exist.   **17.** Limit does not exist.

19. $L = 8$. Let $\delta = \dfrac{0.01}{3} \approx 0.0033$

21. $L = 1$.
    Assume $1 < x < 3$ and let $\delta = \dfrac{0.01}{5} = 0.002$.

23. Limit is 5. Let $\delta = \varepsilon$.   **25.** Limit is 3. Any δ will work.
27. Limit is 0. Let $\delta = \varepsilon^3$.

29. Limit is 2. Let $\delta = \dfrac{\varepsilon}{3}$ for $0 < x < 2$.

31. False, the existence or nonexistence of $f(x)$ at $x = c$ has no bearing on the existence of the limit of $f(x)$ as $x \to c$.

32. True   **33.** False, see Exercise 31.

34. False, the existence or nonexistence of the limit of $f(x)$ as $x \to c$ has no bearing on the existence of $f(c)$.

35. It is not obvious from the graph that the function does not exist at $x = 4$.

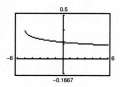

$$\lim_{x \to 4} f(x) = \frac{1}{6}$$

37.

n	$4 \pm [0.1]^n$	$f(4 \pm [0.1]^n)$
1	3.9000	6.9000
2	3.9900	6.9900
3	3.9990	6.9990
4	3.9999	6.9999
4	4.0001	7.0001
3	4.0010	7.0010
2	4.0100	7.0100
1	4.1000	7.1000

41. $\lim_{x \to 0}(1 + x)^{1/x} \approx 2.71828$
(You will study this limit in Chapter 5.)

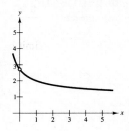

Section 1.2 (*page 74*)

1. a. 1   **b.** 3   **3. a.** $\dfrac{\sqrt{3}}{2}$ **b.** 1   **5.** 16

7. -1 **9.** -4 **11.** 2   **13.** 1   **15.** $\frac{1}{2}$
17. -2 **19.** 1   **21.** -1 **23.** 1   **25.** $\frac{1}{2}$ **27.** -1
29. a. 15   **b.** 5   **c.** 6   **d.** $\frac{2}{3}$
31. a. 64   **b.** 2   **c.** 12   **d.** 8
33.

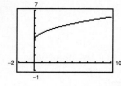

Domain: $\{x : 0 \le x < 9, x > 9\}$
$\lim_{x \to 9} f(x) = 6$
It is not obvious from the graph that the function does not exist at $x = 9$.

35. $f(x) = -\dfrac{1}{x}$, $g(x) = \dfrac{1}{x}$ (Other solutions possible.)

Section 1.3 (*page 82*)

1. a. 1   **b.** 3
$$g(x) = \frac{-2x^2 + x}{x} = -2x + 1, x \neq 0$$

3. a. 2   **b.** 0
$$g(x) = \frac{x^3 - 1}{x - 1} = x^2 + x, x \neq 1$$

5. -2
$$f(x) = \frac{x^2 - 1}{x + 1} = x - 1 = g(x), x \neq -1$$

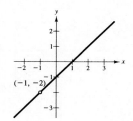

7. 12
$$f(x) = \frac{x^3 + 8}{x + 2} = x^2 - 2x + 4, x \neq -2$$

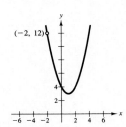

9. $\dfrac{1}{10}$ **11.** $\dfrac{3}{2}$ **13.** $\dfrac{\sqrt{3}}{6}$ **15.** $-\dfrac{1}{4}$

17. 2   **19.** $2x - 2$

21.

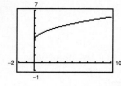

x	-0.1	-0.01	-0.001	0.001	0.01	0.1
$f(x)$	0.358	0.354	0.354	0.354	0.353	0.349

$$\lim_{x \to 0} \frac{\sqrt{x + 2} - \sqrt{2}}{x} \approx 0.354 \quad \left(\text{Actual limit is } \frac{1}{2\sqrt{2}}.\right)$$

23.

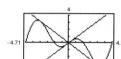

x	1.9	1.99	1.999	1.9999	2.0001	2.001	2.01	2.1
$f(x)$	72.39	79.20	79.92	79.99	80.01	80.08	80.80	88.41

$$\lim_{x\to 2}\frac{x^5 - 32}{x - 2} \approx 80 \quad \text{(Actual limit is 80.)}$$

25. $\frac{1}{5}$ **27.** 0 **29.** 0 **31.** 0 **33.** 1 **35.** 1
37. 3 **39.** 0 **41.** 4
43. 0 **45.** 0

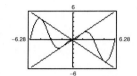

47. 0

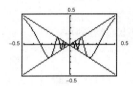

49.

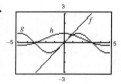

The magnitudes of $f(x)$ and $g(x)$ are approximately equal when x is "close to" 0. Therefore, their ratio is approximately 1.

51. -160 ft/sec **57.** $f(x) = \begin{cases} 4, & x \geq 0 \\ -4, & x < 0 \end{cases}$

59. $\lim_{x\to 0} f(x)$ does not exist.
$\lim_{x\to 0} g(x) = 0$ **61.** $\frac{1}{2}$; $\cos(0.1) \approx .995$

Section 1.4 (*page 92*)

1. a. 1 **b.** 1 **c.** 1
3. a. 0 **b.** 0 **c.** 0
5. a. 3 **b.** -3 **c.** Limit does not exist.
7. $\frac{1}{10}$ **9.** Limit does not exist.
11. Limit does not exist.
13. $-\dfrac{1}{x^2}$ **15.** Limit does not exist.
17. 2 **19.** Limit does not exist.
21. 3 **23.** Discontinuous at $x = -2$ and $x = 2$

25. Discontinuous at every integer
27. Continuous for all real x
29. Continuous for all real x
31. Nonremovable discontinuity at $x = 1$
33. Continuous for all real x
35. Removable discontinuity at $x = 1$;
Nonremovable discontinuity at $x = -2$
37. Nonremovable discontinuity at $x = -2$
39. Continuous for all real x
41. Nonremovable discontinuity at $x = 2$
43. Continuous for all real x
45. Nonremovable discontinuities at integer multiples of $\dfrac{\pi}{2}$
47. Nonremovable discontinuities at each integer
49. $a = 2$ **51.** $a = 4$
53. Continuous for all real x
55. Nonremovable discontinuities at $x = 1$ and $x = -1$
57. Continuous on $(-\infty, \infty)$
59. Continuous on $\ldots, (-2\pi, 0), (0, 2\pi), (2\pi, 4\pi), \ldots$
61. Nonremovable discontinuity at each integer.

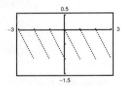

63. Discontinuous at $x = 3$

65.

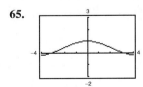

It is not obvious from the graph that the function is discontinuous at $x = 0$.

67. $f(x)$ is continuous on $[2, 4]$.
$f(2) = -1$ and $f(4) = 3$
By the Intermediate Value Theorem, $f(c) = 0$ for at least one value c between 2 and 4.
69. 0.68 **71.** $f(3) = 11$ **73.** $f(2) = 4$

75. Discontinuous at every positive integer

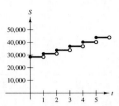

77. Discontinuous at every even positive integer

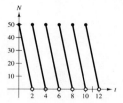

81. True   **82.** True
83. False, the rational function $f(x) = p(x)/q(x)$ has at most n discontinuities where n is the degree of $q(x)$.
84. False, it is discontinuous at $x = 1$.
89. Discontinuous at $x = \pm 1, \pm 2, \pm 3, \ldots$

Section 1.5 (*page 101*)

1. $\lim\limits_{x \to 2^+} \dfrac{1}{(x + 2)^2} = \infty$ **3.** $\lim\limits_{x \to -2^+} \tan \dfrac{\pi x}{4} = -\infty$

$\lim\limits_{x \to -2^-} \dfrac{1}{(x + 2)^2} = \infty$ $\lim\limits_{x \to -2^-} \tan \dfrac{\pi x}{4} = \infty$

5. $\lim\limits_{x \to -3^+} \dfrac{1}{x^2 - 9} = -\infty$ **7.** $\lim\limits_{x \to -3^+} \dfrac{x^2}{x^2 - 9} = -\infty$

$\lim\limits_{x \to -3^-} \dfrac{1}{x^2 - 9} = \infty$ $\lim\limits_{x \to -3^-} \dfrac{x^2}{x^2 - 9} = \infty$

9. $x = 0$ **11.** $x = 2, x = -1$ **13.** $x = \pm 1$
15. $x = 0$ **17.** $x = -2, x = 1$
19. $x = \dfrac{\pi}{4} + \dfrac{n\pi}{2}$, n an integer

21. No vertical asymptote
23. $x = n\pi$, n a nonzero integer
25. Removable discontinuity at $x = -1$
27. Vertical asymptote at $x = -1$
29. $-\infty$ **31.** ∞
33. $\frac{4}{5}$ **35.** $-\infty$ **37.** ∞ **39.** $\frac{1}{2}$ **41.** ∞
43. $-\infty$

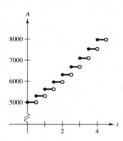

45. ∞ if the constant of proportionality k is positive and $-\infty$ if k is negative.
47. a. $\frac{7}{12}$ ft/sec   **b.** $\frac{3}{2}$ ft/sec   **c.** ∞
49. a. \$176 million   **b.** \$528 million
c. \$1584 million   **d.** ∞

51.

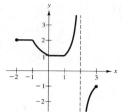

53. False, let $p(x) = x^2 - 1$.
54. False, let $f(x) = \dfrac{1}{x^2}$ and $g(x) = \dfrac{1}{x^4}$.
55. False, let $f(x) = \dfrac{1}{x^2 + 1}$.
56. True
57. False, let $f(x) = \begin{cases} \dfrac{1}{x}, & x \neq 0 \\ 0, & x = 0 \end{cases}$.
58. True

Review Exercises for Chapter 1

1. 7   **3.** 77   **5.** $\frac{10}{3}$ **7.** $-\frac{1}{4}$ **9.** -1 **11.** 75
13. $-\infty$ **15.** $\dfrac{\sqrt{3}}{2}$ **17.** $-\infty$ **19.** $\dfrac{1}{3}$ **21.** $-\infty$
23. $\frac{4}{5}$ **25.** ∞

27.

x	1.1	1.01	1.001	1.0001
$f(x)$	0.5680	0.5764	0.5772	0.5773

$\lim\limits_{x \to 1^+} \dfrac{\sqrt{2x + 1} - \sqrt{3}}{x - 1} \approx 0.577$ $\left(\text{Actual limit is } \dfrac{\sqrt{3}}{3}.\right)$

29. Nonremovable discontinuity at each integer
Continuous on $(k, k + 1)$ for all integers k
31. Removable discontinuity at $x = 1$
Continuous on $(-\infty, 1) \cup (1, \infty)$
33. Nonremovable discontinuity at $x = 2$
Continuous on $(-\infty, 2) \cup (2, \infty)$
35. Nonremovable discontinuity at $x = -1$
Continuous on $(-\infty, -1) \cup (-1, \infty)$
37. Nonremovable discontinuity at each even integer
Continuous on $(2k, 2k + 2)$ for all integers k
39. $c = -\frac{1}{2}$
41. Nonremovable discontinuity every 6 months

43. $x = 0$ **45.** $x = 10$
47. a. \$14,117.65   **b.** \$80,000.00
c. \$720,000.00   **d.** ∞

49. False $\lim\limits_{x \to 0^-} \dfrac{|x|}{x} = -1$ **50.** True   **51.** True

52. False, the existence of the limit of $f(x)$ as $x \to c$ has no bearing on the existence of $f(c)$

53. True   **54.** False, the limit does not exist.   **55.** True

57. Domain: $(-\infty, 0] \cup [1, \infty)$

$\lim\limits_{x \to 0^-} f(x) = 0$

$\lim\limits_{x \to 1^+} f(x) = 0$

CHAPTER 2

Section 2.1   (*page 112*)

1. a. $m = 0$ **b.** $m = -3$

3.

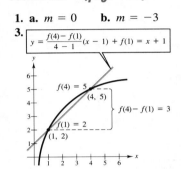

$y = \dfrac{f(4) - f(1)}{4 - 1}(x - 1) + f(1) = x + 1$

$f(4) = 5$

$(4, 5)$

$f(4) - f(1) = 3$

$f(1) = 2$

$(1, 2)$

5. $f'(x) = 0$ **7.** $f'(x) = -5$

9. $f'(x) = 4x + 1$ **11.** $f'(x) = 3x^2 - 12$

13. $f'(x) = \dfrac{-1}{(x - 1)^2}$ **15.** $f'(x) = \dfrac{1}{2\sqrt{x - 4}}$

17. $f'(x) = 2x$

Tangent line: $y = 4x - 3$

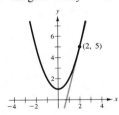

$(2, 5)$

19. $f'(x) = 3x^2$

Tangent line: $y = 12x - 16$

21. $f'(x) = 1 - \dfrac{1}{x^2}$

Tangent line: $y = 2$

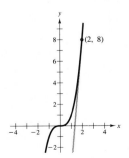

$(2, 8)$

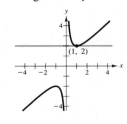

$(1, 2)$

23. $y = 3x - 2$ **25.** $y = 2x + 1$

$\quad\;\; y = 3x + 2$ $\quad\;\;\; y = -2x + 9$

27. b   **28.** e   **29.** c   **30.** a   **31.** f   **32.** d

33.

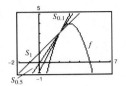

x	-2	-1.5	-1	-0.5	0	0.5	1	1.5	2
$f(x)$	-2	$-\frac{27}{32}$	$-\frac{1}{4}$	$-\frac{1}{32}$	0	$\frac{1}{32}$	$\frac{1}{4}$	$\frac{27}{32}$	2
$f'(x)$	3	$\frac{27}{16}$	$\frac{3}{4}$	$\frac{3}{16}$	0	$\frac{3}{16}$	$\frac{3}{4}$	$\frac{27}{16}$	3

35. a.

$S_{0.1}$

S_1

f

$S_{0.5}$

b. The graphs of S for decreasing values of Δx are secant lines approaching the tangent line to the graph of f at the point $(2, f(2))$.

37. $f(x) = x^2 - 1$

$f'(2) = \lim\limits_{x \to 2} \dfrac{f(x) - f(2)}{x - 2}$

$\quad\;\;\; = \lim\limits_{x \to 2} \dfrac{(x^2 - 1) - 3}{x - 2}$

$\quad\;\;\; = \lim\limits_{x \to 2} (x + 2) = 4$

39. $f(x) = x^3 + 2x^2 + 1$

$f'(-2) = \lim\limits_{x \to -2} \dfrac{f(x) - f(-2)}{x + 2}$

$\quad\;\;\;\;\; = \lim\limits_{x \to -2} \dfrac{(x^3 + 2x^2 + 1) - 1}{x + 2}$

$\quad\;\;\;\;\; = \lim\limits_{x \to -2} x^2 = 4$

41. $f(x) = (x - 1)^{2/3}$

$f'(1) = \lim\limits_{x \to 1} \dfrac{f(x) - f(1)}{x - 1}$

$\quad\;\;\; = \lim\limits_{x \to 1} \dfrac{(x - 1)^{2/3} - 0}{x - 1}$

$\quad\;\;\; = \lim\limits_{x \to 1} \dfrac{1}{(x - 1)^{1/3}}$

Limit does not exist.

f is not differentiable at $x = 1$.

43. $(-\infty, -3), (-3, \infty)$

45. $(-\infty, -1), (-1, \infty)$ **47.** $(-\infty, 3), (3, \infty)$

49. $(1, \infty)$ **51.** $(-\infty, 0), (0, \infty)$

53. f is not differentiable at $x = 1$.

55. $f'(1) = 0$ **57.** f is differentiable at $x = 2$.

59. a. 3   **b.** -3 **61.** True

62. False, let $f(x) = |x|$ at $x = 0$.   **63.** True

64. False, let $f(x) = \begin{cases} x, & x \le 0 \\ 2x, & x > 0 \end{cases}$ at $x = 0$

Section 2.2   (*page 124*)

1. a. $\frac{1}{2}$ **b.** $\frac{3}{2}$ **c.** 2   **d.** 3

3. 0   **5.** 1   **7.** $2x$ **9.** $-4t + 3$ **11.** $3t^2 - 2$

13. $2x + \dfrac{1}{2}\sin x$ **15.** $-\dfrac{1}{x^2} - 3\cos x$

Function	Rewrite	Derivative	Simplify
17. $y = \dfrac{1}{3x^3}$	$y = \dfrac{1}{3}x^{-3}$	$y' = -x^{-4}$	$y' = -\dfrac{1}{x^4}$
19. $y = \dfrac{1}{(3x)^3}$	$y = \dfrac{1}{27}x^{-3}$	$y' = -\dfrac{1}{9}x^{-4}$	$y' = -\dfrac{1}{9x^4}$
21. $y = \dfrac{\sqrt{x}}{x}$	$y = x^{-1/2}$	$y' = -\dfrac{1}{2}x^{-3/2}$	$y' = -\dfrac{1}{2x^{3/2}}$

23. -1 **25.** 0   **27.** 4   **29.** 3

31. $3x^2 - 3 + \dfrac{8}{x^5}$ **33.** $2t + \dfrac{4}{t^2}$

35. $\dfrac{x^3 - 8}{x^3}$ **37.** $3x^2 + 1$ **39.** $\dfrac{4}{5s^{1/5}}$

41. $\dfrac{2}{\sqrt{x}} - 3\sin x$ **43.** $2x + y - 2 = 0$

45. $x + 48y - 20 = 0$

47. $(0, 2), \left(\sqrt{\tfrac{3}{2}}, -\tfrac{1}{4}\right), \left(-\sqrt{\tfrac{3}{2}}, -\tfrac{1}{4}\right)$

49. No horizontal tangents   **51.** (π, π)

53.

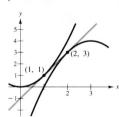

The rate of change of f is constant and therefore f' is a constant function.

55. $y = 2x - 1$ $y = 4x - 4$

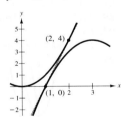

57. $x - 4y + 4 = 0$

59. a.

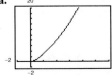

c. It becomes less accurate.

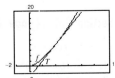

b. $T(x) = 3(x - 4) + 8 = 3x - 4$

d.

Δx	-3	-2	-1	-0.5	-0.1	0	0.1	0.5	1	2	3
$f(4 + \Delta x)$	1	2.828	5.196	6.458	7.702	8	8.302	9.456	11.180	14.697	18.520
$T(4 + \Delta x)$	-1	2	5	6.5	7.7	8	8.3	9.5	11	14	17

61. False, let $f(x) = x$ and $g(x) = x + 1$.   **62.** True

63. False, $dy/dx = 0$ **64.** True

65. a. A and B **b.** Greater

c.

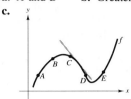

d. B and C, D and E

67. Average rate: 2
Instantaneous rates:
$f'(1) = 2$
$f'(2) = 2$

69. Average rate: $\frac{1}{2}$
Instantaneous rates:
$f'(1) = 1$
$f'(2) = \frac{1}{4}$

71. a. $s(t) = -16t^2 + 1362$
  $v(t) = -32t$
b. -48 ft/sec
c. $s'(1) = -32$ ft/sec
  $s'(2) = -64$ ft/sec
d. $t = \dfrac{\sqrt{1362}}{4} \approx 9.226$ sec
e. -295.242 ft/sec

73. $v(5) = 224$ ft/sec
  $v(10) = 64$ ft/sec

75.

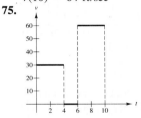

77.

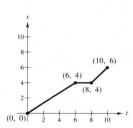

79. a. $T(x) = 0.14x^2 - 3.33x + 58.40$
b.

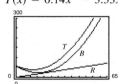

c. $T'(30) = 5.07$ ft/mi/hr
  $T'(40) = 7.87$ ft/mi/hr
  $T'(55) = 12.07$ ft/mi/hr

81. 8m²   **83. a.** $\frac{4}{9}$ **b.** $\frac{1}{3}$ **c.** 0   **d.** $-\frac{5}{9}$

85. $-\$1.91$, $-\$1.93$

87. $\dfrac{dF}{dr} = -2K\dfrac{m_1 m_2}{r^3}$

Force decreases as the distance between the particles increases.

89. $y = 2x^2 - 3x + 1$ **91.** $y = -9x$, $y = -\frac{9}{4}x - \frac{27}{4}$

93. $a = \frac{1}{3}$, $b = -\frac{4}{3}$

21. $-\sqrt[3]{\dfrac{y}{x}},\ -\dfrac{1}{2}$ **23.** $-\dfrac{x^2}{x^2+1},\ 0$ **25.** $-\dfrac{1}{2}$ **27.** 0

29. $x+2y-6=0$

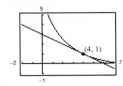

31. a. $y_1=\sqrt{16-x^2}$
$\qquad y_2=-\sqrt{16-x^2}$

b.

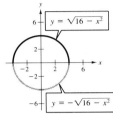

c. $y'=\mp\dfrac{x}{\sqrt{16-x^2}}=-\dfrac{x}{y}$ **d.** $y'=-\dfrac{x}{y}$

33. a. $y_1=\dfrac{3}{4}\sqrt{16-x^2}$
$\qquad y_2=-\dfrac{3}{4}\sqrt{16-x^2}$

b.

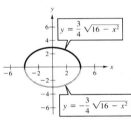

c. $y'=\mp\dfrac{3x}{4\sqrt{16-x^2}}=-\dfrac{9x}{16y}$ **d.** $y'=-\dfrac{9x}{16y}$

35. $\dfrac{10}{x^3}$ **37.** $-\dfrac{16}{y^3}$ **39.** $\dfrac{3y}{4x^2}=\dfrac{3x}{4y}$

41. a. At $(4,3)$:
Tangent line: $4x+3y-25=0$
Normal line: $3x-4y=0$
b. At $(-3,4)$:
Tangent line: $3x-4y+25=0$
Normal line: $4x+3y=0$

45. Horizontal tangents: $(-4,0),\ (-4,10)$
Vertical tangents: $(0,5),\ (-8,5)$

47.

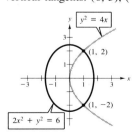

At $(1,2)$:
Slope of ellipse: -1
Slope of parabola: 1
At $(1,-2)$:
Slope of parabola: -1

49.

At $(0,0)$:
Slope of line: -1
Slope of sine curve: 1

51.

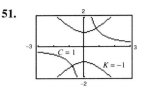   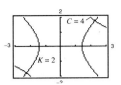

Derivatives: $\dfrac{dy}{dx}=-\dfrac{y}{x},\ \dfrac{dy}{dx}=\dfrac{x}{y}$

53. $-\dfrac{\pi}{2}<y<\dfrac{\pi}{2},\ \dfrac{dy}{dx}=\dfrac{1}{1+x^2}$

57. $-\dfrac{3}{4}$ **59.** $\sqrt{3}$

Section 2.6 (*page 159*)

1. a. $\frac{3}{4}$ **b.** 20 **3. a.** $-\frac{5}{8}$ **b.** $\frac{3}{2}$
5. a. -4 cm/sec   **b.** 0 cm/sec   **c.** 4 cm/sec
$\qquad$ **d.** 12 cm/sec
7. a. 8 cm/sec   **b.** 4 cm/sec   **c.** 2 cm/sec
$\qquad$ **d.** 6.851 cm/sec
9. a. $-2\sqrt{5}\approx-4.472$ cm/sec   **b.** 0 cm/sec
$\qquad$ **c.** $2\sqrt{5}\approx4.472$ cm/sec
$\qquad$ **d.** $\dfrac{126}{\sqrt{109}}\approx12.069$ cm/sec
11. a. 24π in.^{2}/min   **b.** 96π in.^{2}/min
13. b. When $\theta=\dfrac{\pi}{6},\ \dfrac{dA}{dt}=\dfrac{\sqrt{3}}{8}s^2$
$\qquad$ When $\theta=\dfrac{\pi}{3},\ \dfrac{dA}{dt}=\dfrac{1}{8}s^2$
$\qquad$ **c.** If s and $d\theta/dt$ are constant, dA/dt is proportional to $\cos\theta$.
15. a. $\dfrac{5}{\pi}$ ft/min   **b.** $\dfrac{5}{4\pi}$ ft/min
17. a. 36 cm^2/sec   **b.** 360 cm^2/sec
19. $\dfrac{8}{405\pi}$ ft/min   **21. a.** 24.6% **b.** $\frac{1}{64}$ ft/min
23. a. $-\frac{7}{12}$ ft/sec
$\qquad\quad -\frac{3}{2}$ ft/sec
$\qquad\quad -\frac{48}{7}$ ft/sec
$\qquad$ **b.** $\frac{527}{24}$ ft^2/sec
$\qquad$ **c.** $\frac{1}{12}$ rad/sec
25. $\dfrac{dy}{dt}=\dfrac{1}{2}$ ft/sec
$\qquad \dfrac{dx}{dt}=-\dfrac{\sqrt{3}}{6}$ ft/sec
27. a. -750 mph   **b.** 20 min
29. $-\dfrac{28}{\sqrt{10}}\approx-8.85$ ft/sec
31. a. $\frac{25}{3}$ ft/sec   **b.** $\frac{10}{3}$ ft/sec
33. a. 12 sec   **b.** $(0,\sqrt{5})$ **c.** $\dfrac{\sqrt{6}\pi}{24}\approx0.32$ ft/sec
37. $v^{0.3}\left(1.3p\dfrac{dv}{dt}+v\dfrac{dp}{dt}\right)=0$
39. $\frac{1}{20}$ rad/sec

41. a. $\frac{1}{2}$ rad/min   **b.** $\frac{3}{2}$ rad/min   **c.** 1.87 rad/min
43. a. 0 ft/sec   **b.** 10π ft/sec   **c.** $10\sqrt{3}\pi$ ft/sec
45. -0.1808 ft/sec²

Review Exercises for Chapter 2

1. $f'(x) = 2x - 2$
3. a.
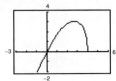
   b. $y = 2x$

c.

Δx	$f(x + \Delta x)$	$f(x)$	$\dfrac{f(x + \Delta x) - f(x)}{\Delta x}$
2	2.8284	0	1.4142
1	1.7321	0	1.7321
0.5	0.9354	0	1.8708
0.1	0.1975	0	1.9748

d. The last column gives the slopes of secant lines. As Δx approaches 0, these slopes approach the slope of the tangent line.

5. $3x(x - 2)$ **7.** $\dfrac{2(x^3 + 1)}{x^3}$ **9.** $-\dfrac{4}{3t^3}$

11. $\dfrac{-3x^2}{2\sqrt{1 - x^3}}$ **13.** $2(6x^3 - 9x^2 + 16x - 7)$
15. $s(s^2 - 1)^{3/2}(8s^3 - 3s + 25)$
17. $-\dfrac{x^2 + 1}{(x^2 - 1)^2}$ **19.** $\dfrac{6x}{(4 - 3x^2)^2}$
21. $-9\sin(3x + 1)$ **23.** $-\csc 2x \cot 2x$
25. $\frac{1}{2}(1 - \cos 2x) = \sin^2 x$
27. $\sin^{1/2} x \cos x - \sin^{5/2} x \cos x = \cos^3 x \sqrt{\sin x}$
29. $-x\sec^2 x - \tan x$ **31.** $\dfrac{x\cos x - 2\sin x}{x^3}$
33. $t(t - 1)^4(7t - 2)$

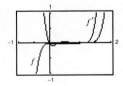

The zeros of f' correspond to the points on the graph of the function where the tangent line is horizontal.

35. $\dfrac{x + 2}{(x + 1)^{3/2}}$
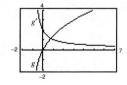

g' is not equal to zero for any x.

37. $\dfrac{5}{6(t + 1)^{1/6}}$ **39.** $-\dfrac{\sec^2\sqrt{1 - x}}{2\sqrt{1 - x}}$

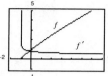 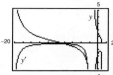

f' has no zeros. y' has no zeros.

41. $4 - 4\sin 2x$ **43.** $2\csc^2 x \cot x$ **45.** $\dfrac{2(t + 2)}{(1 - t)^4}$
47. $2\sec^2 x(x\tan x + 1)$ **49.** $-\dfrac{2x + 3y}{3(x + y^2)}$
51. $\dfrac{2y\sqrt{x} - y\sqrt{y}}{2x\sqrt{y} - x\sqrt{x}}$ **53.** $\dfrac{y\sin x + \sin y}{\cos x - x\cos y}$
55. Tangent line: $3x - y + 7 = 0$
Normal line: $x + 3y - 1 = 0$
57. Tangent line: $x + 2y - 10 = 0$
Normal line: $2x - y = 0$
59. Tangent line: $2x - 3y - 3 = 0$
Normal line: $3x + 2y - 11 = 0$
61. a. $(0, -1), \left(-2, \frac{7}{3}\right)$ **b.** $(-3, 2), \left(1, -\frac{2}{3}\right)$
c. $\left(-1 + \sqrt{2}, \dfrac{2[1 - 2\sqrt{2}]}{3}\right)$
$\left(-1 - \sqrt{2}, \dfrac{2[1 + 2\sqrt{2}]}{3}\right)$
63. a. Yes
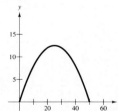
b. No. The derivative from the right and left are not equal.
65. $y'' + y = -(2\sin x + 3\cos x) + (2\sin x + 3\cos x) = 0$
67. a. -18.667 deg/hr   **c.** -3.240 deg/hr
b. -7.284 deg/hr   **d.** -0.747 deg/hr
69. a. 50 vib/sec/lb   **b.** 33.33 vib/sec/lb
71. 56 ft/sec
73. a.   **b.** 50   **c.** $x = 25$
     d. $y' = 1 - 0.04x$
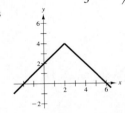

x	0	10	25	30	50
y'	1	0.6	0	-0.2	-1

e. $y'(25) = 0$

77. a. $2\sqrt{2}$ units/sec   **b.** 4 units/sec   **c.** 8 units/sec
79. $\frac{2}{25}$ ft/min   **81.** -120 ft/sec

CHAPTER 3

Section 3.1   (*page 170*)

1. $f'(0) = 0$ **3.** $f'(4) = 0$
5. $f'(-2)$ is undefined   **7.** $x = 0, x = 2$
9. $t = \dfrac{8}{3}, t = 4$ **11.** $x = 0, x = \dfrac{\pi}{3}, \pi, \dfrac{5\pi}{3}$
13. Minimum: $(2, 2)$
Maximum: $(-1, 8)$
15. Minimum: $(0, 0)$ and $(3, 0)$
Maximum: $(\frac{3}{2}, \frac{9}{4})$
17. Minimum: $(-1, -4)$ and $(2, -4)$
Maximum: $(0, 0)$ and $(3, 0)$
19. Minimum: $(0, 0)$
Maximum: $(-1, 5)$
21. Minimum: $(1, 1)$
Maximum: $(4, 4)$
23. Minimum: $(1, -1)$
Maximum: $(0, -\frac{1}{2})$
25. Minimum: $\left(\dfrac{1}{6}, \dfrac{\sqrt{3}}{2}\right)$
Maximum: $(0, 1)$
27. Continuous on $\left[0, \dfrac{\pi}{4}\right]$
Not continuous on $[0, \pi]$
29. a. Yes   **b.** No
31. a. No   **b.** Yes
33. a. Minimum: $(0, -3)$ Maximum: $(2, 1)$
b. Minimum: $(0, -3)$
c. Maximum: $(2, 1)$
d. No extrema
35. Minimum: $(0, 2)$ Maximum: $(3, 36)$
37. Minimum: $(4, 1)$
39. Maximum: $\left| f''\left(\sqrt[3]{-10 + \sqrt{108}}\right) \right| \approx 1.47$
41. Maximum: $\left| f^{(4)}(0) \right| = \frac{56}{81}$
43. Maximum: $P(12) = 72$
45. The part of the lawn farthest from the sprinkler.
47. a.

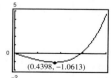

b. $(0.4398, -1.0613)$ Minimum

49. True   **50.** True   **51.** True
52. False, let $f(x) = x^2$ and $g(x) = (x - 1)^2$
53. All real numbers
(Slope is zero at nonintegers and undefined at integers.)

Section 3.2   (*page 177*)

1. $f(0) = f(2) = 0$
f is not differentiable on $(0, 2)$.
3. $f'(1) = 0$
5. $f'\left(\dfrac{6 - \sqrt{3}}{3}\right) = 0$ **7.** Not differentiable at $x = 0$
$f'\left(\dfrac{6 + \sqrt{3}}{3}\right) = 0$
9. Not differentiable at $x = 0$ **11.** $f'(-2 + \sqrt{5}) = 0$
13. $f'\left(\dfrac{\pi}{2}\right) = 0$ **15.** $f'\left(\dfrac{\pi}{4}\right) = 0$
$f'\left(\dfrac{3\pi}{2}\right) = 0$
17. $f'(-0.5756) = 0$ **19.** Not continuous on $[0, \pi]$
21. a. $f(1) = f(2) = 64$
b. Velocity $= 0$ for some t in $[1, 2]$
23. No, let $f(x) = x^2$ on $[-1, 2]$.
25. $f'(-\frac{1}{2}) = -1$ **27.** $f'(\frac{8}{27}) = 1$
29. $f'\left(\dfrac{-2 + \sqrt{6}}{2}\right) = \dfrac{2}{3}$ **31.** $f'\left(\dfrac{\sqrt{3}}{3}\right) = 1$
33. $f'\left(-\dfrac{\pi}{2}\right) = f'\left(\dfrac{\pi}{2}\right) = 1$
35. The function is discontinuous on $[0, 6]$.
37.

(graph with $f(x) = |x|$, points $(-5, 5)$ and $(5, 5)$)

39. a. -48 ft/sec   **b.** $t = \frac{3}{2}$ sec
41. Secant line: $x - 4y + 3 = 0$
Tangent line: $c = 4, x - 4y + 4 = 0$

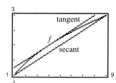

43. False, f is not continuous on $[-1, 1]$.
44. False, let $f(x) = \dfrac{x^3 - 4x}{x^2 - 1}$.
45. True   **46.** True   **47.** True   **48.** True

57. $f(x) = \cos x$, $g(x) = \sin x$

Section 3.3   (*page 186*)

1. Increasing on $(3, \infty)$
   Decreasing on $(-\infty, 3)$
3. Increasing on $(-\infty, -2)$ and $(2, \infty)$
   Decreasing on $(-2, 2)$
5. Increasing on $(-\infty, 0)$
   Decreasing on $(0, \infty)$
7. Critical number: $x = 1$
   Increasing on $(-\infty, 1)$
   Decreasing on $(1, \infty)$
   Relative maximum: $(1, 5)$
9. Critical number: $x = 3$
   Increasing on $(3, \infty)$
   Decreasing on $(-\infty, 3)$
   Relative minimum: $(3, -9)$
11. Critical numbers: $x = -2, 1$
   Increasing on $(-\infty, -2)$ and $(1, \infty)$
   Decreasing on $(-2, 1)$
   Relative maximum: $(-2, 20)$
   Relative minimum: $(1, -7)$
13. Critical numbers: $x = -1, 1$
   Increasing on $(-\infty, -1)$ and $(1, \infty)$
   Decreasing on $(-1, 1)$
   Relative maximum: $(-1, \frac{4}{5})$
   Relative minimum: $(1, -\frac{4}{5})$
15. Critical number: $x = 0$
   Increasing on $(-\infty, \infty)$
   No relative extrema
17. Critical number: $x = 5$
   Increasing on $(-\infty, 5)$
   Decreasing on $(5, \infty)$
   Relative maximum: $(5, 5)$
19. Critical number: $x = 0$
   Discontinuities: $x = -3, 3$
   Increasing on $(-\infty, -3)$ and $(-3, 0)$
   Decreasing on $(0, 3)$ and $(3, \infty)$
   Relative maximum: $(0, 0)$
21. Critical numbers: $x = 0, 4$
   Increasing on $(-\infty, 0)$ and $(4, \infty)$
   Decreasing on $(0, 4)$
   Relative maximum: $(0, 15)$
   Relative minimum: $(4, -17)$

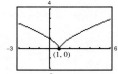

23. Critical number: $x = 1$
   Increasing on $(1, \infty)$
   Decreasing on $(-\infty, 1)$
   Relative minimum: $(1, 0)$

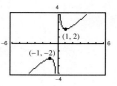

25. Critical numbers: $x = -1, 1$
   Discontinuity: $x = 0$
   Increasing on $(-\infty, -1)$ and $(1, \infty)$
   Decreasing on $(-1, 0)$ and $(0, 1)$
   Relative maximum: $(-1, -2)$
   Relative minimum: $(1, 2)$

27. Critical numbers: $x = -3, 1$
   Discontinuity: $x = -1$
   Increasing on $(-\infty, -3)$ and $(1, \infty)$
   Decreasing on $(-3, -1)$ and $(-1, 1)$
   Relative maximum: $(-3, -8)$
   Relative minimum: $(1, 0)$

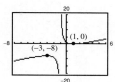

29. Critical numbers: $x = \dfrac{\pi}{6}, \dfrac{5\pi}{6}$

   Increasing on $\left(0, \dfrac{\pi}{6}\right)$, $\left(\dfrac{5\pi}{6}, 2\pi\right)$

   Decreasing on $\left(\dfrac{\pi}{6}, \dfrac{5\pi}{6}\right)$

   Relative maximum: $\left(\dfrac{\pi}{6}, \dfrac{[\pi + 6\sqrt{3}]}{12}\right)$

   Relative minimum: $\left(\dfrac{5\pi}{6}, \dfrac{[5\pi - 6\sqrt{3}]}{12}\right)$

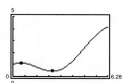

31. Critical numbers: $x = \dfrac{\pi}{2}, \dfrac{7\pi}{6}, \dfrac{3\pi}{2}, \dfrac{11\pi}{6}$

   Increasing on $\left(0, \dfrac{\pi}{2}\right)$, $\left(\dfrac{7\pi}{6}, \dfrac{3\pi}{2}\right)$, $\left(\dfrac{11\pi}{6}, 2\pi\right)$

   Decreasing on $\left(\dfrac{\pi}{2}, \dfrac{7\pi}{6}\right)$, $\left(\dfrac{3\pi}{2}, \dfrac{11\pi}{6}\right)$

   Relative maxima: $\left(\dfrac{\pi}{2}, 2\right)$, $\left(\dfrac{3\pi}{2}, 0\right)$

   Relative minima: $\left(\dfrac{7\pi}{6}, -\dfrac{1}{4}\right)$, $\left(\dfrac{11\pi}{6}, -\dfrac{1}{4}\right)$

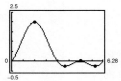

33. a. $f'(x) = \dfrac{2(9 - 2x^2)}{\sqrt{9 - x^2}}$
   b.

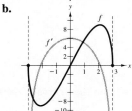

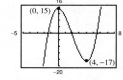

c. Critical numbers: $x = \pm \dfrac{3\sqrt{2}}{2}$

d. $f' > 0$ on $\left(-\dfrac{3\sqrt{2}}{2}, \dfrac{3\sqrt{2}}{2}\right)$

$f' < 0$ on $\left(-3, -\dfrac{3\sqrt{2}}{2}\right), \left(\dfrac{3\sqrt{2}}{2}, 3\right)$

35. a. $f'(t) = t(t\cos t + 2\sin t)$

b.

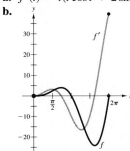

c. Critical numbers: $x = 2.2889, 5.0870$

d. $f' > 0$ on $(0, 2.2889), (5.0870, 2\pi)$

$f' < 0$ on $(2.2889, 5.0870)$

37. $g'(0) < 0$ **39.** $g'(-6) < 0$ **41.** $g'(0) > 0$

43.

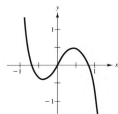

45.

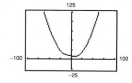

Minimum at the approximate critical number $x = -0.40$.
Maximum at the approximate critical number $x = 0.48$.

47. Yes; $\theta = \dfrac{\pi}{2}$

49. $r = \dfrac{2R}{3}$

51. Decreasing when $0 < t < 6.02$ days
Increasing when $6.02 < t < 14$ days

53. a. $T = 10°, R \approx 8.3666 \ \Omega$

b.

55. $f(x) = -\dfrac{1}{2}x^3 + \dfrac{3}{2}x^2$ **57.** True

58. False, let $f(x) = x$, and $g(x) = x$ on the interval $(-\infty, 0)$.

59. True **60.** False, let $f(x) = x^3$. **61.** True

62. False, let $f(x) = x^3$ and $c = 0$.

Section 3.4 (*page 194*)

1. Concave upward: $(-\infty, \infty)$

3. Concave upward: $(-\infty, 1)$
Concave downward: $(1, \infty)$

5. Concave upward: $(-\infty, -1), (1, \infty)$
Concave downward: $(-1, 1)$

7. Relative maximum: $(3, 9)$

9. Relative minimum: $(5, 0)$

11. Relative maximum: $(0, 3)$
Relative minimum: $(2, -1)$

13. Relative minimum: $(3, -25)$

15. Relative minimum: $(0, -3)$

17. Relative maximum: $(-2, -4)$
Relative minimum: $(2, 4)$

19. No relative extrema since f is non-increasing.

21. Relative maximum: $(-2, 16)$
Relative minimum: $(2, -16)$
Point of inflection: $(0, 0)$

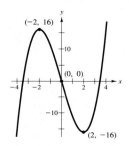

23. Point of inflection: $(2, 0)$

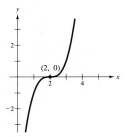

25. Relative minima: $(\pm 2, -4)$
Relative maximum: $(0, 0)$

Points of inflection: $\left(\pm\dfrac{2}{\sqrt{3}}, -\dfrac{20}{9}\right)$

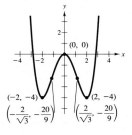

27. Relative minimum: $(1, -27)$
Points of inflection: $(2, -16)$, $(4, 0)$

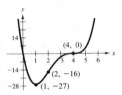

29. Relative minimum: $(-2, -2)$

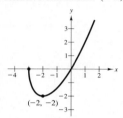

31. Relative minimum: $(3\pi, -1)$
Relative maximum: $(\pi, 1)$
Point of inflection: $(2\pi, 0)$

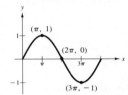

33. Relative minima: $\left(\dfrac{\pi}{2}, 1\right)$, $\left(\dfrac{5\pi}{2}, 1\right)$

Relative maxima: $\left(\dfrac{3\pi}{2}, -1\right)$, $\left(\dfrac{7\pi}{2}, -1\right)$

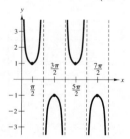

35. Relative minimum: $\left(\dfrac{5\pi}{3}, -2.598\right)$

Relative maximum: $\left(\dfrac{\pi}{3}, 2.598\right)$

Points of inflection: $(\pi, 0)$,
$(1.823, 1.452)$, $(4.46, -1.452)$

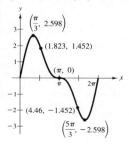

37. a. $f'(x) = 0.2x(x - 3)^2(5x - 6)$
$f''(x) = 0.4(x - 3)(10x^2 - 24x + 9)$
b. Relative maximum: $(0, 0)$
Relative minimum: $(1.2, -1.6796)$
Points of inflection: $(0.4652, -0.7049)$,
$(1.9348, -0.9049)$, $(3, 0)$
c.

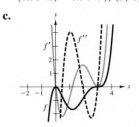

39. a. $f'(x) = \cos x - \cos 3x + \cos 5x$
$f''(x) = -\sin x + 3\sin 3x - 5\sin 5x$
b. Relative maximum: $(\pi/2, 1.53333)$
Points of inflection:
$(0.5236, 0.2667)$, $(1.1731, 0.9638)$,
$(1.9685, 0.9637)$, $(2.6180, 0.2667)$
c.

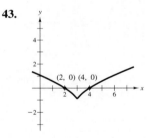

41.

43.

45.

47.

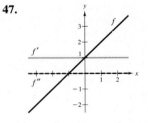

49.

51.

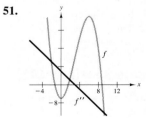

53. $f(x) = (x - c)^n$ has a point of inflection at $(c, 0)$ if n is odd and $n \geq 3$.

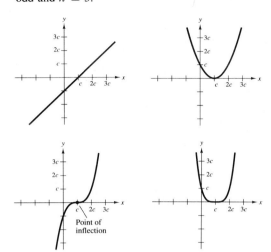

55. $f(x) = \frac{1}{2}x^3 - 6x^2 + \frac{45}{2}x - 24$

57. a. $f(x) = \frac{1}{32}x^3 + \frac{3}{16}x^2$

    b. Two miles from touchdown

61. $x = \left(\dfrac{15 - \sqrt{33}}{16} \right) L \approx 0.578\, L$ **63.** $x = 100$ units

65. $\theta = \dfrac{\pi}{2} + 2n\pi, \; \theta = \dfrac{3\pi}{2} + 2n\pi$

67.

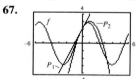

The values of f, P_1, and P_2 and their first derivatives are equal to $x = 0$.

69.

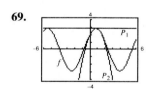

The values of f, P_1, and P_2 and their first derivatives are equal to $x = \pi/4$.

71. a. $S'' > 0$ **b.** $S'' < 0$ **c.** $S' = C, S'' = 0$

    d. $S' = 0, S'' = 0$ **e.** $S' < 0, S'' > 0$ **f.** $S' > 0$

73. True   **74.** False, 0 is not in the domain of f.

75. False, the maximum value is $\sqrt{13} \approx 3.60555$.

76. True   **79.** $(1, 0)$

Section 3.5 (*page 203*)

1. h   **2.** c   **3.** e   **4.** a   **5.** d

6. g   **7.** b   **8.** f   **9.** $\frac{2}{3}$ **11.** 0

13. Limit does not exist.   **15.** Limit does not exist.

17. 5   **19.** -1 **21.** 2   **23.** 1

25. 0   **27.** 0   **29.** 1   **31.** 0

33. $-\frac{1}{2}$

35.

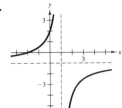

37.

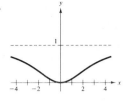

39.

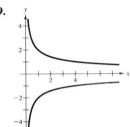

41.

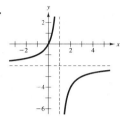

43.

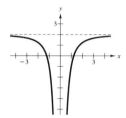

45.

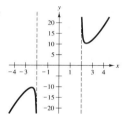

47.

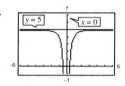

49.

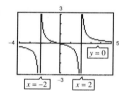

51.

53.

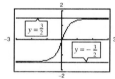

55. a.

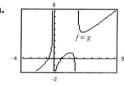

c.

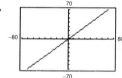

The slant asymptote $y = x$.

57.

x	10^0	10^1	10^2	10^3	10^4	10^5	10^6
$f(x)$	1.000	0.513	0.501	0.500	0.500	0.500	0.500

$$\lim_{x \to \infty} x - \sqrt{x(x-1)} = \frac{1}{2}$$

59.

x	10^0	10^1	10^2	10^3	10^4	10^5	10^6
$f(x)$	0.479	0.500	0.500	0.500	0.500	0.500	0.500

$$\lim_{x \to \infty} x \sin \frac{1}{2x} = \frac{1}{2}$$

61. 0.5   **63.** 100%

65. False, let $f(x) = \dfrac{2x}{\sqrt{x^2 + 2}}$

$f'(x) > 0$ for all real numbers.

66. False, let $f(x) = \begin{cases} -\frac{1}{8}x^2 + \frac{1}{2}x + 1, & x < 0 \\ \sqrt{x + 1}, & x \geq 0 \end{cases}$

$f''(x) < 0, f(x)$ increases without bound.

69.

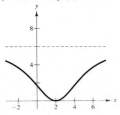

Section 3.6 (*page 211*)

1.

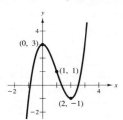

3.

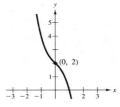

5.

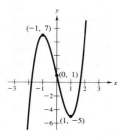

7.

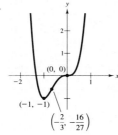

9.

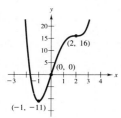

11.

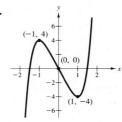

13.

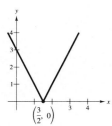

15.

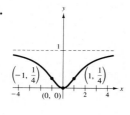

17.

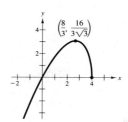

19.

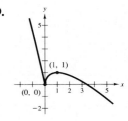

21.

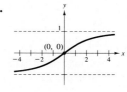

23.

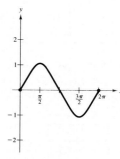

25.

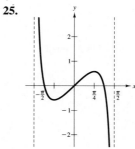

27.

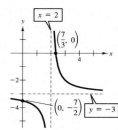

29.

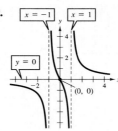

31.

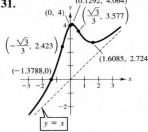

33.

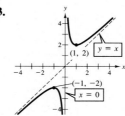

35.

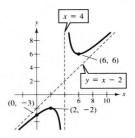

37.

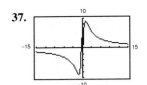

39.

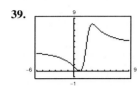

The graph crosses the horizontal asymptote $y = 4$. The graph of f does not cross its vertical asymptote $x = c$ since $f(c)$ does not exist.

41.

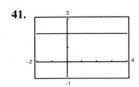

The rational function is not reduced to lowest terms.

43.

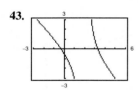

The graph appears to approach the line $y = -x + 1$ which is the slant asymptote.

45. $y = \dfrac{1}{x - 5}$　　**47.** $y = \dfrac{3x^2 - 13x - 9}{x - 5}$

49. a. The horizontal asymptote is $y = a$.
　　b. The vertical asymptote is $x = b$.

51. $a < 0$ and $b^2 < 3ac$

53. $a < 0$ and $b^2 = 3ac$

55. $a < 0$ and $b^2 > 3ac$

57.

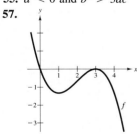

59.

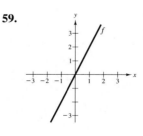

61.

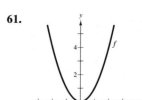

63.

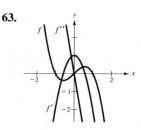

Section 3.7　(*page 218*)

1. a.

First number, x	Second number	Product, P
10	110−10	$10(110-10) = 1000$
20	110−20	$20(110-20) = 1800$
30	110−30	$30(110-30) = 2400$
40	110−40	$40(110-40) = 2800$
50	110−50	$50(110-50) = 3000$
60	110−60	$60(110-60) = 3000$

　　b. $P = x(110 - x)$　　**c.** 55 and 55

　　d.

First number, x	Second number	Product, P
10	110−10	$10(110-10) = 1000$
20	110−20	$20(110-20) = 1800$
30	110−30	$30(110-30) = 2400$
40	110−40	$40(110-40) = 2800$
50	110−50	$50(110-50) = 3000$
60	110−60	$60(110-60) = 3000$
70	110−70	$70(110-70) = 2800$
80	110−80	$80(110-80) = 2400$
90	110−90	$90(110-90) = 1800$
100	110−100	$100(110-100) = 1000$

　　e.

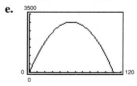

3. $\sqrt{192}$ and $\sqrt{192}$　　**5.** 1 and 1　　**7.** $l = w = 25$ ft

9. $l = w = 8$ ft　　**11.** $\left(\dfrac{7}{2}, \sqrt{\dfrac{7}{2}}\right)$　　**13.** $x = \dfrac{Q_0}{2}$

15. 600 m $\times$ 300 m

17. a. $A = 150$ in.^{2}
　　　　$V = 99$ in.^{3}
　　b. $A = 150$ in.^{2}
　　　　$V = 125$ in.^{3}
　　c. $A = 150$ in.^{2}
　　　　$V = 117$ in.^{3}

19. a.

Height, x	Length and width	Volume, V
1	$24 - 2(1)$	$1[24 - 2(1)]^2 = 484$
2	$24 - 2(2)$	$2[24 - 2(2)]^2 = 800$
3	$24 - 2(3)$	$3[24 - 2(3)]^2 = 972$
4	$24 - 2(4)$	$4[24 - 2(4)]^2 = 1024$
5	$24 - 2(5)$	$5[24 - 2(5)]^2 = 980$
6	$24 - 2(6)$	$6[24 - 2(6)]^2 = 864$

b. $V = x(24 - 2x)^2$ **c.** $x = 4$, $V = 1024$

d.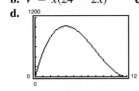

21. $\dfrac{5 - \sqrt{7}}{6}$ ft $\times \dfrac{1 + \sqrt{7}}{3}$ ft $\times \dfrac{4 + \sqrt{7}}{3}$ ft

23. Rectangular portion: $\dfrac{16}{\pi + 4}$ ft $\times \dfrac{32}{\pi + 4}$ ft

25. $x = 3$, $y = \frac{3}{2}$ **27.** $(0, 0)$, $(4, 0)$, $(0, 6)$

29. Width: $\dfrac{5\sqrt{2}}{2}$; Length: $5\sqrt{2}$

31. Bases: r and $2r$; altitude: $\dfrac{\sqrt{3}r}{2}$

33. a.

Radius, r	Height	Surface area, S
0.2	$\dfrac{22}{\pi(0.2)^2}$	$2\pi(0.2)\left[0.2 + \dfrac{22}{\pi(0.2)^2}\right] \approx 220.3$
0.4	$\dfrac{22}{\pi(0.4)^2}$	$2\pi(0.4)\left[0.4 + \dfrac{22}{\pi(0.4)^2}\right] \approx 111.0$
0.6	$\dfrac{22}{\pi(0.6)^2}$	$2\pi(0.6)\left[0.6 + \dfrac{22}{\pi(0.6)^2}\right] \approx 75.6$
0.8	$\dfrac{22}{\pi(0.8)^2}$	$2\pi(0.8)\left[0.8 + \dfrac{22}{\pi(0.8)^2}\right] \approx 59.0$

b. $S = 2\pi r\left(r + \dfrac{22}{nr^2}\right)$ **c.** $r = \sqrt[3]{\dfrac{11}{\pi}}$, $h = 2r$

d.

Radius, r	Height	Surface area, S
0.2	$\dfrac{22}{\pi(0.2)^2}$	$2\pi(0.2)\left[0.2 + \dfrac{22}{\pi(0.2)^2}\right] \approx 220.3$
0.4	$\dfrac{22}{\pi(0.4)^2}$	$2\pi(0.4)\left[0.4 + \dfrac{22}{\pi(0.4)^2}\right] \approx 111.0$
0.6	$\dfrac{22}{\pi(0.6)^2}$	$2\pi(0.6)\left[0.6 + \dfrac{22}{\pi(0.6)^2}\right] \approx 75.6$
0.8	$\dfrac{22}{\pi(0.8)^2}$	$2\pi(0.8)\left[0.8 + \dfrac{22}{\pi(0.8)^2}\right] \approx 59.0$
1.0	$\dfrac{22}{\pi(1.0)^2}$	$2\pi(1.0)\left[1.0 + \dfrac{22}{\pi(1.0)^2}\right] \approx 50.3$
1.2	$\dfrac{22}{\pi(1.2)^2}$	$2\pi(1.2)\left[1.2 + \dfrac{22}{\pi(1.2)^2}\right] \approx 45.7$
1.4	$\dfrac{22}{\pi(1.4)^2}$	$2\pi(1.4)\left[1.4 + \dfrac{22}{\pi(1.4)^2}\right] \approx 43.7$

Radius, r	Height	Surface area, S
1.6	$\dfrac{22}{\pi(1.6)^2}$	$2\pi(1.6)\left[1.6 + \dfrac{22}{\pi(1.6)^2}\right] \approx 43.6$
1.8	$\dfrac{22}{\pi(1.8)^2}$	$2\pi(1.8)\left[1.8 + \dfrac{22}{\pi(1.8)^2}\right] \approx 44.8$
2.0	$\dfrac{22}{\pi(2.0)^2}$	$2\pi(2.0)\left[2.0 + \dfrac{22}{\pi(2.0)^2}\right] \approx 47.1$

e.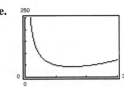

35. 18 in. $\times$ 18 in. $\times$ 36 in.

37. $\dfrac{32\pi r^3}{81}$ **39.** $r = \sqrt[3]{\dfrac{9}{\pi}} \approx 1.42$ in.

41. Side of square: $\dfrac{10\sqrt{3}}{9 + 4\sqrt{3}}$

Side of triangle: $\dfrac{30}{9 + 4\sqrt{3}}$

43. a. $\dfrac{10\pi}{\pi + 3 + 2\sqrt{2}} \approx 3.5$ ft   **b.** 10 ft

45. $w = 8\sqrt{3}$, $h = 8\sqrt{6}$ **47.** $h = \sqrt{2}$ ft

49. 1 mile from the nearest point on the coast

53. $\theta = \arctan k$, $F = \dfrac{kW}{\sqrt{k^2 + 1}}$

55. $\theta = \dfrac{2\pi}{3}\left(3 - \sqrt{6}\right) \approx 66°$

57. 14.1421×7.071

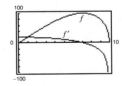

59. $42.1°$

Section 3.8 (*page 228*)

1.

n	x_n	$f(x_n)$	$f'(x_n)$	$\dfrac{f(x_n)}{f'(x_n)}$	$x_n - \dfrac{f(x_n)}{f'(x_n)}$
1	1.7000	-0.1100	3.4000	-0.0324	1.7324
2	1.7324	0.0012	3.4648	0.0003	1.7321

3.

n	x_n	$f(x_n)$	$f'(x_n)$	$\dfrac{f(x_n)}{f'(x_n)}$	$x_n - \dfrac{f(x_n)}{f'(x_n)}$
1	3	0.1411	-0.9900	-0.1425	3.1425
2	3.1425	-0.0009	-1.0000	0.0009	3.1416

5. 0.682   **7.** 1.146   **9.** 3.317   **11.** -0.489

13. 0.569   **15.** 4.493   **17.** 0.74

33.

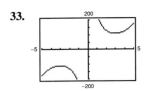

Relative minimum: (3, 108)
Relative maximum: $(-3, -108)$

35.

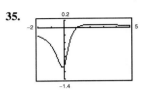

Relative minimum: $(-0.155, -1.077)$
Relative maximum: $(2.155, 0.077)$

37. $f'\left(\dfrac{2744}{729}\right) = \dfrac{3}{7}$

39. $f'(0) = 1$ **41.** No, f is discontinuous at $x = 0$

43. $c = \dfrac{x_1 + x_2}{2}$ **45.** $t \approx 4.92 \approx 4{:}55$ P.M.
$d \approx 64$ mi

47. $(0, 0), (5, 0), (0, 10)$ **51.** 14.05 ft
53. $3(3^{2/3} + 2^{2/3})^{3/2} \approx 21.07$ ft

55. a. $y = \dfrac{1}{4}$ in., $v = 4$ in./sec

c. Period: $\dfrac{\pi}{6}$ Frequency: $\dfrac{6}{\pi}$

57. $-0.347, -1.532, 1.879$ **59.** $-1.164, 1.453$

61. $dS = \pm 1.8\pi$ in.^{2}, $\dfrac{dS}{S} \times 100 \approx \pm 0.56\%$

$dV = \pm 8.1\pi$ in.^{3}, $\dfrac{dV}{V} \times 100 \approx \pm 0.83\%$

63. \$48   **65.** 120   **67.** $x = \sqrt{\dfrac{2Qs}{r}}$

69. Maximum: (1, 3)
Minimum: (1, 1)
71. False, let $f(x) = x^3$ and $c = 0$.
72. False, the horizontal asymptotes of
$f(x) = 2x/\sqrt{x^2 + 2}$ are $y = 2$ and $y = -2$.
73. The first and second derivatives of the deficit
function are both positive.

CHAPTER 4 (page 256)

Section 4.1

1. $y = t^3 + C$ **3.** $y = \dfrac{2}{5}x^{5/2} + C$

Given	Rewrite	Integrate	Simplify
5. $\displaystyle\int \sqrt[3]{x}\,dx$	$\displaystyle\int x^{1/3}\,dx$	$\dfrac{x^{4/3}}{4/3} + C$	$\dfrac{3}{4}x^{4/3} + C$
7. $\displaystyle\int \dfrac{1}{x\sqrt{x}}\,dx$	$\displaystyle\int x^{-3/2}\,dx$	$\dfrac{x^{-1/2}}{-1/2} + C$	$-\dfrac{2}{\sqrt{x}} + C$
9. $\displaystyle\int \dfrac{1}{2x^3}\,dx$	$\dfrac{1}{2}\displaystyle\int x^{-3}\,dx$	$\dfrac{1}{2}\left(\dfrac{x^{-2}}{-2}\right) + C$	$-\dfrac{1}{4x^2} + C$

11. $\dfrac{1}{4}x^4 + 2x + C$ **13.** $\dfrac{2}{5}x^{5/2} + x^2 + x + C$

15. $\dfrac{3}{5}x^{5/3} + C$ **17.** $-\dfrac{1}{2x^2} + C$

19. $\dfrac{2}{15}x^{1/2}(3x^2 + 5x + 15) + C$ **21.** $x^3 + \dfrac{1}{2}x^2 - 2x + C$
23. $\dfrac{2}{7}y^{7/2} + C$ **25.** $x + C$
27. $-2\cos x + 3\sin x + C$ **29.** $t + \csc t + C$
31. $\tan\theta + \cos\theta + C$ **33.** $\tan y + C$

35. 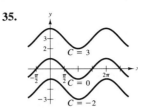   **37.**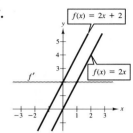

39.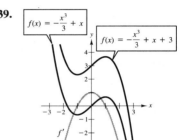

41. $y = x^2 - x + 1$ **43.** $y = \sin x + 4$
45. $f(x) = x^2 + x + 4$
47. $f(x) = -4x^{1/2} + 3x = -4\sqrt{x} + 3x$

49. a. $h(t) = \dfrac{t^2}{4} + 2t + 5$ **b.** 26 in.

53. $v_0 \approx 187.617$ ft/sec
55. a. $\dfrac{154}{39} \approx 3.95$ ft/sec^2 **b.** $\dfrac{1859}{3} \approx 619.67$ ft
57. a. 300 ft   **b.** 60 ft/sec ≈ 41 mph

61. $C(x) = x^2 - 12x + 50$ **63.** $R = x(100 - \frac{5}{2}x)$

$\overline{C}(x) = x - 12 + \dfrac{50}{x}$ $p = 100 - \frac{5}{2}x$

65. True   **66.** True   **67.** True   **68.** True
69. 320 m, -32 m/sec

71.

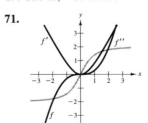

Section 4.2 (page 267)

1. 35   **3.** $\dfrac{158}{85}$ **5.** $4c$ **7.** $\displaystyle\sum_{i=1}^{9} \dfrac{1}{3i}$

9. $\displaystyle\sum_{j=1}^{8}\left[2\left(\dfrac{j}{8}\right) + 3\right]$ **11.** $\dfrac{2}{n}\displaystyle\sum_{i=1}^{n}\left[\left(\dfrac{2i}{n}\right)^3 - \left(\dfrac{2i}{n}\right)\right]$

13. $\dfrac{3}{n}\displaystyle\sum_{i=1}^{n}\left[2\left(1 + \dfrac{3i}{n}\right)^2\right]$ **15.** 420   **17.** 2470

19. $\dfrac{1015}{n^3}$ **21.** $\dfrac{8}{3}$ **23.** $\dfrac{81}{4}$ **25.** 9

27. $\displaystyle\lim_{n\to\infty}\left[8\left(\dfrac{n^2+n}{n^2}\right)\right]=8$

29. $\displaystyle\lim_{n\to\infty}\dfrac{1}{6}\left[\dfrac{2n^3-3n^2+n}{n^3}\right]=\dfrac{1}{3}$

31. $\displaystyle\lim_{n\to\infty}2\left[\dfrac{10n^4+13n^3+4n^2}{n^4}\right]=20$

33. $S\approx 0.768$ **35.** $S\approx 0.746$ **37.** $S\approx 0.859$
$s\approx 0.518$ $s\approx 0.646$ $s\approx 0.659$

39. a.

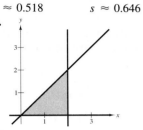

e.

n	5	10	50	100
$s(n)$	1.6	1.8	1.96	1.98
$S(n)$	2.4	2.2	2.04	2.02

41. $A=2$ **43.** $A=\dfrac{7}{3}$

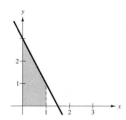
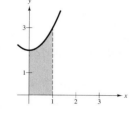

45. $A=34$ **47.** $A=\dfrac{2}{3}$

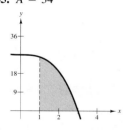
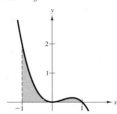

49. $A=6$

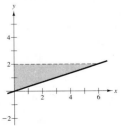

51. $\dfrac{69}{8}$ **53.** 0.345

55.

n	4	8	12	16	20
Approximate area	5.3838	5.3523	5.3439	5.3403	5.3384

57.

n	4	8	12	16	20
Approximate area	2.2223	2.2387	2.2418	2.2430	2.2435

59. b   **61.** True   **62.** True

Section 4.3 (*page 277*)

1. $\displaystyle\int_0^5 3\,dx$ **3.** $\displaystyle\int_{-4}^4(4-|x|)\,dx$ **5.** $\displaystyle\int_{-2}^2(4-x^2)\,dx$

7. $\displaystyle\int_0^\pi \sin x\,dx$ **9.** $\displaystyle\int_0^2 y^3\,dy$

11. $A=12$ **13.** $A=8$

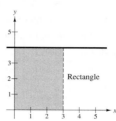
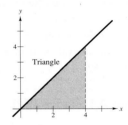

15. $A=14$ **17.** $A=1$

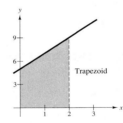
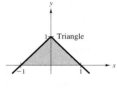

19. $A=\dfrac{9\pi}{2}$

21. a. 13   **b.** -10 **c.** 0   **d.** 30
23. a. 8   **b.** -12 **c.** -4 **d.** 30
25. 36   **27.** 0   **29.** $\dfrac{10}{3}$

31. $\displaystyle\int_{-1}^5(3x+10)\,dx$ **33.** $\displaystyle\int_0^3\sqrt{x^2+4}\,dx$

35.

n	4	8	12	16	20
$L(n)$	3.6830	3.9956	4.0707	4.1016	4.1177
$M(n)$	4.3082	4.2076	4.1838	4.1740	4.1690
$R(n)$	3.6830	3.9956	4.0707	4.1016	4.1177

33. 16   **35.** 0   **37.** 2   **39.** $\dfrac{422}{5}$ **41.** $\dfrac{28\pi}{15}$ **43.** 2

45. 6

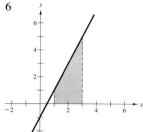

47. $\frac{10}{3}$

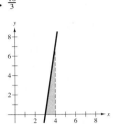

49. $\frac{1}{4}$

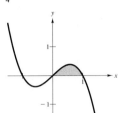

51. 16

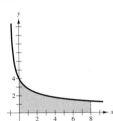

53. $\sqrt{3}$

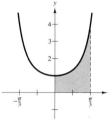

55. Average value $= \frac{2}{5}$, $x = \frac{29}{4}$

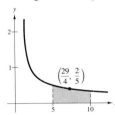

57. Average value $= 2$, $x = 2$

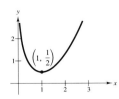

59. 0.254   **61.** 1.6234 liters
63. a. $C \approx \$9.17$ **b.** $C \approx \$3.14$ Savings $\approx \$6.03$
65. a. $\dfrac{19{,}800}{M}$ **b.** $\dfrac{22{,}800}{M}$
67. a. $0.025 = 2.5\%$ **b.** $0.736 = 73.6\%$
68. False, only constants can be taken through the integral sign.
69. False, $\dfrac{d}{dx}\left[-\dfrac{1}{x^2}\right] \neq \dfrac{1}{x}$.   **70.** True   **71.** True
72. False, $\displaystyle\int \tan x\,dx = -\ln|\cos x| + C$.

3. b   **4.** d   **5.** a   **6.** c
7. $f(x) = 3\ln x$
Domain: $x > 0$
9. $f(x) = \ln 2x$
Domain: $x > 0$

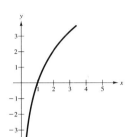

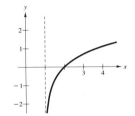

11. $f(x) = \ln(x - 1)$
Domain: $x > 1$

13. a. 1.7917   **b.** -0.4055 **c.** 4.3944   **d.** 0.5493
15. $\ln 2 - \ln 3$ **17.** $\ln x + \ln y - \ln z$ **19.** $\frac{3}{2}\ln 2$
21. $3[\ln(x + 1) + \ln(x - 1) - 3\ln x]$
23. $\ln z + 2\ln(z - 1)$ **25.** $\ln\dfrac{x - 2}{x + 2}$
27. $\ln\sqrt[3]{\dfrac{x(x + 3)^2}{x^2 - 1}}$ **29.** $\ln\dfrac{9}{\sqrt{x^2 + 1}}$ **31.** 3   **33.** 2
35. $\dfrac{2}{x}$ **37.** $\dfrac{4(\ln x)^3}{x}$ **39.** $\dfrac{2x^2 - 1}{x(x^2 - 1)}$ **41.** $\dfrac{1 - x^2}{x(x^2 + 1)}$
43. $\dfrac{1 - 2\ln t}{t^3}$ **45.** $\dfrac{2}{x\ln x^2} = \dfrac{1}{x\ln x}$ **47.** $\dfrac{1}{1 - x^2}$
49. $\dfrac{-4}{x(x^2 + 4)}$ **51.** $\dfrac{\sqrt{x^2 + 1}}{x^2}$ **53.** $\cot x$
55. $-\tan x + \dfrac{\sin x}{\cos x - 1}$ **57.** $\dfrac{3\cos x}{(\sin x - 1)(\sin x + 2)}$
59. $\dfrac{2}{x}(\sin 2x + x\cos 2x\ln x^2)$ **61.** $\dfrac{2xy}{3 - 2y^2}$
63. $5x - y - 2 = 0$ **65.** $xy'' + y' = x\left(\dfrac{-2}{x^2}\right) + \dfrac{2}{x} = 0$
67. Relative minimum: $(1, \frac{1}{2})$

CHAPTER 5

Section 5.1   (*page 324*)

1.

x	0.5	1.5	2	2.5	3	3.5	4
$\int_1^x 1/t\,dt$	-0.6932	0.4055	0.6932	0.9163	1.0987	1.2529	1.3865

69. Relative minimum: $(e^{-1}, -e^{-1})$

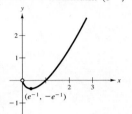

71. Relative minimum: (e, e)

Point of inflection: $\left(e^2, \dfrac{e^2}{2}\right)$

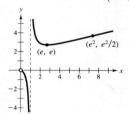

73.

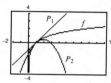

The values of f, P_1, and P_2, and their first derivatives agree at $x = 1$. The values of the second derivatives of f and P_2 agree at $x = 1$.

75. 0.567   **77.** $\dfrac{2x^2 - 1}{\sqrt{x^2 - 1}}$ **79.** $\dfrac{3x^3 - 15x^2 + 8x}{2(x - 1)^3\sqrt{3x - 2}}$

81. $\dfrac{(2x^2 + 2x - 1)\sqrt{x - 1}}{(x + 1)^{3/2}}$

83. $\beta = \dfrac{10}{\ln 10}(\ln I + 16 \ln 10)$

60 db

85. a.

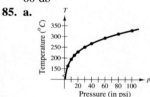

b. $p = 10$: 4.75 deg/lb/in.^{2}
$p = 70$: 0.97 deg/lb/in.^{2}

87. $g'(x) = \dfrac{f'(x)}{f(x)}, f(x) > 0$ **a.** yes   **b.** yes

Therefore the signs of $g'(x)$ and f' are the same.

89. For large values of x, g increases at a higher rate than f in both cases. The natural logarithm function increases very slowly for large values of x.

a.

b.

91.

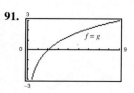

93. False, $\ln x + \ln 25 = \ln 25x$.   **94.** True   **95.** True

96. False, $y' = 0$.

Section 5.2 (*page 333*)

1. $\ln|x + 1| + C$ **3.** $-\frac{1}{2}\ln|3 - 2x| + C$

5. $\ln\sqrt{x^2 + 1} + C$ **7.** $\dfrac{x^2}{2} - 4\ln|x| + C$

9. $\frac{1}{3}\ln|x^3 + 3x^2 + 9x| + C$ **11.** $\frac{1}{3}(\ln x)^3 + C$

13. $2\sqrt{x + 1} + C$

15. $x + 6\sqrt{x} + 18\ln|\sqrt{x} - 3| + C$

17. $2\ln|x - 1| - \dfrac{2}{x - 1} + C$

19. $\ln|\sin\theta| + C$ **21.** $-\frac{1}{2}\ln|\csc 2x + \cot 2x| + C$

23. $\ln|1 + \sin t| + C$

25. $\ln|\sec x - 1| + C$ **27.** $-3\ln|2 - x| + C$

29. $-\ln\sqrt{|\cos 2\theta|} + C$ **31.** $\frac{5}{3}\ln 13 \approx 4.275$ **33.** $\frac{7}{3}$

35. $-\ln 3$ **37.** $\ln\left|\dfrac{2 - \sin 2}{1 - \sin 1}\right| \approx 1.929$

39. $2\left[\sqrt{x} - \ln\left(1 + \sqrt{x}\right)\right] + C$ **41.** $-\sin(1 - x) + C$

43. $\ln(\sqrt{2} + 1) - \dfrac{\sqrt{2}}{2} \approx 0.174$ **49.** $\dfrac{1}{x}$ **51.** 0

53. d   **55.** $\frac{15}{2} + 8\ln 2 \approx 13.045$ square units

57. $P(t) = 1000[12\ln|1 + 0.25t| + 1]$
$P(3) \approx 7715$

59. \$168.27   **61.** False, $\frac{1}{2}(\ln x) = \ln x^{1/2}$.

62. False, $\dfrac{d}{dx}[\ln x] = \dfrac{1}{x}$.   **63.** True

64. False, the integrand, $1/x$, has a nonremovable discontinuity in the interval $[-1, e]$.

65. $\lim_{k \to 0} f_k(x) = \ln x$

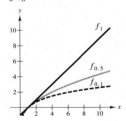

Section 5.3 (*page 341*)

1.

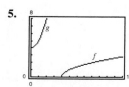

3.

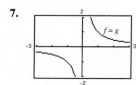

5.

7.

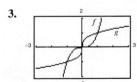

9. $f^{-1}(x) = \dfrac{x+3}{2}$ **11.** $f^{-1}(x) = x^{1/5}$

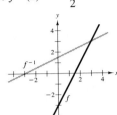
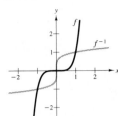

13. $f^{-1}(x) = x^2, \quad x \geq 0$

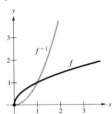

15. $f^{-1}(x) = \sqrt{4 - x^2}, \quad 0 \leq x \leq 2$

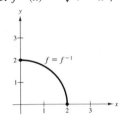

17. $f^{-1}(x) = x^3 + 1$ **19.** $f^{-1}(x) = x^{3/2}, \quad x \geq 0$

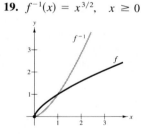

21. $f^{-1}(x) = \dfrac{\sqrt{7}x}{\sqrt{1 - x^2}}, \quad -1 < x < 1$

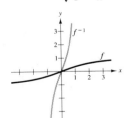

23. $f^{-1}(x) = \begin{cases} \dfrac{1 - \sqrt{1 + 16x^2}}{2x} & \text{if } x \neq 0 \\ 0 & \text{if } x = 0 \end{cases}$

25.

x	1	2	3	4
$f^{-1}(x)$	0	1	2	4

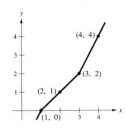

27. Inverse exists   **29.** Inverse does not exist
31. One-to-one   **33.** One-to-one

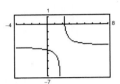
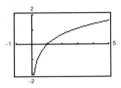

35. Not one-to-one

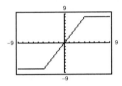

37. Inverse exists   **39.** Inverse does not exist
41. Inverse exists   **43.** $f'(x) = 2(x - 4) > 0$ on $(4, \infty)$

45. $f'(x) = -\dfrac{8}{x^3} < 0$ on $(0, \infty)$

47. $f'(x) = -\sin x < 0$ on $(0, \pi)$

49. Not continuous at $\dfrac{(2n - 1)\pi}{2}$

51. One-to-One   **53.** One-to-one
  $f^{-1}(x) = x^2 + 2, x \geq 0$ $f^{-1}(x) = 2 - x, x \geq 0$
55. $f^{-1}(x) = \sqrt{x} + 3, x \geq 0$

57. $f^{-1}(x) = x - 3, x \geq 0$ **59.** $\dfrac{1}{5}$ **61.** $\dfrac{2\sqrt{3}}{3}$

63. $\frac{1}{13}$ **65.** $f'(\frac{1}{2}) = \frac{3}{4}, (f^{-1})'(\frac{1}{8}) = \frac{4}{3}$
67. $f'(5) = \frac{1}{2}, (f^{-1})'(1) = 2$ **69.** 32   **71.** 600

73. $(g^{-1} \circ f^{-1})(x) = \dfrac{x+1}{2}$ **75.** $(f \circ g)^{-1}(x) = \dfrac{x+1}{2}$

81. False, let $f(x) = x^2$.   **82.** True   **83.** True

84. False, let $f(x) = \dfrac{1}{x}$.

85. No, let $f(x) = \begin{cases} x, & 0 \leq x \leq 1 \\ 1 - x, & 1 < x \leq 2 \end{cases}$.   **87.** $\sqrt{17}$

Section 5.4 (*page 350*)

1. a. $\ln 1 = 0$ **b.** $\ln 7.389 \ldots = 2$
3. a. $e^{0.6931\cdots} = 2$ **b.** $e^{2.128\cdots} = 8.4$
5. a. $x = 4$ **b.** $x = \frac{3}{2}$ **7. a.** $x = e^2$ **b.** $x = \ln 4$
9.   **11.**

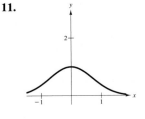

13. a.

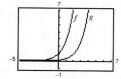

Translation 2 units to the right

b.

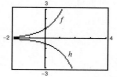

Reflection in the x-axis and a vertical shrink

c.

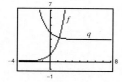

Reflection in the y-axis and a translation 3 units upward

15.

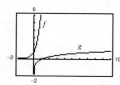

17.

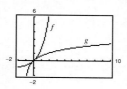

19. c   **20.** d   **21.** a   **22.** b   **23.** $2.7182805 < e$

25. a. 3   **b.** -3 **27.** $2e^{2x}$ **29.** $2(x-1)e^{-2x+x^2}$

31. $\dfrac{e^{\sqrt{x}}}{2\sqrt{x}}$ **33.** $3(e^{-t}+e^t)^2(e^t-e^{-t})$ **35.** $2x$

37. $\dfrac{2e^{2x}}{1+e^{2x}}$ **39.** $\dfrac{-2(e^x-e^{-x})}{(e^x+e^{-x})^2}$ **41.** x^2e^x

43. $e^{-x}\left(\dfrac{1}{x}-\ln x\right)$ **45.** $2e^x\cos x$ **47.** $\dfrac{10-e^y}{xe^y+3}$

49. $3(6x+5)e^{-3x}$

53. Relative maximum: $\left(0, 1/\sqrt{2\pi}\right)$
Points of inflection: $\left(\pm 1, 1/\sqrt{2\pi e}\right)$

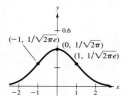

55. Relative minimum: $(0, 1)$

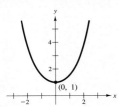

57. Relative minimum: $(0, 0)$
Relative maximum: $(2, 4e^{-2})$
Points of inflection: $\left(2 \pm \sqrt{2}, \left(6 \pm 4\sqrt{2}\right)e^{-(2\pm\sqrt{2})}\right)$

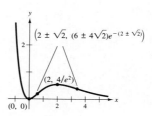

59.

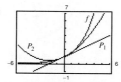

The values of f, P_1, and P_2, and their first derivatives agree at $x = 0$. The values of the second derivatives of f and P_2 agree at $x = 0$.

61. $A = \sqrt{2}e^{-1/2}$ **63.** 0.567

65. a.

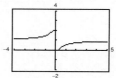

b. When x increases without bound, $1/x$ approaches zero, and $e^{1/x}$ approaches 1. Therefore, $f(x)$ approaches $\frac{2}{1+1} = 1$. Thus, $f(x)$ has a horizontal asymptote at $y = 1$. As x approaches zero from the right, $1/x$ approaches ∞, $e^{1/x}$ approaches ∞ and $f(x)$ approaches 0. As x approaches zero from the left, $1/x$ approaches $-\infty$, $e^{1/x}$ approaches 0, and $f(x)$ approaches 2. The limit does not exist since the left limit does not equal the right limit. Therefore, $x = 0$ is a nonremovable discontinuity.

67. $e^{5x} + C$ **69.** $\dfrac{e^2-1}{2e^2}$

71. $x - \ln(e^x+1) + C_1$ or $-\ln(1+e^{-x}) + C_2$

73. $\dfrac{e}{3}(e^2-1)$ **75.** $-\dfrac{2}{3}(1-e^x)^{3/2} + C$

77. $\ln|e^x - e^{-x}| + C$ **79.** $-\frac{5}{2}e^{-2x} + e^{-x} + C$

81. $\dfrac{1}{\pi}e^{\sin \pi x} + C$ **83.** $\ln|\cos e^{-x}| + C$

85. $\dfrac{1}{2a}e^{ax^2} + C$ **87.** $f(x) = \dfrac{1}{2}(e^x + e^{-x})$

89. $e^5 - 1 \approx 147.413$ **91.** $1 - e^{-1} \approx 0.632$

93. a. Midpoint Rule: 92.1898
Trapezoidal Rule: 93.8371
Simpson's Rule: 92.7385
b. Midpoint Rule: 1.1906
Trapezoidal Rule: 1.1827
Simpson's Rule: 1.1880

Section 5.5   (*page 359*)

1. -3 **3.** 0   **5. a.** $\log_2 8 = 3$ **b.** $\log_3(1/3) = -1$

7. a. $10^{-2} = 0.01$ **b.** $(1/2)^{-3} = 8$

9. a. $x = 3$ **b.** $x = -1$ **11. a.** $x = \frac{1}{3}$ **b.** $x = \frac{1}{16}$
13. a. $x = -1, 2$ **b.** $x = \frac{1}{3}$

15. 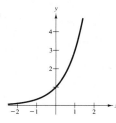   **17.**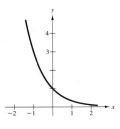

19. 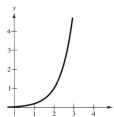   **21.**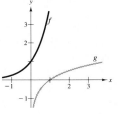

23. a. False   **b.** True   **c.** True   **d.** False
25. $(\ln 4)4^x$ **27.** $(\ln 5)5^{x-2}$ **29.** $t\,2^t(t \ln 2 + 2)$
31. $\dfrac{1}{x(\ln 3)}$ **33.** $\dfrac{x-2}{(\ln 2)x(x-1)}$ **35.** $\dfrac{x}{(\ln 5)(x^2-1)}$
37. $2(1 - \ln x)x^{(2/x)-2}$
39. $(x-2)^{x+1}\left[\dfrac{x+1}{x-2} + \ln(x-2)\right]$
41. $g(x) = x^x, k(x) = 2^x, h(x) = x^2, f(x) = \log_2 x$
43. a. \$40.64
  b. $C'(1) \approx 0.051P, C'(8) \approx 0.072P$
  c. $\ln 1.05$

45.

n	1	2	4	12	365	Continuous compounding
A	\$2061.03	\$2088.15	\$2102.35	\$2112.06	\$2116.84	\$2117.00

47.

n	1	2	4	12	365	Continuous compounding
A	\$17,449.40	\$18,679.19	\$19,358.15	\$19,837.40	\$20,077.29	\$20,085.54

49.

t	1	10	20	30	40	50
P	\$91,393.12	\$40,656.97	\$16,529.89	\$6720.55	\$2732.37	\$1110.90

51.

t	1	10	20	30	40	50
P	\$90,521.24	\$36,940.70	\$13,646.15	\$5040.98	\$1862.17	\$687.90

53. c

55. a. \$332.01   **b.** \$604.96   **c.** \$1102.32

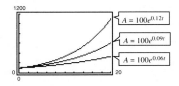

57. $p'(1) \approx 113.5$ fish/month
  $p'(10) \approx 403.2$ fish/month
  $t = 5 \ln 19 \approx 14.72$

59. a.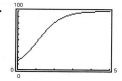

  b. 80.3%   **c.** $x \approx 1.546$ or 1546 egg masses
  d. $x \approx 1.105$ or 1105 egg masses
61. $-\dfrac{4^{-x}}{\ln 4} + C$ **63.** 4   **65.** $-\dfrac{7^{(3-x^2)}}{2 \ln 7} + C$
67. \$2825.51

69.

x	1	10^{-1}	10^{-2}	10^{-4}	10^{-6}
$(1+x)^{1/x}$	2	2.594	2.705	2.718	2.718

71. $y = 600(1.05)^t$ **72.** False, e is an irrational number.
73. True   **74.** True   **75.** True   **76.** True   **77.** True

Section 5.6 *(page 367)*

1. $y^2 - 5x^2 = C$ **3.** $y = Ce^{(2x^{3/2})/3}$
5. $y = C(1 + x^2)$
7. $\dfrac{dQ}{dt} = \dfrac{k}{t^2}$ **9.** $\dfrac{dN}{ds} = k(250 - s)$

$Q = -\dfrac{k}{t} + C$ $N = -\dfrac{k}{2}(250 - s)^2 + C$

11. $y = \frac{1}{4}t^2 + 10$ **13.** $y = 10e^{-t/2}$
15. $y = \frac{1}{2}e^{0.4605t}$ **17.** $y = 0.6687e^{0.4024t}$
19. Amount after 1000 years: 6.52 grams
Amount after 10,000 years: 0.14 gram
21. Initial quantity: 6.70 grams
Amount after 1000 years: 5.94 grams
23. Initial quantity: 2.16 grams   **25.** 95.81%
Amount after 10,000 years: 1.63 grams
27. Time to double: 5.78 years
Amount after 10 years: \$3320.12
29. Annual rate: 8.94%
Amount after 10 years: \$1833.67
31. Annual rate: 9.50%   **33.** \$112,087.09
Time to double: 7.30 years
35. a. 6.64 years   **b.** 6.33 years
    c. 6.30 years   **d.** 6.30 years
37. $y \approx 4.22e^{0.0430t}$
9.97 million
39. k. The larger the value of k, the greater the rate of growth
of the population.
41. 527.06 mm Hg
43. a. $N \approx 30(1 - e^{-0.0502t})$ **b.** 36 days
45. a. $S \approx 30e^{-1.7918/t}$ **b.** 20,965 units
    c.

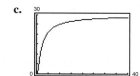

47. 2010 $(t = 16)$
49. a. 20 db   **b.** 70 db   **c.** 95 db   **d.** 120 db
51. a. $10^{8.3} \approx 199,526,231.5$ **b.** 10^R **c.** $\dfrac{1}{I \ln 10}$
53. 22.35°

Section 5.7 *(page 377)*

1. $\dfrac{\pi}{6}$ **3.** $\dfrac{\pi}{3}$ **5.** $\dfrac{\pi}{6}$ **7.** $-\dfrac{\pi}{4}$
9. 2.50   **11.** $\arccos(\frac{1}{1.269}) \approx 0.66$
13. The range of $y = \arctan x$ is $-\dfrac{\pi}{2} < y < \dfrac{\pi}{2}$.
15.

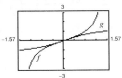

17. -0.1
19. a. $\dfrac{1}{2}$ **b.** $\dfrac{\sqrt{3}}{2}$

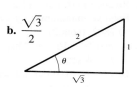

21. a. $\frac{3}{5}$ **b.** $\frac{5}{3}$

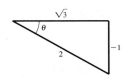

23. a. $-\sqrt{3}$

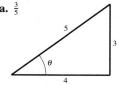

b. $-\frac{13}{5}$

25. x **27.** $\sqrt{1 - 4x^2}$ **29.** $\dfrac{\sqrt{x^2 - 1}}{x}$
31. $\dfrac{\sqrt{x^2 - 9}}{3}$ **33.** $\dfrac{\sqrt{x^2 + 2}}{x}$ **35.** $\arcsin\left(\dfrac{9}{\sqrt{x^2 + 81}}\right)$
39.

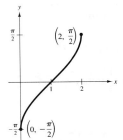

41.

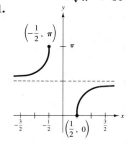

43. $x = \frac{1}{3}[\sin(\frac{1}{2}) + \pi] \approx 1.207$ **45.** $x = \frac{1}{3}$
47. $\dfrac{2}{\sqrt{2x - x^2}}$ **49.** $-\dfrac{3}{\sqrt{4 - x^2}}$
51. $\dfrac{a}{a^2 + x^2}$ **53.** $\dfrac{3x - \sqrt{1 - 9x^2}\,\arcsin 3x}{x^2\sqrt{1 - 9x^2}}$
55. $\dfrac{-6}{1 + 36x^2}$ **57.** $-\dfrac{t}{\sqrt{1 - t^2}}$ **59.** 0   **61.** $\dfrac{1}{1 - x^4}$
63. $\arcsin x$
65. $y = -2x + \left(\dfrac{5\pi}{6} - \sqrt{3}\right)$ **67.**

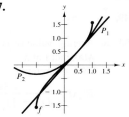

$y = -2x + \left(\dfrac{\pi}{6} + \sqrt{3}\right)$

37. $f^{-1}(x) = \sqrt{\dfrac{x}{2}} + 4$ **39.** $-2x$

41. $te^t(t + 2)$

43. $\dfrac{e^{2x} - e^{-2x}}{\sqrt{e^{2x} + e^{-2x}}}$ **45.** $3^{x-1} \ln 3$

47. $\dfrac{x(2 - x)}{e^x}$ **49.** $(1 - x^2)^{-3/2}$

51. $\dfrac{x}{|x|\sqrt{x^2 - 1}} + \operatorname{arcsec} x$ **53.** $(\arcsin x)^2$

55. $2 - \dfrac{\sinh \sqrt{x}}{2\sqrt{x}}$ **57.** $\dfrac{-y}{x(2y + \ln x)}$

59. $-\dfrac{2x \sin x^2 + e^y}{xe^y}$

61. a. ax^{a-1} **b.** $(\ln a)a^x$
   c. $x^x(1 + \ln x)$ **d.** 0

63. $-\frac{1}{6}e^{-3x^2} + C$

65. $\dfrac{e^{4x} - 3e^{2x} - 3}{3e^x} + C$

67. $\ln|e^x - 1| + C$ **69.** $\frac{1}{2}\arctan(e^{2x}) + C$

71. $\frac{1}{2}\arcsin x^2 + C$ **73.** $\frac{1}{2}\ln(16 + x^2) + C$

75. $\dfrac{1}{4}\left(\arctan\dfrac{x}{2}\right)^2 + C$ **77.** $\frac{1}{2}\ln(\sqrt{x^4 - 1} + x^2) + C$

79. $y = -e^{-t^2/2} + C$ **81.** $y = -\frac{1}{2}\ln(1 + e^{-2x}) + C$

83. $A = \ln 2$

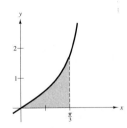

85. $-\dfrac{1}{2}(e^{-16} - 1) \approx 0.500$ **87.** 1.346

89. a. \$525.64   **b.** \$824.36   **c.** \$74,206.58

91. \$3499.38   **93.** $A = 500e^{-0.0128t}$

95. a. -24.26% **b.** -14.72%

97. a. 0.3935 **b.** 0.7769
   c. 0.2492 **d.** 0.9502

99. a. $v(t) = \dfrac{1}{k}[32 + (kv_0 - 32)e^{kt}], \; k < 0$

   b. $\dfrac{32}{k}$

   c. $s(t) = \dfrac{32}{k}t - \dfrac{1}{k^2}(kv_0 - 32)(1 - e^{kt}) + s_0$

101. a. 157 words/min
   b. $t = 5$: 3.55 words/min/week
     $t = 14$: 4.71 words/min/week

CHAPTER 6

Section 6.1   (*page 409*)

1. $A = 36$ **3.** $A = 9$ **5.** $A = \frac{3}{2}$

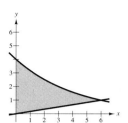
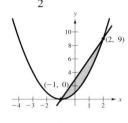

11. d

13. $A = \frac{32}{3}$ **15.** $A = \dfrac{9}{2}$

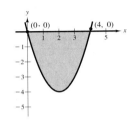

17. $A = 1$ **19.** $A = \frac{37}{12}$

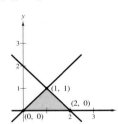
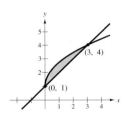

21. $A = \frac{64}{3}$ **23.** $A = \frac{3}{2}$

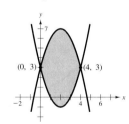

25. $A = \dfrac{\pi}{2} - \dfrac{1}{3} \approx 1.237$ **27.** $A = \dfrac{9}{2}$

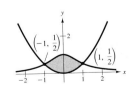
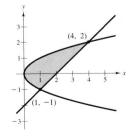

29. $A = 6$

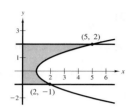

31. $A = 8 \ln 2 \approx 5.545$

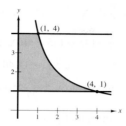

33. $A \approx 10.612$

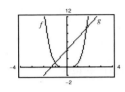

35. $A = 2(1 - \ln 2) \approx 0.614$

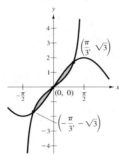

37. $A = 4$

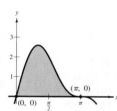

39. $A = \dfrac{1}{2}\left(1 - \dfrac{1}{e}\right) \approx 0.316$

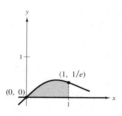

41. $A = 2(\ln 5)^2 \approx 5.181$ **43.** $A = \dfrac{1}{2} ac$

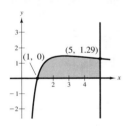

45. $b = 9\left(1 - \dfrac{1}{\sqrt[3]{4}}\right) \approx 3.330$

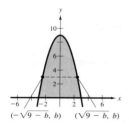

47. $x^4 - 2x^2 + 1 \le 1 - x^2$ on $[-1, 1]$

$$A = \int_{-1}^{1} [(1 - x^2) - (x^4 - 2x^2 + 1)]\,dx = \frac{4}{15}$$

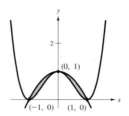

49. $A = \displaystyle\int_{-2}^{1} [x^3 - (3x - 2)]\,dx = \dfrac{27}{4}$

51. 1.7587   **53.** 4.7731

55. $\dfrac{1}{6}$ **57.** \$1.625 billion

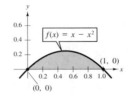

59. a.

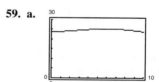

b. 8.9583 billion
61. a. 6.031 m^2 **b.** 12.062 m^3 **c.** 60,310 lb
63. Consumer surplus = 1600
Producer surplus = 400
65. Consumer surplus = 50,000
Producer surplus = 25,497
67. True   **68.** True   **69.** $|c - d|$

Section 6.2   (*page 420*)

1. $\dfrac{\pi}{3}$ **3.** $\dfrac{16\pi}{3}$ **5.** $\dfrac{15\pi}{2}$ **7.** $\dfrac{2\pi}{35}$ **9.** 8π

11. $\dfrac{\pi}{4}$ **13. a.** 8π **b.** $\dfrac{128\pi}{5}$ **c.** $\dfrac{256\pi}{15}$ **d.** $\dfrac{192\pi}{5}$

15. a. $\dfrac{32\pi}{3}$ **b.** $\dfrac{64\pi}{3}$ **17.** 18π

19. $\pi(8 \ln 4 - \frac{3}{4}) \approx 32.49$

21. $\dfrac{208\pi}{3}$ **23.** $\dfrac{384\pi}{5}$ **25.** $\pi \ln 4$ **27.** $\dfrac{3\pi}{4}$

29. $\dfrac{\pi}{2}\left(1 - \dfrac{1}{e^2}\right) \approx 1.358$ **31.** π **33.** a

35. a. $\dfrac{512\pi}{15}$

b. No, the solid has only been translated horizontally.

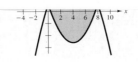

5. $\displaystyle\int u\,du$ **7.** $\displaystyle\int \dfrac{}{u}$
$u = 3x - 2, n = 4$ $u = 1 - 2\sqrt{x}$

9. $\displaystyle\int \frac{du}{\sqrt{a^2 - u^2}}$ **11.** $\displaystyle\int \sin u\, du$

$u = t,\ a = 1$ $u = t^2$

13. $\displaystyle\int e^u\, du$ **15.** $-\dfrac{1}{5}(-2x + 5)^{5/2} + C$

$u = \sin x$

17. $\dfrac{1}{2}v^2 - \dfrac{1}{6(3v - 1)^2} + C$

19. $-\dfrac{1}{3}\ln\left|-t^3 + 9t + 1\right| + C$

21. $\dfrac{1}{2}x^2 + x + \ln|x - 1| + C$ **23.** $\dfrac{1}{3}\ln\left|\dfrac{3x - 1}{3x + 1}\right| + C$

25. $\dfrac{x}{15}(12x^4 + 20x^2 + 15) + C$ **27.** $\dfrac{1}{4\pi}\sin 2\pi x^2 + C$

29. $-\dfrac{1}{\pi}\csc \pi x + C$ **31.** $\dfrac{1}{5}e^{5x} + C$

33. $2\ln(1 + e^x) + C$ **35.** $\ln|\sec x(\sec x + \tan x)| + C$

37. $\ln(t^2 + 4) - \dfrac{1}{2}\arctan\dfrac{t}{2} + C$

39. $-\dfrac{1}{2}\arcsin(2t - 1) + C$ **41.** $\dfrac{1}{2}\ln\left|\cos\dfrac{2}{t}\right| + C$

43. $3\arcsin\dfrac{x - 3}{3} + C$ **45.** $\dfrac{1}{4}\arctan\dfrac{2x + 1}{8} + C$

47. $y = \dfrac{1}{2}e^{2x} + 2e^x + x + C$ **49.** $s = \dfrac{1}{2}\arcsin t^2 + C$

51. $y = \dfrac{1}{2}\arctan\dfrac{\tan x}{2} + C$ **53.** $\dfrac{1}{2}$

55. $\dfrac{1}{2}(1 - e^{-1}) \approx 0.316$ **57.** 4   **59.** $\dfrac{\pi}{18}$

61. $\dfrac{1}{3}\arctan\left(\dfrac{x + 2}{3}\right) + C$ **63.** $2 - \sqrt{2}$ **65.** a   **67.** $\dfrac{4}{3}$

69. $a = \dfrac{1}{2}$

71. a. $\pi(1 - e^{-1}) \approx 1.986$

b. $b = \sqrt{\ln\left(\dfrac{3\pi}{3\pi - 4}\right)} \approx 0.743$

73. $\dfrac{2}{\arcsin(4/5)} \approx 2.157$ **75.** 1.0320   **77.** True

78. False, if $u = \sin x$, then $du = \cos x\, dx$.

79. False, $\displaystyle\int u^n\, du,\ n = -\dfrac{1}{2}$.   **80.** True

81. $a = \sqrt{2},\ b = \dfrac{\pi}{4}$

$-\dfrac{1}{\sqrt{2}}\ln\left|\csc\left(x + \dfrac{\pi}{4}\right) + \cot\left(x + \dfrac{\pi}{4}\right)\right| + C$

Section 7.2   (*page 486*)

1. a. $x\sin x$ **b.** $x^2\cos x$ **c.** $x^2 e^x$ **d.** $\ln x$
3. $u = x,\ dv = e^{2x}\, dx$ **5.** $u = (\ln x)^2,\ dv = dx$

7. $u = x,\ dv = \sec^2 x\, dx$ **9.** $-\dfrac{1}{4e^{2x}}(2x + 1) + C$

11. $e^x(x^3 - 3x^2 + 6x - 6) + C$ **13.** $\dfrac{1}{3}e^{x^3} + C$
15. $\dfrac{1}{4}[2(t^2 - 1)\ln|t + 1| - t^2 + 2t] + C$
17. $\dfrac{(\ln x)^3}{3} + C$ **19.** $\dfrac{e^{2x}}{4(2x + 1)} + C$

21. $(x - 1)^2 e^x + C$ **23.** $\dfrac{2(x - 1)^{3/2}}{15}(3x + 2) + C$

25. $x\sin x + \cos x + C$
27. $x\arctan x - \dfrac{1}{2}\ln(1 + x^2) + C$
29. $\dfrac{1}{5}e^{2x}(2\sin x - \cos x) + C$ **31.** $y = \dfrac{1}{2}e^{x^2} + C$
33. $y = \dfrac{2}{405}(27t^2 - 24t + 32)\sqrt{2 + 3t} + C$

35. $\sin y = x^2 + C$ **37.** $-\dfrac{\pi}{2}$

39. $\dfrac{e[\sin(1) - \cos(1)] + 1}{2} \approx 0.909$

41. $\dfrac{\pi}{2} - 1$ **43.** $\dfrac{e^{2x}}{4}(2x^2 - 2x + 1) + C$

45. $(3x^2 - 6)\sin x - (x^3 - 6x)\cos x + C$
47. $x\tan x + \ln|\cos x| + C$

49. $-\dfrac{e^{-4t}}{128}(32t^3 + 24t^2 + 12t + 3) + C$

51. $\dfrac{1}{13}(2e^{-\pi} + 3) \approx 0.2374$ **53.** $\dfrac{2}{5}(2x - 3)^{3/2}(x + 1) + C$
55. $\dfrac{1}{3}\sqrt{4 + x^2}(x^2 - 8) + C$

57. $n = 0$: $x(\ln x - 1) + C$ **65.** $\dfrac{x^4}{16}(4\ln x - 1) + C$

$n = 1$: $\dfrac{x^2}{4}(2\ln x - 1) + C$

$n = 2$: $\dfrac{x^3}{9}(3\ln x - 1) + C$

$n = 3$: $\dfrac{x^4}{16}(4\ln x - 1) + C$

$n = 4$: $\dfrac{x^5}{25}(5\ln x - 1) + C$

$\displaystyle\int x^n\ln x\, dx = \dfrac{x^{n+1}}{(n + 1)^2}[(n + 1)\ln x - 1] + C$

67. $\dfrac{e^{2x}}{13}(2\cos 3x + 3\sin 3x) + C$ **69.** $1 - \dfrac{5}{e^4} \approx 0.908$

71. $\dfrac{\pi}{1 + \pi^2}\left(\dfrac{1}{e} + 1\right) \approx 0.395$

73. a. 1
b. $\pi(e - 2) \approx 2.257$
c. $\dfrac{(e^2 + 1)\pi}{2} \approx 13.177$
d. $\left(\dfrac{e^2 + 1}{4}, \dfrac{e - 2}{2}\right) \approx (2.097, 0.359)$

75. a. $3.2(\ln 2) - 0.2 \approx 2.018$
b. $12.8(\ln 4) - 7.2(\ln 3) - 1.8 \approx 8.035$
77. \$131,528.68
81. For any integratable function, $\int f(x)\, dx = C + \int f(x)\, dx$, but this cannot be used to imply that $C = 0$.

83. $s(t) = -16t^2 + 12,000t\left[1 + \ln\dfrac{50,000}{50,000 - 400t}\right]$

$+ 1,500,000\ln\dfrac{50,000 - 400t}{50,000}$

When $t = 100,\ s(100) \approx 557,168.626$ feet.

Section 7.3   (*page 496*)

1. $-\dfrac{1}{4}\cos^4 x + C$ **3.** $\dfrac{1}{12}\sin^6 2x + C$
5. $-\dfrac{1}{3}\cos^3 x + \dfrac{2}{5}\cos^5 x - \dfrac{1}{7}\cos^7 x + C$
7. $\dfrac{1}{12}(6x + \sin 6x) + C$
9. $\dfrac{1}{8}(2x^2 - 2x\sin 2x - \cos 2x) + C$

15. $\frac{1}{3}\ln|\sec 3x + \tan 3x| + C$

17. $\frac{1}{15}\tan 5x(3 + \tan^2 5x) + C$

19. $\frac{1}{2\pi}(\sec \pi x \tan \pi x + \ln|\sec \pi x + \tan \pi x|) + C$

21. $\tan^4\left(\frac{x}{4}\right) - 2\tan^2\left(\frac{x}{4}\right) - 4\ln\left|\cos\frac{x}{4}\right| + C$

23. $\frac{1}{2}\tan^2 x + C$ **25.** $\frac{\tan^3 x}{3} + C$ **27.** $\frac{\sec^6 4x}{24} + C$

29. $\frac{1}{3}\sec^3 x + C$

31. $r = \frac{1}{32\pi}(12\pi\theta - 8\sin 2\pi\theta + \sin 4\pi\theta) + C$

33. $y = \frac{1}{9}\sec^3 3x - \frac{1}{3}\sec 3x + C$

35. $-\frac{1}{10}(\cos 5x + 5\cos x) + C$

37. $\frac{1}{8}(2\sin 2\theta - \sin 4\theta) + C$

39. $\frac{1}{4}(\ln|\csc^2 2x| - \cot^2 2x) + C$

41. $-\cot\theta - \frac{1}{3}\cot^3\theta + C$

43. $\ln|\csc t - \cot t| + \cos t + C$

45. $\ln|\csc x - \cot x| + \cos x + C$ **47.** $t - 2\tan t + C$

49. π **51.** $\frac{1}{2}(1 - \ln 2)$ **53.** $\ln 2$ **55.** $\frac{4}{3}$

57. $\frac{1}{16}(6x + 8\sin x + \sin 2x) + C$

59. $\frac{1}{4\pi}[\sec^3 \pi x \tan \pi x$

$\quad + \frac{3}{2}(\sec \pi x \tan \pi x + \ln|\sec \pi x + \tan \pi x|)] + C$

61. $\frac{1}{5\pi}\sec^5 \pi x + C$ **63.** $\frac{3\sqrt{2}}{10}$ **65.** $\frac{3\pi}{16}$

67. $\frac{\tan^6 3x}{18} + \frac{\tan^4 3x}{12} + C_1$

$\quad = \frac{\sec^6 3x}{18} - \frac{\sec^4 3x}{12} + C_2$

69. $\frac{1}{2}$ **71. a.** $\frac{\pi^2}{2}$ **b.** $(\bar{x}, \bar{y}) = \left(\frac{\pi}{2}, \frac{\pi}{8}\right)$

77. $-\frac{1}{15}\cos x(3\sin^4 x + 4\sin^2 x + 8) + C$

79. $\frac{5}{6\pi}\tan\frac{2\pi x}{5}\left(\sec^2\frac{2\pi x}{5} + 2\right) + C$

83. a. $H(t) = 55.46 - 23.88\cos\frac{\pi t}{6} - 3.34\sin\frac{\pi t}{6}$

b. $L(t) = 39.34 - 20.78\cos\frac{\pi t}{6} - 4.33\sin\frac{\pi t}{6}$

c. Summer

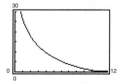

85. a. $\frac{2T}{ug}\sinh\frac{ugL}{2T}$ feet

b. $\frac{4}{g}v\sinh\frac{ugL}{2T}$

Section 7.4 (page 506)

1. $\displaystyle\int \frac{\sqrt{x^2 + 16}}{x}\,dx$ **3.** $\displaystyle\int \arcsin\frac{x}{4}\,dx$

---

5. $\frac{x}{25\sqrt{25 - x^2}} + C$

7. $5\ln\left|\frac{5 - \sqrt{25 - x^2}}{x}\right| + \sqrt{25 - x^2} + C$

9. $\ln\left|x + \sqrt{x^2 - 4}\right| + C$

11. $\frac{1}{15}(x^2 - 4)^{3/2}(3x^2 + 8) + C$ **13.** $\frac{1}{3}(1 + x^2)^{3/2} + C$

15. $\frac{1}{2}\left(\arctan x + \frac{x}{1 + x^2}\right) + C$

17. $\frac{1}{2}x\sqrt{4 + 9x^2} + \frac{2}{3}\ln\left|3x + \sqrt{4 + 9x^2}\right| + C$

19. $\sqrt{x^2 + 9} + C$ **21.** 2π

23. $\ln\left|x + \sqrt{x^2 - 9}\right| + C$ **25.** $-\frac{(1 - x^2)^{3/2}}{3x^3} + C$

27. $-\frac{1}{3}\ln\left|\frac{\sqrt{4x^2 + 9} + 3}{2x}\right| + C$ **29.** $-\frac{1}{\sqrt{x^2 + 3}} + C$

31. $\frac{1}{3}(1 + e^{2x})^{3/2} + C$

33. $\frac{1}{2}\left(\arcsin e^x + e^x\sqrt{1 - e^{2x}}\right) + C$

35. $\frac{1}{4}\left(\frac{x}{x^2 + 2} + \frac{1}{\sqrt{2}}\arctan\frac{x}{\sqrt{2}}\right) + C$

37. $x\,\text{arcsec}\,2x - \frac{1}{2}\ln\left|2x + \sqrt{4x^2 - 1}\right| + C$

39. $\arcsin\left(\frac{x - 2}{2}\right) + C$

41. $\sqrt{x^2 + 4x + 8} - 2\ln\left|\sqrt{x^2 + 4x + 8} + (x + 2)\right| + C$

43. $\sqrt{3} - \frac{\pi}{3} \approx 0.685$ **45.** $9(2 - \sqrt{2}) \approx 5.272$

47. $\frac{1}{2}(x - 15)\sqrt{x^2 + 10x + 9}$

$\quad + 33\ln\left|\sqrt{x^2 + 10x + 9} + (x + 5)\right| + C$

49. $\frac{1}{2}\left(x\sqrt{x^2 - 1} + \ln\left|x + \sqrt{x^2 - 1}\right|\right) + C$

51. πr^2 **53.** $6\pi^2$

55. $\ln\left[\frac{5(\sqrt{2} + 1)}{\sqrt{26} + 1}\right] + \sqrt{26} - \sqrt{2} \approx 4.367$

57. $100\sqrt{2} + 50\ln\left(\frac{\sqrt{2} + 1}{\sqrt{2} - 1}\right) \approx 229.559$

59. 187.2π lb **61. a.** 121.3 lb **b.** 92.98 lb

63. $\frac{\pi}{32}\left[102\sqrt{2} - \ln(3 + 2\sqrt{2})\right] \approx 13.989$

65. b. $y = -12\ln\left(\frac{12 - \sqrt{144 - x^2}}{x}\right) - \sqrt{144 - x^2}$

c. $x = 0$ **d.** 5.2 ft

67. True **68.** False, $\displaystyle\int \frac{\sqrt{x^2 - 1}}{x}\,dx = \int \tan^2\theta\,d\theta$

69. False, $\displaystyle\int_0^{\sqrt{3}} \frac{dx}{(1 + x^2)^{3/2}} = \int_0^{\pi/3} \cos\theta\,d\theta$. **70.** True

Section 7.5 (page 517)

1. $\frac{A}{x} + \frac{B}{x - 10}$ **3.** $\frac{A}{x} + \frac{Bx + C}{x^2 + 10}$

71. a. \$4,637,228.40 **b.** \$5,555,555.56

73. $0.015846 < \displaystyle\int_{2}^{\infty} \frac{1}{x^5 - 1}\, dx < 0.015851$

77. False, $\displaystyle\int \frac{\ln x^2}{x}\, dx = \frac{1}{2}\int (\ln x^2)\frac{2}{x}\, dx = \frac{1}{2}\int u\, du.$ **78.** True

79. False, $\displaystyle\int_{-1}^{1} \sqrt{x^2 - x^3}\, dx = \int_{-1}^{1} |x|\sqrt{1 - x}\, dx.$ **80.** True

CHAPTER 8

Section 8.1   (*page 557*)

1. 2, 4, 8, 16, 32   **3.** $-\frac{1}{2}, \frac{1}{4}, -\frac{1}{8}, \frac{1}{16}, -\frac{1}{32}$

5. $-1, -\frac{1}{4}, \frac{1}{9}, \frac{1}{16}, -\frac{1}{25}$ **7.** $3, \frac{9}{2}, \frac{27}{6}, \frac{81}{24}, \frac{243}{120}$

9. 3, 4, 6, 10, 18   **11.** 14, 17   **13.** $\frac{3}{16}, -\frac{3}{32}$

15. $10 \cdot 9$ **17.** $n + 1$ **19.** $\dfrac{1}{(2n + 1)(2n)}$ **21.** $3n - 2$

23. $n^2 - 2$ **25.** $\dfrac{n + 1}{n + 2}$ **27.** $\dfrac{(-1)^{n-1}}{2^{n-2}}$ **29.** $\dfrac{n + 1}{n}$

31. $\dfrac{n}{(n + 1)(n + 2)}$ **33.** $\dfrac{(-1)^{n-1}}{1 \cdot 3 \cdot 5 \cdots (2n - 1)} = \dfrac{(-1)^{n-1}2^n n!}{(2n)!}$

35. Converges to 1   **37.** Diverges   **39.** Converges to $\frac{3}{2}$

41. Diverges   **43.** Converges to 0   **45.** Converges to 0

47. Diverges   **49.** Converges to 0   **51.** Converges to 0

53. Converges to e^k **55.** Monotonic, bounded

57. Not monotonic, bounded   **59.** Not monotonic, bounded

61. Monotonic, bounded   **63.** Not monotonic, bounded

65. 5   **67.** $\frac{1}{3}$

69. a. $a_n = 10 - \dfrac{1}{n}$

b. A monotonic, bounded sequence must converge (Theorem 8.5)

c. $a_n = \dfrac{3n}{4n + 1}$

d. The unbounded sequence does not converge.

71. a. No

b.

n	1	2	3	4	5
A_n	\$9086.25	\$9173.33	\$9261.24	\$9349.99	\$9439.60

n	6	7	8	9	10
A_n	\$9530.06	\$9621.39	\$9713.59	\$9806.68	\$9900.66

73. a. $\$2,500,000,000(0.8)^n$

b.

Year	1	2	3	4
Budget	\$2,000,000,000	\$1,600,000,000	\$1,280,000,000	\$1,024,000,000

c. Converges to 0

75.

n	0	1	2	3	4	5
a_n	\$127.42	\$144.79	\$162.16	\$179.53	\$196.90	\$214.27

n	6	7	8	9	10
a_n	\$231.64	\$249.01	\$266.38	\$283.75	\$301.12

1995 Cost: \$387.97

77. $S_6 = 240$, $S_7 = 440$, $S_8 = 810$, $S_9 = 1490$, $S_{10} = 2740$

79. a. $a_9 = a_{10} = \dfrac{1,562,500}{567}$

b. Decreasing

c. Factorials increase more rapidly than exponentials.

81. 1, 1.4142, 1.4422, 1.4142, 1.3797, 1.3480
Converges to 1

83. a. 1, 1, 2, 3, 5, 8, 13, 21, 34, 55, 89, 144

b. 1, 2, 1.5, 1.6667, 1.6, 1.6250, 1.6154, 1.6190, 1.6176, 1.6182

c. $\rho = \dfrac{1 + \sqrt{5}}{2} \approx 1.6180$

85. True   **86.** True   **87.** True   **88.** True

89. 1.4142, 1.8478, 1.9616, 1.9904, 1.9976
$\displaystyle\lim_{x \to \infty} a_n = 2$

Section 8.2   (*page 566*)

1. 1, 1.25, 1.361, 1.424, 1.464

3. 3, -1.5, 5.25, -4.875, 10.3125

5. 3, 4.5, 5.25, 5.625, 5.8125   **7.** $\displaystyle\lim_{n \to \infty} a_n = 1 \neq 0$

9. $\displaystyle\lim_{n \to \infty} a_n = 1 \neq 0$ **11.** Geometric series: $r = \frac{3}{2} > 1$

13. Geometric series: $r = 1.055 > 1$ **15.** $\displaystyle\lim_{n \to \infty} a_n = \frac{1}{2} \neq 0$

17. Geometric series: $r = \frac{3}{4} < 1$

19. Geometric series: $r = 0.9 < 1$

21. Telescoping series: $a_n = \dfrac{1}{n} - \dfrac{1}{n + 1}$ **23.** 2

25. $\frac{2}{3}$ **27.** $\frac{10}{9}$ **29.** $\frac{9}{4}$ **31.** $\frac{3}{4}$ **33.** 3   **35.** $\frac{1}{2}$

37. $\dfrac{4}{9}$ **39.** $\displaystyle\sum_{n=0}^{\infty} \frac{3}{40}(0.01)^n = \frac{5}{66}$ **41.** Diverges

43. Converges   **45.** Diverges   **47.** Converges

49. Diverges   **51.** Diverges   **53.** $\dfrac{1}{1-x}, \ |x| < 1$

55.

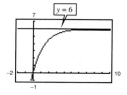

Horizontal asymptote: $y = 6$
The horizontal asymptote is the sum of the series.

57. The required term for each series is $n = 100$ and $n = 5$, respectively. The second series converges at a faster rate.

59. 20

n	5	10	20	50	100
S_n	8.1902	13.0264	17.5685	19.8969	19.9995

The terms of the series decrease in magnitude relatively slowly and the sequence of partial sums approaches the sum of the series relatively slowly.

61. $\frac{40}{3}$

n	5	10	20	50	100
S_n	13.3203	13.3333	13.3333	13.3333	13.3333

The terms of the series decrease in magnitude relatively rapidly and the sequence of partial sums approaches the sum of the series relatively rapidly.

63. $80,000(1 - 0.9^n)$ **65.** 152.42 ft   **67.** $\frac{1}{8}$
69. a. 126 in.^{2} **b.** 128 in.^{2} **71.** \$3,623,993.23
73. \$3048.1 million   **75. a.** \$26,046.33   **b.** \$26,111.12
77. a. \$632,407.96   **b.** \$640,501.61

83. $\displaystyle\sum_{n=0}^{\infty} 1, \ \sum_{n=0}^{\infty} (-1)$ (Answer is not unique.)

85. True   **86.** True
87. False, the series must begin with $n = 0$ in order for the limit to be $a/(1 - r)$.
88. True

91. $L - \dfrac{1}{4}L - 2\left(\dfrac{1}{16}\right)L - 4\left(\dfrac{1}{64}\right)L - 8\left(\dfrac{1}{256}\right)L$

$= L - L\left(\dfrac{1}{4} + \dfrac{1}{8} + \dfrac{1}{16} + \dfrac{1}{32} + \cdots\right)$

$= L - L\displaystyle\sum_{n=0}^{\infty} \dfrac{1}{4}\left(\dfrac{1}{2}\right)^n = L\left(1 - \dfrac{1/4}{1 - 1/2}\right) = \dfrac{1}{2}L$

The remaining pieces are getting smaller and smaller, thus making the table appear to disappear.

Section 8.3   (*page 573*)

1. Diverges   **3.** Converges   **5.** Converges
7. Diverges   **9.** Diverges   **11.** Converges
13. Diverges   **15.** Diverges   **17.** Converges
19. Converges   **21.** Diverges   **23.** Converges
25. Converges   **27.** Diverges   **29.** Diverges
31. Converges   **33.** $p > 1$

35. a.

M	2	4	6	8
N	4	31	226	1673

b. No, since the magnitude of the terms of the series are approaching zero, it requires more and more terms to increase the partial sum by 2.

39. $R_6 \approx 0.0015$
$S_6 \approx 1.0811$

41. $R_{10} \approx 0.0997$ **43.** $R_4 \approx 5.6 \times 10^{-8}$
$S_{10} \approx 0.9818$ $S_6 \approx 0.4049$

45. $N \geq 7$ **47.** $N \geq 2$

49. a.

n	5	10	20	50	100
S_n	3.7488	3.7500	3.7500	3.7500	3.7500

b.

n	5	10	20	50	100
S_n	1.4636	1.5498	1.5962	1.6251	1.6350

In part a, the magnitude of the terms of the series approaches 0 more rapidly and the sequence of partial sums approaches the sum of the series more quickly.

51. b. $\displaystyle\sum_{n=2}^{\infty} \dfrac{1}{n^{1.1}} = 0.4665 + 0.2987 + 0.2176$
$+ 0.1703 + 0.1393 + \cdots$

$\displaystyle\sum_{n=2}^{\infty} \dfrac{1}{n \ln n} = 0.7213 + 0.3034 + 0.1803$
$+ 0.1243 + 0.0930 + \cdots$

c. $n > e^{40}$
53. $-\ln 2$

Section 8.4   (*page 579*)

1. Converges   **3.** Diverges   **5.** Converges
7. Diverges   **9.** Converges   **11.** Converges
13. Diverges   **15.** Diverges   **17.** Converges
19. Diverges   **21.** Converges   **23.** Diverges
25. Diverges   **27.** Diverges; p-Series Test
29. Converges; Comparison Test with

$\displaystyle\sum_{n=1}^{\infty} \left(\dfrac{1}{3}\right)^n$

31. Diverges; nth Term Test
33. Converges; Integral Test   **37.** Diverges
39. Converges

43. b.

n	5	10	20	50	100
S_n	1.1839	1.2087	1.2212	1.2287	1.2312

c. 0.1226
d. 0.0277
e. No, only a finite sum has been subtracted from the sum of the series.

47. False, let $a_n = \dfrac{1}{n^3}$ and $b_n = \dfrac{1}{n^2}$.   **48.** True   **49.** True

50. False, let $a_n = \dfrac{1}{n}$, $b_n = \dfrac{1}{n^2}$, and $c_n = \dfrac{10}{n}$.

Section 8.5   (*page 587*)

1. Converges   **3.** Converges   **5.** Diverges
7. Converges   **9.** Diverges   **11.** Diverges
13. Converges   **15.** Converges   **17.** Converges

19. Converges   **21.** Converges absolutely
23. Converges conditionally   **25.** Diverges
27. Converges conditionally   **29.** Converges absolutely
31. Converges absolutely   **33.** Converges conditionally
35. Converges absolutely   **37.** 0.368   **39.** 0.842
41. 0.693   **43.** 7

45. a.

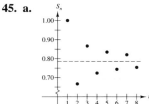

b.

n	1	2	3	4	5	6	7	8
S_n	1.0000	0.6667	0.8667	0.7238	0.8349	0.7440	0.8209	0.7543

d. The points alternate sides of the horizontal line that represents the sum of the series. The distance between the successive points and the line decreases. That distance is always less than the magnitude of the next term of the series.

49. a. $-1 < x < 1$
   b. $-1 \le x < 1$

51. True   **52.** True   **53.** False, let $a_n = \dfrac{(-1)^n}{n}$.

54. True

Section 8.6   (*page 594*)

5. Diverges   **7.** Converges   **9.** Converges
11. Diverges   **13.** Converges   **15.** Diverges
17. Converges   **19.** Converges   **21.** Diverges
23. Converges   **27.** Converges   **29.** Converges
31. Diverges   **33.** Converges
35. Converges; Alternating Series Test
37. Converges; p-Series Test   **39.** Diverges; nth-Term Test
41. Diverges; Ratio Test
43. Converges; Limit Comparsion Test with $b_n = \dfrac{1}{2^n}$

45. Converges; Comparision Test with $b_n = \dfrac{1}{2^n}$

47. Converges; Ratio Test   **49.** Converges; Ratio Test
51. Converges; Ratio Test   **53.** a. and c.

55. $\displaystyle\sum_{n=0}^{\infty} \dfrac{n+1}{4^{n+1}}$ **57.** -0.7769

59. No, the series $\displaystyle\sum_{n=1}^{\infty} \dfrac{1}{n+10,000}$ diverges.

Section 8.7   (*page 604*)

1. d   **2.** c   **3.** a   **4.** b
5. $1 - x + \frac{1}{2}x^2 - \frac{1}{6}x^3$ **7.** $1 + 2x + 2x^2 + \frac{4}{3}x^3 + \frac{2}{3}x^4$
9. $x - \frac{1}{6}x^3 + \frac{1}{120}x^5$ **11.** $x + x^2 + \frac{1}{2}x^3 + \frac{1}{6}x^4$
13. $1 - x + x^2 - x^3 + x^4$ **15.** $2 - 3x^3 + x^4$
17. $1 - (x-1) + (x-1)^2 - (x-1)^3 + (x-1)^4$
19. $(x-1) - \frac{1}{2}(x-1)^2 + \frac{1}{3}(x-1)^3 - \frac{1}{4}(x-1)^4$

21. a. $P_3(x) = x + \dfrac{1}{3}x^3$

   b. $P_5(x) = x + \dfrac{1}{3}x^3 + \dfrac{2}{15}x^5$

   c. $Q_3(x) = 1 + 2\left(x - \dfrac{\pi}{4}\right) + 2\left(x - \dfrac{\pi}{4}\right)^2 + \dfrac{8}{3}\left(x - \dfrac{\pi}{4}\right)^3$

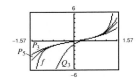

23. a.

x	0	0.25	0.50	0.75	1.00
$\sin x$	0	0.2474	0.4794	0.6816	0.8415
$P_1(x)$	0	0.25	0.50	0.75	1.00
$P_3(x)$	0	0.2474	0.4792	0.6797	0.8333
$P_5(x)$	0	0.2474	0.4794	0.6817	0.8417
$P_7(x)$	0	0.2474	0.4794	0.6816	0.8415

   b.

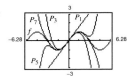

25. a. $P_3(x) = x + \frac{1}{6}x^3$

   b.

x	-1	-0.75	-0.50	-0.25
$f(x)$	-1.571	-0.848	-0.524	-0.253
$P_3(x)$	-1.167	-0.820	-0.521	-0.253

x	0	0.25	0.50	0.75	1
$f(x)$	0	0.253	0.524	0.848	1.571
$P_3(x)$	0	0.253	0.521	0.820	1.167

   c.

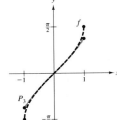

27. 0.6042   **29.** 0.1823   **31.** $R_4 \le 2.03 \times 10^{-5}$

33. $R_3 \leq 7.82 \times 10^{-3}$ **35.** 3   **37.** 9

39. $-0.3936 < x < 0$

41. $e^x : P_4(x) = 1 + x + \frac{1}{2}x^2 + \frac{1}{6}x^3 + \frac{1}{24}x^4$

$xe^x : Q_4(x) = x + x^2 + \frac{1}{2}x^3 + \frac{1}{6}x^4$

$= xP_4(x) - \frac{1}{24}x^4$

47.

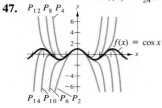

Section 8.8 (*page 613*)

1. $R = 1$ **3.** $R = \frac{1}{2}$ **5.** $R = \infty$ **7.** $(-2, 2)$

9. $(-1, 1]$ **11.** $(-\infty, \infty)$ **13.** $x = 0$ **15.** $(-4, 4)$

17. $(0, 10]$ **19.** $(0, 2]$ **21.** $(0, 2c)$ **23.** $(-\frac{1}{2}, \frac{1}{2})$

25. $(-\infty, \infty)$ **27.** $(-1, 1)$ **29.** $x = 3$

31. a. $(-2, 2)$ **b.** $(-2, 2)$ **c.** $(-2, 2)$ **d.** $[-2, 2)$

33. a. $(0, 2]$ **b.** $(0, 2)$ **c.** $(0, 2)$ **d.** $[0, 2]$

35. a. For $f(x)$: $(-\infty, \infty)$

For $g(x)$: $(-\infty, \infty)$

d. $f(x) = \sin x$

$g(x) = \cos x$

39. c.

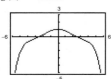

d. 0.92

41. a. $\frac{8}{5}$ **b.** $\frac{8}{11}$

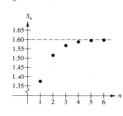

c. The alternating series converges more rapidly. The partial sums of the series of positive terms approach the sum from below. The partial sums of the alternating series alternate sides of the horizontal line representing the sum.

d.

M	10	100	1000	10,000
N	4	9	15	21

43. $f(x) = \dfrac{1}{1 + x}$ **45.** $f(x) = \cos x$

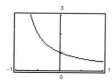

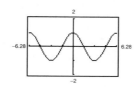

47. False, let $a_n = \dfrac{(-1)^n}{n\,2^n}$.   **48.** True   **49.** True

50. True

Section 8.9 (*page 620*)

1. $\displaystyle\sum_{n=0}^{\infty} \frac{x^n}{2^{n+1}}$ **3.** $\displaystyle\sum_{n=0}^{\infty} \frac{(-1)^n x^n}{2^{n+1}}$

$(-2, 2)$ $(-2, 2)$

5. $\displaystyle\sum_{n=0}^{\infty} \frac{(x-5)^n}{(-3)^{n+1}}$ **7.** $-3\displaystyle\sum_{n=0}^{\infty}(2x)^n$

$(2, 8)$ $(-\frac{1}{2}, \frac{1}{2})$

9. $-\dfrac{1}{11}\displaystyle\sum_{n=0}^{\infty}\left[\frac{2}{11}(x+3)\right]^n$ **11.** $\dfrac{3}{2}\displaystyle\sum_{n=0}^{\infty}\left(\frac{x}{-2}\right)^n$

$\left(-\dfrac{17}{2}, \dfrac{5}{2}\right)$ $(-2, 2)$

13. $\displaystyle\sum_{n=0}^{\infty}\left[\frac{1}{(-2)^n} - 1\right]x^n$ **15.** $2\displaystyle\sum_{n=0}^{\infty}x^{2n}$

$(-1, 1)$ $(-1, 1)$

17. $2\displaystyle\sum_{n=0}^{\infty}x^{2n}$ **19.** $\displaystyle\sum_{n=1}^{\infty}n(-1)^n x^{n-1}$

$(-1, 1)$ $(-1, 1)$

21. $\displaystyle\sum_{n=0}^{\infty}\frac{(-1)^n x^{n+1}}{n+1}$ **23.** $\displaystyle\sum_{n=0}^{\infty}(-1)^n x^{2n}$ **25.** $\displaystyle\sum_{n=0}^{\infty}(-1)^n (2x)^{2n}$

$(-1, 1]$ $(-1, 1)$ $(-\frac{1}{2}, \frac{1}{2})$

27.

x	0.0	0.2	0.4	0.6	0.8	1.0
S_2	0.000	0.180	0.320	0.420	0.480	0.500
$\ln(x+1)$	0.000	0.182	0.336	0.470	0.588	0.693
S_3	0.000	0.183	0.341	0.492	0.651	0.833

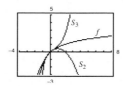

29. 0.245   **31.** 0.125

33. $\displaystyle\sum_{n=0}^{\infty} nx^{n-1}$

$(-1, 1)$

35. 2, since the probability of obtaining a head on a single toss is $\frac{1}{2}$, it is expected that, on average, a head will be obtained in 2 tosses.

39. 3.14   **41.** $\ln\frac{3}{2} \approx 0.4055$ **43.** $\ln\frac{7}{5} \approx 0.3365$

45. $\arctan\frac{1}{2} \approx 0.4636$

47. The series of Exercise 44 converges to its sum at a slower rate because its terms approach 0 to a much slower rate.

Section 8.10 (*page 630*)

1. $\displaystyle\sum_{n=0}^{\infty}\frac{(2x)^n}{n!}$ **3.** $\dfrac{\sqrt{2}}{2}\displaystyle\sum_{n=0}^{\infty}\frac{(-1)^{n(n+1)/2}}{n!}\left(x - \frac{\pi}{4}\right)^n$

5. $\displaystyle\sum_{n=0}^{\infty} \frac{(-1)^n(x-1)^{n+1}}{n+1}$ **7.** $\displaystyle\sum_{n=0}^{\infty} \frac{(-1)^n(2x)^{2n+1}}{(2n+1)!}$

9. $1 + \dfrac{x^2}{2!} + \dfrac{5x^4}{4!} + \cdots$

11. $\displaystyle\sum_{n=0}^{\infty} (-1)^n(n+1)x^n$

13. $\dfrac{1}{2}\left[1 + \displaystyle\sum_{n=1}^{\infty} \frac{(-1)^n 1\cdot 3\cdot 5 \cdots (2n-1)x^{2n}}{2^{3n}n!} \right]$

15. $1 + \dfrac{x^2}{2} + \displaystyle\sum_{n=2}^{\infty} \frac{(-1)^{n+1}1\cdot 3\cdot 5 \cdots (2n-3)x^{2n}}{2^n n!}$

17. $1 + \dfrac{x^2}{2} + \dfrac{x^4}{2^2 2!} + \dfrac{x^6}{2^3 3!} + \cdots$ **19.** $\displaystyle\sum_{n=0}^{\infty} \frac{(-1)^n(2x)^{2n+1}}{(2n+1)!}$

21. $\displaystyle\sum_{n=0}^{\infty} \frac{(-1)^n x^n}{(2n)!}$ **23.** $\displaystyle\sum_{n=0}^{\infty} \frac{(-1)^n x^{2n}}{(2n+1)!}$ **25.** $\displaystyle\sum_{n=0}^{\infty} \frac{x^{2n+1}}{(2n+1)!}$

27. $\dfrac{1}{2}\left[1 + \displaystyle\sum_{n=0}^{\infty} \frac{(-1)^n(2x)^{2n}}{(2n)!} \right]$ **29.** $\displaystyle\sum_{n=0}^{\infty} \frac{(-1)^n x^{2n+1}}{(2n+1)!}$

31. $P_5(x) = x + x^2 + \dfrac{1}{3}x^3 - \dfrac{1}{30}x^5 + \cdots$

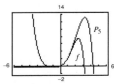

33. $P_5(x) = x - \dfrac{1}{2}x^2 - \dfrac{1}{6}x^3 + \dfrac{3}{40}x^5 + \cdots$

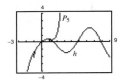

35. $P_4(x) = x - x^2 + \dfrac{5}{6}x^3 - \dfrac{5}{6}x^4 + \cdots$

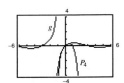

37. $\displaystyle\sum_{n=0}^{\infty} \frac{(-1)^{(n+1)}x^{2n+3}}{(2n+3)(n+1)!}$ **39.** 0.8415   **41.** 0.6931

43. 0   **45.** 0.9461   **47.** 0.5312   **49.** 0.2010

51. 0.3413

53. $P_5(x) = x - 2x^3 + \dfrac{2}{3}x^5$

$\left[-\dfrac{3}{4}, \dfrac{3}{4}\right]$

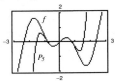

55. $P_5(x) = (x-1) - \dfrac{1}{24}(x-1)^3 + \dfrac{1}{24}(x-1)^4$
$- \dfrac{71}{1920}(x-1)^5$

$\left[\dfrac{1}{4}, 2\right]$

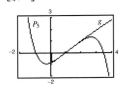

59. a.

c. $\displaystyle\sum_{n=0}^{\infty} 0x^n = 0 \neq f(x)$

Review Exercises for Chapter 8

1. $a_n = \dfrac{1}{n!}$ **3.** Converges to 0   **5.** Diverges

7. Converges to 0   **9.** Converges to 0

11. a.

n	1	2	3	4	5	6	7	8
A_n	\$5100.00	\$5202.00	\$5306.04	\$5412.16	\$5520.40	\$5630.81	\$5743.43	\$5858.30

b. \$11,040.20

13. 1, 2.5, 4.75, 8.125, 13.3875
15. 0.5, 0.45833, 0.45972, 0.45970, 0.45970
17. 3   **19.** $\frac{1}{2}$ **21.** $\frac{1}{11}$ **23.** $45\frac{1}{3}$ ft
25. $5087.14   **27.** Diverges   **29.** Converges
31. Converges   **33.** Diverges   **35.** Diverges
37. Converges

39. a.

N	5	10	20	30	40
$\sum_{n=1}^{N} \frac{1}{n^p}$	1.4636	1.5498	1.5962	1.6122	1.6202
$\int_{N}^{\infty} \frac{1}{x^p}dx$	0.2000	0.1000	0.0500	0.0333	0.0250

b.

N	5	10	20	30	40
$\sum_{n=1}^{N} \frac{1}{n^p}$	1.0367	1.0369	1.0369	1.0369	1.0369
$\int_{N}^{\infty} \frac{1}{x^p}dx$	0.0004	0.0000	0.0000	0.0000	0.0000

The series of part b converges more rapidly. This is evident from the integrals which give the remainders of the partial sums.

41. $(-10, 10)$ **43.** $[1, 3]$ **45.** Converges only at $x = 2$
47. $\frac{\sqrt{2}}{2} \sum_{n=0}^{\infty} \frac{(-1)^{n(n+1)/2}}{n!}\left(x - \frac{3\pi}{4}\right)^n$ **49.** $\sum_{n=0}^{\infty} \frac{(x \ln 3)^n}{n!}$
51. $-\sum_{n=0}^{\infty} (x + 1)^n$ **53.** $\sum_{n=0}^{\infty} \frac{2}{3}\left(\frac{x}{3}\right)^n$
55. $1 + 2x + 2x^2 + \frac{4}{3}x^3$ **57.** $f(x) = \dfrac{3}{3 - 2x}$
$\left(-\frac{3}{2}, \frac{3}{2}\right)$
59. $\sum_{n=0}^{\infty} \frac{(-1)^n x^{2n+1}}{(2n+1)(2n+1)!}$ **61.** $\sum_{n=0}^{\infty} \frac{(-1)^n x^{n+1}}{(n+1)^2}$
63. 0   **65.** 0.996   **67.** 0.560
69. a. 4   **b.** 6   **c.** 5   **d.** 10

CHAPTER 9

Section 9.1 (*page 640*)

1. e   **3.** a   **5.** d
7. Vertex: (0, 0)
Focus: $(0, \frac{1}{16})$
Directrix: $y = -\frac{1}{16}$

9. Vertex: (0, 0)
Focus: $(-\frac{3}{2}, 0)$
Directrix: $x = \frac{3}{2}$

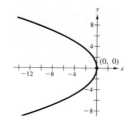

11. Vertex: (0, 0)
Focus: (0, −2)
Directrix: $y = 2$

13. Vertex: (1, −2)
Focus: (1, −4)
Directrix: $y = 0$

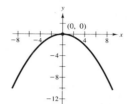
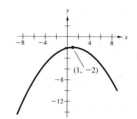

15. Vertex: $(5, -\frac{1}{2})$
Focus: $(\frac{11}{2}, -\frac{1}{2})$
Directrix: $x = \frac{9}{2}$

17. Vertex: (1, 1)
Focus: (1, 2)
Directrix: $y = 0$

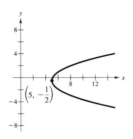
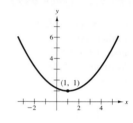

19. Vertex: $(-1, 2)$
Focus: (0, 2)
Directrix: $x = -2$

21. Vertex: $(2, -2)$
Focus: $(0, -2)$
Directrix: $x = 4$

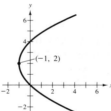
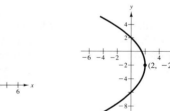

23. Vertex: $(-2, 1)$
Focus: $(-2, -\frac{1}{2})$
Directrix: $y = \frac{5}{2}$

25. Vertex: $(\frac{1}{4}, -\frac{1}{2})$
Focus: $(0, -\frac{1}{2})$
Directrix: $x = \frac{1}{2}$

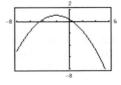
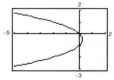

27. $x^2 + 6y = 0$ **29.** $y^2 - 4y + 8x - 20 = 0$
31. $x^2 + 24y + 96 = 0$ **33.** $y^2 - 8x - 4y + 4 = 0$
35. $x^2 + y - 4 = 0$ **37.** $5x^2 - 14x - 3y + 9 = 0$
39. $(x - h)^2 = -8(y + 1)$ **41.** $3x - 2y^2 = 0$
43. $\frac{9}{4}$ ft   **45.** $4x - y - 8 = 0$ **47.** $y = 2ax_0 x - ax_0^2$
49. Tangent lines: $2x + y - 1 = 0$
$2x - 4y - 1 = 0$
Point of intersection: $(\frac{1}{2}, 0)$
(on the directrix)

23. Center: $(0, 0)$
Vertices: $(\pm\sqrt{3}, 0)$
Foci: $(\pm\sqrt{5}, 0)$

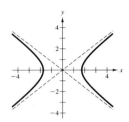

25. Center: $(1, -3)$
Vertices: $(1, -3 \pm \sqrt{2})$
Foci: $(1, -3 \pm 2\sqrt{5})$

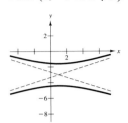

5. $\dfrac{(x' - 3\sqrt{2})^2}{16} - \dfrac{(y' - \sqrt{2})^2}{16} = 1$

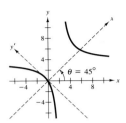

27. Center: $(1, -3)$
Vertices: $(-1, -3), (3, -3)$
Foci: $(1 \pm \sqrt{10}, -3)$

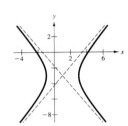

7. $\dfrac{(x')^2}{3} + \dfrac{(y')^2}{2} = 1$ **9.** $x' = -(y')^2$

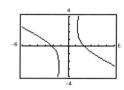 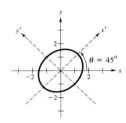

29. $\dfrac{y^2}{4} - \dfrac{x^2}{12} = 1$ **31.** $\dfrac{x^2}{1} - \dfrac{y^2}{9} = 1$

33. $\dfrac{(x - 3)^2}{9} - \dfrac{(y - 2)^2}{4} = 1$ **35.** $\dfrac{y^2}{9} - \dfrac{(x - 2)^2}{9/4} = 1$

37. $\dfrac{(x - 6)^2}{9} - \dfrac{(y - 2)^2}{7} = 1$

11. $y' = \dfrac{(x')^2}{6} - \dfrac{x'}{3}$ **13.** $\theta = 45°$

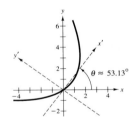 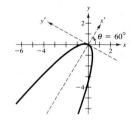

41. $x \approx 110.3$ mi   **43. a.** $\dfrac{64x^2}{225} - \dfrac{64y^2}{31} = 1$ **b.** No

45. a. At $(6, \sqrt{3})$: $2x - 3\sqrt{3}y - 3 = 0$
At $(6, -\sqrt{3})$: $2x + 3\sqrt{3}y - 3 = 0$
b. At $(6, \sqrt{3})$: $9x + 2\sqrt{3}y - 60 = 0$
At $(6, -3)$: $9x - 2\sqrt{3}y - 60 = 0$

47. Volume $= \dfrac{4\pi}{3}$

Surface area $= \pi\left[2\sqrt{7} - 1 + \dfrac{\sqrt{2}}{2}\ln\left(\dfrac{\sqrt{2} + 1}{2\sqrt{2} + \sqrt{7}}\right)\right]$
≈ 11.66

51. False, $y^2 - x^2 + 2x + 2y = 0$ yields two intersecting lines.

52. True

53. False, the equation of a hyperbola is second degree in both variables.

54. True   **57.** Parabola   **59.** Circle
61. Circle   **63.** Hyperbola

15. $\theta \approx 26.57°$ **17.** $\theta \approx 31.72°$

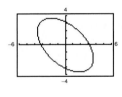 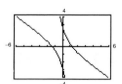

19. $\left(0, \pm\dfrac{2\sqrt{15}}{5}\right)$, $\dfrac{dy}{dx} = \dfrac{1}{5}$ **21.** Parabola   **23.** Ellipse

25. Hyperbola   **27.** Parabola
29. Two lines   **31.** Two parallel lines

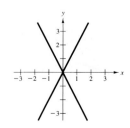 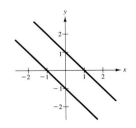

Section 9.4 (*page 664*)

1. $\dfrac{(y')^2}{2} - \dfrac{(x')^2}{2} = 1$ **3.** $\dfrac{(x')^2}{1/4} - \dfrac{(y')^2}{1/6} = 1$

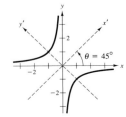 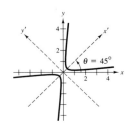

33. Two lines

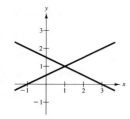

39. $x^2 + y^2 - 2xy - 2x - 2y + 1 = 0$
    $0 \le x \le 1, 0 \le y \le 1$

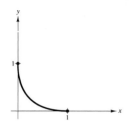

Review Exercises for Chapter 9

1. h   **2.** a   **3.** e   **4.** i   **5.** f
6. b   **7.** c   **8.** j   **9.** g   **10.** d
11. Circle
    Center: $(\frac{1}{2}, -\frac{3}{4})$
    Radius: 1

13. Hyperbola
    Center: $(-4, 3)$
    Vertices: $(-4 \pm \sqrt{2}, 3)$

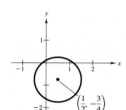

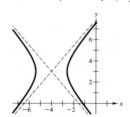

15. Ellipse
    Center: $(2, -3)$
    Vertices: $\left(2, -3 \pm \dfrac{\sqrt{2}}{2}\right)$

17. Parabola
    Vertex: $(3, 0)$

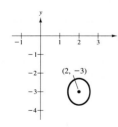

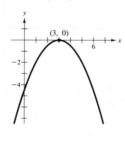

19. Ellipse
    Center: $(1, -\frac{1}{2})$
    Vertices: $(1 \pm \frac{3}{4}, -\frac{1}{2})$

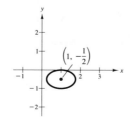

At $t = -1, \dfrac{dy}{dx} = 1, \quad \dfrac{d^2y}{dx^2} = 2$

21. Parabola
    Vertex: $\left(-\dfrac{\sqrt{2}}{4}, \dfrac{\sqrt{2}}{4}\right)$

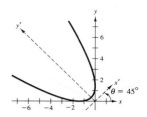

23. $x^2 - 8x + 8y = 0$ **25.** $y^2 - 4y - 12x + 4 = 0$
27. $4x + 4y - 7 = 0$ **29.** $\dfrac{(x-2)^2}{25} + \dfrac{y^2}{21} = 1$
31. $\dfrac{2x^2}{9} + \dfrac{y^2}{36} = 1$ **33.** $\dfrac{x^2}{4} + \dfrac{3y^2}{16} = 1$
35. 3 feet on either side of center   **41.** 192π ft^2
43. 4.212 ft   **45.** 15.87
47. $\dfrac{y^2}{1} - \dfrac{x^2}{8} = 1$ **49.** $\dfrac{x^2}{4} - \dfrac{y^2}{12} = 1$
51. $\dfrac{5(x-4)^2}{16} - \dfrac{5y^2}{64} = 1$ **53.** $a = \sqrt{5}$

CHAPTER 10

Section 10.1   (*page 674*)

1. a.

t	0	1	2	3	4
x	0	1	$\sqrt{2}$	$\sqrt{3}$	2
y	1	0	-1	-2	-3

b.

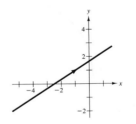

c. $y = 1 - x^2, x \ge 0$
3. $2x - 3y + 5 = 0$ **5.** $y = (x-1)^2$

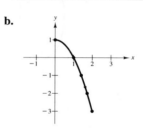

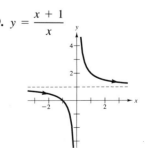

7. $y = \dfrac{1}{2}x^{2/3}$ **9.** $y = \dfrac{x+1}{x}$

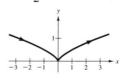

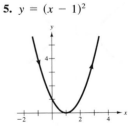

51. $\dfrac{3\pi}{8}$ **53.** $\dfrac{3\pi}{2}$ **55.** $\left(\dfrac{3}{4}, \dfrac{8}{5}\right)$ **57.** 36π

59. a.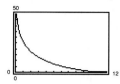

b. The parameter can be considered as time and the orientation of the graph gives the direction of movement of the weight.

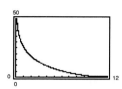

61. False,
$$\dfrac{d^2 y}{dx^2} = \dfrac{\dfrac{d}{dt}\left[\dfrac{g'(t)}{f'(t)}\right]}{f'(t)} = \dfrac{f'(t)g''(t) - g'(t)f''(t)}{[f'(t)]^3}.$$

62. False, the graph of $y = x^{2/3}$ does not have a horizontal asymptote at the origin.

63. True   **64.** True

Section 10.3   (*page 694*)

1.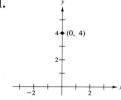

3.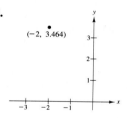

5.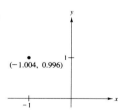

7. $\left(\sqrt{2}, \dfrac{\pi}{4}\right), \left(-\sqrt{2}, \dfrac{5\pi}{4}\right)$

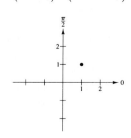

9. $(5, 2.214), (-5, 5.356)$

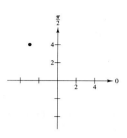

11. $r = a$ **13.** $r = 4\csc\theta$

15. $r = -\dfrac{2}{3\cos\theta - \sin\theta}$ **17.** $r = 9\csc^2\theta\cos\theta$

19. $x^2 + y^2 = 9$ **21.** $x^2 + y^2 - y = 0$

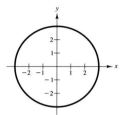

23. $\sqrt{x^2 + y^2} = \arctan\dfrac{y}{x}$ **25.** $x - 3 = 0$

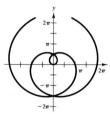   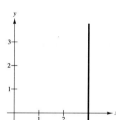

27.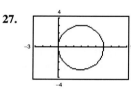

$-\dfrac{\pi}{2} \le \theta \le \dfrac{\pi}{2}$

Horizontal tangents: 2

29.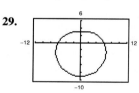

$0 \le \theta \le 2\pi$

Horizontal tangents: 2

31. $(x - h)^2 + (y - k)^2 = h^2 + k^2$
Center: (h, k)
Radius: $\sqrt{h^2 + k^2}$

33. $2\sqrt{5}$ **35.** 5.6

37. $\dfrac{dy}{dx} = \dfrac{2\cos\theta(3\sin\theta + 1)}{6\cos^2\theta - 2\sin\theta - 3}$

$\left(5, \dfrac{\pi}{2}\right), \dfrac{dy}{dx} = 0$

$(2, \pi), \dfrac{dy}{dx} = -\dfrac{2}{3}$

$\left(-1, \dfrac{3\pi}{2}\right), \dfrac{dy}{dx} = 0$

39. $\dfrac{(1 + 2\cos\theta)(1 - \cos\theta)}{\sin\theta(2\cos\theta - 1)}, -1$

41. $\dfrac{2\sin\theta\cos\theta}{1 - 2\sin^2\theta}, -\sqrt{3}$

43. Horizontal: $\left(2, \dfrac{\pi}{2}\right), \left(\dfrac{1}{2}, \dfrac{7\pi}{6}\right), \left(\dfrac{1}{2}, \dfrac{11\pi}{6}\right)$

Vertical: $\left(\dfrac{3}{2}, \dfrac{\pi}{6}\right), \left(\dfrac{3}{2}, \dfrac{5\pi}{6}\right)$

45. $\left(5, \dfrac{\pi}{2}\right), \left(1, \dfrac{3\pi}{2}\right)$

47. $(0, 0), (1.4142, 0.7854), (1.4142, 2.3562)$

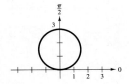

49. $(7, 1.5708), (3, 4.7124)$ **51.** $\theta = 0$

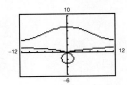 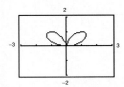

53. $\theta = \dfrac{\pi}{6}, \dfrac{\pi}{2}, \dfrac{5\pi}{6}$ **55.** $\theta = 0, \dfrac{\pi}{2}$

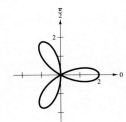 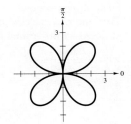

57.   **59.**

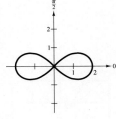 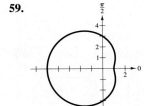

61.   **63.**

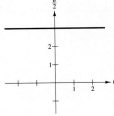 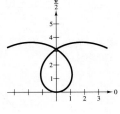

65. $0 \le \theta \le 2\pi$ **67.** $0 \le \theta < 2\pi$

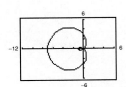 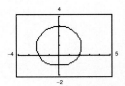

69. $0 \le \theta < 4\pi$ **71.** $0 \le \theta < \pi$

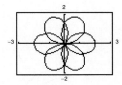 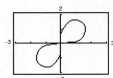

73.   **75.**

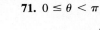
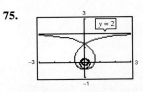 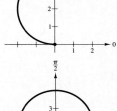

77. a.   **b.**

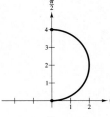 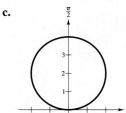

c.   **d.**

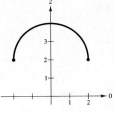

81. a. $r = 2 - \sin\left(\theta - \dfrac{\pi}{4}\right)$ **b.** $r = 2 + \cos\theta$

$= 2 - \dfrac{\sqrt{2}(\sin\theta - \cos\theta)}{2}$

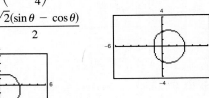

c. $r = 2 + \sin\theta$ **d.** $r = 2 - \cos\theta$

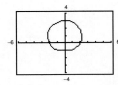 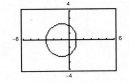

83. a.

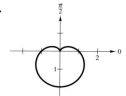

b.

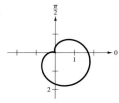

85. True   **86.** True   **87.** True   **88.** True
89. False, the graph of $r = \cos\theta$ has a vertical tangent at $(1, 0)$.
90. False, the diameter is 1.

93.

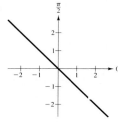

95.

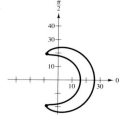

Section 10.4 (*page 703*)

1. 16π **3.** $\dfrac{\pi}{3}$ **5.** $\dfrac{\pi}{8}$ **7.** $\dfrac{3\pi}{2}$

9. $\dfrac{2\pi - 3\sqrt{3}}{2}$ **11.** $\pi + 3\sqrt{3}$

13. $\left(1, \dfrac{\pi}{2}\right), \left(1, \dfrac{3\pi}{2}\right), (0, 0)$

15. $\left(\dfrac{2 - \sqrt{2}}{2}, \dfrac{3\pi}{4}\right), \left(\dfrac{2 + \sqrt{2}}{2}, \dfrac{7\pi}{4}\right), (0, 0)$

17. $\left(\dfrac{3}{2}, \dfrac{\pi}{6}\right), \left(\dfrac{3}{2}, \dfrac{5\pi}{6}\right), (0, 0)$ **19.** $(2, 4), (-2, -4)$

21. $\left(2, \dfrac{\pi}{12}\right), \left(2, \dfrac{5\pi}{12}\right), \left(2, \dfrac{7\pi}{12}\right), \left(2, \dfrac{11\pi}{12}\right)$
$\left(2, \dfrac{13\pi}{12}\right), \left(2, \dfrac{17\pi}{12}\right), \left(2, \dfrac{19\pi}{12}\right), \left(2, \dfrac{23\pi}{12}\right)$

23. $(0.581, \pm 0.535), (2.581, \pm 1.376)$

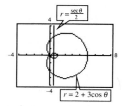

25. $(0, 0), (0.935, 0.363), (0.535, -1.006)$
The graphs reach the pole at different times (θ-values).

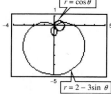

27. $\dfrac{4}{3}\left(4\pi - 3\sqrt{3}\right)$ **29.** $11\pi - 24$
31. $\dfrac{2}{3}\left(4\pi - 3\sqrt{3}\right)$

33. $\dfrac{5\pi a^2}{4}$ **35.** $\dfrac{a^2}{2}(\pi - 2)$

37. a. $(x^2 + y^2)^{3/2} = ax^2$
b.

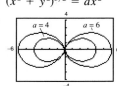

c. $\dfrac{15\pi}{2}$

39. $2\pi a$ **41.** 8
43. $\dfrac{\pi}{4}\sqrt{\pi^2 + 4} + \ln\left(\dfrac{\pi + \sqrt{\pi^2 + 4}}{2}\right)$
45. $\ln\left(\dfrac{\sqrt{4\pi^2 + 1} + 2\pi}{\sqrt{\pi^2 + 1} + \pi}\right) + \dfrac{2\sqrt{\pi^2 + 1} - \sqrt{4\pi^2 + 1}}{2\pi}$
47. $A \approx 0.667, s \approx 4.439$

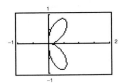

49. 4π **51.** $\dfrac{2\pi\sqrt{1 + a^2}}{1 + 4a^2}(e^{\pi a} - 2a)$ **53.** 21.87
55. $4\pi^2 ab$
57. False, the area is given by $\displaystyle\int_0^{\frac{\pi}{2}} \sin^2\theta\, d\theta$.
58. False, the graphs of $f(\theta) = 1$ and $g(\theta) = -1$ coincide.
59. False, if $f(\theta) = 0$ and $g(\theta) = \sin 2\theta$, then there is only one point of intersection.
60. True, the area enclosed by the first is $\pi/2$ and the area enclosed by the second is $\pi/4$.
63. $y^2 = \dfrac{x^2(1 + x)}{1 - x}$

$A = 2 - \dfrac{\pi}{2}$

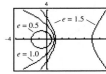

Section 10.5 (*page 710*)

1.

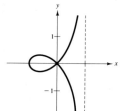

3.

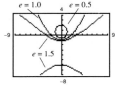

5. c   **7.** a   **9.** b
11. Parabola

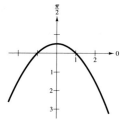

13. Ellipse

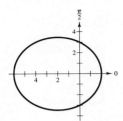

15. Ellipse

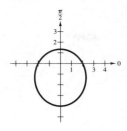

17. Hyperbola

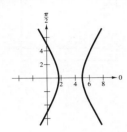

19. Hyperbola

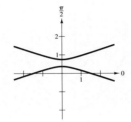

21. $\pi/4$ radians counterclockwise

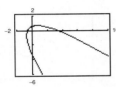

23. $\pi/6$ radians clockwise

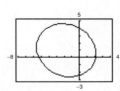

25. $r = \dfrac{1}{1 - \cos\theta}$

27. $r = \dfrac{1}{2 + \sin\theta}$ **29.** $r = \dfrac{2}{1 + 2\cos\theta}$

31. $r = \dfrac{2}{1 - \sin\theta}$ **33.** $r = \dfrac{16}{5 + 3\cos\theta}$

35. $r = \dfrac{9}{4 - 5\sin\theta}$ **39.** $r^2 = \dfrac{9}{1 - (16/25)\cos^2\theta}$

41. $r^2 = \dfrac{-16}{1 - (25/9)\cos^2\theta}$ **43.** 10.88

47. $\dfrac{\pi}{2}$ **49.** 0 **51.** $\dfrac{\pi}{3}$ **53.** $r = \dfrac{8200}{1 + \sin\theta}$, 1466.67 mi

57. $r = \dfrac{92{,}931{,}075.2223}{1 - 0.0167\cos\theta}$

Perihelion: 91,404,618 mi
Aphelion: 94,509,382 mi

59. $r = \dfrac{5.537 \times 10^9}{1 - 0.2481\cos\theta}$

Perihelion: 4.436×10^9 k
Aphelion: 7.364×10^9 k

61. a. 9.341×10^{18} k^2
   21.867 yr
 b. 0.899 rad, larger
 c. a. 2.559×10^9 k, 1.17×10^8 k/yr
   b. 4.118×10^9 k, 1.88×10^8 k/yr

Review Exercises for Chapter 10

1. a. $\dfrac{dy}{dx} = -\dfrac{3}{4}$
   Horizontal tangents: None
 b. $y = \dfrac{-3x + 11}{4}$
 c.

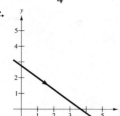

3. a. $\dfrac{dy}{dx} = -2t^2$
   Horizontal tangents: None
 b. $y = 3 + \dfrac{2}{x}$
 c.

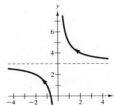

5. a. $\dfrac{dy}{dx} = \dfrac{(t - 1)(2t + 1)^2}{t^2(t - 2)^2}$
   Horizontal tangents: $\left(\dfrac{1}{3}, -1\right)$
 b. $y = \dfrac{4x^2}{(5x - 1)(x - 1)}$
 c.

7. a. $\dfrac{dy}{dx} = -\dfrac{5}{2}\cot\theta$
   Horizontal tangents: $(3, 7)$, $(3, -3)$
 b. $\dfrac{(x - 3)^2}{4} + \dfrac{(y - 2)^2}{25} = 1$
 c.

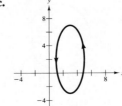

9. a. $\dfrac{dy}{dx} = -4\tan\theta$

Horizontal tangents: $(\pm 1, 0)$

b. $x^{2/3} + (y/4)^{2/3} = 1$

c.

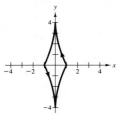

11. a. $\dfrac{dy}{dx} = \dfrac{2\cos 2\theta}{-\csc^2\theta}$

Horizontal tangents: $(1, 1), (-1, -1)$

b.

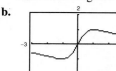

13. $x = -3 + 4\cos\theta$
$y = 4 + 3\sin\theta$

15.

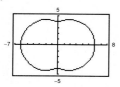

19. $\dfrac{\pi^2 r}{2}$

21. Circle   **23.** Line

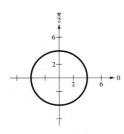

25. Cardioid   **27.** Limaçon

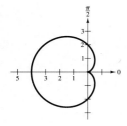

29. Rose curve   **31.** Rose curve

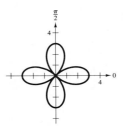

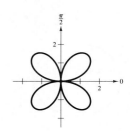

33. Parabola   **35.**

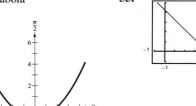

37.

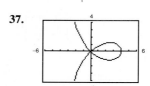

39. $x^2 + y^2 - 3x = 0$
41. $(x^2 + y^2 + 2x)^2 = 4(x^2 + y^2)$
43. $(x^2 + y^2)^2 = x^2 - y^2$
45. $y^2 = x^2\left(\dfrac{4 - x}{4 + x}\right)$ **47.** $r = a\cos^2\theta\sin\theta$
49. $r^2 = a^2\theta^2$ **51.** $r = 10\sin\theta$
53. $r = \dfrac{4}{1 - \cos\theta}$ **55.** $r = \dfrac{5}{3 - 2\cos\theta}$

57. a. $\pm\dfrac{\pi}{3}$

b. Vertical: $(-1, 0), (3, \pi), (\tfrac{1}{2}, \pm 1.318)$
Horizontal: $(-0.686, \pm 0.568), (2.186, \pm 2.206)$

c.

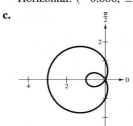

61. $\dfrac{9\pi}{2}$ **63.** $\dfrac{\pi}{32}$ **65.** a^2 **67.** $\dfrac{8\pi - 6\sqrt{3}}{3}$

69. $8a$ **71.** $\arctan\left(\dfrac{2\sqrt{3}}{3}\right) \approx 49.1°$

CHAPTER 11
Section 11.1 *(page 722)*

1. $\langle 4, 2 \rangle$

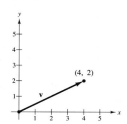

3. $\langle -7, 0 \rangle$

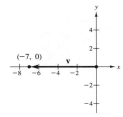

5. $\langle 4, 3 \rangle$

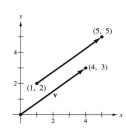

7. $\langle -4, -3 \rangle$

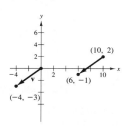

9. $\langle 0, 4 \rangle$

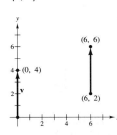

11. $\langle -1, \frac{5}{3} \rangle$

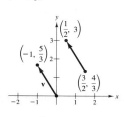

13. a. $\langle 4, 6 \rangle$ **b.** $\langle -6, -9 \rangle$

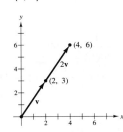
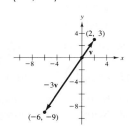

c. $\langle 7, \frac{21}{2} \rangle$ **d.** $\langle \frac{4}{3}, 2 \rangle$

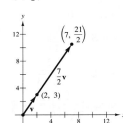
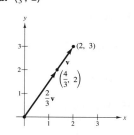

15. $\langle 3, -\frac{3}{2} \rangle$

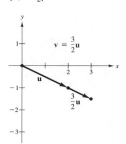

17. $\langle 4, 3 \rangle$

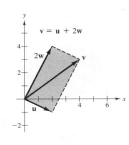

19. $\langle \frac{7}{2}, -\frac{1}{2} \rangle$ **21.** $a = 1, b = 1$

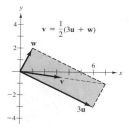

23. $a = 1, b = 2$ **25.** $a = \frac{2}{3}, b = \frac{1}{3}$

27. $(3, 5)$ **29.** 5   **31.** $\sqrt{61}$ **33.** 4

35. a. $\sqrt{2}$ **b.** $\sqrt{5}$ **c.** 1   **d.** 1   **e.** 1   **f.** 1

37. a. $\sqrt{5}/2$ **b.** $\sqrt{13}$ **c.** $\sqrt{85}/2$

     d. 1   **e.** 1   **f.** 1

41. $\langle 2\sqrt{2}, 2\sqrt{2} \rangle$ **43.** $\langle 1, \sqrt{3} \rangle$

45. a. $\pm \dfrac{1}{\sqrt{10}} \langle 1, 3 \rangle$ **b.** $\pm \dfrac{1}{\sqrt{10}} \langle 3, -1 \rangle$

47. a. $\pm \dfrac{1}{5} \langle -4, 3 \rangle$ **b.** $\pm \dfrac{1}{5} \langle 3, 4 \rangle$

49. $\langle 3, 0 \rangle$ **51.** $\langle -\sqrt{3}, 1 \rangle$ **53.** $\left(\dfrac{3 + \sqrt{2}}{\sqrt{2}} \right) \mathbf{i} + \left(\dfrac{3}{\sqrt{2}} \right) \mathbf{j}$

55. $(2 \cos 4 + \cos 2) \mathbf{i} + (2 \sin 4 + \sin 2) \mathbf{j}$

57. $-\dfrac{\sqrt{2}}{2} \mathbf{i} + \dfrac{\sqrt{2}}{2} \mathbf{j}$ **59.** 1.33, 132.5°

61. 12.3°, 82.2 lb   **63.** 71.3°, 228.5 lb

65. Tension in the rope: 1.1547 lb
     Magnitude of **u**: 0.5774 lb

67. Tensions: 44.65 lb and 65.27 lb
     Vertical components: 38.67 lb and 61.33 lb

69. N 85.13° E, 416.15 mph   **71.** $(-4, -1), (6, 5), (10, 3)$

73. $T_2 = 157.316$
     $T_3 = 3692.482$

77. True   **78.** True   **79.** True   **80.** False, $a = b = 0$

81. False, $\| a\mathbf{i} + b\mathbf{j} \| = \sqrt{2} |a|$ **82.** True

31. $4x - 3y + 4z = 10$ **33.** $z = 3$

35. $x + y + z = 5$ **37.** $7x + y - 11z = 5$

39. $y - z = -1$

41. Orthogonal   **43.** $83.5°$ **45.** Parallel

47.

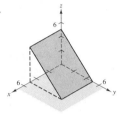

49.

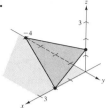

51.

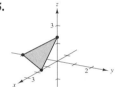

53.

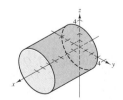

55.

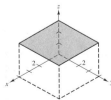

57. $x = 2$
$y = 1 + t$
$z = 1 + 2t$

59. $(2, -3, 2)$ **61.** Nonintersecting   **63.** 0

65. $\dfrac{6\sqrt{14}}{7}$ **67.** $\dfrac{2\sqrt{26}}{13}$ **69.** $\dfrac{10\sqrt{26}}{13}$

71. a. Sphere
$x^2 + y^2 + z^2 - 6x + 4y - 10z + 22 = 0$
b. Planes
$4x - 3y + z = 10 \pm 4\sqrt{26}$

73. $\arccos \frac{1}{65} \approx 89.1°$ **75.** True

76. False, they may be nonintersecting.
(See Exercise 61.)

Section 11.6   (*page 771*)

1. c   **2.** e   **3.** f   **4.** b   **5.** d   **6.** a

7. Plane   **9.** Right circular cylinder

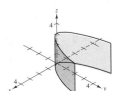

11. Parabolic cylinder   **13.** Elliptic cylinder

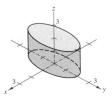

15. Cylinder

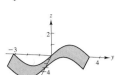

17. a. $(20, 0, 0)$
    b. $(10, 10, 20)$
    c. $(0, 0, 20)$
    d. $(0, 20, 0)$

19. Ellipsoid

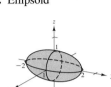

21. Hyperboloid of one sheet

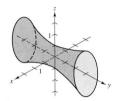

23. Elliptic paraboloid

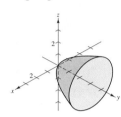

25. Hyperbolic paraboloid

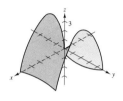

27. Cone

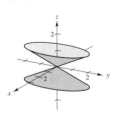

29. Ellipsoid

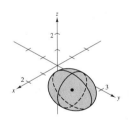

31. Cylinder

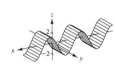

33. Surface of Revolution

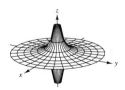

35. Elliptic cone

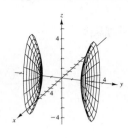

37. Hyperboloid of two sheets

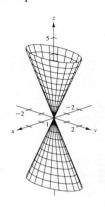

39.

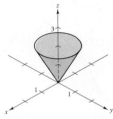

41.

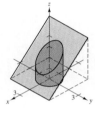

43. $x^2 + z^2 = 4y$ **45.** $4x^2 + 4y^2 = z^2$

47. $y^2 + z^2 = \dfrac{4}{x^2}$ **49.** $y = \sqrt{2z}$ **51.** $\dfrac{128\pi}{3}$

53. a. Major axis: $4\sqrt{2}$
   Minor axis: 4
   Foci: $(0, \pm 2, 2)$
   b. Major axis: $8\sqrt{2}$
   Minor axis: 8
   Foci: $(0, \pm 4, 8)$

55. $\dfrac{x^2}{3963^2} + \dfrac{y^2}{3963^2} + \dfrac{z^2}{3942^2} = 1$ **57.** No

Section 11.7 (*page 778*)

1. $\left(5, \dfrac{\pi}{2}, 1\right)$ **3.** $\left(2, \dfrac{\pi}{3}, 4\right)$ **5.** $\left(2\sqrt{2}, -\dfrac{\pi}{4}, -4\right)$

7. $(5, 0, 2)$ **9.** $\left(1, \sqrt{3}, 2\right)$ **11.** $\left(-2\sqrt{3}, -2, 3\right)$

13. $x^2 + y^2 = 4$ **15.** $x - \sqrt{3}y = 0$

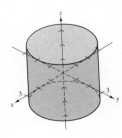
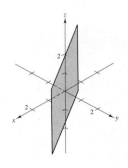

17. $x^2 + y^2 - 2y = 0$ **19.** $x^2 + y^2 + z^2 = 4$

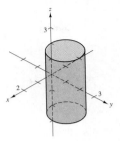
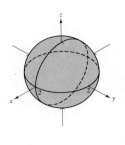

21. $\left(4, 0, \dfrac{\pi}{2}\right)$ **23.** $\left(4\sqrt{2}, \dfrac{2\pi}{3}, \dfrac{\pi}{4}\right)$ **25.** $\left(4, \dfrac{\pi}{6}, \dfrac{\pi}{6}\right)$

27. $\left(\sqrt{6}, \sqrt{2}, 2\sqrt{2}\right)$ **29.** $(0, 0, 12)$

31. $\left(\dfrac{5}{2}, \dfrac{5}{2}, -\dfrac{5\sqrt{2}}{2}\right)$

33. $x^2 + y^2 + z^2 = 4$ **35.** $3x^2 + 3y^2 - z^2 = 0$

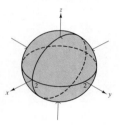
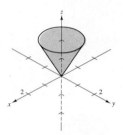

37. $x^2 + y^2 + (z - 2)^2 = 4$ **39.** $x^2 + y^2 = 1$

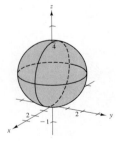
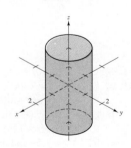

41. $\left(4, \dfrac{\pi}{4}, \dfrac{\pi}{2}\right)$ **43.** $\left(2\sqrt{13}, -\dfrac{\pi}{6}, \arccos\left[\dfrac{3}{\sqrt{13}}\right]\right)$

45. $\left(13, \pi, \arccos\left[\dfrac{5}{13}\right]\right)$ **47.** $\left(10, \dfrac{\pi}{6}, 0\right)$

49. $\left(3\sqrt{3}, -\dfrac{\pi}{6}, 3\right)$ **51.** $\left(4, \dfrac{7\pi}{6}, 4\sqrt{3}\right)$

Rectangular	*Cylindrical*	*Spherical*
53. (4, 6, 3)	(7.211, 0.983, 3)	(7.810, 0.983, 1.177)
55. (4.698, 1.710, 8)	$\left(5, \dfrac{\pi}{9}, 8\right)$	(9.434, 0.349, 0.304)
57. (−7.071, 12.247, 14.142)	(14.142, 2.094, 14.142)	$\left(20, \dfrac{2\pi}{3}, \dfrac{\pi}{4}\right)$

59. d   **60.** e   **61.** c   **62.** a   **63.** f   **64.** b

65. a. $r^2 + z^2 = 16$ **b.** $\rho = 4$

67. a. $r^2 + (z - 1)^2 = 1$ **b.** $\rho = 2 \cos \phi$

69. a. $r = 4 \sin \theta$ **b.** $\rho = \dfrac{4 \sin \theta}{\sin \phi} = 4 \sin \theta \csc \phi$

71. a. $r^2 = \dfrac{9}{\cos^2 \theta - \sin^2 \theta}$ **b.** $\rho^2 = \dfrac{9 \csc^2 \phi}{\cos^2 \theta - \sin^2 \theta}$

73. 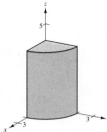   **75.**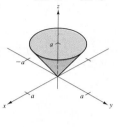

77.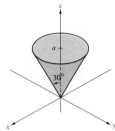

79. Rectangular: $0 \le x \le 10$
$0 \le y \le 10$
$0 \le z \le 10$

81. Spherical: $4 \le \rho \le 6$

83. a. Los Angeles: (4000, −118.24°, 55.95°)
Rio de Janeiro: (4000, −43.22°, 112.90°)
   b. Los Angeles: (−1568.2, −2919.7, 2239.7)
Rio de Janeiro: (2685.2, −2523.3, −1556.5)
   c. 91.18° ≈ 1.59 radians
   d. 6366 mi

85. Ellipse

Review Exercises for Chapter 11

1. a. $\mathbf{u} = 3\mathbf{i} - \mathbf{j}$
$\mathbf{v} = 4\mathbf{i} + 2\mathbf{j}$
   b. $2\sqrt{5}$ **c.** 10   **d.** $10\mathbf{i}$ **e.** $2\mathbf{i} + \mathbf{j}$ **f.** $\mathbf{i} - 2\mathbf{j}$

3. a. $\mathbf{u} = -\mathbf{i} + 4\mathbf{j}$ **b.** 3
$\mathbf{v} = -3\mathbf{i} + 6\mathbf{j}$
   c. $24\mathbf{i} + 6\mathbf{j} + 12\mathbf{k}$ **d.** $4x + y + 2z = 20$
   e. $x = 4 - t, y = 4 + 4t, z = 0$

5. Parallel   **7.** $\theta = \arccos\left(\dfrac{\sqrt{2} + \sqrt{6}}{4}\right) = 15°$

9. π **11.** $-2\sqrt{2}\mathbf{i} + 2\sqrt{2}\mathbf{j}$

13. $\dfrac{3}{\sqrt{26}}\mathbf{i} - \dfrac{9}{\sqrt{26}}\mathbf{j} + \dfrac{12}{\sqrt{26}}\mathbf{k}$ **15.** $\sqrt{14}$

19. $\langle -\frac{15}{14}, \frac{10}{14}, -\frac{1}{14} \rangle$ **23.** 4

25. $\overline{AC}$: 21.7 lb   **27.** $\dfrac{27\sqrt{2}}{2} \approx 19.1$ in.
$\overline{BC}$: 17.7 lb

29. a. $x = 1, y = 2 + t, z = 3$ **b.** None

31. a. $x = t, y = -1 + t, z = 1$
   b. $x = y + 1, z = 1$

33. $x + y + z = 6$

35. $x + 2y = 1$ **37.** $\dfrac{8}{7}$ **39.** $\dfrac{\sqrt{35}}{7}$ **41.** $\dfrac{\sqrt{3}}{3}$

43. 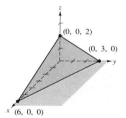   **45.**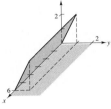

47. 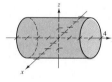   **49.**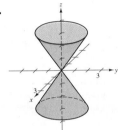

51. 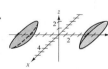   **53.**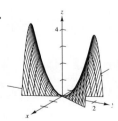

55.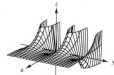

57. a. $x^2 + y^2 - 2z + 2 = 0$
   b. $8\pi \approx 25.1$ cm³
   c. $\dfrac{495\pi}{64} \approx 24.3$ cm³

59. a. $\left(4, \dfrac{3\pi}{4}, 2\right)$
   b. $\left(2\sqrt{5}, \dfrac{3\pi}{4}, \arccos\left[\dfrac{\sqrt{5}}{5}\right]\right)$

61. a. $r^2 \cos 2\theta = 2z$
  b. $\rho = 2 \sec 2\theta \cos \phi \csc^2 \phi$
63. $x^2 - y^2 + z^2 = 1$ **65.** $x^2 + y^2 = 1$

CHAPTER 12

Section 12.1 (*page 788*)

1. $(-\infty, 0), (0, \infty)$ **3.** $(0, \infty)$
5. $[0, \infty)$ **7.** $(-\infty, \infty)$
9. $\sqrt{1 + t^2}$ **11.** b **13.** d
15. a. $(-20, 0, 0)$ **b.** $(10, 20, 10)$
  c. $(0, 0, 20)$ **d.** $(20, 0, 0)$

17. 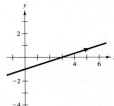 **19.**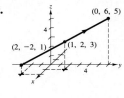

21. 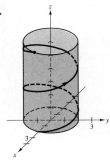 **23.**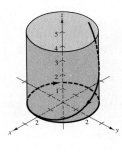

25.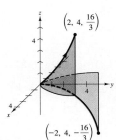

27. Parabola **29.** Helix **31.** $\mathbf{r}(t) = t\mathbf{i} + (4 - t)\mathbf{j}$
33. $\mathbf{r}(t) = 5\cos t\,\mathbf{i} + \sin t\,\mathbf{j}$
35. $\mathbf{r}(t) = t\mathbf{i} - t\mathbf{j} + 2t^2\mathbf{k}$ **37.** $\mathbf{r}(t) = 2\sin t\,\mathbf{i} + 2\cos t\,\mathbf{j} + 4\sin^2 t\,\mathbf{k}$

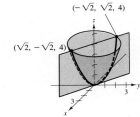 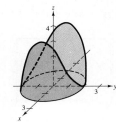

39. $\mathbf{r}(t) = (1 + \sin t)\mathbf{i} + \sqrt{2}\cos t\,\mathbf{j} + (1 - \sin t)\mathbf{k}$
and
  $\mathbf{r}(t) = (1 + \sin t)\mathbf{i} - \sqrt{2}\cos t\,\mathbf{j} + (1 - \sin t)\mathbf{k}$

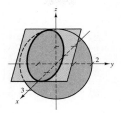

41. $\mathbf{r}(t) = t\mathbf{i} + t\mathbf{j} + \sqrt{4 - t^2}\,\mathbf{k}$

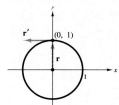

43. $2\mathbf{i} + 2\mathbf{j} + \frac{1}{2}\mathbf{k}$ **45.** 0
47. Limit does not exist **49.** $(-\infty, 0), (0, \infty)$
51. $[-1, 1]$ **53.** $\left(-\dfrac{\pi}{2} + n\pi, \dfrac{\pi}{2} + n\pi\right)$ **59.** True

Section 12.2 (*page 796*)

1. $\mathbf{r}(2) = 4\mathbf{i} + 2\mathbf{j}$
  $\mathbf{r}'(2) = 4\mathbf{i} + \mathbf{j}$

3. $\mathbf{r}\left(\dfrac{\pi}{2}\right) = \mathbf{j}$
  $\mathbf{r}'\left(\dfrac{\pi}{2}\right) = -\mathbf{i}$

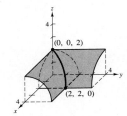 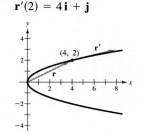

5. a., b.

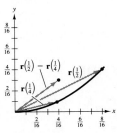

c. The vector
$$\frac{\mathbf{r}\left(\frac{1}{2}\right) - \mathbf{r}\left(\frac{1}{4}\right)}{\frac{1}{2} - \frac{1}{4}}$$
approximates the tangent vector $\mathbf{r}'(\frac{1}{4})$.

7. $\mathbf{r}\left(\dfrac{3\pi}{2}\right) = -2\mathbf{j} + \left(\dfrac{3\pi}{2}\right)\mathbf{k}$

$\mathbf{r}'\left(\dfrac{3\pi}{2}\right) = 2\mathbf{j} + \mathbf{k}$

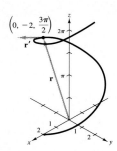

9. $\dfrac{\mathbf{r}'(-\frac{1}{4})}{\|\mathbf{r}'(-\frac{1}{4})\|} = \dfrac{1}{\sqrt{4\pi^2 + 1}}(\sqrt{2}\pi\mathbf{i} + \sqrt{2}\pi\mathbf{j} - \mathbf{k})$

$\dfrac{\mathbf{r}''(-\frac{1}{4})}{\|\mathbf{r}''(-\frac{1}{4})\|} = \dfrac{1}{2\sqrt{\pi^2 + 4}}(-\sqrt{2}\pi^2\mathbf{i} + \sqrt{2}\pi^2\mathbf{j} + 4\mathbf{k})$

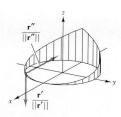

11. $6\mathbf{i} - 14t\mathbf{j} + 3t^2\mathbf{k}$
13. $-3a\cos^2 t\,\mathbf{i} + 3a\sin^2 t\cos t\,\mathbf{j}$ **15.** $-e^{-t}\mathbf{i}$
17. $\langle \sin t + t\cos t,\ \cos t - t\sin t,\ 1\rangle$
19. **a.** $\mathbf{i} + 3\mathbf{j} + 2t\mathbf{k}$ **b.** $2\mathbf{k}$ **c.** $8t + 9t^2 + 5t^4$
   d. $-\mathbf{i} + (9 - 2t)\mathbf{j} + (6t - 3t^2)\mathbf{k}$
   e. $8t^3\mathbf{i} + (12t^2 - 4t^3)\mathbf{j} + (3t^2 - 24t)\mathbf{k}$
   f. $\dfrac{10 + 2t^2}{\sqrt{10 + t^2}}$
21. $(-\infty, 0),\ (0, \infty)$ **23.** $\left(\dfrac{n\pi}{2}, \dfrac{(n+1)\pi}{2}\right)$
25. $(-\infty, \infty)$ **27.** $t^2\mathbf{i} + t\mathbf{j} + t\mathbf{k} + \mathbf{C}$
29. $\ln t\,\mathbf{i} + t\mathbf{j} - \frac{2}{5}t^{5/2}\mathbf{k} + \mathbf{C}$
31. $e^t\mathbf{i} - \cos t\,\mathbf{j} + \sin t\,\mathbf{k} + \mathbf{C}$
33. $\tan t\,\mathbf{i} + \arctan t\,\mathbf{j} + \mathbf{C}$ **35.** $2e^{2t}\mathbf{i} + 3(e^t - 1)\mathbf{j}$
37. $600\sqrt{3}t\,\mathbf{i} + (-16t^2 + 600t)\mathbf{j}$
39. $\left(\dfrac{2 - e^{-t^2}}{2}\right)\mathbf{i} + (e^{-t} - 2)\mathbf{j} + (t + 1)\mathbf{k}$
41. $4\mathbf{i} + \dfrac{1}{2}\mathbf{j} - \mathbf{k}$ **43.** $a\mathbf{i} + a\mathbf{j} + \dfrac{\pi}{2}\mathbf{k}$

53. False, let $\mathbf{r}(t) = \cos t\,\mathbf{i} + \sin t\,\mathbf{j} + \mathbf{k}$, then $\dfrac{d}{dt}[\|\mathbf{r}(t)\|] = 0$,

  but $\|\mathbf{r}'(t)\| = 1$.
54. False, $D_t[\mathbf{r}(t) \cdot \mathbf{u}(t)] = \mathbf{r}(t) \cdot \mathbf{u}'(t) + \mathbf{r}'(t) \cdot \mathbf{u}(t)$

Section 12.3 (*page 804*)

1. $\mathbf{v}(t) = 3\mathbf{i} + \mathbf{j}$ **3.** $\mathbf{v}(t) = 4\mathbf{i} + \mathbf{j}$
   $\mathbf{a}(t) = \mathbf{0}$ $\mathbf{a}(t) = 2\mathbf{i}$

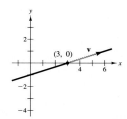   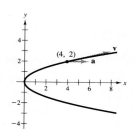

5. $\mathbf{v}(t) = -\sqrt{2}\mathbf{i} + \sqrt{2}\mathbf{j}$ **7.** $\mathbf{v}(t) = 2\mathbf{i}$
   $\mathbf{a}(t) = -\sqrt{2}\mathbf{i} - \sqrt{2}\mathbf{j}$ $\mathbf{a}(t) = -\mathbf{j}$

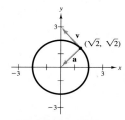   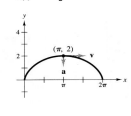

9. $\mathbf{v}(t) = \mathbf{i} + 2\mathbf{j} + 3\mathbf{k}$ **11.** $\mathbf{v}(t) = \mathbf{i} + 2t\mathbf{j} + t\mathbf{k}$
   $s(t) = \sqrt{14}$ $s(t) = \sqrt{1 + 5t^2}$
   $\mathbf{a}(t) = \mathbf{0}$ $\mathbf{a}(t) = 2\mathbf{j} + \mathbf{k}$

13. $\mathbf{v}(t) = \mathbf{i} + \mathbf{j} - \dfrac{t}{\sqrt{9 - t^2}}\mathbf{k}$

  $s(t) = \sqrt{\dfrac{18 - t^2}{9 - t^2}}$

  $\mathbf{a}(t) = \dfrac{-9}{(9 - t^2)^{3/2}}\mathbf{k}$

15. $\mathbf{v}(t) = 4\mathbf{i} - 3\sin t\,\mathbf{j} + 3\cos t\,\mathbf{k}$
   $s(t) = 5$
   $\mathbf{a}(t) = -3\cos t\,\mathbf{j} - 3\sin t\,\mathbf{k}$
17. $x = 1 + t$ **19.** $\mathbf{v}(t) = t(\mathbf{i} + \mathbf{j} + \mathbf{k})$
   $y = -1 - 2t$ $\mathbf{r}(t) = \dfrac{t^2}{2}(\mathbf{i} + \mathbf{j} + \mathbf{k})$
   $z = \dfrac{1}{4} + \dfrac{3}{4}t$ $\mathbf{r}(2) = 2(\mathbf{i} + \mathbf{j} + \mathbf{k})$
   $(1.100, -1.200, 0.325)$

21. $\mathbf{v}(t) = \left(\dfrac{t^2}{2} + \dfrac{9}{2}\right)\mathbf{j} + \left(\dfrac{t^2}{2} - \dfrac{1}{2}\right)\mathbf{k}$

  $\mathbf{r}(t) = \left(\dfrac{t^3}{6} + \dfrac{9}{2}t - \dfrac{14}{3}\right)\mathbf{j} + \left(\dfrac{t^3}{6} - \dfrac{1}{2}t + \dfrac{1}{3}\right)\mathbf{k}$

  $\mathbf{r}(2) = \dfrac{17}{3}\mathbf{j} + \dfrac{2}{3}\mathbf{k}$

23. $\mathbf{r}(t) = 44\sqrt{3}t\,\mathbf{i} + (10 + 44t - 16t^2)\mathbf{j}$

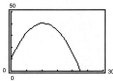

25. $v_0 = 40\sqrt{6}$ ft/sec, 78 ft

27. a. 54.1 ft/sec   **b.** 22.0 ft   **c.** 2.0 sec

29. $v_0 = 32$ ft/sec, $\theta = 45°$

31. a. $\theta = \dfrac{\pi}{4}$ **b.** $\theta = \dfrac{\pi}{2}$ **33.** 96.7 ft/sec

37. $\mathbf{v}(t) = b\omega[(1 - \cos\omega t)\mathbf{i} + \sin\omega t\,\mathbf{j}]$

$\mathbf{a}(t) = b\omega^2[\sin\omega t\,\mathbf{i} + \cos\omega t\,\mathbf{j}]$

a. $\|\mathbf{v}(t)\| = 0$ when $\omega t = 0, 2\pi, 4\pi, \ldots$

b. $\|\mathbf{v}(t)\|$ is maximum when $\omega t = \pi, 3\pi, \ldots$

39. $\mathbf{v}(t) = -b\omega\sin\omega t\,\mathbf{i} + b\omega\cos\omega t\,\mathbf{j}$

$\mathbf{v}(t)\cdot\mathbf{r}(t) = 0$

41. $\mathbf{a}(t) = -b\omega^2[\cos\omega t\,\mathbf{i} + \sin\omega t\,\mathbf{j}] = -\omega^2\mathbf{r}(t)$

43. $8\sqrt{10}$ ft/sec   **49.** $\mathbf{r}_3{}'(t) = \omega\mathbf{r}_1{}'(t)$

$\mathbf{r}_3{}''(t) = \omega^2\mathbf{r}_1{}''(t)$

Section 12.4   (*page 814*)

1. $\mathbf{T}(0) = \dfrac{\sqrt{2}}{2}(\mathbf{i} + \mathbf{k})$ **3.** $\mathbf{T}(0) = \dfrac{\sqrt{5}}{5}(2\mathbf{j} + \mathbf{k})$

$x = t$ $x = 2$

$y = 0$ $y = 2t$

$z = t$ $z = t$

5. $\mathbf{T}\left(\dfrac{\pi}{4}\right) = \dfrac{1}{2}\langle -\sqrt{2}, \sqrt{2}, 0\rangle$

$x = \sqrt{2} - \sqrt{2}t$

$y = \sqrt{2} + \sqrt{2}t$

$z = 4$

7. $\mathbf{T}(3) = \frac{1}{19}\langle 1, 6, 18\rangle$

$x = 3 + t$

$y = 9 + 6 + 6t$

$z = 18 + 18t$

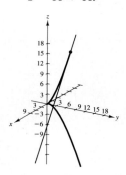

9. $\mathbf{v}(t) = 4\mathbf{i}$

$\mathbf{a}(t) = \mathbf{0}$

$\mathbf{T}(t) = \mathbf{i}$

$\mathbf{N}(t) =$ undefined

The path is a line and the speed is constant.

11. $\mathbf{v}(t) = 8t\,\mathbf{i}$

$\mathbf{a}(t) = 8\mathbf{i}$

$\mathbf{T}(t) = \mathbf{i}$

$\mathbf{N}(t) = \mathbf{0}$

The path is a line and the speed is variable.

13. $\mathbf{T} = \dfrac{\sqrt{2}}{2}(\mathbf{i} - \mathbf{j})$ **15.** $\mathbf{T} = \dfrac{\sqrt{2}}{2}(-\mathbf{i} + \mathbf{j})$

$\mathbf{N} = \dfrac{\sqrt{2}}{2}(\mathbf{i} + \mathbf{j})$ $\mathbf{N} = -\dfrac{\sqrt{2}}{2}(\mathbf{i} + \mathbf{j})$

$a_\mathbf{T} = -\sqrt{2}$ $a_\mathbf{T} = \sqrt{2}e^{\pi/2}$

$a_\mathbf{N} = \sqrt{2}$ $a_\mathbf{N} = \sqrt{2}e^{\pi/2}$

17. $\mathbf{T} = (\cos\omega t_0)\mathbf{i} + (\sin\omega t_0)\mathbf{j}$

$\mathbf{N} = (-\sin\omega t_0)\mathbf{i} + (\cos\omega t_0)\mathbf{j}$

$a_\mathbf{T} = \omega^2$

$a_\mathbf{N} = \omega^3 t_0$

19. $\mathbf{T}(t) = -\sin(\omega t)\mathbf{i} + \cos(\omega t)\mathbf{j}$

$\mathbf{N}(t) = -\cos(\omega t)\mathbf{i} - \sin(\omega t)\mathbf{j}$

$a_\mathbf{T} = 0$

$a_\mathbf{N} = a\omega^2$

21. $\|\mathbf{v}(t)\| = a\omega$

The speed is constant since $a_\mathbf{T} = 0$.

23. $\mathbf{r}(2) = 2\mathbf{i} + \dfrac{1}{2}\mathbf{j}$

$\mathbf{T}(2) = \dfrac{\sqrt{17}}{17}(4\mathbf{i} - \mathbf{j})$

$\mathbf{N}(2) = \dfrac{\sqrt{17}}{17}(\mathbf{i} + 4\mathbf{j})$

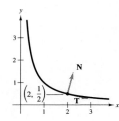

25. a. Cycloid

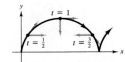

b. $t = \dfrac{1}{2}: a_\mathbf{T} = \dfrac{\sqrt{2}\pi^2}{2},\ a_\mathbf{N} = \dfrac{\sqrt{2}\pi^2}{2}$

$t = 1: a_\mathbf{T} = 0,\ a_\mathbf{N} = \pi^2$

$t = \dfrac{3}{2}: a_\mathbf{T} = \dfrac{\sqrt{2}\pi^2}{2},\ a_\mathbf{N} = \dfrac{\sqrt{2}\pi^2}{2}$

c. $t = \frac{1}{2}$: Increasing

$t = 1$: Maximum

$t = \frac{1}{2}$: Decreasing

27. $\mathbf{T}(t) = \dfrac{\sqrt{14}}{14}(\mathbf{i} + 2\mathbf{j} - 3\mathbf{k})$

$\mathbf{N}(t) = \mathbf{0}$

$a_\mathbf{T} = 0$

$a_\mathbf{N} = 0$

29. $\mathbf{T} = \dfrac{\sqrt{6}}{6}(\mathbf{i} + 2\mathbf{j} + \mathbf{k})$

$\mathbf{N} = \dfrac{\sqrt{30}}{30}(-5\mathbf{i} + 2\mathbf{j} + \mathbf{k})$

$\mathbf{a} \cdot \mathbf{T} = \dfrac{5\sqrt{6}}{6}$

$\mathbf{a} \cdot \mathbf{N} = \dfrac{\sqrt{30}}{6}$

31. $\mathbf{T} = \dfrac{1}{5}(4\mathbf{i} - 3\mathbf{j})$ **33.** $\mathbf{T}\left(\dfrac{\pi}{2}\right) = \dfrac{\sqrt{17}}{17}(-4\mathbf{i} + \mathbf{k})$

$\mathbf{N} = -\mathbf{k}$ $\mathbf{N}\left(\dfrac{\pi}{2}\right) = -\mathbf{j}$

$\mathbf{a} \cdot \mathbf{T} = 0$ $\mathbf{B}\left(\dfrac{\pi}{2}\right) = \dfrac{\sqrt{17}}{17}(\mathbf{i} + 4\mathbf{k})$

$\mathbf{a} \cdot \mathbf{N} = 3$

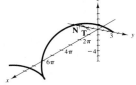

35. $a_{\mathbf{T}} = \dfrac{-32(v_0 \sin\theta - 32t)}{\sqrt{v_0^2 \cos^2\theta + (v_0 \sin\theta - 32t)^2}}$

$a_{\mathbf{N}} = \dfrac{32v_0 \cos\theta}{\sqrt{v_0^2 \cos^2\theta + (v_0 \sin\theta - 32t)^2}}$

37. a. Centripetal component is quadrupled
   b. Centripetal component is halved

39. 4.83 mi/sec   **41.** 4.67 mi/sec

Section 12.5 (*page 825*)

1. $4\sqrt{10}$ **3.** $6a$

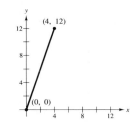

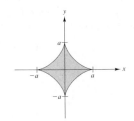

5. $2\sqrt{15}$ **7.** $2\pi\sqrt{a^2 + b^2}$

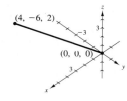

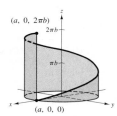

9. 8.37

11. a. $s = \sqrt{5}t$

   b. $\mathbf{r}(t) = 2\cos\dfrac{s}{\sqrt{5}}\mathbf{i} + 2\sin\dfrac{s}{\sqrt{5}}\mathbf{j} + \dfrac{s}{\sqrt{5}}\mathbf{k}$

   c. $s = \sqrt{5}$: $(1.081, 1.683, 1.000)$
   $s = 4$: $(-0.433, 1.953, 1.789)$

13. $K = 0$ **15.** $K = \frac{2}{5}$ **17.** $K = 0$

19. $\dfrac{\sqrt{2}}{2}$ **21.** $\dfrac{1}{4}$ **23.** $\dfrac{1}{a}$ **25.** $\dfrac{\sqrt{2}}{2}e^{-t}$ **27.** $\dfrac{1}{\omega t}$

29. $\dfrac{\sqrt{5}}{(1 + 5t^2)^{3/2}}$ **31.** $\dfrac{3}{25}$ **33.** $K = 0$, undefined

35. $K = \dfrac{4}{(17)^{3/2}}$ **37.** $K = \dfrac{1}{a}, \dfrac{1}{K} = a$

39. a. $\left(x - \dfrac{\pi}{2}\right)^2 + y^2 = 1$

   b. Since the curvature is not as great, the radius of
   curvature is greater.

41. $(x - 1)^2 + \left(y - \dfrac{5}{2}\right)^2 = \left(\dfrac{1}{2}\right)^2$

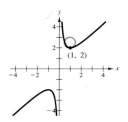

43. $(x + 2)^2 + (y - 3)^2 = 8$

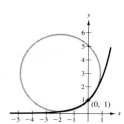

45. a. $(1, 3)$ **b.** 0   **47. a.** $K \to \infty$ as $x \to 0$ **b.** 0

49. Yes $(-1, 3)$

53. $a = \frac{1}{4}, b = 2$

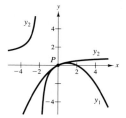

55. 56.27 mph   **57.** $\dfrac{3}{2\sqrt{2}(1 + \sin\theta)}$

59. $\dfrac{2}{|a|}$ **61. a.** 0   **b.** 0   **63.** $\dfrac{1}{4}$

67. $a_{\mathbf{T}} = 6t$ **69.** 55 lb
   $a_{\mathbf{N}} = 6$

71. a. a **73.** $K = \dfrac{1}{4a}\sec\dfrac{\theta}{2}$
   b. πa
   c. $K = \pi a$ Minimum: $K = \dfrac{1}{4a}$

There is no maximum.

Review Exercises for Chapter 12

1. a. All reals except $n\pi$, n is an integer
b. $t = n\pi$, n is an integer
3. a. $(0, \infty)$
b. Continuous

5.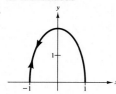

7.

9.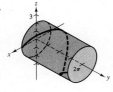

11.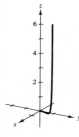

13. $x = t$, $y = -t$, $z = 2t^2$ **15.** $4\mathbf{i} + \mathbf{k}$

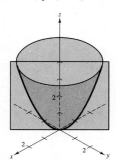

17. a. $3\mathbf{i} + \mathbf{j}$ **b.** $\mathbf{0}$ **c.** $4t + 3t^2$
d. $-5\mathbf{i} + (2t - 2)\mathbf{j} + 2t^2\mathbf{k}$ **e.** $\dfrac{10t - 1}{\sqrt{10t^2 - 2t + 1}}$
f. $\left(\dfrac{8}{3}t^3 - 2t^2\right)\mathbf{i} - 8t^3\mathbf{j} + (9t^2 - 2t + 1)\mathbf{k}$
19. $x = -\sqrt{2} - \sqrt{2}t$
$y = \sqrt{2} - \sqrt{2}t$
$z = \dfrac{3\pi}{4} + t$
21. $\sin t\,\mathbf{i} + (t\sin t - \sin t)\mathbf{j} + \mathbf{C}$
23. $\frac{1}{2}(t\sqrt{1 + t^2} + \ln|t + \sqrt{1 + t^2}|) + \mathbf{C}$
25. $\mathbf{r}(t) = (t^2 + 1)\mathbf{i} + (e^t + 2)\mathbf{j} - (e^{-t} + 4)\mathbf{k}$
27. $\frac{32}{3}\mathbf{j}$ **29.** 152 ft **31.** 111.56 ft/sec
33. $\mathbf{v} = 4\mathbf{i} - 3\mathbf{j}$
$\|\mathbf{v}\| = 5$
$\mathbf{a} = \mathbf{0}$
$\mathbf{a} \cdot \mathbf{T} = 0$
$\mathbf{a} \cdot \mathbf{N} = 0$
$K = 0$

35. $\mathbf{v} = 2\mathbf{i} - \dfrac{2}{(t + 1)^2}\mathbf{j}$
$\|\mathbf{v}\| = \dfrac{2\sqrt{(t + 1)^4 + 1}}{(t + 1)^2}$
$\mathbf{a} = \dfrac{4}{(t + 1)^3}\mathbf{j}$
$\mathbf{a} \cdot \mathbf{T} = \dfrac{-4}{(t + 1)^3\sqrt{(t + 1)^4 + 1}}$
$\mathbf{a} \cdot \mathbf{N} = \dfrac{4}{(t + 1)\sqrt{(t + 1)^4 + 1}}$
$K = \dfrac{(t + 1)^3}{[(t + 1)^4 + 1]^{3/2}}$

37. $\mathbf{v} = e^t\mathbf{i} - e^{-t}\mathbf{j}$
$\|\mathbf{v}\| = \sqrt{e^{2t} + e^{-2t}}$
$\mathbf{a} = e^t\mathbf{i} + e^{-t}\mathbf{j}$
$\mathbf{a} \cdot \mathbf{T} = \dfrac{e^{2t} - e^{-2t}}{\sqrt{e^{2t} + e^{-2t}}}$
$\mathbf{a} \cdot \mathbf{N} = \dfrac{2}{\sqrt{e^{2t} + e^{-2t}}}$
$K = \dfrac{2}{(e^{2t} + e^{-2t})^{3/2}}$

39. $\mathbf{v} = \mathbf{i} + 2t\mathbf{j} + t\mathbf{k}$
$\|\mathbf{v}\| = \sqrt{1 + 5t^2}$
$\mathbf{a} = 2\mathbf{j} + \mathbf{k}$
$\mathbf{a} \cdot \mathbf{T} = \dfrac{5t}{\sqrt{1 + 5t^2}}$
$\mathbf{a} \cdot \mathbf{N} = \dfrac{-5\sqrt{5}}{\sqrt{1 + 5t^2}}$
$K = \dfrac{\sqrt{5}}{(1 + 5t^2)^{3/2}}$

41. $\dfrac{\sqrt{5}\pi}{2}$ **43.** 4.56 mi/sec
45. The curvature changes abruptly from zero to a nonzero constant.

CHAPTER 13

Section 13.1 (*page 839*)

1. a. $\dfrac{3}{2}$ **b.** $-\dfrac{1}{4}$ **c.** 6 **d.** $\dfrac{5}{y}$ **e.** $\dfrac{x}{2}$ **f.** $\dfrac{5}{t}$
3. a. 5 **b.** $3e^2$ **c.** $\dfrac{2}{e}$ **d.** $5e^y$ **e.** xe^2 **f.** te^t
5. a. $\frac{2}{3}$ **b.** 0 **7. a.** $\sqrt{2}$ **b.** $3\sin 1$
9. a. 4 **b.** 6 **11. a.** $2x + \Delta x$ **b.** -2
13. Domain: $\{(x, y): x^2 + y^2 \le 4\}$
Range: $0 \le z \le 2$
15. Domain: $\{(x, y): -1 \le x + y \le 1\}$
Range: $-\dfrac{\pi}{2} \le z \le \dfrac{\pi}{2}$
17. Domain: $\{(x, y): y < -x + 4\}$
Range: All real numbers
19. Domain: $\{(x, y): x \ne 0, y \ne 0\}$
Range: All real numbers
21. Domain: $\{(x, y): y \ne 0\}$
Range: $0 < z$
23. Domain: $\{(x, y): x \ne 0, y \ne 0\}$
Range: $0 < |z|$
25. a. $(20, 0, 0)$ **b.** $(-15, 10, 20)$
c. $(20, 15, 25)$ **d.** $(20, 20, 0)$
27. c **29.** b

31.

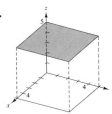

33.

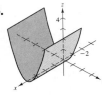

35.

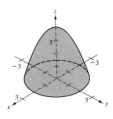

37.

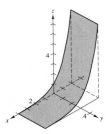

39.

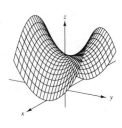

41.

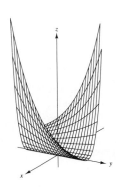

43.

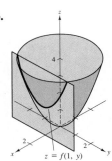

$z = f(1, y)$

$z = f(x, 1)$

45. Lines: $x + y = c$

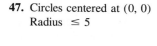

47. Circles centered at $(0, 0)$
Radius ≤ 5

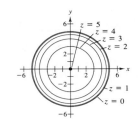

49. Hyperbolas: $xy = c$

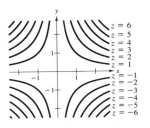

51. Circles passing through $(0, 0)$

Centered at $\left(\dfrac{1}{2c}, 0\right)$

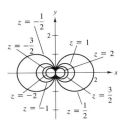

53. No. $z = e^{-(x^2+y^2)}$

55.

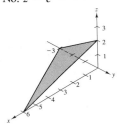

57.

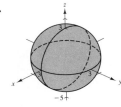

59.

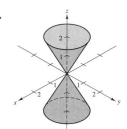

61.

Tax Rate	Inflation Rate		
	0	0.03	0.05
0	$2593.74	$1929.99	$1592.33
0.28	$2004.23	$1491.34	$1230.42
0.35	$1877.14	$1396.77	$1152.40

63. a. 243 board-feet   **b.** 507 board-feet

65.

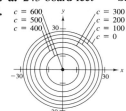

67. $C = 0.75xz + 0.80(xz + yz)$

69. a. $k = 1300$ **b.** $P = \dfrac{1300T}{V}$

The level curves are lines.

71. a. C   **b.** A   **c.** B

Section 13.2 (*page 849*)

1. 2   **3.** 15   **5.** 5, Continuous

7. -3, Continuous for $x \neq y$

9. 0, Continuous for $xy \neq -1$, $y \neq 0$, $\left|\dfrac{x}{y}\right| \leq 1$

11. 1, Continuous

13. $2\sqrt{2}$, Continuous for $x + y + z \geq 0$

15. 1, Continuous   **17.** Continuous except at $(0, 0)$; $-\infty$

19. Continuous except at $(0, 0)$
$y = 0 : 0$
$y = x : \frac{1}{2}$
Limit does not exist.

21. Continuous except at $(0, 0)$
$x = y^2 : -\frac{1}{2}$
$x = -y^2 : \frac{1}{2}$
Limit does not exist.

23. 1   **25.** Limit does not exist.

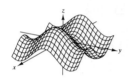   

27. 1   **29.** 0   **31.** Continuous except at $(0, 0, 0)$

33. Continuous   **35.** Continuous

37. Continuous for $y \neq \dfrac{3x}{2}$ **39. a.** $2x$ **b.** -4

41. a. $2 + y$ **b.** $x - 3$ **45.** True

46. False, let $f(x, y) = \dfrac{xy}{x^2 + y^2}$.

47. False, let $f(x, y) = \begin{cases} \ln(x^2 + y^2), & x \neq 0, y \neq 0 \\ 0, & x = 0, y = 0. \end{cases}$

48. True

Section 13.3 (*page 858*)

1. $f_x(x, y) = 2$ **3.** $f_x(x, y) = \sqrt{y}$
$f_y(x, y) = -3$ $f_y(x, y) = \dfrac{x}{2\sqrt{y}}$

5. $f_x(x, y) = 2xe^{2y}$
$f_y(x, y) = 2x^2 e^{2y}$

7. $f_x(x, y) = \dfrac{2x}{x^2 + y^2}$ **9.** $f_x(x, y) = \dfrac{-2y}{x^2 - y^2}$
$f_y(x, y) = \dfrac{2y}{x^2 + y^2}$ $f_y(x, y) = \dfrac{2x}{x^2 - y^2}$

11. $f_x(x, y) = -2xe^{-(x^2+y^2)}$
$f_y(x, y) = -2ye^{-(x^2+y^2)}$

13. $f_x(x, y) = \dfrac{x}{\sqrt{x^2 + y^2}}$
$f_y(x, y) = \dfrac{y}{\sqrt{x^2 + y^2}}$

15. $f_x(x, y) = 2\sec^2(2x - y)$
$f_y(x, y) = -\sec^2(2x - y)$

17. $f_x(x, y) = ye^y \cos xy$
$f_y(x, y) = e^y(x \cos xy + \sin xy)$

19. $f_x(x, y) = 1 - x^2$ **21.** $f_x(x, y) = 2$
$f_y(x, y) = y^2 - 1$ $f_y(x, y) = 3$

23. $f_x(x, y) = \dfrac{1}{2\sqrt{x + y}}$ **25.** $g_x(1, 1) = -2$
$f_y(x, y) = \dfrac{1}{2\sqrt{x + y}}$ $g_y(1, 1) = -2$

27. $\dfrac{\partial z}{\partial x} = -1$ **29.** $\dfrac{\partial z}{\partial x} = \dfrac{1}{4}$ **31.** $\dfrac{\partial z}{\partial x} = -\dfrac{1}{4}$

$\dfrac{\partial z}{\partial y} = 0$ $\dfrac{\partial z}{\partial y} = \dfrac{1}{4}$ $\dfrac{\partial z}{\partial y} = \dfrac{1}{4}$

33. $-\frac{1}{2}$ **35.** 18

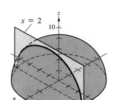   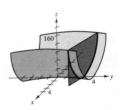

37. $\dfrac{\partial^2 z}{\partial x^2} = 2$

$\dfrac{\partial^2 z}{\partial y^2} = 6$

$\dfrac{\partial^2 z}{\partial y \, \partial x} = \dfrac{\partial^2 z}{\partial x \, \partial y} = -2$

39. $\dfrac{\partial^2 z}{\partial x^2} = \dfrac{y^2}{(x^2 + y^2)^{3/2}}$

$\dfrac{\partial^2 z}{\partial y^2} = \dfrac{x^2}{(x^2 + y^2)^{3/2}}$

$\dfrac{\partial^2 z}{\partial y \, \partial x} = \dfrac{\partial^2 z}{\partial x \, \partial y} = \dfrac{-xy}{(x^2 + y^2)^{3/2}}$

41. $\dfrac{\partial^2 z}{\partial x^2} = e^x \tan y$

$\dfrac{\partial^2 z}{\partial y^2} = 2e^x \sec^2 y \tan y$

$\dfrac{\partial^2 z}{\partial y \, \partial x} = \dfrac{\partial^2 z}{\partial x \, \partial y} = e^x \sec^2 y$

43. $\dfrac{\partial^2 z}{\partial x^2} = \dfrac{2xy}{(x^2 + y^2)^2}$

$\dfrac{\partial^2 z}{\partial y^2} = \dfrac{-2xy}{(x^2 + y^2)^2}$

$\dfrac{\partial^2 z}{\partial y \, \partial x} = \dfrac{\partial^2 z}{\partial x \, \partial y} = \dfrac{y^2 - x^2}{(x^2 + y^2)^2}$

33. 0.082 in., 0.63%   **35.** π in.

ALGEBRA

Factors and Zeros of Polynomials

Let $p(x) = a_n x^n + a_{n-1} x^{n-1} + \cdots + a_1 x + a_0$ be a polynomial. If $p(a) = 0$, then a is a *zero* of the polynomial and a solution of the equation $p(x) = 0$. Furthermore, $(x - a)$ is a *factor* of the polynomial.

Fundamental Theorem of Algebra

An nth degree polynomial has n (not necessarily distinct) zeros. Although all of these zeros may be imaginary, a real polynomial of odd degree must have at least one real zero.

Quadratic Formula

If $p(x) = ax^2 + bx + c$, and $0 \leq b^2 - 4ac$, then the real zeros of p are $x = (-b \pm \sqrt{b^2 - 4ac})/2a$.

Special Factors

$$x^2 - a^2 = (x - a)(x + a) \qquad\qquad x^3 - a^3 = (x - a)(x^2 + ax + a^2)$$

$$x^3 + a^3 = (x + a)(x^2 - ax + a^2) \qquad\qquad x^4 - a^4 = (x^2 - a^2)(x^2 + a^2)$$

Binomial Theorem

$$(x + y)^2 = x^2 + 2xy + y^2 \qquad\qquad (x - y)^2 = x^2 - 2xy + y^2$$

$$(x + y)^3 = x^3 + 3x^2 y + 3xy^2 + y^3 \qquad\qquad (x - y)^3 = x^3 - 3x^2 y + 3xy^2 - y^3$$

$$(x + y)^4 = x^4 + 4x^3 y + 6x^2 y^2 + 4xy^3 + y^4 \qquad\qquad (x - y)^4 = x^4 - 4x^3 y + 6x^2 y^2 - 4xy^3 + y^4$$

$$(x + y)^n = x^n + nx^{n-1} y + \frac{n(n-1)}{2!} x^{n-2} y^2 + \cdots + nxy^{n-1} + y^n$$

$$(x - y)^n = x^n - nx^{n-1} y + \frac{n(n-1)}{2!} x^{n-2} y^2 - \cdots \pm nxy^{n-1} \mp y^n$$

Rational Zero Theorem

If $p(x) = a_n x^n + a_{n-1} x^{n-1} + \cdots + a_1 x + a_0$ has integer coefficients, then every *rational zero* of p is of the form $x = r/s$, where r is a factor of a_0 and s is a factor of a_n.

Factoring by Grouping

$$acx^3 + adx^2 + bcx + bd = ax^2(cx + d) + b(cs + d) = (ax^2 + b)(cx + d)$$

Arithmetic Operations

$$ab + ac = a(b + c) \qquad \frac{a}{b} + \frac{c}{d} = \frac{ad + bc}{bd} \qquad \frac{a + b}{c} = \frac{a}{c} + \frac{b}{c}$$

$$\frac{\left(\dfrac{a}{b}\right)}{\left(\dfrac{c}{d}\right)} = \left(\frac{a}{b}\right)\left(\frac{d}{c}\right) = \frac{ad}{bc} \qquad \frac{\left(\dfrac{a}{b}\right)}{c} = \frac{a}{bc} \qquad \frac{a}{\left(\dfrac{b}{c}\right)} = \frac{ac}{b}$$

$$a\left(\frac{b}{c}\right) = \frac{ab}{c} \qquad \frac{a - b}{c - d} = \frac{b - a}{d - c} \qquad \frac{ab + ac}{a} = b + c$$

Exponents and Radicals

$$a^0 = 1, \quad a \neq 0 \qquad (ab)^x = a^x b^x \qquad a^x a^y = a^{x+y} \qquad \sqrt{a} = a^{1/2} \qquad \frac{a^x}{a^y} = a^{x-y} \qquad \sqrt[n]{a} = a^{1/n}$$

$$\left(\frac{a}{b}\right)^x = \frac{a^x}{b^x} \qquad \sqrt[n]{a^m} = a^{m/n} \qquad a^{-x} = \frac{1}{a^x} \qquad \sqrt[n]{ab} = \sqrt[n]{a}\,\sqrt[n]{b} \qquad (a^x)^y = a^{xy} \qquad \sqrt[n]{\frac{a}{b}} = \frac{\sqrt[n]{a}}{\sqrt[n]{b}}$$